THE BEDSIDE
ESQUIRE

THE BEDSIDE
ESQUIRE

Edited by

ARNOLD GINGRICH

Editor of *Esquire*

TUDOR PUBLISHING COMPANY

New York

INTRODUCTION

A PUBLISHER REFUSED TO ALLOW ONE OF HIS AUTHORS TO BE represented in this book, on the grounds that it would not be dignified for a writer of his stature to be included in "a bedside anything."

And that's the only reason why this book, which would otherwise need no introduction, must be introduced, if not explained, herewith.

This book is not a bedside anything. It is a bedside something. Something to have at hand, say on your night table, to be picked up when you want to read for ten minutes or an hour. It is a big assortment of some of the best of Esquire, assembled in bulk, let's say, or by volume, if we want to strain for a pun. If it were designed for reading at one galloping gulp, it could have been called *The Weekend Esquire*. But it isn't. It's designed for off-and-on sampling and savoring. That's why it has deliberately been chopped up into four separate sections, each calculated to be a more or less exact fit for one of four moods in which you may pick this book up.

But you don't have to go to bed with it. The good publisher who apparently thought so was badly confused. Lest you share his confusion, we hasten to assure you that this book is not by intent either aphrodisiac or sedative.

Esquire has been absorbed, with recorded enjoyment, by the minds and eyes of such disparate folk as William Lyon Phelps and the late little-lamented John Dillinger. It is highly improbable, of course, that they enjoyed the same things in it. For, as Raymond Gram Swing once exclaimed with an air of discovery, the combination of Esquire's text and pictures is as surprising as would be that of the mind of Madame Curie and the body of Sally Rand.

Any oaf can enjoy a picture. Esquire's have been cut out and hung up in Congo huts as well as American college dormitories. But it takes a mind to make the most of words. That's why it's only natural that Esquire has been much more widely looked at than read. It simply confirms the obvious truth of that synthetic Chinese proverb in which a latter day Confucius gauged the penetrating power of one picture as equaling that of a thousand words.

Sunny side up, Esquire is just a picture book, wherein the Petty girl's is the face that has launched a thousand quips. There's your darling of the dormitories and belle of the barber shops. How that one gets around!

But it has another side. Call it the under side, or even the shady side, because it has been so heavily overshadowed by the pictures. (Sometimes this editor, weary of hearing the cartoons talked about as if they characterized the content as a whole, has been tempted to term it The Esquire Nobody Knows.) At any rate, it's from this other side of Esquire that this book has been fashioned.

Out of Esky's other rib, as it were, comes this Lilith, that first wife of Adam, forgotten in the fame of Eve.

This is the solid side. One might call it, for contrast, the serious side, except for the hazard that "serious" might carry such unwarranted connotations as "sober" and "solemn".

The point is not one to be labored unduly, and yet it should be made, to justify and clarify the extreme diversity and apparent disparity of this book's contents. It is, in a word, such stuff as literature is made of, and literature, like industry, comes both light and heavy.

That's why room was found, between these covers, both for a *Latins are Lousy Lovers* and a *Snows of Kilimanjaro*. That's why a Steinbeck is here found cheek by jowl with a Pegler, a Dreiser with a Lardner, and so on down through a seemingly most heterogeneous list. Which brings us squarely back to the matter of your moods and how this book will try to match them.

It is divided into four parts, and it's by no means all gall and/or wormwood. *Part One* starts it off, about as quietly as a string of cannon crackers. This is a group of "Shockers," all of these stories or articles enjoying as their common denominator the fact that their appearance in print occasioned something of a nine day wonder or, at least, a seven day sensation. Included in this group are two standout "discoveries": *No More Trouble for Jedwick*, Louis Paul's first published story, which won the O. Henry Memorial Award for the year 1934, and *Christ in Concrete*, Pietro di Donato's first published story, later expanded and extended into the novel bearing the same title, which was a Book-of-the-Month selection of the summer of 1939. With these two exceptions, all the pieces in this group possessed, to greater or less degree, rabble-rousing elements (for instance, one offended dog-lovers, another mother-worshippers) which snowed us under with letters of the "Sir, you cur" variety. The furor over *A Good Job Gone* actually reached the point where there were serious exchanges of challenges to duels between Damyanks and professional Suthinuhs in the vox pop pages, while *Latins are Lousy Lovers* so enraged the good folk South of the Border and more especially Down Cuba Way, that while it obviously left its own point unproved it conclusively proved another: the Latin lack of a sense of humor. Six otherwise unoffending (and probably equally offended) Havana newsdealers were solemnly hoosegowed for having given stack-room on their newsstands to the issue of Esquire containing that article, for months afterward tourists' copies of the magazine were furiously confiscated, and serious representations were actually made to the U. S. Chamber of Commerce if not, as rumor ran, to the State Department.

On second thought, maybe that section won't match one of your moods. Maybe you have to be in the mood for it.

Part Two, however, is a pure relaxer, prescribed as a chaser to be taken for comic relief whenever the going gets too tough in any one of the other sections. If you're in a mood for getting away from it all this will get you there in a hurry. It includes Ring Lardner's last story and one of the last from Thorne Smith. Also the Graffis classic on the "bust-belly and behind business," *A Breast of the Times*. For this editor, if for nobody else, there is also interest in the fact that this section contains, in *Little Augie and The Davis Cup*, the first manuscript ever submitted to Esquire, when the magazine was no more than a first-whispered and un-confirmed rumor in the publishing trade, as well as the story that is a ranking contender for, if not undisputed possessor of, the title of most-frequently rejected manuscript ever published by *Esquire* or anybody else: *Keeping Cool at Conneaut*. This came to us with the brash announcement that it had been "turned down by every paying market in America and England, and most of the non-paying markets too". Intrigued, we published it to resounding applause.

Part Three really ought not to carry any comment, spanning as it does such peaks as Hemingway's *Snows of Kilimanjaro* (which Jesse Stuart calls "all of Hemingway's best stories in one hunk") and Steinbeck's unforgettable *Ears of Johnny Bear*. All the pieces in this section seem to us to classify as Literature, but none is offered as such. Rather, we proffer this portion when your mood is for "a good story, even if it *is* Literature."

Part Four could be called the section *For Men Only*, because it is not only next to null in interest to women readers but also goes, in good part, directly against the grain of the influence (not to say domination) of women readership on general magazine contents. This section is literally strewn with the tablets of broken taboos. For instance, for some obscure and possibly atavistic reason women don't like to read about snakes (featured in *A Shipment of Mute Fate*, and *A Snake of One's Own*), nor about rats (with which *Three Skeleton Key* is literally lousy) nor about their erring sisters (vide *Queen in the Parlour Car, Hide Your Eyes* and *Deutschland Weber Alles*) nor about messy details of human or animal cruelty (*So Smells Defeat, Leiningen versus the Ants*), so this section is mostly made up of what most editors avoid. Perhaps the indicated mood is one of feeling contrary.

So there it is. If the title led you to expect something else, and this clarification is disappointing, maybe you can still hurry back with it if you've kept this copy reasonably clean. But if you still venture beyond this point, at least you can't say you weren't warned, can you?

Since this preface was conceived in pique at a publisher who held out a wanted author, it ought, in decency, to end in gratitude to those publishers who, having acquired book rights to certain of these pieces since their original publication in Esquire, graciously waived them. It does.

ARNOLD GINGRICH

CONTENTS

PART IV.

PART I

PART I.

SWEET FACES AND FOUL MINDS

By George Jean Nathan

THAT, TAKING ONE WITH ANOTHER, WOMEN'S MINDS ARE LESS CLEAN than men's is a fact which, while sufficiently recognized by men in the mass, has yet strangely, so far as I know, not found its commentator and analyst on paper. We have had a few general epigrams on the subject, and we have thought, now and again, that we were about to read some sharp and penetrating statement on the matter, but in both cases delicate evasion and polite half-statement have been the only reward of our curiosity. In the interests of lovely truth, therefore, let us make bold to pursue the inquiry a bit further.

Any man who moves about in feminine society and who is not deaf in both ears can testify to the fact that women's conversation, whatever the specific nature of its initial impulse, sooner or later is inevitably bound to get around to sex. The manoeuvre may be contrived indirectly and with a certain spurious show of neo-Victorian modesty—in some instances, but once it gains a measure of confidence it stalks into the topic like a bouncer into a barroom. Whereas men, when they enter into the subject, customarily enter into it, often somewhat disconcertingly, with what may metaphorically be described as both feet, women begin by skirting around its edges, by tossing out innuendo, and by playing ping-pong with suggestiveness before getting to the main business of the conversational meeting. A man will say, frankly, openly, and plainly, what is in his mind; a woman will by verbal by-play and insinuation convert what would otherwise be forthrightly clean into something that is vaguely dirty. Women seldom, in sex matters, use the straightforward, clean-cut, appropriate terms. They rely upon circumlocutions and synonyms which, like burlesque show strippers, are twice as suggestive as the naked words. They drape their colloquies in gauze veils and, slowly and with deliberately timed oral movements and gestures, remove them, to their twofold—or sevenfold—eroticism.

15

For this, the still remaining double standard of sex—it still remains for all the vociferous verbal and physical promiscuity of a relative handful of females and for all the editorial fulminations in liberal publications edited by unwanted old maids or fed-up married men who have eyes for their stenographers and obliquely wish to give their wives the gate—the still operative double standard, as I say, is doubtless responsible. Women, under its terms, are denied the privilege of directness and honesty and must perforce take refuge in an arsenal of allusive hints and winks. Their thoughts may be the same as men's thoughts, but the forbidden direct articulation of them serves by repression to make them gradually stagnant and fungus-covered. A man, as the saying is, gets them off his chest and is done with them; a woman is not equally permitted to get them off her mind, and there they remain to crawl about with their increasingly slimy worminess.

This enforced repression seeking vicarious outlet is indicated, among other things, by the stuff that women read. Who are the chief consumers of cheap sex novels and the magazines of so-called "snappy" fiction? The sales statistics show, and emphatically, that they are women—young, medium, and pretty old. The phrase, "shop-girl fiction," tells its own story. On the higher literary but equally sexy level, who have been and are the chief worshipers of D. H. Lawrence, particularly in his "Lady Chatterley's Lover" mood? The answer is too obvious to be recorded.

Women think of sex in the daytime as well as at night, whereas men in general seldom find their thoughts hovering about the topic when the sun is shining. Even Frenchmen and the Viennese hardly begin before twilight. And speculation is inflammation. I have known many men in my lifetime, but I have yet to encounter one who talked or thought about sex at lunch. The majority of women, on the other hand, even those who work for a living, allow their imaginations and conversation to play around it from the first application of the morning lipstick to the last dab of cold cream at night. Like hatred, sex must be articulated or, like hatred, it will produce a disturbing internal malaise. The edicts of polite society are responsible to no small degree for women's dirty minds.

Any psychoanalyst or practitioner of psychopathology will tell you that, out of every ten customers and patients, nine are women. And out of the nine, at least eight will be found to be troubled with sex complexes. These sex complexes, the aforesaid professors need hardly tell you, are the result of repressions, and the aforesaid repressions are responsible for all kinds of mental quirks. The injunction, "Get it out of your mind," suggests the nature of the mind and its thoughts. These thoughts are not healthy, but diseased. Concentration on sex, though sometimes unsuspected, has brought with it a species of mental corruption.

Plays dealing with abnormality always find their chief customers among women. When "The Captive" was, previous to its enforced withdrawal by the police, shown in New York, the box-office statistics revealed that five women to every man attended it, and the matinées were patronized almost exclusively by women.

Such pornographic literary trash as Elinor Glyn's "Three Weeks," Ethel M. Dell's "The Sheik" and Arlen's "The Green Hat" finds itself in the best-seller class solely because of women.

The sex moving pictures, with Mae West's alone excepted (and they are humourous rather than erotically stimulating), are patronized overwhelmingly, the exhibitors' records assure us, by women.

The heroines of men are Joan of Arc, Florence Nightingale and Edith Cavell. The heroines of women are Du Barry, Pompadour and Gabriele d'Annunzio.

I have lately had the privilege of scrutinizing the account books of the four leading purveyors of so-called erotica in New York City. Not the cheap dispensers of contemptible pink-backs, but the sellers of books, that, for one reason or another, are not supposed to be read by the moral element in the community. The account books of the first, covering the period from January first, 1934, to July first, 1934, showed that his customers numbered 1,810 women as against 254 men. The books of the second, covering a like period, showed 927 women as against 46 men. Those of the third, covering the time between January first, 1934, to September first, 1934, showed 737 women and only 34 men. And those of the fourth, covering the period from February first, 1934, to August first, 1934, disclosed 462 women as against just 14 men. I am not acquainted with the sellers of pink-backs and so, unfortunately, cannot offer statistics in that quarter. But the story on the somewhat higher sexy level is sufficiently illuminating. Men usually outgrow their taste for pornography after they have completed, at an early age, the prescribed course of "Only a Boy," "Fanny Hill," and "Green Girls in Paris." But women's taste for pornography seems seldom to abate.

Perhaps in no clearer way may we appreciate the dubious quality of the feminine mind than by referring to the question of motion picture censorship and observing the peculiar aberrations of that mind when it serves on the various state censorship committees whose business it is to pass on the morality of the films. Through various esoteric channels, I have managed to glean certain facts and certain information in this direction that offer tasty reading. I herewith present my findings:

1. The male members of three of these censorship boards—there are state boards at the present time in New York, Maryland, Virginia, Ohio, Kansas, Pennsylvania, and for Sunday films, in Massachusetts—found nothing particularly dirty in such words and phrases as "naked," "twin beds," "mistress," "birth control" and "long, lonely nights," but were compelled to demand their deletion upon the insistence of women members of the boards.

2. It was the women on the boards of two state censorship bodies who, against the male members' indifference, forced the elimination from certain films of such innocent spectacles as women's underclothing hanging on a clothes line and a husband appearing in his wife's presence in his B. V. D.'s.

3. The deletion of such childishly harmless lines as "I wonder if Molly's mother has told her everything" (spoken by the husband on his wedding night), as "You made her so dizzy she had to go in and lie down" (spoken after a kiss), as "I'm from America"—"What part?"—"All of me," as "If you think Americans are good at the Black Bottom, just watch those Africans," and as "Come in, young man. Don't be frightened. It's much warmer here than on the balcony," were all ordered out not by the male members but by the female.

4. Although the male censors could not discern anything excessively foul in a view of a nude little baby, of a girl sitting on a couch with a man's head in her lap, of a man in pajamas, of a girl drawing her feet up on a bench, of nightgowns arranged on a bed, of a nude figure carved on a pipe, and of table book-ends showing a female figure's single nude breast, the women censors apparently could.

5. The censorship ladies also saw something extremely filthy in the following lines: "Corinne thinks a mistress is something you read about in a French novel"; "You know, experience should have taught you, my dear, that the name Smith is always suspicious on the hotel register"; "You mustn't think of the man in me, only the artist"; "It wasn't love"; "What's your name?" "Eve," "Mine's Adam"; "Is friend husband out of town again?"; and "This girl, painted as a harlot, met death with a smile."

Under beautiful rose-beds, it would seem, there are often sewers.

WASHING THE HANDS

By AIKEN A. DEHAN

FALSE MODESTY IN THE EXTREME FORM WHICH CHARACTERIZED life in the Victorian Era has to a large extent disappeared in more modern times. Most of us today call a spade a spade and do not refer to a girl's leg as a limb. But we still cling stubbornly to many other objectionable forms of polite hypocrisy and prudery and the most objectionable of these is in connection with—to put it baldly—the washing of hands.

I thoroughly agree with Mr. Hemingway in his advocacy of the use of words which are even downright dirty when they are necessary to draw a character true to life. But these good old Anglo-Saxon words; strong, simple but highly expressive words, are even more necessary in ordinary conversation, even in polite society. I see no good reason why we should refer to a simple necessary action like the washing of hands by more or less obscure synonyms.

We all find it highly necessary, several times a day, to wash our hands. Why in the name of common sense and honesty should we think it necessary to refer to this simple natural act as "seeing a man about a dog," "watering the stock," "sharpening the skates," or as the French so subtly put it, "changer le poisson d'eau"? There are probably hundreds of such expressions in every language in the world, all designed to avoid the necessity of coming out, point-blank, and saying what we mean.

In some cases the suggestion implied in the synonym is obvious but in others it may be more or less in the nature of a convention and like so many conventions, not universally understood. Now-a-days when every home is equipped with a bath-room scale a man at a mixed gathering has only to bring up the subject of weight and the intelligent host or hostess knows that he wants to wash his hands. But I know of an actual case where this simple subterfuge gave rise to a heated controversy which finally resulted in the entire assembled company trooping out to stand in the hallway while a man weighed himself on the bath-room scale—a man who had practically no interest in his weight but did want to wash his hands, in privacy. If he had had the courage to come out openly and say he wanted to wash his hands no one would have thought any the less of him for his frankness.

The considerate host or hostess makes provision for the washing of the hands of the guests at frequent intervals but how few hosts and hostesses are truly and unselfishly considerate these days. Women are the worse offenders in this respect. ESQUIRE is an outspoken men's magazine. It is not intended for women and if any of them read this article and choose to take offense at what I say, they will have themselves to blame. Women seem to be so constituted that they can go for hours and hours without ever thinking of washing their hands. There is probably some biological reason for it. A camel can go for nine hours—or is it nine days?—without drinking water. It must be quite the contrary with most women.

Being constituted as they are, most women fail to appreciate the weakness of the stronger sex in this respect and make little or no provision for it in their social arrangements. Think of the untold distress and actual suffering that has resulted from this lack of common consideration.

The male guest may be chilly or tired or may have been sitting still for hours, all of which tend to aggravate matters. Now that alcohol has once more taken its proper place at social gatherings the necessity of frequent hand washings has increased enormously. The guest may have got himself jammed into a corner, behind a bridge table or something, unable to escape without knocking over the furniture. He may be sitting in a conspicuous place in front of all the company where his slightest movement is obvious to all. Unless the hostess comes to his rescue he may feel that he has to sit and suffer till the buoyancy of his back teeth is put to a severe test.

On account of the constitutional peculiarities I have already referred to, the hostess may be absolved in many cases from blame in this connection; but not so the host. Even in a mixed gathering where false modesty is rampant he can with a little ingenuity and originality give his male guests opportunities to relieve their distress and do it in an unobtrusive, inconspicuous way. It is a simple matter for the host himself to slip out at any time on the pretense of answering the phone or a ring at the door bell but the guest has no such opportunities. An understanding and unselfish host can, from time to time, pick out a dummy at a bridge table and suggest that he ought to go out and turn over the engine of his car, seeing it is such a cold night, or that he might like to come down and see the new blower on the furnace, or if he cannot think of anything better, that the guest really should come upstairs and see Junior's white mice. It all seems terribly complicated when all that is really necessary is to come right out and ask him if he wants to wash his hands. But what else can you do with confirmed male prudes?

The ideal host gives his male guests an opportunity to perform the necessary ablutions as soon as they arrive. It may be a cold night, they may have driven a long way or they may have recently taken copious draughts of fluids or large quantities of salt or sugar, all of which tend to soil the hands. He gives them frequent opportunities during the evening and always a final opportunity before they leave for home. But hosts like this are few and far between.

The ideal architect designs and equips houses so that the guest can wash unobtrusively. He puts complete bathrooms, that is complete except for the bath, at the far corner of the cloakroom on the ground floor and in the basement. He has at least two bathrooms, complete in all details upstairs, out of sight of each other. But who ever heard of an ideal architect? Most architects are positively inhuman. They put bathrooms in conspicuous places, usually in full sight of the room where the women leave their wraps and put on their war paint. They equip these bathrooms with fixtures that make distinctive noises. They fail to provide adequate bolts for the doors and hide the lights and switches. They make a more or less personal matter, like washing the hands, a sort of semi-public ceremony.

Of course some men are not bothered with this hand-washing urge at all and there are others, hardy spirits, who refuse to suffer in silence. I hope by giving this matter publicity to alleviate in some small measure the sufferings of those who still retain a certain amount of modesty, false or otherwise.

There are some cases where even the frankest individual must use discretion. I go a few times a year to play bridge with three old maids, three of the dearest old ladies in the world but also three of the most perfect examples of Middle Victorianism, extant. The evening is usually an ordeal of mixed pleasure for they make no provision whatever for the washing of the guest's hands.

Not long ago I started on one of these duty visits. For hours in advance I had rigidly abstained from drinking fluids or eating sugar or salt. I was all set to spend the evening with the minimum of hand-washing. It isn't the passage of time that bothers most of us; it is the mental hazard; the knowledge that hand-washing is impossible makes the need seem more urgent.

But the heater of the car broke down and I got caught in a traffic jam and had to sit in the cold till I was chilled to the bone. I had almost decided to break the engagement when I had a brilliant idea. I stopped the car a few doors away from the house, lifted the hood and smeared grease over both hands. Then I drove up and went in, explaining my delay was due to engine trouble.

Let me make myself perfectly clear. I didn't say anything about washing my hands. I needn't go into details. You will just have to take my word for it that they were not the kind of old ladies you could talk to, about washing hands. I held out my greasy paws and they rose to the occasion in perfect accord. They escorted me upstairs to the bathroom. One went ahead and switched on the light. Another rushed off for some of those embroidered atrocities they call guest towels. The third sister put in the plug and filled the basin. I thought for one awful moment they were going to wash my hands for me but they finally left me and stood at the head of the stairs and waited for me. I finished washing my hands, dried them on the slippery-elm towels and quietly locked the door. Then I turned around and had my first good look at the bathroom. In addition to the wash-basin and soap holder it was equipped with a large bath, a towel rack, a bathroom scale, a couple of ample mirrors, a medicine chest, let into the wall, and a framed, hand-embroidered motto which read "Cleanliness Is Next to Godliness"—and that was absolutely all.

The architect, with that diabolical perversity that is so common among architects, had put the missing equipment in a separate room—somewhere else in the house.

LATINS ARE LOUSY LOVERS

Anonymous

FIRST OF ALL, I WANT TO MAKE IT CLEAR THAT THIS IS NOT THE WAIL of a downhearted frail who was scorned and is therefore taking a cad's revenge. The following observations are not based on personal experience alone, but on the testimony of other disillusioned damsels, as well. I have listened to their plaints in ladies' rooms, night clubs, tearooms, boudoirs, on boats and on beaches; and I wish to acknowledge my indebtedness to those unwept, unhonored and unsung American women who have trusted and Given All in Cuba and Mexico, Central and South America, Spain and Puerto Rico—not to mention various encounters with visiting Latins on their own hearthstones in Ohio, Maine, Mississippi and both Dakotas. I, myself, have just returned from five months in Cuba, where I did a little field work on my own; and I believe that it is high time someone exploded the mythical superiority of Latins as lovers and relegated it to its proper place, along with other half-baked, but quaint, traditions, such as the saying that ashes in your coffee make you drunk, that if you don't save all your baby teeth, your second set will be puppies' teeth, or that if you don't move, the bee won't sting you. (Ah, so you've been caught on that one, too!)

It is a common belief all over the world that Latin men are the best lovers and Americans the worst. With an American flag of washable bunting draped prominently—but with careless grace—around my chest, and balancing an American eagle on my head, I hereby rise to state that this is a hoax. I will not only state it; hell, I will prove it. In order to facilitate matters, let us divide the subject into three parts: The Latin at Large, The Latin at Home, and The Latin in Bed. All right, Miss America, take it away!

THE LATIN AT HOME

From now on, I will say Cubans, because I have taken a special course in Cubans, but you can substitute Venezuelans or Andalusians or Argentines, because, from what the rest of the girls say, they are practically interchangeable as far as this subject is concerned.

In the first place, they are generally short in stature. When anyone asks you if you want to meet another Cuban, it's customary to say, "All right. Is he over five foot four?" (She Stoops to Conquer Cubans can be taken physically, therefore, as well as morally and spiritually.) They are not only short; they are thin, too, with narrow shoulders and wide hips: in other words, like the Flapper Age trousers—bell-bottomed. Their teeth—if any—are either frayed stumps or dazzling with gold. They wear straw Kellys too large or too small, badly fitting suits, and shoes that pinch their feet—and they have little feet. Of course, they do have nice eyes—that is, when they aren't cross-eyed. Their hair is oily and usually needs cutting. They spit a great deal. They are always scratching themselves.

That is the typical Cuban for you. That is, that is what they're like if they look like Cubans. Most Cubans don't look like Cubans. They look like Germans, Italians, Swedes, Polacks, and clerks from Yonkers. It makes my heart bleed to think of the boatloads of hopeful females who go down there every year on cruises, trusting to find a nation of Cesar Romeros. If they do find one, the odds are ten to one that he's another American tourist. As one more disappointed maiden put it, on her return to Manhattan, "The worst Americans are better than the best Cubans. I mean, the Americans you see here digging ditches or driving ice wagons or riding in the subways are all handsomer and better built than the most highly publicized Don Juans in Havana."

In the second place, although part of their claim to superiority in amorous dalliance is based on an assumption of gallantry, they are not gallant in a practical way. They meet you at a bar for cocktails at five-thirty, make violent love to you—and then go home for dinner. They will meet you afterward and renew their spirited attack, but for the space of a couple of hours, their mad love is abated. They appreciate their home cooking, and, of course, foreign young women cannot be invited—or, at any rate, they aren't—into the sanctity of the typical Cuban home. They pay you fantastic compliments that no half-wit would believe, but they never send you flowers or give you presents. I take that back. A South American gave a girl I know an old coin, and a New York blonde once got a clock and an Eversharp pencil from a Cuban who said he was enslaved by her eyes, that he was blinded by the golden sunshine of her hair, that he would cut off his right arm for her, in short, that he would die for her. (They are fond of fancying themselves as impetuous, violent folk, ready to draw their machetes at the drop of a sombrero.) They are, however, great on photographs and practically the moment they meet you, will pull out their pictures, inscribe them passionately, and present them to you, blissfully confident that forever afterward you sleep with their images under your pillow by night and plastered onto your mirror by day, where you can spend long hours in adoration.

They are convinced that all American women worship them; and they love American women because they're so free and easy. With their money, they forget to add. There are very few who object to acting as amiable escorts to American girls who foot the bills. In fact, some of them can be said really to live only during the tourist season, when they emerge like butterflies to meet all in-coming ships. The rest of the year, they just languish around, recounting their exploits and saving their strength.

They are good dancers, as a rule, although the belief that every Cuban is a born hoofer is a fallacy. When they *are* good, they are superlatively so, but there are plenty of them who can step on your feet just as often and just as heavy as the boys back home. They are definitely not good drinkers. A couple of highballs and they are sitting on top of the world. One more, and they slip down in their chairs, practically parallel with the floor. All Latins have trouble with their livers and if they drink too much they get very sick. One Cuban says, "When I drink more than two drinks, my kidneys resent it, and my liver abets them." Their sense of humor expresses itself for the most part in jokes which were thrown out of the Minsky circuit ten years ago. They adore American slang but are always five to ten years behind. (Last winter I met a Cuban who had just caught up with "It's the cat's pajamas!") Anything approaching subtlety will leave them blankfaced and untouched but the simplest reference to the bathroom and the elimination processes of the digestive tract will plunge them into uncontrollable hysterics. They also appreciate any suggestion of sex, provided it is elementary enough. Judged by their standards, the greatest wits in the world have been the little boys who scribble on fences and the comfort station wall decorators. The national type of joke most prevalent is a charming little game known as the *pega*. It is couched in the form of question and answer and is the ultimate in obscene simplicity. Naturally, examples cannot be given at this time, but the question is frequently something like, "Have you got a few minutes to spare?" And when the victim answers "Yes, why?"— (and they always answer; even though they've been hearing this form of joke daily all their lives, they never seem to catch on)— the answer is, "Well then, do thus and so"—(fill in with any of the dirtier phrases you remember from your childhood.) This will render them incapacitated by laughter for ten minutes.

While the above may seem irrelevant, I believe it to have a bearing on the general subject, since it depicts sidelights on the qualities of the Latin at Large as a companion. And after all, a certain amount of companionship—sometimes known as the pre-liminaries—is customary before getting down to the brass tacks of *amor*.

The Latin at Home

In his own home, the Cuban man is absolute king, lord and master. He demands service and he gets it—hand and foot. Although he practically never takes his wife out—and seldom stays home with her—he is insanely jealous and keeps constant tab on her by bribing the servants, tapping the telephone wires, and a general spy system as elaborate as that of the Jesuits. He telephones his home every hour or so as part of the check-up. If his wife says she is going to the hairdresser's, the modiste's or the milliner's, he makes sure to telephone there, too. If she goes to a movie, he runs over and sees the same picture so that he can question her on it during dinner that night. When he stays out all night, he almost never notifies his wife, but if he telephones and says he won't be home, he makes a point of going home within an hour.

The Cuban husband is practically never at home, except for meals. He goes out night after night, to political meetings, the club, poker games, jai-alai games, cock fights, cabarets, dances, parties, dinners, sidewalk cafes—or to visit his mistress—and his wife stays home. Once a month, he may spend an evening at the movies with her; a couple of times a year he takes her to large charity fiestas; and on special occasions, like the Fourth of July or the President's

Saint's Day, he may invite her out and buy her a glass of sherry. One man I know married his wife when she was sixteen and has never let her out at night since. She is now thirty-two. She has never even been permitted to go alone in the daytime to do her shopping or to a beauty parlor or to the movies. Although she is the mother of three children, the only person she can go to these places with is her older sister, and then she must travel in a closed automobile, never in a street car or bus, where other men might look at her. Her husband initiated her into this regime immediately after they returned from their honeymoon. Right then, he began leaving her in the house while he went out; and night after night, she used to sit at an upstairs window alone and watch him sitting in a gay party at the sidewalk café across the street. Nor is he an ignorant country yokel. He is a member of Congress; he has traveled in the United States and in Europe; he likes music, dancing and night life; and he is considered worldly and charming by the women he meets outside of his home.

This is by no means an isolated case, although not all Cubans carry the system to such extremes. However, they do not take their wives to night clubs, cabarets or public restaurants. When they go out for a good time—which is about six nights out of the week— their helpmates stay at home. As one man said, "Certainly my wife stays home where she belongs. Furthermore, I never allow her to have girl friends. When she starts to become friendly with another woman—go to the movies with her or to the hairdresser's, right away I forbid her to see her any more. Women together talk and breed trouble. My wife must live for me alone and for what time I can find to give her." Which might be said to be the definitive word on the subject.

The Latin in Bed

And now we come to the point of the piece. God knows, the Cuban man spends enough time on the subject of sex. He devotes his life to it. He talks it, dreams it, reads it, sings, dances it, eats it, sleeps it—does everything but do it. That last is of course not literally true, but it is a fact that they spend far more time in words than in action. Sitting in their offices, rocking on the sidewalk in front of their clubs, drinking at cafés, they talk hour after hour about sex. When the University of Habana had a football team, they used to drive their American coach crazy by sitting in the dressing-room before a game and describing their exploits—play by play—with the girls they took out the night before. A smart American who makes an appointment to discuss business with a Cuban at a café always makes the Cuban sit with his back to the street; because if he does not, the Cuban will eye every woman who passes, and, like as not, at a crucial point of the business transaction, will interrupt to make anatomical comments on some pretty who is just going by. They telephone each other at their offices during business hours to describe in minute detail a new conquest. According to them, they always had their first affair at the age of two. This may account for their being all worn out at twenty-three. Makers of aphrodisiacs do a thriving business: Spanish fly, yohimbim, marihuana cigarets, cocaine, Baum Bengue. (Even the horses at Oriental Park have ginger put under their tails.) You can pick up any Cuban newspaper and see, on the second or third page, right smack in the middle of the news, a big ad—"Men! Let Science help you! Merely a matter of the hormones. Etc., etc."

This lack of masculine energy does not prevent them from talking a great game. They boast of their prowess, their anatomical proportions, and their methods. (To hear them talk of what is known to Drs. Van der Velde, Stopes, *et al.* as the love-play, you'd think they invented it. Certain they are, at least, that it has been revealed to them alone out of all mankind in a sort of divine and mystic annunciation kept secret from the rest of the world.) But if you believe the testimony of their women-folk, when it actually comes to the test, they apparently suffer from tropical amnesia. In other words, they're talkers, not doers.

According to Cuban technique, love is a game of chess. Now it's your move; now its mine—whoops, I caught you! If I do this, she will do that. If she says that, it means I should do this. They will spend hours figuring out unnecessary progressive steps in an amorous campaign, and when their objective is finally obtained, they are apparently too exhausted by strategy to do much about it. Through the years, they have managed to work out an extraordinarily and elaborately complicated system of sexual attack, which only they know the meaning of; and they are perfectly happy to putter around with this for months at a time, making telephone calls, writing notes, conferring with their friends (they are inveterate gossips and cannot make an amorous move without running off beforehand and afterward to consult with all their male friends), and making a great to-do about symbols and signals and point counter point.

They believe in quantity, not quality, also. Every man has his wife and his mistress of the moment. In addition, he has to find time to attend to the demi-mondaines (dancers, singers, night-club hostesses or just women about town), the concubines (maids, dance-hall girls, little *achinadas* and *mulaticas*), and to the regular professional prostitutes. (They are great frequenters of houses of ill fame, making their rounds as a matter of course, and Mr. Dewey would have a difficult time in Habana. He certainly would lack the taxpayers' wholehearted support.) Besides this, in each one of these classes of women, he has someone he's working up to the proper pitch of surrender—dropping in to see occasionally, buying a glass of beer for, calling on the telephone—and, also in each class, he has someone he's got marked out to start paying attention to when he gets around to it, or when a vacancy occurs in the regular lists or on the scrub team. You can easily see how all of this keeps him extremely busy—he even has to devote afternoons, and frequently mornings, to it—so that he doesn't find quite so much time for actual practice.

Nevertheless, living in this constant aura of sex, the Cuban grows serenely sure that he is more adept amorously than other men—particularly Americans. In this impenetrable vanity of theirs, they are unlike any other nation. The elderly American, at least, occasionally lets a bit of cynicism slip into his attitude. He admits that the gift of a diamond bracelet, a mink coat or a car may possibly have influenced the young lady of his choice, but the Cuban, be he ever so ancient, fat, bald and wrinkled, is perpetually convinced that his personal charms alone are what render him irresistible. To see him is to love him, he reasons.

They are a curious mixture of Spanish tradition, American imitation and insular limitation. This explains why they never catch on to themselves. I think the reason for their initial vanity is that, early in life, they start frequenting what, for want of a better word, are known as fancy women. (I know a better word but I won't use it here.) These women, for obvious business reasons, flatter them extravagantly, make them think they're superlative lovers—and the men never find out otherwise. I suppose no one ever has the heart to tell them. And everything with which they come in contact the rest of their lives serves to perpetuate the myth: the books they read, the songs they sing, the testimony of their fellow countrymen—who are, as I have said, anything but reticent—and the continued plaudits of their womenfolk. One case I heard of—submitted by a fellow field worker—had to do with a noted Casanova, famed not only in Habana but as far as Pinar del Rio for his amatory skill. When subjected to an impartial test, it turned out that his routine could be classified as Amateur College Boy, Class G-6, but that immediately on completion of said simple routine, he sat up in bed and exclaimed delightedly, "Am I not wonderful? Am I not wonderful?"

In short, as the result of an extensive female survey, my conclusions are that offhand I would swap you five Cubans, three South Americans and two slightly used Spaniards for one good Irish-American any night in the week. I feel sorry for the women of Cuba. Theirs not to reason why, theirs but to try and try.

I am hereby offering a plea for Latin womanhood. Too long have they suffered under adversity's rod. Any upstanding American man who wants to do a humane deed knows where to go now. My advice to the American male is, Go South, young man, Go South. It's open season for putting the horns on Cuban manhood. They'll look like a race of moose when you get through with them, and you will have served to remove a national stigma and explode a world-wide myth.

If this all sounds like an embittered and chauvinistic diatribe against Cubans, I can only say that I did not mean it as such. It is merely that I happen to like American men, and I have been aroused to a high pitch of indignation by hearing them constantly maligned. You cannot spend an hour in the society of any Latin male without hearing what bad lovers Americans are. "Of course, American men know nothing of sex!" is the theme song of the tropics. I thought that our own home boys might like to know that they've been severely underrated and that they no longer need tremble before foreign competition in the most popular of all indoor sports.

THE WENCH IS NOT AMUSED

Anonymous

ANY GIRL, IF THE BODY SHE POSSESSES ISN'T ACTUALLY DEFORMED and the face badly moth-bitten, is going to become acquainted with the gentle art of seduction fairly early in life. As for myself, I've had what I now recognize as more than my share of experience.

Not at the risk of sounding vain, because I know I am vain, I'll say that when men look at me in the street I know why. They've good reason to. In 1930, when the agency I was working for folded, I posed for several commercial photographers. I've seen strange men studying my picture in a magazine and, though their eyes generally started at the ankles and worked up by degrees, I'm pleased to admit that they looked twice at the face, too. And I've read a book, I dance well because I love it, I know how to listen as well as talk, I can tell a touchback from a safety, I can hold my likker as well as my men—when I want to—and I know most of the right words. I seldom buy my own dinner.

I know that sounds conceited as the devil but, darn it, it's true. I'll lay twenty to one I can make any nine out of ten males, provided they are neither puling infants nor doddering antiquarians, ask for my phone number within any given half-hour.

So, when I say I've had more than the average experience with the technique of seduction (horrible phrase) I think I'm stating a simple truth.

When a gal is first turned loose in the world of man the game of seduction—win, lose or draw—is pretty exciting. And it continues to be for some years. At first, either your parents or your school keep you under observation and you're only exposed to younger men. Their approach, naturally, isn't as polished as that which you'll encounter later. Also, the fact that you are under some sort of surveillance means that you'll be exposed only occasionally and for brief periods of time and not to the extensive and intensive campaigns you'll have to face when you become what is so quaintly known as a "bachelor girl." During my last four years of school, a year abroad, and my first three or four years in New York I must admit that I thoroughly enjoyed the whole tiresome process; particularly so when I learned that, so long as I kept my head, the game could be played according to my own rules without ever hurting the boy friend's sense of masculine superiority in the least.

It was always a thrilling battle and the campaign itself was often more exciting than the storming, or attempted storming of one's last citadel. How many times I've lost in this warfare is entirely a matter of my own business. But I will say this: no campaigner, no matter how hardened, ever overcame my last line of defense unless I deliberately chose that he should—and that can hardly be counted a total defeat.

In the past year, sadly enough, I've come to realize that what was once an enthralling game is now a deadly bore. And I contend it's *all* the men's fault. A seduction should be above all things glamorous and exciting. But can there be glamor in a story repeated a dozen, yea a hundred times? Can glamor be expected to survive the hundredth ardent whispering of non-poetic time-worn words? Can there be excitement in a card game played eternally, with both players forever holding the same cards? There cannot!

Why don't men vary their approaches? Damn it, haven't they any originality? Must they be so monotonous?

Why is it that each man has at his command three or four of the seven standard approaches to seduction and selects his approach according to what he fondly believes to be his shrewd analysis of the character of the wench he is lusting for?

This is all wrong. And something should be done about it. Why don't men realize that an injection of originality or novelty into their love-making will get them further with the gal of their temporary choice than any pet phrases or standard passes the gibbering idiots can produce?

Repetition is so damned boring. The fun is all gone if, after the first kiss and the first declamation, you can, from past experience, anticipate practically every word and gesture that is to follow, be it a one night stand or a three week siege. And that isn't right—sex should be fun.

If you're a girl who hasn't given this matter any objective

thought, stop now and take stock. You'll be saddened and dis-illusioned to see what well-worn ruts your young men pursue.

And you, lad, believing yourself to be a Casanova as you do, cast your eyes over the following catalog—and blush for your sex's limitations. Blush, too, for yourself, for you have nothing more on the ball than any other man. You're unoriginal and trite. That swell build-up you were planning to use tonight and which you rather expected to send darling little Jean into a swoon will be the same build-up John used on her two months ago, Paul the week before, Ronald last year, and so on back to the days when she bought her first lipstick and lace panties. And you actually expected her to fall for it tonight? Fooey! Those girlish peals of laughter will probably be *at* you, rather than *with* you. But you have only to get yourself a new aproach, my lad, really new, and your path will be paved with recumbent maidens.

The following list contains what I've found to be the seven funda-mental approaches. There are, of course, variants but they are all variants of these basic seven. At least, my own experience and the experience of the attractive girls I know leads me to believe that this is a complete list. If it isn't, I've been neglected and I resent that. And if the young man will step forward to present credentials proving that he is in possession of an Approach Number Eight I'll be glad to meet him on his home grounds, winner take all.

APPROACH ONE
The Crudest

Simple, and very raw. The idea is for the male to ply you with likker until you lose control. The man who uses this approach is obviously a louse, obviously without resources, and so unsubtle that he is easily seen through and a cinch to out-smart. This technique is so bad it doesn't merit serious discussion. The only ones who will succumb to this attack are the completely foolish, those who are particularly light-headed drinkers and potential nymphomaniacs.

APPROACH TWO
The Cheapest

As crude in its way as *One*. This man tries to get at you through passionate declarations of love. He may even plead with you to marry him, *sometimes* soon. Meanwhile, since you are already man and wife in the eyes of God or, at the very least, two hearts that beat as one—how about it? The man who uses these tactics is probably an even greater louse than the likker-plying-male. The "I-love-you"-chanted-soulfully method will succeed only with susceptible virgins (any age) and those stridently emotional wenches of meager intelligence whose *métier* in life is rocking the cradle. The gal who has been around will merely enjoy her laugh, when approached in this manner, and promptly send the man back to the minor leagues, where he belongs.

Approach Three
The Ham-iest

The long-bearded "misunderstood husband" gag. No elucidation is needed. Only fools fall for this chestnut and it is doubtful if, after falling, they deserve any sympathy. It has been my experience that married men are seldom worth the trouble. It is generally wisest to send them home to the little woman, in short order.

Approach Four
The Outright Purchase

Like the Greeks, they come bearing gifts; generally expensive and so tendered that it is possible for the semi-prostitute to accept her wages without feeling too professional. The man who pulls this one isn't fooling. He means business and wants it tacitly understood that there are to be no strings attached to this business deal. And he is intelligent enough to know that the average female is capable of very long distance rationalizing and thus can graciously and righteously accept a fur coat or a diamond ring whereas she would regard the offer of actual cash as a terrific insult. This system, probably because it has a sound economic and not emotional basis, is liable to work with any of us who haven't been born heiresses. If the man is anywhere near as attractive as his gift it is sometimes necessary for a gal to summon up her last bit of will power to say "No." But it is usually worth it, if only to preserve those few remaining shreds of self respect.

APPROACH FIVE
The Big Brother Act

This predatory gent is an insidious operator where the unwary female is concerned. In the first place, he is patient. This, in itself, is unusual enough to throw you off. He starts off on a "just friends" basis and worms his way into your heart as a confidant and pal. Before you know it you are, on those odd nights, telling him all about your joys or sorrows with whichever Tom, Dick or Harry you are at the moment involved. He is very sweet, sympathetic and understanding. But he is playing a waiting game. He knows that eventually, human nature being what it is, there'll be a bust-up between you and the boy of the moment . . . and when it comes you'll find his broad shoulder there for you to weep on. You weep and you weep. You're on the rebound and desperately in need of masculine comforting. And suddenly you find that you're getting it in a very big, and totally unexpected way. And because you are weak and blue and emotionally drained and in need of some male tenderness you all at once become aware of the fact that your Big Brother is much sweeter and more desirable than you had ever found him to be before. And if he realizes this at the same time that you awaken . . . you're lost. When he puts on the pressure you're defenceless. I know that this approach depends upon extenuating circumstances but they occur far more frequently than one ever suspects. And a girl on the rebound is in no fit condition to put up an adequate defence. My only solution is this: never trust a man who tries to build up a *platonic* friendship with you. At the time it may seem to you that it would be *such* a relief to know a man like that, but you can with impunity bet your last garter-belt that you're wrong because, some place in the back of his mind, he'll have an idea or two . . .

APPROACH SIX
The Pseudo-Sophisticated

This approach has three subdivisions but they are all based on the same fundamental sophistry:

6-A. *The Philosophical.* The life-is-real, life-is-earnest, opportunity-knocks-but-once, so grab-each-fleeting-moment-while-you-may school. This is, of course, the veriest hokum, fit only for children in their teens. Every woman beyond the age of adolescence knows that this unique opportunity the gentleman is so magnanimously offering her is an opportunity that knocks all too damn frequently. Why any man who isn't completely witless ever thinks a girl will believe him to be the only one who will ever offer her a chance to indulge in a life of sin is beyond me. So, girls, the next time a man pulls this, "Tonight is ours!" line on you, control your laughter, let him down gently, and send him on his way. The stronger sex? Physically, yes.

6-B. *The Pagan.* This lad is likely to have long hair. He has read *Ulysses* and has a glib knowledge of neo-realistic painting or something of that sort. He thinks very highly of individualism and can quote Nietzsche's remarks about the Superman (himself). He tells you that the old, conventional moral standards of our fathers are outmoded (news to you?) and insists that today we see such things as sexual relations with a new vision, a proper perspective. "After all, we want each other, and what is there to stop us?" he asks. "Aren't we free people, free to live our own lives?" You are also free to point out to him that "we want each other" is taking altogether too much for granted. You explain, in as tactful and gentle terms as the situation requires, that a fairly ardent kiss or two, permitted in a moment of weakness, doesn't exactly establish the fact that you are willing to turn over the body beautiful. He'll never believe, of course, that it wasn't your inhibitions which prevented you from succumbing and he'll go on his way, still proud of his free and soaring spirit, in search of a girl with low heels and spectacles, who thinks Communism would be nice. And he'll say to her "Look at Russia," and get away with it. I don't want to look at Russia. Blouses and smocks? Not with my torso.

6-C. *The Physical.* Whereas the first chap in this category went at you on a philosophical plane, so-called and the second tried to weaken you on a moral and individualistic grounds the "Physical" lad goes to the root of the matter and attacks you with body blows. His weapons are psychiatry, Freudian psychology and your glands. These physical realists always have your well being at heart. They explain at great length that sex is an appetite which must be satisfied if one isn't to become a victim of all sorts of fetishes and suppressed desires. Now, no girl would want to become amorous in public with a Shetland pony or become addicted to horsewhipping her grandmother. It isn't being done. The obvious solution is to permit whichever physical realist is at the moment spouting his propaganda to come between you and the tragedies of perversion. The whole affairs is, of course, to be conducted in your own best interests.

We may very well be animals and victims of appetites which must be satisfied in order to prevent complexes and frustrations. I'm willing to admit that the boys may have something there. But, so far, I've been able to order my own meals and I think I'll continue to do so. When I'm hungry I'll eat, if the proper food is available, and no one is going to force improperly prepared food on me when I'm not hungry . . . and my grandmother will have to take her chances.

APPROACH SEVEN

The "Forcing" Method

Or perhaps I should call it the cat-and-mouse attack. In any event, the glib gentleman who works this approach on you is primarily concerned with forcing *you* to make the final move and "Safety First" is obviously his motto.

The opening lines generally read something like this, "I don't love you and I know you don't love me—but I can't help wanting you. Why pretend? I think you're swell—sex excluded—but you're so damned attractive that, no matter how hard I try, when I'm with you I want you." Then he adds, oh very frankly and fairly, "I like you so much that I have to be honest with you. If I continue to see you I'll make love to you, I can't help myself. If you want me to stop coming around, now that you know, you've only to say so." The only catch in this last speech is that he only produces it when he is pretty damn sure that you like him a lot and enjoy being with him. Of course you, liking him as you do and feeling on safe terrain because he hasn't so much as touched you, laugh it off and take your chances.

But after a night or two of conversation in the same vein but growing progressively more intense, the chances are that he will kiss you; ardently, of course, and probably with considerable finesse—and you've given the inch that may cost you your virtue.

Gently and insidiously the campaign progresses. Each night it will become a little more intense and each night your defences will fall back an inch or two. But he will never use force, never put on any obvious pressure. Each time you feel called upon to say "Stop," he'll stop—to your growing annoyance. And, though you probably won't realize it, that is one word you'll come to use less and less frequently.

Slowly and inevitably the tide, to use a figure of speech, creeps up and up until that night when you've forgotten even the meaning of the word—and then the louse stops of his own accord!

The speeches at this point are liable to be on the impassioned side and to deal at some length with his desire for you and your many darling qualities and so on far into the night. Eventually he gets around to asking you if you, too, desire him. After what has just transpired you wonder if he is a complete idiot, then reassure him in your own subtle way.

This generally calls for a clinch and the addition of fuel to the flame. After a proper interval he pulls the Remorse-stop. It goes something like this and is generally delivered in a somewhat throaty voice, "I want you *soooo* much (pause) but I can't let you do this unless you are sure in your own mind. We're excited now, my dear, (he's telling you!) and I wouldn't want you to do anything you'd later regret. I want you more than anyone I've ever known, (this is standard; note careful evasion of the word *love*) but this is too beautiful an adventure to rush into headlong." While you're wondering just how he would have you rush into said adventure he makes a suggestion, "Sleep on it tonight and think it over in the clear light of day, tomorrow. We'll meet for dinner, and then you can give me your decision."

You agree, and this leads to another scene that wouldn't get by the Will Hays' office and considerable incoherent and what he thinks is poetic talk about how much he hopes you'll feel tomorrow night as you do tonight.

Then to the much discussed sleep and "thinking (if any) in the light of day." It would serve the gent right if the daylight led to a decision he wouldn't like but for some darned reason it seldom does.

When you meet him the next night he is pretty solemn about the whole thing (but you can be sure he'll give you the best dinner he can afford, with a rather obvious emphasis on the wine list). Once you get back to whichever apartment is the scene of combat you'll find that tenderness is the preliminary mood of the evening. He may not use his arms and hands as they were intended to be used at all, but if he does he'll be very, very gentle. In desperation you finally take him by the hand, figuratively speaking, and lead him to the bedroom.

It may be several days before you begin to realize that you've been *had* in more ways than one. And if this realization doesn't come to you shortly you are in an even worse position because you've been had so thoroughly that your heart may well be in your young man's hands—and that is one section of your anatomy which should remain permanently yours.

There is a mild variant to this approach. In this method the man, at the critical point, doesn't suggest a little daylight thought on the subject but, instead, goes dramatic and says, "No, this can't be. The price you pay is too large," or words to that effect. It works out in exactly the same way. One says, "Perhaps," and the other says, "No," and in the end you are unconsciously forced into taking them both by the hand . . .

This is probably the most difficult form of seduction to work clear of—because you've been allowed to work yourself into it.

These are the standardized versions of sexual Blind Man's Buff, Tag, You're It, or whatever you want to call it, as I know them. There are probably others, depending on race, color or previous condition of servitude but I wager that they in their way are just as standardized. What to do about it?

Sometimes I think I'd rather be attacked. Or at least meet a man direct enough to say bluntly and without preamble, "I think you're swell and I'd like to make love to you. I warn you, if you say no I'll ask you the same thing tomorrow night. What will it be, milady's boudoir or the movies?"

The hell of it is, experience has so conditioned me that I'd probably choose the movies and be forced to sit through a Hollywood version of the preliminaries of one of the stereotyped brands of seduction I've listed. There's no escape.

ESSAY ON JIGGLING

By George A. McNamara

SPRING IS HERE. THE GIRLS HAVE EMERGED FROM THEIR WINTER cocoons of cloth and fur and the jiggle is once more abroad in the land. All winter long the jiggle, that gayest decoration of the public scene, that champagne of movement which can be accomplished only by the human female, has been obscured from the public gaze by heavy fabrics and voluminous draperies. With the coming of spring, it has blossomed forth once more, lightly clothed in gay prints, to charm and adorn a drab and care-worn world. It gets more delighted attention than all of Mother Earth's new-born and colorful horticultural display. It inspires more of the bubbly, electric feeling of well-being than all of the conventional, publicized harbingers of spring together. Everybody sees the jiggling and each one is charmed by it. But no one has a kind word to say for it. It is treated as an infirmity, partly physical and partly moral and better not spoken of at all. Even the poets ignore it. They twang their lyres to the birds and the bees, the sunshine and the trees, they make grateful mention of the maiden herself, her eyes and her sighs, her dresses and her tresses but they say nothing at all about her pleasingly complicated mode of locomotion. They, like everyone else, avoid jiggling, in words, if not in the flesh.

This graceless convention has penetrated even to the irresponsible and carefree as I learned one day when I made, to a very young lady, a light and passing allusion to the girls' jiggling. She looked concerned for a moment. Then she leaned closer to me and in a confidential voice she implied a mild reproof. "They can't help it," she whispered. She sat back with such a pleased air of having been helpful and informative upon a delicate subject that only a brute could have said he thanked God they couldn't help.

This hypocritical shushing of something everyone sees and enjoys is a vestige of puritanism still successfully murdering the esthetic and charming. A lovely girl makes pleasant and cheerful

41

any scene at all and she confers a favor upon each person who sees her. People look at her and after her because the sight of her pleases them. And she pleases them with no cold and static beauty.

The museums are full of classic marble compositions but their aisles are empty except for a few nearsighted grinds hunting for culture. She offers living beauty, youth in motion, cheerful and hopeful and gay. However serious her errand she proceeds to its discharge by a series of complicated evolutions which make everybody who sees her feel better. She jiggles. And in spite of all the shushing, in spite of her own earnest endeavors to proceed in only one direction at one time, various portions of her persist in swinging along on their own harmonic lines of motion. And the faster she hurries, the faster she jiggles. Even the Board of Education which has ruined more young women than any other force or agency is helpless before the jiggle and its young teachers are as entertaining as they are instructive. Advancing years, of course, take away their entertaining qualities and their cheerfulness but advancing years would do that almost as quickly without any help from the Board. The essential point is that all the girls, however admonished or instructed, continue to jiggle for the delight of the common people without any sanction from society or any intention of their own. Everybody sees it and enjoys it but only God approves of it.

In view of the conspiracy of silence on the subject, it is remarkable that we have such a word as jiggle. The meaning of the word is definite and widely understood—jiggling is what happens when a young woman walks. Or turns or bends or reaches or stamps her foot. And she approaches the absolutely ultimate in jiggling when she runs. Hers is a purely human achievement in this machine age. Machines may shake, they may vibrate or oscillate but they can never, never jiggle.

Although the meaning of the word is clear and definite, it is difficult to describe the jiggle because it is an integral part of the intricate succession of exercises by which women propel themselves from one spot to another. Of course women wiggle and the wiggling causes jiggling but the wiggling is beside the point. Wiggling is neither here nor there, we will confine ourselves to jiggling. A jiggle occurs when some portion of the body, having been left behind when the major portion was in motion and wishing to catch up, gives a sprightly bounce. In its anxiety not to be left alone, it overleaps its proper position and finding itself without support from the main body, it quickly retires too far, whereupon a secondary jiggle ensues. It is all liveliness and eagerness and gaiety. And as some parts are sliding back while others are catching up, each in its own tempo and arc, yet all somehow holding to the central movement, the effect is indescribably spirited and jolly. It is a symphony of motion *allegretto*, a symphony of joy and hope, a symphony with a message. It says in the language of the emotions, which is the proper language of a symphony, that it is not good for man to use all his energies in the grubby business of acquiring goods or to give all his thought to the injustices of society or to the dour contemplation of the future of his race. It presents, most appealingly, the lovely and the lively. And it makes plain that these things, with the good nature inherent in them, can give more happiness than all the efficiency and forethought in the world. Everybody sees the girls walking along and everybody is pleased and cheered up.

And the remarkable part of it is that the girls themselves have little to do with the cheer and good feeling they disseminate. Young ladies are essentially serious creatures. They lay deep plans for the most trifling adventures and they worry enormously over the most trivial eventualities. It is only their bodies which are lively and irresponsible and which, by their antics, keep them smiling and gay. And all the attractiveness they bring to the public scene is due to their brightness and eagerness and their general effect of uncontrollable but charming activity.

Consider Lois as she hurries to the office at a canter. She is all anxiety at what the boss will have to say if she is late. She is possessed of one idea. She is feverish with haste and concern. But does she present a picture of harassed distraction? Not at all, not at all. Her garments have been chosen in a more leisurely moment for their brightness and appeal. Her face and hair and hat have been pleasingly tended. But more than all this, she moves so brightly and eagerly in a fascinating blend of so many small, epicycloidal lines of motion that the effect is entrancing—she jiggles. Who shall say how many worn householders have brightened at the sight and having felt the blue devils within them weaken for a moment, gritted their teeth and resolved to hold onto the ancestral home in Teaneck? Or how many fat industrialists, gloomily contemplating the state of business and tempted to dump a line on the market, have held their hands at the vague memory of a vast and promising busyness recently beheld? The industrialists may not remember but the vast busyness was just Lois and her sisters trotting, very seriously, about their inconsequential affairs. And these are no special instances for there are girls like Lois jiggling up and down every street and avenue, every lane and highway in the country, broadcasting a message of joy and hope. Spring is here.

It is a melancholy thought that each one of them will, some day, lose her jiggle. With advancing years the jiggle becomes a menace. A woman is in grave danger of flying to pieces. To prevent any such unpleasantness, she binds herself into one solid, inelastic lump and thereafter jiggles no more.

With her person in close and continual restraint, she carries on under difficulties particularly in warm weather. No longer does she scatter good cheer all about but saves her smiles until the favor she wishes is most immediate. And then, one awful day, comes the realization that nobody looks at her any more. Nobody even listens to her. This soul-shaking irreparable loss of her audience so deranges her psyche that she develops the disposition and facial expression of a spitting cobra. In her confusion of spirit, she falls into futile vindictiveness and she treats each member of the calloused and inattentive human race with the screeching animosity she formerly showed only to mice, snakes and things that crawled out from under flat stones. Animosity and vindictiveness are catching and as she composes twenty-five per cent of our population, her unsettling effect on the body politic is enormous. We are able to maintain a stable form of government only because all males engaged in her service have adopted a universal incantation which, muttered to themselves immediately upon her departure, exorcises the residue of her visit and leaves them free to be bland and conciliatory to the next customer.

A world from which the jiggle had been removed and all women were like that is an impossibility. Nobody would ever have any children. The will to live would be irritated right out of the human race and no one would wait for his physical envelope to wear out before having a look at the next world.

It is sufficiently distressing to remember that is the state to which all the happy, smiling girls about us must some day come. But let us be glad we have them with us, to brighten and animate the daily scene for a short time, before they settle down to being a helpmate for some one man and a nest of scorpions to everyone else in the world. Let us be glad their lively mode of locomotion is largely outside their control and not to be modified by any silly notions which staid elders may put in their heads. And lastly let us be glad for the gay, lively, hopeful air which they disseminate through a medium which so successfully attracts the eye. For though you may never have noticed the great social significance of the jiggle, you do notice the jiggle itself. And so does your old man. Spring is here.

A REPORT ON MAN'S BEST FRIEND

By LAWRENCE MARTIN

FOR TWO YEARS MY ASSISTANTS AND I HAVE BEEN STUDYING THE DOG situation. We have interviewed dog men; visited pounds; inspected the booming dog industry; perused the dog press; pondered the overtones of Irene Castle McLaughlin's annual Pooch Ball; compiled statistics, and mastered the vast literature of the subject, including the Dog Encyclopedia which answers 10,000 questions about Hydrocephalus, Dingo, and Dewclaws. We are ready to report.

At the outset we must see this thing in perspective. It means sketching in the philosophical background.

Men everywhere face three problems, the solution of which is the major chore of living. First they must maintain themselves on the earth—must eat, must shelter and clothe themselves, and have enough left over for the annual pilgrimage to the old home town. This, the economic problem, poses the second: how the takings of harvest and shop are to be divided, and who will boss the show— roughly, the political trouble. From the solution of these two stems the third: by what philosophies, cosmic genuflections, gadgets, toys, arts, and other eloquent self-deceptions men will be able to kid themselves into believing that it is all worth the toil and suffering;—that, in fact, whatever the current setup (barbarism, feudalism, capitalism, fascism, or plain slavery) it is the only thinkable and decent arrangement.

This is the Cultural Problem, the problem of cushioning life; and the dog is part of it. For this animal, in his present multitudinous incarnations and mongrelisms, is a creation of man. Though designed to help on Problem One (sheep dogs, Belgian, Dutch, and Danish hounds pulling tradesmen's carts) and Problem Two (watch and police dogs), the beast is mainly a cultural contraption. His function, that is, resides in enabling us to crowd out of our consciousness the intrinsic ennui, the undependability, the treacherous lonesomeness of life.

46

We cannot rely upon one another for companionship or fidelity. But when all things fail, a man's Schnauzer will still walk with him, or look up from the domestic rug with utter trust and solicitude. A middle-aged matron may present three chins to the world, but to her Peke she is Juno. Socially dogs serve a like purpose. A pup in the living room keeps the conversation from dying out among a miscellany of people with nothing to say to one another, having only a need to huddle together, to be un-alone.

The emancipated intellect, free from dogphilia, loathes the dog-mindedness of man with its parade of pooches led night and morning to physiological rendezvous and leaving on the city streets nasty tokens of success. But those of us who don't need a dog-pal to buck us up must realize the subject is big, that the dog, like art museums, libraries, Wagnerian operas, Rotary luncheons, and the sports page, is an institution devised to keep the Ultimate Un-thinkable Uselessness of things at bay.

Realizing this, he will understand why the dog population of his country stands at twelve million. Why the dog items in our leading newspaper, the New York *Times*, average slightly better than one a day, and not a Man Bites Dog among them. Why there is a tradition and practice of dog-humaneness that often puts child care to shame. Why a far-flung business in and around dogs flourishes, from orphan puppy nipples, through clinics, dietetics, booties, cosmetics, sex aids and discouragers, to the final tombstone or crematory urn. And the world being, as O'Casey put it, "in a turrible state o' chassis," it should occasion no surprise that the dogreliance of spiritually insecure man held its own through the weary depression—especially in the United States, which has pushed Great Britain out of first place as the dog haven of the world.

Aside from their psychic value, dogs are nuisances. Their utility has been grossly exaggerated. Innumerable canines, it is true, run little errands, chiefly to the meat market to fetch their own supper. Maybe your Collie goes to the corner drugstore for the paper, but can he be relied upon to pick the *Christian Science Monitor* from among tabloids and Hearst? On Monday we read of the dog Susie turning in a fire alarm, but on Tuesday it appears that a jewelry store thief has stolen the watch dog along with the diamonds.

The subtle propaganda of the anti-vivisection societies, with their picture of a St. Bernard dog wearing his rescue kit as a necklace, hides the greater truth that the dog is more helped than helper. That the animals, like Horatio Alger heroes, do a lot of rescue work, such as saving babies from burning houses or boys from treacherous swimming holes, is a myth. More often it's the other way around. Babies are continually rescuing dogs from conflagrations, and boys have been drowned trying to pull Fido out of the mere. In a celebrated recent case in New York State the dog Idaho was tried for playfully drowning a lad. The village of three thousand divided on his guilt; the dog had character witnesses and an alibi. He might have been innocent, but a mugg that approximated Idaho did it, for the boy stayed drowned. And when he's being useful, the dog likely as not overdoes it, like the one that stopped a fight by biting three Negroes and a cop. How he overlooked the innocent bystanders is a mystery. The research of two years puts the dog in a pathetic light. The touted rescuer is forever being rescued. He falls down crevasses. He gets marooned on ice floes (always managing to freeze his tail to the cake). He gets caught in chicken wire fences or lost in flues and ventilators. Not infrequently he may cost his owner fifty dollars for the services of six men to pry him out of a no-dog place like a culvert. A Pennsylvania freight train limped into its destination hours late because the crew stopped out in the prairie to extricate a beagle hound who was hanging by his hind leg to a wire fence. A fox terrier stopped five trains on the subway and caused rush-hour chaos while a posse gathered him in from among the furrows of live rails. Dogs are always leaping from ocean liners and being hauled in by the coast guard.

Not even bloodhounds always know their stuff. One ran down a footpad suspect, but the lie detector contradicted him. Another was put on the case of a missing girl. It kept leading the police and the neighborhood down to a slip by the river. The river was dragged, and everything but a little girl was brought up. Eventually the child was found sleeping in a neighbor's hammock. A Solomon of a judge once neatly decided a litigation over ownership of a dog by having the parties call to the object of their legal quarrel. It unfailingly answered one and not the other. Weeks later a similar case came up, and this dog came at the call of both parties, and also of the judge, bailiff, court clerk, reporters and spectators. The thing ended in a hilarious riot. It was a willing dog, but not smart.

In addition to the well meaning who are forever making trouble, there is the problem of canines bent on malicious mischief, and getting into the courts and eventually into the death chamber. This extends from the Scotties that just had to bite people and the Pinscher who was an incorrigible tipperover of garbage cans, to the wild spirits that live for the kill. In a single year in one state dogs destroyed: fowls, 24,473; head of cattle, 273; sheep and lambs, 10,729—a rather imposing score. Two co-operating Black Legion curs disposed of 35 chickens in a single raid, and a pack of Fascist mongrels annihilated 293 hens before they were rounded up.

Thus the degree of UD (Utility Dog) which is the highest rating conferred on the élite, is in no danger of attaining wholesale distribution. The lower rating, CDX, or Companion Dog Excellent, has a wider spread, for the trial balance of the dog, decidedly on the debit side, shows psychic worth as an antidote to the inferiority complex. Some dogs are hard to love, like the Loebell Brussels Griffon, a rare species but not rare enough. The animal has one eye, bowlegs, a bad heart, asthma, and a fretful disposition, but probably for reasons cited in the earlier paragraphs manages to stay in the family. A couple of years ago the tourist-third passengers on the *S. S. Rotterdam* were all atwitter because a college sophomore daily grew to look more like the Welsh terrier he was bringing back as a vacation souvenir. I knew a gaffer in Wales who had grown to look like his old Sealyham, sideburns and all. Nor does this sort of thing happen only abroad or on the high seas. Every day a man goes by my club leading a Chow, and either the Chow has grown to look like him, or he like the Chow—the family resemblance is unmistakable.

The affinity of man and dog being, then, not only psychological but in cases physical, it should shock no one that human beings go to strange lengths to see that their pet wants little here below, nor wants that little long. My agents have pried out fourteen magazines that serve the dog public. The Morris couple of Lenox, Massachusetts, were so gone on their Peke, Miss Rose, that they listed her in the Social Register.

More than thirty different brands of dog food are nationally advertised, and in any large city one can have the doggie dinner delivered. Take Kanine Kitchens, for example: it gives a balanced diet for a Chow at $1.53 a week; for a smaller dog, say a Peke, at

$0.94. The food is delivered three times a week. This leaves an extra day on which, presumably, the pup subsists on leftovers, like his master dallying with the meat loaf. These Rover Rations contain meat, calcium, cereals, roughage, phosphorus, and cod-liver oil. All the vitamins and calories are there; and if this news stacks up grimly against the little known fact that one-third of American children are undernourished (in some Southern counties, 73%), the answer of a notorious dogwoman is in point: "If children are undernourished it doesn't mean that dogs should be too." A Princeton chap a couple of years ago started a dog restaurant. He now serves 15,000 pounds of beef to 6,000 dogs, has branches throughout the East and has opened a London joint. Professional dog feeding grows as more people live in apartment hotels. The meals come on paper plates done up in cellophane and waxed paper. The stuff is accurately weighed, the menus built by dieticians. The dogs even go on a Friday fish course. There are special slenderizing diets for prize dogs facing the ordeal of the show.

Chicago, a representative city, contains 38 dog hospitals, which includes one clock-around ambulance service. For the proletarian dog there is the free clinic of the Anti-Cruelty Society. When your pet fails to get over whatever ails him (and even aristocrats die —Bunjie, the $10,000 Boston Bull, passed out in a heat wave in spite of electric fans in the kennel, ice packs, and oxygen), you can give him a fancy funeral, depositing the remains in a dog cemetery which concedes nothing in beauty to the best final parking places awaiting you and me. There is one out west of where I live, on a hill, covering six and a half acres of beautifully wooded ground. People who care enough for their pets to give them funerals take good care of the graves; they bring wreaths and plant flowers. The caretaker tells of a widow who every Sunday passes up her ex-spouse's grave to deposit a floral tribute on the resting place of her pet. The "package price" burial for a small dog (they have some way of deciding when Pal is over-package) is $25.00. Caskets are white silk-lined pine boxes. Monuments run from $14.50 to $300; they usually display the name and vital facts, perhaps a picture. They run to sentiment: "To My Faithful Pet," "Here Lies Darling Bunny." Brash epitaphs like the 18th Century's "Here lies his Highness' dog of Kew; Pray tell me, sir, whose dog are you?" no longer rate. Cremation costs $6—ashes in plain box if your intent is to scatter them over the garden or bury them in a favorite spot; $6.50 if you prefer them in an urn suitable for the mantel.

Every dog has its day, and the paths of the dog-walking services lead but to the grave. In the meantime, between the Kanine Kitchen Kutlets and the final urn, you can get your dog aired for twenty-five cents the walk, or cut rates by the week. Private schools flourish, where the curriculum consists of manners, tricks, and not wetting the carpet. Of the many dog laundries (they wash the dog, not the dog linen) the most famous is that of little Marcia, braintruster Tugwell's enterprising daughter. When in Washington with your pet, get the animal a Tugwell rubdown, thirty cents and up. The dog industrial boom has made it relatively easy to take the creature on an extended motor trip. Along the more frequent highways like the Boston Post Road will be found concessions where dogs can get special meals while master and mistress dine and dance next door.

Nor need rain and weather longer be harsh experiences for your tender penthouse pet. For the rain which falls on blue-ribbon Borzoi and alley outcast alike, there are rubber boots at five dollars the set, and coats of rubberized cellophane in green, red, and yellow. For the shrewd winds there are sweaters, and coats in rakish plaids, even imitation leopard skins. If the pavement is hard on Prince's tootsies, you can get leather boots made to order.

No longer is it necessary for the family quadruped to eat out of a decrepit tin picpan or push a bone around on an old newspaper spread in the kitchen hallway. The new order of things which includes special feeding spoons for the little ones and nursing bottles for orphan puppies, has devised the Doggie Dinette, a two-bowler on a wooden stand, made by (of all people) the Period Furniture Company of Dayton. The old burlap sack is outmoded, and in its place "pure cedar bedding," pillows of green denim with red tufting, the Kumfort Dog Mattress—a nice ensemble with everything except a canopy and monogrammed draw-curtains, 24 x 30 and only $6.18.

A hundred years ago Americans were crude people, as the old travel books of Europeans testify. They ate pie and ice cream with a knife, picked their teeth at table, at formal parties spat on carpets and portieres, and regarded a bath as a health risk. Nowadays even a dog has better manners. In those days American dogs were mean curs whose chief use was as scavengers of the garbage dumped in the gutter in front of houses. All is changed. In the bright pampered age of Emily Post and Elizabeth Arden the dog must be as clean as a hound's tooth, and then some. If your dog isn't as sweet as your stenographer, whose fault is it, with these items in the local bazaar?—

Manicure set in leather case.
Wash-up Kit—towel, spray, powder.
Emergency kit for traveling.
Dude—exclusive dog shampoo.
Sleekote Deodorant and Hair Dressing in fancy bottle, smartly packaged to resemble doghouse (smells like bay rum).
Kosmetic Kit in pale blue box containing screw-top bottles and jars with shampoo, deodorant, tonic, and freshener, talcum, salve, and boric acid cream.

The high point, though, is registered by Bonwit Teller's new creation "Leash." Let them tell about it:

DO YOUR DOGS OFFEND?

Every summer an increasing number of women come in to buy cologne for their pets. And they say even the sternest mastiffs are pleased because it makes them socially acceptable at all times. Dogs hate to be banished from company. So we've had an exclusive deodorizing cologne with a nice, clean woodsy scent brewed specially for them. Nothing sissy about it.

The dog industry is new and booming. It is based on the aristocracy which, represented by the American Kennel Club and its registrations, has a longer history than many things American. More than a million pedigreed dogs have checked in during the last half century. The 1936 registrations, estimated at 84,000, will exceed 1935's by a good per cent, to constitute the all time American high in the fancy dog line. A hundred thousand dogs in the nation are in training—not for anything in particular but just against one another. On the fancy breeds, the "noble and well-born," more than thirty million dollars was spent for feed, kennels, medicines, etc., in the first part of 1936, an increase of 23% over the same period of 1935. If the twelve million run-of-the-mill hounds of the country eat the average ration of a well-fed Peke, our annual dog food bill runs to $624,000,000. Add the other costs and you wonder how the pet budget is ever balanced.

Among other odds and ends needing mention is the fact that even civilized whelps have sex urges. In these the master class interferes in its own interest. On the one hand it invents and applies "Cupid Chaser," a dope foisted upon the lady in season, guaranteed to make her offensive even to the Casanovas of the species. On the other it engineers a program of planned sex, as in this come-on in the magazine ads:

> Prospective Matrons
> Sire: Ari of Kettle Cove
> (Sg. Lux ex Anita by Troll)
> Dam: ch. Lady Anna v. Seigrist
> (Int. Ch. Favoriet ex Ch. Trail 'Em)
> Ready to Breed

Dogs were among the world war heroes, and there was some agitation for a dog bonus. Lieutenant Bobby, the only dog officer, is retired. Rags, an alley pup, carried messages under fire in a lousier war than dogs could ever have contrived; he was gassed and wounded, and on his death rated both monument and biography. Another famous dog was Nellie, the mascot of a couple of hundred newspaper men and gals at the front in the ignoble spectacle, The State versus Bruno. The reporters adopted him and kept him down in the basement of Flemington's Union Hotel, where they had converted a poolroom into a bar. Here, between the liquor and being nice to Nellie, they tried to forget the tripe they had to turn out by the toilettissue reel: another argument for Dog as Escape.

The importance of the dog in human relations is placed in a new light by these remarks in the London *Evening Standard*:

"In these days of international stress it is a relief to hear of the formation, under distinguished patronage, of a vital society to be called the Fellowship of Faithful Friends. The 'F.F.F.,' as it is to be called for short, qualifies the extent of its friendship with four more 'F.'s'—'four-footed, furry, and feathered.' The founders maintain that in our treatment of animals lies the vital factor in eliminating war and lessening unemployment, hence they propose to organize 'dog parties, cat parties, bird parties, monkey parties (if enough) and other pet parties.'"

What strange complications the future holds as dogs become more ubiquitous, egregious, and cultured only astrologers can tell who practice under the sign of Canus Major, and maybe not they. The case of the lad Bert Long who ran away from home with his pup is a small portent. Stranded in Florida, Bert wrote home for carfare. The Longs sent a money order made out to boy and dog both. After a lot of trouble a judge was finally found who waived the pup's signature.

But the time will come when dogs who have hit the human trail will be able to sign their own names. When those days arrive, Sugar-Plum, CDX, UD, the literary Pekinese, rising up from her silken cushion after her Doggie Dessert, will neglect her deodorant, her manicure, her tonic, her freshener, her shampoo, her talcum, her salve, her boric acid cream, her anti-belch medicine, and her Cupid Chaser, to write a Report on the Human Situation and man's too desperate dependence on the dog. I will bet the price of a pooch pudding, nay of a bitch banquet, that the report will hark back to the smelly old days when men were men and dogs gamboled in the garbage.

CHRIST IN CONCRETE

By Pietro di Donato

MARCH WHISTLED STINGING SNOW AGAINST THE BRICK WALLS AND up the gaunt girders. Geremio, the foreman, swung his arms about, and gaffed the men on.

Old Nick, the "Lean," stood up from over a dust-flying brick pile, and tapped the side of his nose.

"Master Geremio, the devil himself could not break his tail any harder than we here."

Burly Vincenzo of the walrus mustache and known as the "Snoutnose," let fall the chute door of the concrete hopper and sang over in the Lean's direction. "Mari-Annina's belly and the burning night will make of me once more a milk-mouthed stripling lad. . . ."

The Lean loaded his wheelbarrow and spat furiously. "Sons of two-legged dogs . . . despised of even the devil himself! Work! Sure! For America beautiful will eat you and spit your bones into the earth's hole! Work!" And with that his wiry frame pitched the barrow violently over the rough floor.

Snoutnose waved his head to and fro and with mock pathos wailed, "Sing on, oh guitar of mine. . . ."

Short, cheery-faced Joe Chiappa, the scaffoldman, paused with hatchet in hand and tenpenny spike sticking out from small dice-like teeth to tell the Lean as he went by, in a voice that all could hear, "Ah, father of countless chicks, the old age is a carrion!"

Geremio chuckled and called to him. "Hey little Joe, who are you to talk? You and big-titted Cola can't even hatch an egg, whereas the Lean has just to turn the doorknob of his bedroom and old Philomena becomes a balloon!"

Coarse throats tickled and mouths opened wide in laughter.

Mike, the "Barrel-mouth" pretended he was talking to himself and yelled out in his best English . . . he was always speaking English while the rest carried on in their native Italian. "I don't

55

know myself, but somebodys whose gotta bigga buncha keeds and he alla times talka from somebodys elsa!"

Geremio knew it was meant for him and he laughed. "On the tomb of Saint Pimple-legs, this little boy my wife is giving me next week shall be the last! Eight hungry little Christians to feed, is enough for any man."

Joe Chiappa nodded to the rest. "Sure, Master Geremio had a telephone call from the next bambino. Yes, it told him it had a little bell there instead of a rose bush. . . . It even told him its name!"

"Laugh, laugh all of you," returned Geremio, "but I tell you that all my kids must be boys so that they some day will be big American builders. And then I'll help them to put the gold away in the basements for safe keeping!"

A great din of riveting shattered the talk among the fast-moving men. Geremio added a handful of "Honest" tobacco to his corncob, puffed strongly, and cupped his hands around the bowl for a bit of warmth. The chill day caused him to shiver, and he thought to himself, "Yes, the day is cold, cold . . . but who am I to complain when the good Christ himself was crucified?

"Pushing the job is all right, (when has it been otherwise in my life?) but this job frightens me. I feel the building wants to tell me something; just as one Christian to another. I don't like this. Mr. Murdin tells me, 'Push it up!' That's all he knows. I keep telling him that the underpinnings should be doubled and the old material removed from the floors, but he keeps the inspector drunk and . . . 'Hey, Ashes-ass! Get away from under that pilaster! Don't pull the old work. Push it away from you or you'll have a nice present for Easter if the wall falls on you!' . . . Well, with the help of God I'll see this job through. It's not my first, nor the . . . 'Hey, Patsy number two! Put more cement in that concrete; we're putting up a building, not an Easter cake!' "

Patsy hurled his shovel to the floor and gesticulated madly. "The padrone Murdin-sa tells me, 'Too much, too much! Lil' bit is plenty!' And you tell me I'm stingy! The rotten building can fall after I leave!"

Six floors below, the contractor called. "Hey Geremio! Is your gang of dagos dead!"

Geremio cautioned to the men. "On your toes, boys. If he writes out slips, someone won't have big eels on the Easter table."

The Lean cursed that "the padrone could take the job and shove it . . . !"

Curly-headed Sandino, the roguish, pigeon-toed scaffoldman, spat a clod of tobacco juice and hummed to his own music. . . . "Yes, certainly yes to your face, master padrone . . . and behind, this to you and all your kind!"

The day, like all days, came to an end. Calloused and bruised bodies sighed, and numb legs shuffled towards shabby railroad flats. . . .

"Ah, *bella casa mio*. Where my little freshets of blood, and my good woman await me. Home where my broken back will not ache so. Home where midst the monkey chatter of my piccolinos I will float off to blessed slumber with my feet on the chair and the head on the wife's soft full breast."

These great child-hearted ones leave each other without words or ceremony, and as they ride and walk home, a great pride swells the breast. . . .

"Blessings to Thee, oh Jesus. I have fought winds and cold. Hand to hand I have locked dumb stones in place and the great building rises. I have earned a bit of bread for me and mine."

The mad day's brutal conflict is forgiven, and strained limbs prostrate themselves so that swollen veins can send the yearning blood coursing and pulsating deliciously as though the body mountained leaping streams.

The job alone remained behind . . . and yet, they too, having left the bigger part of their lives with it. The cold ghastly beast, the Job, stood stark, the eerie March wind wrapping it in sharp shadows of falling dusk.

That night was a crowning point in the life of Geremio. He bought a house! Twenty years he had helped to mold the New World. And now he was to have a house of his own! What mattered that it was no more than a wooden shack? It was his own!

He had proudly signed his name and helped Annunziata to make her x on the wonderful contract that proved them owners. And she was happy to think that her next child, soon to come, would be born under their own rooftree. She heard the church chimes, and cried to the children, "Children, to bed! It is near midnight. And remember, shut-mouth to the *paesanos*! Or they will send the evil eye to our new home even before we put foot."

The children scampered off to the icy yellow bedroom where three slept in one bed and three in the other. Coltishly and friskily they kicked about under the covers; their black iron-cotton stockings not removed . . . what! and freeze the peanut-little toes?

Said Annunziata, "The children are so happy, Geremio; let them be, for even I, would a Tarantella dance." And with that she turned blushing. He wanted to take her on her word. She patted his hands, kissed them, and whispered. "Our children will dance for us . . . in the American style someday."

Geremio cleared his throat and wanted to sing. "Yes, with joy I could sing in a richer feeling than the great Caruso." He babbled little old country couplets and circled the room until the tenant below tapped the ceiling.

Annunziata whispered, "Geremio, to bed and rest. Tomorrow is a day for great things . . . and the day on which our Lord died for us."

The children were now hard asleep. Heads under the cover, over . . . moist noses whistling, and little damp legs entwined.

In bed Geremio and Annunziata clung closely to each other. They mumbled figures and dates until fatigue stilled their thoughts. And with chubby Johnnie clutching fast his bottle and warmed between them . . . life breathed heavily, and dreams entertained in far, far worlds, the nation builder's brood.

But Geremio and Annunziata remained for a while staring into darkness, silently.

"Geremio?"

"Yes?"

"This job you are now working. . . ."

"So?"

"You used always to tell me about what happened on the jobs . . . who was jealous, and who praised. . . ."

"You should know by now that all work is the same. . . ."

"Geremio. The month you have been on this job, you have not spoken a word about the work. . . . And I have felt that I am walking into a dream. Is the work dangerous? Why don't you answer . . . ?"

Job loomed up damp, shivery gray. Its giant members waiting. Builders quietly donned their coarse robes, and waited.

Geremio's whistle rolled back into his pocket and the symphony of struggle began.

Trowel rang through brick and slashed mortar rivets were machine-gunned fast with angry grind Patsy number one check Patsy number two check the Lean three check Vincenzo four steel bellowed back at hammer donkey engines coughed purple Ashes-ass Pietro fifteen chisel point intoned stone thin steel whirred and wailed through wood liquid stone flowed with dull rasp through iron veins and hoist screamed through space Carmine the Fat twenty-four and Giacomo Sangini check. . . . The multitudinous voices of a civilization rose from the surroundings and melded with the efforts of the Job.

To the intent ear, Nation was voicing her growing pains, but, hands that create are attached to warm hearts and not to calculating minds. The Lean as he fought his burden on looked forward to only one goal, the end. The barrow he pushed, he did not love. The stones that brutalized his palms, he did not love. The great God Job, he did not love. He felt a searing bitterness and a fathomless consternation at the queer consciousness that inflicted the ever mounting weight of structures that he HAD TO! HAD TO! raise above his shoulders! When, when and where would the last stone be? Never . . . did he bear his toil with the rhythm of song! Never . . . did his gasping heart knead the heavy mortar with lilting melody! A voice within him spoke in wordless language.

The language of worn oppression and the despair of realizing that his life had been left on brick piles. And always, there had been hunger and her bastard, the fear of hunger.

Murdin bore down upon Geremio from behind and shouted:

"Goddamnit Geremio, if you're givin' the men two hours off today with pay, why the hell are they draggin' their tails! And why don't you turn that skinny old Nick loose, and put a young wop in his place!"

"Now listen-a to me, Mister Murdin ——"

"Don't give me that! And bear in mind that there are plenty of good barefoot men in the streets who'll jump for a day's pay!"

"Padrone—padrone, the underpinning gotta be make safe and . . ."

"Lissenyawopbastard! If you don't like it, you know what you can do!"

And with that he swung swaggering away.

The men had heard, and those who hadn't knew instinctively.

The new home, the coming baby, and his whole background, kept the fire from Geremio's mouth and bowed his head. "Annunziata speaks of scouring the ashcans for the children's bread in case I didn't want to work on a job where . . . But am I not a man, to feed my own with these hands? Ah, but day will end and no boss in the world can then rob me of the joy of my home!"

Murdin paused for a moment before descending the ladder.

Geremio caught his meaning and jumped to, nervously directing the rush of work. . . . No longer Geremio, but a machine-like entity.

The men were transformed into single, silent, beasts. Snoutnose steamed through ragged mustache whip-lashing sand into mixer Ashes-ass dragged under four by twelve beam Lean clawed wall knots jumping in jaws masonry crumbled dust billowed thundered choked. . . .

At noon, Geremio drank his wine from an old-fashioned magnesia bottle and munched a great pepper sandwich . . . no meat on Good Friday. Said one, "Are some of us to be laid off? Easter is upon us and communion dresses are needed and . . ."

That, while Geremio was dreaming of the new house and the joys he could almost taste. Said he, "Worry not. You should know Geremio." It then all came out. He regaled them with his wonderful joy of the new house. He praised his wife and children one by one. They listened respectfully and returned him well wishes and blessings. He went on and on. . . . "Paul made a radio—all by himself mind you! One can hear Barney Google and many American songs! How proud he."

The ascent to labor was made, and as they trod the ladder, heads turned and eyes communed with the mute flames of the brazier whose warmth they were leaving, not with willing heart, and in that fleeting moment, the breast wanted so, so much to speak, of hungers that never reached the tongue.

About an hour later, Geremio called over to Pietro. "Pietro, see if Mister Murdin is in the shanty and tell him I must see him! I will convince him that the work must not go on like this . . . just for the sake of a little more profit!"

Pietro came up soon. "The padrone is not coming up. He was drinking from a large bottle of whiskey and cursed in American words that if you did not carry out his orders ——"

Geremio turned away disconcerted, stared dumbly at the structure and mechanically listed in his mind's eye the various violations on construction safety. An uneasy sensation hollowed him. The Lean brought down an old piece of wall and the structure palsied. Geremio's heart broke loose and out-thumped the floor's vibrations, a rapid wave of heat swept him and left a chill touch in its wake. He looked about to the men, a bit frightened. They seemed usual, life-size, and moved about with the methodical deftness that made the moment then appear no different than the task of toil had ever been.

Snoutnose's voice boomed into him. "Master Geremio, the concrete is re—ady!"

"Oh yes, yes Vincenz." And he walked gingerly towards the chute, but, not without leaving behind some part of his strength, sending out his soul to wrestle with the limbs of Job, who threatened in stiff silence. He talked and joked with Snoutnose. Nothing said anything, nor seemed wrong. Yet a vague uneasiness was to him as certain as the foggy murk that floated about Job's stone and steel.

"Shall I let the concrete down now, Master Geremio?"

"Well, let me see—no, hold it a minute. Hey Sandino! Tighten the chute cables!"

Snoutnose straightened, looked about, and instinctively rubbed the sore small of his spine. "Ah," sighed he, "all the men feel as I— yes, I can tell. They are tired but happy that today is Good Friday and we quit at three o'clock—" And he swelled in human ecstasy at the anticipation of food, drink, and the hairy flesh-tingling warmth of life, and then, extravagant rest. In truth, they all felt as Snoutnose, although perhaps, with variations on the theme.

It was the Lean only, who had lived, and felt otherwise. His

soul, accompanied with time, had shredded itself in the physical
war to keep the physical alive. Perhaps he no longer had a soul,
and the corpse continued from momentum. May he not be the
Slave, working on from the birth of Man—He of whom it was said,
"It was not for Him to reason?" And probably He, who, never
asking, taking, nor vaunting, created God and the creatable? Nevertheless, there existed in the Lean a sense of oppression suffered, so
vast, that the seas of time could never wash it away.

Geremio gazed about and was conscious of seeming to understand many things. He marveled at the strange feeling which permitted him to sense the familiarity of life. And yet—all appeared
unreal, a dream pungent and nostalgic. Life, dream, reality, unreality, spiraling ever about each other. "Ha," he chuckled, "how
and from where do these thoughts come?"

Snoutnose had his hand on the hopper latch and was awaiting the
word from Geremio. "Did you say something, Master Geremio?"

"Why yes, Vincenz, I was thinking—funny! A—yes, what is the
time—yes, that is what I was thinking."

"My American can of tomatoes says ten minutes from two
o'clock. It won't be long now, Master Geremio."

Geremio smiled. "No, about an hour . . . and then, home."

"Oh, but first we stop at Mulberry Street, to buy their biggest
eels, and the other finger-licking stuffs."

Geremio was looking far off, and for a moment happiness came
to his heart without words, a warm hand stealing over. Snoutnose's
words sang to him pleasantly, and he nodded.

"And Master Geremio, we ought really to buy the seafruits with
the shells—you know, for the much needed steam they put into
the ——"

He flushed despite himself and continued. "It is true, I know it—
especially the juicy clams . . . uhmn, my mouth waters like a
pump."

Geremio drew on his unlit pipe and smiled acquiescence. The
men around him were moving to their tasks silently, feeling of their
fatigue, but absorbed in contemplations the very same as Snoutnose's. The noise of labor seemed not to be noise, and as Geremio
looked about, life settled over him a gray concert—gray forms,
atmosphere and gray notes. . . . Yet his off-tone world felt so
near, and familiar.

"Five minutes from two," swished through Snoutnose's mustache.

Geremio automatically took out his watch, rewound, and set it. Sandino had done with the cables. The tone and movement of the scene seemed to Geremio strange, differently strange, and yet, a dream familiar from a timeless date. His hand went up in motion to Vincenzo. The molten stone gurgled low, and then with heightening rasp. His eyes followed the stone-cementy pudding and to his ears there was no other sound than its flow. From over the roofs somewhere, the tinny voice of *Barney Google* whined its way, hooked into his consciousness and kept itself a revolving record beneath his skull-plate.

"Ah, yes, Barney Google, my son's wonderful radio machine . . . wonderful Paul." His train of thought quickly took in his family, home and hopes. And with hope came fear. Something within asked, "Is it not possible to breathe God's air without fear dominating with the pall of unemployment? And the terror of production for Boss, Boss and Job? To rebel is to lose all of the very little. To be obedient is to choke. Oh dear Lord, guide my path."

Just then, the floor lurched and swayed under his feet. The slipping of the underpinning below rumbled up through the undetermined floors.

Was he faint or dizzy? Was it part of the dreamy afternoon? He put his hands in front of him and stepped back, and looked up wildly. "No! No!"

The men poised stricken. Their throats wanted to cry out and scream but didn't dare. For a moment they were a petrified and straining pageant. Then the bottom of their world gave way. The building shuddered violently, her supports burst with the crackling slap of wooden gunfire. The floor vomited upward. Geremio clutched at the air and shrieked agonizingly. "Brothers, what have we done? Ahhhh-h children of ours!" With the speed of light, balance went sickeningly awry and frozen men went flying explosively. Job tore down upon them madly. Walls, floors, beams became whirling, solid, splintering waves crashing with detonations that ground man and material in bonds of death.

The strongly shaped body that slept with Annunziata nights and was perfect in all the limitless physical quantities, thudded as a worthless sack amongst the giant debris that crushed fragile flesh and bone with centrifugal intensity.

Darkness blotted out his terror and the resistless form twisted, catapulted insanely in its directionless flight, and shot down neatly and deliberately between the empty wooden forms of a foundation wall pilaster in upright position, his blue swollen face pressed against the form and his arms outstretched, caught securely through the meat by the thin round bars of reinforcing steel.

The huge concrete hopper that was sustained by an independent structure of thick timber, wavered a breath or so, its heavy concrete rolling uneasily until a great sixteen-inch wall caught it squarely with all the terrific verdict of its dead weight and impelled it downward through joists, beams and masonry until it stopped short, arrested by two girders, an arm's length above Geremio's head; the gray concrete gushing from the hopper mouth, and sealing up the mute figure.

Giacomo had been thrown clear of the building and dropped six floors to the street gutter, where he lay writhing.

The Lean had evinced no emotion. When the walls descended, he did not move. He lowered his head. One minute later he was hanging in mid-air, his chin on his chest, his eyes tearing loose from their sockets, a green foam bubbling from his mouth and his body spasming, suspended by the shreds left of his mashed arms pinned between a wall and a girder.

A two-by-four hooked little Joe Chiappa up under the back of his jumper and swung him around in a circle to meet a careening I-beam. In the flash that he lifted his frozen cherubic face, its shearing edge sliced through the top of his skull.

When Snoutnose cried beseechingly, "Saint Michael!" blackness enveloped him. He came to in a world of horror. A steady stream, warm, thick, and sickening as hot wine bathed his face and clogged his nose, mouth, and eyes. The nauseous syrup that pumped over his face, clotted his mustache red and drained into his mouth. He gulped for air, and swallowed the rich liquid scarlet. As he breathed, the pain shocked him to oppressive semi-consciousness. The air was wormingly alive with cries, screams, moans and dust, and his crushed chest seared him with a thousand fires. He couldn't see, nor breathe enough to cry. His right hand moved to his face and wiped at the gelatinizing substance, but it kept coming on, and a heart-breaking moan wavered about him, not far. He wiped his eyes in subconscious despair. Where was he? What kind of a dream was he having? Perhaps he wouldn't wake up in time for work, and then what? But how queer; his stomach beating him, his chest on fire, he sees nothing but dull red, only one hand moving about, and a moaning in his face!

The sound and clamor of the rescue squads called to him from far off.

Ah, yes, he's dreaming in bed and far out in the streets, engines are going to a fire. Oh poor devils! Suppose his house were on fire? With his children scattered about in the rooms he could not remember! He must do his utmost to break out of this dream! He's swimming under water, not able to raise his head and get to the air. He must get back to consciousness to save his children!

He swam frantically with his one right hand, and then felt a face beneath its touch. A face! It's Angelina alongside of him! Thank God, he's awake! He tapped her face. It moved. It felt cold, bristly, and wet. "It moves so. What is this?" His fingers slithered about grisly sharp bones and in a gluey, stringy, hollow mass, yielding as wet macaroni. Gray light brought sight, and hysteria punctured his heart. A girder lay across his chest, his right hand clutched a grotesque human mask, and suspended almost on top of him was the switching, faceless body of Joe Chiappa. Vincenzo fainted with an inarticulate sigh. His fingers loosed and the bodyless-headless face dropped and fitted to the side of his face while the drippings above came slower and slower.

The rescue men cleaved grimly with pick and axe.

Geremio came to with a start . . . far from their efforts. His brain told him instantly what had happened and where he was. He shouted wildly. "Save me! Save me! I'm being buried alive!"

He paused exhausted. His genitals convulsed. The cold steel rod upon which they were impaled, froze his spine. He shouted louder and louder. "Save me! I am hurt badly! I can be saved I can—save me before it's too late!" But the cries went no farther than his own ears. The icy wet concrete reached his chin. His heart appalled. "In a few seconds I will be entombed. If I can only breathe, they will reach me. Surely, they will!" His face was quickly covered, its flesh yielding to the solid sharp-cut stones. "Air! Air!" screamed his lungs as he was completely sealed. Savagely, he bit into the wooden form pressed upon his mouth. An eighth of an inch of its surface splintered off. Oh, if he could only hold out long enough to bite even the smallest hole through to air! He must! There can be no other way! He is responsible for his family! He cannot leave them like this! He didn't want to die! This could not be the answer to life! He had bitten half way through when his teeth snapped off to the gums in the uneven conflict. The pressure of the concrete was such, and its effectiveness so thorough, that the wooden splinters, stumps of teeth, and blood never left the choking mouth.

Why couldn't he go any farther?

Air! Quick! He dug his lower jaw into the little hollowed space and gnashed in choking agonized fury. "Why doesn't it go through? Mother of Christ, why doesn't it give? Can there be a notch, or two-by-four stud behind it? Sweet Jesu! No! No! Make it give. . . . Air! Air!"

He pushed the bone-bare jaw maniacally; it splintered, cracked, and a jagged fleshless edge cut through the form, opening a small hole to air. With a desperate burst the lung-prisoned air blew an opening through the shredded mouth and whistled back greedily a gasp of fresh air. He tried to breathe, but it was impossible. The heavy concrete was settling immutably and its rich cement-laden grout ran into his pierced face. His lungs would not expand and were crushing in tighter and tighter under the settling concrete.

"Mother mine—mother of Jesu-Annunziata—children of mine—dear, dear, for mercy, Jesu-Guiseppe e' Maria," his blue foamed tongue called. It then distorted in a shuddering coil and mad blood vomited forth. Chills and fire played through him and his tortured tongue stuttered, "Mercy, blessed Father—salvation, most kind Father—Savior—Savior of His children help me—adored Savior—I kiss Your feet eternally—you are my Lord—there is but one God—you are my God of infinite mercy—Hail Mary divine Virgin—our Father who art in heaven hallowed be thy—name—our Father—my Father," and the agony excruciated with never-ending mount, "our Father—Jesu, Jesu, soon Jesu, hurry dear Jesu Jesu! Je-sssu. . . . !" His mangled voice trebled hideously, and hung in jerky whimperings.

The unfeeling concrete was drying fast, and shrinking into monolithic density. The pressure temporarily desensitized sensation; leaving him petrified, numb, and substanceless. Only the brain, remained miraculously alive.

"Can this be death? It is all too strangely clear. I see nothing nor feel nothing, my body and senses are no more, my mind speaks as it never did before. Am I or am I not Geremio? But I am Geremio! Can I be in the other world? I never was in any other world except the one I knew of; that of toil, hardship, prayer . . . of my wife who awaits with child for me, of my children and the first home I was to own. Where do I begin in this world? Where do I leave off? Why? I recall only a baffled life of cruelty from every direction. And hope was always as painful as fear, the fear of displeasing, displeasing the people and ideas whom I could never understand; laws, policemen, priests, bosses, and a rag with colors waving on a stick. I never did anything to these things. But what have I done with my life? Yes, my life! No one else's! Mine—mine—MINE—Geremio! It is clear. I was born hungry, and have always been hungry for freedom—life! I married and ran away to America so as not to kill and be killed in Tripoli for things they call, 'God and Country.' I've never known the freedom I wanted in my heart. There was always an arm upraised to hit at me. What have I done to them? I did not want to make them toil for me. I did not raise my arm to them. In my life I could never breathe, and now without air, my mind breathes clearly for me. Wait! There has been a terrible mistake! A cruel crime! The world is not right! Murderers! Thieves! You have hurt me and my kind, and have taken my life from me! I have long felt it—yes, yes, yes, they have cheated me with flags, signs and fear. . . . I say you can't take my life! I want to live! My life! To tell the cheated to rise and fight! Vincenz! Chiappa! Nick! Men! Do you hear me? We must follow the desires within us for the world has been taken from us; we, who made the world! Life!"

Feeling returned to the destroyed form.

"Ahhh-h, I am not dead yet. I knew it—you have not done with me. Torture away! I cannot believe you, God and Country, no longer!" His body was fast breaking under the concrete's closing wrack. Blood vessels burst like mashed flower stems. He screamed. "Show yourself now, Jesu! Now is the time! Save me! Why don't you come! Are you there! I cannot stand it—ohhh, why do you let it happen—it is bestial—where are you! Hurry, hurry, hurry! You do not come! You make me suffer, and what have I done! Come, come—come now—now save me, save me now! Now, now, now! If you are God, save me!"

The stricken blood surged through a weltering maze of useless pipes and exploded forth from his squelched eyes and formless nose, ears and mouth, seeking life in the indifferent stone.

"Aie—aie, aie—devils and Saints—beasts! Where are you—quick, quick, it is death and I am cheated—cheat—ed! Do you hear, you whoring bastards who own the world? Ohhh-ohhhh aie-aie—hahahaha!" His bones cracked mutely and his sanity went sailing distorted in the limbo of the subconscious.

With the throbbing tones of an organ in the hollow background, the fighting brain disintegrated and the memories of a baffled life-time sought outlet.

He moaned the simple songs of barefoot childhood, scenes flashed desperately on and off in disassociated reflex, and words and parts of words came pitifully high and low from his inaudible lips, the hysterical mind sang cringingly and breathlessly, "Jesu my Lord my God my all Jesu my Lord my God my all Jesu my Lord my God my all Jesu my Lord my God my all," and on as the whirling tempo screamed now far, now near, and came in soul-sickening waves as the concrete slowly contracted and squeezed his skull out of shape.

THEY ORDER IT BETTER IN FRANCE

ANONYMOUS

I TOOK A FRIEND, A FRENCHMAN, WHO HAPPENS TO BE IN NEW YORK, out to lunch. We went to a certain restaurant on East Fifty-Fifth Street where I knew the food was good and the place itself quiet. Always a few people; never a crowd.

We had some business to discuss.

At the table on our right were three very pretty women. No one likes looking at a pretty woman better than I do.

At the table on our left, were three women, one a girl as pretty as paint. One blonde and smart. The third a brunette. That was all right for me too. I like a feminine background for a business talk.

Opposite us were several couples. A woman per couple; I didn't notice them at first.

We ordered our luncheon.

Knowing my friend, and my France, I expected we'd start off with a certain amount of appreciation of so much female beauty, near by. Actually, I myself am not a bad judge of feminine looks; and of what used to be called "It."

So I gave my friend a lead.

"Pretty, isn't she? The girl in the red scarf?"

He didn't answer at once. I'd forgotten in my long absence from France that I'd asked a question which would immediately provoke expert reflection before I got a considered opinion.

My friend the Frenchman looked at the pretty girl and then said:

"Y . . . yes. She is *pretty*," in a tone implying that that was all that could be said about her.

"Why I think she's *awfully* pretty," I defended, "she looks like Myrna Loy."

He agreed, helping himself to *hors d'oeuvres*, that she was like Myrna Loy. "But Myrna Loy is not 'excitante' (i.e., physically disturbing)," he said.

"Well then," I said, "perhaps you prefer the woman next her? The blonde with the gold clips in her sweater?"

Again the pause. Then:

"She has very pretty eyes, and mouth. But I am afraid of some thing in her . . ."

"What?"

He slightly shook his head and bit an olive. "I am afraid that she would be less well naked. She does not look well formed. I detest experiencing the hip bones of a woman."

By now my host instinct was roused; and, feeling that I wanted to make him feel properly entertained, I hastened to offer him the third woman at the table, a perfectly ravishing little brunette, plump enough to obviate the risk of anyone experiencing any bones anywhere. "What about her?" I said.

She was sitting near to us so we had an excellent view of her.

"She is *better*. She is much better. A pretty nose, and a ravishing smile. A charming little stomach. Only I'm afraid of one thing about her. . . . She has an expression, a look, which is too—intelligent! A look that is more observant than warm. . . . A warm look in a woman is a great thing, with an intellectual woman one arrives with difficulty at great pleasures! . . . Now, that woman opposite," he said. "She has atrocious arms, but she has a little vicious air which pleases me! One sees very well that she understands Love."

I looked at her. To me she was large and frog-faced. I could imagine "love" with her being about as satisfying as with a Fifth Avenue bus. . . . I turned my eyes to the table at our right. The waiter brought our steaks. I realized it would be some time before we got around to talking "business." So I picked him yet another daisy. "Well now *there*," I insisted, "is an absolutely *glorious girl*. You couldn't see anything easier to look at anywhere!"

She was, too. A blonde, tall, with a divine figure. She was sitting sort of away from the table, sprawling like a schoolgirl and smoking cigarettes. As far as I was concerned, she was tops. And I envied the man who had put a big sapphire ring on her engagement finger.

My French friend looked her over. His contemplative glance raked her from the top of her perfectly heavenly little head, down to the tips of her pumps. Finally he conceded, as he cut his steak across—"She has excellent thighs . . . *Altogether* charming thighs," then, having eaten two mouthfuls, while he stared at the woman, of the couple opposite us, whom I hardly noticed, for the good reason that she wasn't too easy to look at, he said,

"Now *there*—my friend—*Voila une bonne affaire!*"

So I took a look. She was a square-rigged dame with a brownish skin, a large mouth, her eyes made up black all around. She wasn't chic, and she wasn't by any means young. She seemed to be eating well and laughing a great deal.

But when a Frenchman gives a lady the once over and says "*C'est une bonne affaire*," which roughly translates "She has boudoir talent" you needn't have any more doubts about her. Because he's one of a nation of Experts! And if you ask him why he thinks so, he can give you a highly reasoned bit of anatomical chapter and verse and to demonstrate the amorous capabilities of the question. For instance a good curve in and out at the back of the waist is an encouraging sign . . . whereas thin arms and wrists are very discouraging and mean "coldness." A good firm neck and not too much length of leg, is what is wanted. And the face must be *lively*. But it must *not* be intellectual. "Too intellectual for pleasure" is a well-known dismissal for girls with college honors. And a certain amount of plumpness is liked. Though a girl I know was told by her French boyfriend, "You are a little too fat, cherie. I prefer it for love. But it is not becoming when you are dressed." Another symptom that raises hope is a readiness to laugh—A woman who laughs easily is easy to love!

The fact is that the Frenchman's eye in the matter of picking a lady is very highly trained to discern ability for love. (Put it that way!) He can pick a girl the way an Englishman of a certain type picks a horse—He sees the "points" right away that are going to guarantee him satisfaction. The whole American idealization of "Dream Girls," "Pretty Kids" and what not, doesn't enter his consciousness. The Frenchman's looking for a good time; not for a picture to hang over his bed—which all means that he's got a lot less liking than we tender-hearted, misty-eyed Americans have for "baby" qualities in girls. He isn't captivated by big eyes and lisps and bows and what not. (Something symptomatic, I always think, this calling a girl "Baby.") And in fact his whole idea about the "right age" for a woman to be is practically opposite to ours.

I suppose The Traveling Salesman in any country is probably

about as good an index as you can get of average taste in girls for
any nation. (Except in England where the salesmen are called
Commercial Travelers and go to Temperance Inns and spend their
evenings talking to one another!) But when the American salesman
gets to talking to you, you soon can tell what sort of dames he
looks for when he arrives at his destination, because he never talks
about anything else.

Roughly speaking his ideal is something young enough and coy
and fluffy. . . . And if she's not such hotstuff really when he gets
down to it—well then he gets an enormous kick out of the idea
(seldom correct) that she's a virgin! It's wonderful what a sense
of outraging Innocence will do for the Nordic man's self esteem.
The Tired Business Man likes to think of his love of the moment
as his "little girl" and a certain newspaper lately gave great promi-
nence to a gentleman in a western state who achieved the enviable
feat of combining rape and good-citizenship by marrying a girl
eleven years old. Incidentally, he was backed up by his mother-
in-law who declared her profound certainty that the Almighty was
tickled to death by the marriage.

But our French friends like it all the other way. "Ripeness" is
one of the things they're after. Most Frenchmen will assert that
a woman isn't worth considering until she's thirty. Vintage Women
in fact. And whereas a pair of sheer stockings, a pinafore and a
baby-blue hair riband symbolizes our own Ideal of Womanhood,
you've only got to read *Cheri*—that stirring description of an idyll
between a boy of sixteen and a lady of (certainly) fifty, to realize
how Grandmothers get Glorified in France—when every fresh
wrinkle is a path of mystery, and a double chin does for the Frenchman what a double Scotch does for us—makes him feel better just
to think about it.

However—the Frenchman's a practical man. He has his "ideal"
but he knows he doesn't meet it every day. And in the meantime
he isn't going to waste his opportunities. So he doesn't as we're apt
to do, keep on kidding himself that every new girl *is* an ideal. On
the contrary. He's a cheerful realist. He's trained to spot the re-
deeming graces as adroitly as a highly bred pig sniffs truffles. And
faced with the homeliest dame he'll work over her until he can
say, "Yes—she's certainly homely, but she has 'delightful ears' ";
or "an exciting back to her neck"; or "provocative biceps." And

the worst he cares to admit about any woman is "Yes, she is very ugly, but she has 'something' (*Elle a quelque chose*)." And if you get him in a cynical but wholesome mood he'll indicate that after all, "All cats are grey at night!"

The same practical view which prompts him to make the best of what he gets, and never to leave a lady unturned so to speak, had an instructive influence a year ago on the conduct of the big strikes in Paris, France.

When the Trades Union Leaders ordered a sit-down strike and got the men in the factories, they sent out motor lorries from Paris full of the gayest possible gals—to sit in with them.

Which seems to be an idea anyway for Brightening Up Industrial Disputes. (American Labor Leaders please copy.)

NO MORE TROUBLE FOR JEDWICK

By LOUIS PAUL

JEDWICK SMILED AT THE WOMAN DRAWING WATER FROM THE WELL. "Kin I have me a drink, ma'am?" he drawled, his broad shoulders drooped shyly in a half bow.

She was tall and dark. The sun blazed down on the white hot Virginia highway. Jedwick's clothes were saturated with sweat. Scintillant beads shone like translucent jewels against his shiny skin. The black man shook his head like a hound dog coming up out of a creek.

"I reckon," she nodded. The Negro woman, lighter than Jedwick, was not wholly at ease. Her husband was in the village getting groceries. Roamin' niggers . . .

"Yas ma'am," Jedwick said, and dipped into the barrel.

The woman dried her hands on her apron. "Y'all f'om round hyeah?"

Jedwick stared at her a moment. "I ain't f'om hyeah," he murmured between immense gulps, "ner neither I ain't gonna stay hyeah. Whereat I git to Alexandria?"

"Right smart piece yonder."

"How fur?"

She speculated. "Eight-twelve mile."

Jedwick finished his water and looked at the blue and gold cauldron over his head. "Hot, ain't it?"

"Do git hot."

"Yo' man wuk in town?"

"No. He after groceries."

Jedwick glanced down the hill toward the little village. The view was empty.

She understood his movement.

He smiled. He had fine healthy teeth. She was aware of a frightened sensation in the pit of her stomach. Jedwick bent and rubbed his ankle as though that were an habitual gesture. The flaming orb in the sky shone down remorselessly. Something about the Negro's beautiful black arms hypnotized her. She stood poised, enchanted, like a statue: made to flee, but forever motionless. The midday silence was oppressive, like the sun. She waited.

"I ain't seed no woman fo' a long time," Jedwick said, almost in apology.

"He after groceries."

Closer to hers, his face was more strikingly handsome than ever. His lips were very cool, strangely. Perspiration came off on her mouth and cheeks . . .

Later he said, "Thank you sho' nuff fo' that there water, ma'am. Ain't they some law gin doin' much wawkin' thisyere state highways?"

"Is," she looked up at the stranger, embarrassed, "if them troopers ketches you."

Jedwick nodded and suddenly disappeared down the embankment. Couldn't trust the road from here in. Stick to the tracks.

He wrapped a long red handkerchief around his shoulders to keep his neck from frying, and stepped gingerly along the single-tracked roadbed, trying to pace the ties to his long swinging gait. Oughta lay these hyeah ties out even, so's a man could wawk. Wa'nt no cinder path like usual. Say ten mile. 'Bout fo' hours in thisyere sun. Should be makin' up a string o' boxes fo' Manhattan Junction in Alex some'rs round six.

He wanted after an hour to crawl under the shade of some green leafy trees. Lay out yo' legs an' sleep. Thoughts that came like hunger or dreams, unwanted; but they were only a whip-flick to sting the flesh of his determination. Gits me out o' the sun in one o' them boxes in Alex, yassuh! There I rests. He visualized a phrase: Jedwick escapes.

Waves of hypnotic steel-gray heat shimmered up off the two metal radiators that converged in the distance. His eyes began to burn. He thought it would be nice to be rich. He would buy a boat with a motor in it, all covered with a striped canvas canopy, and sail out of sight of land. There would be a breeze off in the ocean. Nice gal, that there brown lady by the highway crossin'. Like a scared cottontail. She liked him. They all liked Jedwick. Lovin' ain't harmin' no gal, he thought.

Bugs. Chrissakes! Little gnats and fuzzy things and leg-squirming beetles popped up in front of him; some kind of a locust whanged with a flat noise on his chest, and he slapped it down. Flies and ticks smelled your sweat. A breath of wind floated lazily over the treetops, but died itself of the heat. Jedwick sighed.

Sighing wasn't natural to him. He thought he'd sing. He bugled a tentative air.

A slick-tawkin' man f'om Bumminham . . .

The plaintive lyric echoed magnificently between the banks of woods. Jedwick's cello-like bass rose through the dazzling, brain-sizzling heat to heaven, and he laughed about some dimly-felt deliciousness in solitude's freedom. His voice took up the lilt.

> A slick-tawkin' man f'om Bumminham
> Come up my way, an' his name was Sam;
> I pay no attention, ner I din give a damn,
> Till he stoled my gal away.

He hummed the rest of the melody: it was too hot to think of the words.

A little garter snake, sunning itself under the vast ceiling of broiling light, was startled and jiggled off noisily into the brush. Maybe, he confided to the vanished reptile, maybe tomor' I gonna be in *New* York. Yassuh. Wonder how fur they is after me? Think they can ketch thisyere Jedwick? Yo' completely crazy. How fur I is to Alex, I wonder? Damn me! but it do git hot!

Three mile an hour, 'bout. 'Thout stoppin' I git me in them yards fo sundown. Yassuh. Sundown. Don't seem like ole sun ever gone go down.

> I hates t' see
> Thet evenin' sun go down . . .

Nossuh. Man said that jes crazy's that snake.

There was a shack directly around a bend, and the white man saw him first. "Where you going to, boy?"

He had a wrinkled skin and sandy grey hair and wore grey uniform pants.

"I goin' t' ask you fo' some water, has you got any?" Jedwick smiled brightly with his thick lips.

"Where you goin'?" the man repeated.

"Well, y'see, cap'n, well, suh, I'm goin' in t' the Districk. Yassuh. Dassit."

"Washin'ton? What you traipsin' up here for?"

"Don't like to wawk on the highway, cap'n, boss. 'S y'all got a little water?"

"Alexandria's along up hyeah. You makin' for one of them boxes?"

"Nossuh, nossuh! Ain't layin' over no place, cap'n, suh. Ole friend in town gonna ride me into the Districk."

"You must be runnin' away, boy," the man in the shack said, squinting lowered eyes at the big sweating Negro.

"Me? I ain't runnin' no place, suh, cap'n," he protested. "Why fo' I gonna run any place?"

The white man fetched up an iron pail and handed him a different dipper. "Too hot," he said, shaking his head, "to hit them ties 'less yo-all runnin' away. Why ain't you takin' a sleep in some cool place?"

"Me, suh? I gotta git in D. C. Yassuh. I got me friends in the Districk, suh."

The wrinkled man glanced down at Jedwick's right ankle.

"Goin' git me a job," Jedwick stammered uncertainly, "in—like, suh, now, a 'partment house. Dassit," he said. "Yassuh."

"Take all you want," the other said about the water; "they's a crick below here. Ain't my business where-at you're runnin' to."

"Nossuh, cap'n. I ain't runnin'."

"Matter o' fact, they's some empties makin' up in Alexandria about seven tonight. You going t' New York," he stated.

Jedwick was amazed. "How you figger that there, boss?"

"If'n I don't know a chain-gang nigger," he told Jedwick calmly, "I'll go and jump in that there crick."

The big Negro's face curled into a magnificent smile. "Come f'om thataway?"

"Been around," the man said expressionlessly.

"Yassuh," murmured Jedwick. He added, "Thank y'all fo' that water."

"Not 'tall."

"Thank y'all," he repeated.

The man drew himself in out of the heat. Jedwick started off toward Alexandria, but caught a phrase which he thought was the man calling him back—until he analyzed it.

"I want Colonel Saunders, yessum," he was saying, "the police chief in——"

Jedwick sauntered back, and the man in the shack stepped away from the phone when he saw him. His hand slipped into a drawer and the Negro saw a pearl butt come out. Jedwick muttered softly as he crashed over the flimsy table, rolling the white man backward out of his chair. He twisted, and leapt again. They bowled heavily through the door, rocking the flimsy shack. The leather-faced, wiry man struggled up almost successfully, but Jedwick got his feet on him. The black kicked scientifically, as a boxer uses his hands.

In a moment the white man lay still, his head battered. His shirt was torn where his stomach had been gashed. Jedwick felt very sorry for him. How foolish the man had been. Jedwick hated to hurt anybody.

He stopped long enough to bundle the body inside the shack, take another drink and dip his face in the bucket of cool water. It seemed hotter in the sun that ever.

Now he dumped the pail empty and resumed his trek in the oily tropical sun's glare. In a few moments the water he had drunk sank through the pores of his skin and oozed out in driblets. If it's hotter down in Africa, he joked to himself, I'm glad my folks done been slaves. Yassuh.

Slaves.

At least it wasn't too hot to whistle. Instead of his bit of excoriation of a slick-tawkin' man from Bumminham the great black figure chanted a whistley refrain as he trudged on tirelessly toward his destination. He loped along, picking the ties carefully. The song was a monotonous, fugitive melody about a man named Joe, who

—Done his Susie wrong, yassuh,
But he love her all the same.

He seemed almost to skip along the ties to that repetitious lilt.

Jedwick was, as he saw the shacks of Alexandria's outskirts loom glaringly in the terrific blaze of afternoon, neither blithe nor desperate, neither coward nor cruel. He was escaping. A criminal—or any man—would. He felt very sorry for the grey-haired man, did he not? Of course. Glimpsing the freight-yards of Alexandria, Virginia, he lapsed into the weakness of a sigh again. Like when the cap'n blowed his whistle at sundown and yo' pick drapped outn yo' fingers . . . like when the las' sack o' cotton was drug down t' the baler, an'—, 'assuh. He shook these memories off. Jedwick wasn't really a sighing man.

He hadn't eaten for forty hours. You travels light and fast and lives offn yo' flesh. But yo' gits hongry. Whereat you kin promote a vittle or that in Alex? Better crawl in one of them cars. They gonna trace that phone cawl. Find that wrinkled man an' they gonna be hell poppin' round Alex.

Down in behind the fence. That was the place. He saw a bum duck between two cars and hop over the coupling, coming toward him.

"Hi," he greeted this specimen.

"Know what time d'Junction empties goin' out t'night?" the bum screwed up a weather-scarred face.

"Yassuh. Seven."

"You eat?"

"No suh!"

"Where ya come in?"

Jedwick thumbed his hand back.

"Leggin'—you out in that there sun?"

"Sho nuff, likely, brother," Jedwick answered.

"Got a coupla hours," said the bum. "They's a jungle overn 'em weeds. Some liver here, an' haffa loaf o' breard."

Jedwick thanked the man from the North.

They toasted the liver. The bum, whose name was Sully, dug some whole coffee beans out of a bag, battered them on a rock, and had a can going. They split the 'breard' and the big Negro was very grateful. After the meal Sully pulled a razor from a leather bag around his neck and began to shave a light beard. Jedwick, in payment for the bum's life-giving coffee, related the incidents of his story. The man shaving exhibited a great curiosity concerning the details of Jedwick's encounter with the brown up on the hill yonder. He chuckled, vicariously amused.

Jedwick added that he had killed the trackman.

Sully squinted. "You must be one o' dese tough black boys."

"Nossuh," said Jedwick, particular not to be misunderstood. "Whut else I gonna do?"

"Coulda flattened him, or tied him up." Sully put away his razor.

"Sho.' You figger out jes' whut to do. That man had a big gun. He gonna blow off my haid ifn I don't git him."

"Every man fer himself, sonny," the bum shrugged his shoulders. "You set?"

"Les go git stowed away fo some no-count railroad bull git rampagin' round."

They idled through the yard, trained soldiers expertly taking cover back of every bump in the topography. Jedwick pried a loose door. Sully was boosted half way up. A metallic voice startled them.

"What you guys doin'?"

Sully's wits left him and he stared up at the man blankly. Jedwick grinned with silly surprise. "We's jes gonna ride in, suh."

"Oh, yer jist gonna ride in?"

"Yassuh," he said innocently.

"Just gonna ride in." The voice was pregnant with unpleasant suggestions.

Jedwick wrinkled his brow into a puzzled expression. "Yassuh, cap'n, boss. Ain't it aw right?"

"Ain't it aw right?" he mimicked, and spat. "Where you two bums from?"

"We, suh?"

"Who the hell y' think I'm talkin' to?"

"Yassuh. I got a fren in New York, boss," he explained. "He gits me a job in a big apartment house. Sully hyeah goin' try to git a job too, cap'n."

"Well, maybe I don't know stiffs no more," the man said. "Don't you know you can't ride on no freight train?"

"Can't ride on no freight train?" Jedwick almost believed in this innocence himself. "Nossuh, boss, nossuh. Is thisyere a freight train? Look like they is all epty. I never know they is hahm in ridin' in epty car. Never would come in hyeah did we knows that, suh. Dassit." He was talking fast—for his life. "Yassuh, boss, gentman, suh."

The train-bull shook himself impatiently. "Better take yourselfs outa here big and pronto," he said with positiveness, "or you'll be gittin' about sixty days apiece for vags."

" 'Scuse us, mister cap'n, boss, suh, yassuh," Jedwick murmured with elegant unctuousness, "we is goin'."

The Law swung himself up the side ladder and disappeared momentarily along the line of cars.

"You gittin' in?" the black man whispered to Sully coolly.

Sully backed away. "Not me!" he exclaimed hoarsely.

Jedwick shook a finger, said "Hi!" got his belly up on the platform, clipped the door to, and disappeared into the black interior.

He heard the bull coming back, tapping on each door. "Hey, you, come outa there!" He got to Jedwick's door and cried, "Hey, you, come outa there!" There was only silence inside. Footsteps crunched away along the gravel.

Jedwick lay motionless for an unconscionable time. At last the train gave three bone-rattling jerks that knocked him into another corner. The couplings shrieked, another gentle bump, and the train moved slowly out of the yards. The engineer's hoot-hoot sounded to Jedwick's ears like a wild pæan to freedom. The car was like a furnace, but of course he didn't care.

He crawled over to the door and lay with his head to the floor crack, afraid to push the thing ajar.

Wonder and excitement to freedom! The train rattled on, carriages hitting track-cracks, with ever-increasing crescendo. Fool, anyone who risked life unnecessarily. That trackman. Why hadn't he let well enough alone? Dead now, and nothing gained. Never would *he* risk the quickness of life except in the defense of his own.

On into the night the bumping freight train sped. North. Where he could achieve that departure from the old and sink into the blissful anonymity of its millions, renascence, born again, with only dead memories to remind him of the past. Yassuh, he speculated. Dassit. Goin' git free in *New* York. But gotta watch out fo' that bull. Whereat I wonder is fust division stop on thisyere line? Some'rs 'long hyeah. He pried the door open a crack. The sun had set and blue darkness had fallen over the countryside that bobbed swiftly by his limited vision. A hot wind blew in his face.

Yassuh. Like sho' nuff git me a lettle sheteye, can't takin' no chances. Bull goin' look in these hyeah cars fust crack outn the box do we make a division stop. We git in the Junction mornin' sometime . . . then, nigger, you is free. Yassuh. Dassit—free! The thought made his brain spin airily. No more trouble for Jedwick!

Well, no more later; but just now the cars pulled up under brakes and came to a jerking halt. He shoved open the door and glanced out. Blackness. Tall brush alongside the cinder roadbed. Lucky. Jedwick was always lucky. He jumped down and squatted behind the weeds. Sure enough. The bull had a flash, and he peered into the recesses of every car. Another train, a passenger, thundered on past in the opposite direction. Jedwick waited until the freight train began to move, then he hopped out like a big rabbit scooting across an open space, and swung himself up into the car. That was all right. He was good for another hour.

That hour found him asleep. Fatigue fells all men. Jedwick fell asleep, woke when the train stopped again—which was too late. He was on his knees when the light flashed in.

"What the hell you doin' in there?" the bull shouted.

Jedwick, a thinking animal in danger, murmured in a much broader accent than his own, "Can't po' man rahd in disyere train, yo' honah?"

"Comin' outa there?"

"Sho gwine come out, yassuh."

He jumped down, but squatted his great frame into a much smaller figure. The railroad bull clicked his light into Jedwick's face. "Say, ain't you the same nigger I chased in Alexandria?"

"Whut Alesandria?"

"Din I tell yer to stay outa them cars?"

"Me, yo' honah? Nossuh," Jedwick exhibited surprise.

"Hell I ain't!"

"Nossuh," Jedwick said gently but firmly.

"Where'd y' git on?"

"Bout a nour back yander, yo' honah, suh. Ah bo'd de train when de cyahs stoppin' sahd them there weeds. 'Scuse me, suh."

"Well," said the man, not exactly satisfied, "git on outa here. You can't ride in these here trains. An' I ketch y' ridin' agin," he showed Jedwick an army Colt strapped to his trousers, "I'm gonna plug ya." He meant it. "I see you again," the white man added, "you git it."

Jedwick hunched his shoulders. "I'se so'y, yo honah. Ah gone git away f'om hyeah jes lahk y'all say. Gone right now." He started off toward the rear of the train. "Ain't meant nary hahm, suh," he murmured.

"See you stay 'way," the bull called after him.

When the freight train pulled out again Jedwick was on it. After the next stop the bull knew he was on it. It was a game of hide and seek. At each stop the Negro ran for cover in the weeds, and thanked the night for being darker than the ace of spades. He saw the blue steel of a gun behind the flash as the detective prowled through the cars.

Jedwick wondered why the man wouldn't let well enough alone. Damn me!, but people sho' huntin' trouble wid big guns. Why fo' ever body come messin' 'round me? What I wanna harm nobody fo'? They keeps messin' 'round stid leavin' me be, an' mo' trouble happen fo' you know it. That 'man goin' kill me ifn he ketches me, he thought, or I goin' try to kill him. Why anybody want kill someone else?

The bull wouldn't of course, let well enough alone. He knew there was only one way to nab the black bastard—that was on the moving train. There was some danger in that, but the bull didn't consider danger. His job was to get that pernicky nigger the hell and gone off his train.

Crawling along the tops of the cars, he swung himself down over the one he suspected. He gently wedged it open and slipped in. Jedwick sat square in front of the door, his legs spread and tensed, waiting. The bull plopped between the black man's outstretched legs, and Jedwick caught him full in the face with a large but cunning heel. The man's pistol cracked against the side of the car, and the white bull's body dropped out like a sack of potatoes and hit the cinders with a thud. Jedwick sighed as at the completion of an unpleasant duty. Trouble, he thought philosophically; why people allus huntin' 'round fo' trouble?

The sunrise got pink in the east. He sized up the land about him. Wasn't but a few minutes out of the Junction. Better slip off before that cop was missed. Shortly the freight slowed. He hopped it from the ladder.

It was a mile or so to the highway. The sun was just blazing up properly. Another boiling day. A truck was the thing.

Free. Escape was almost certain now. They couldn't pin the

railroad bull's accident on him. And Alabama would never get him if he reached New York. Of course he'd reach New York. One of those wonderful red vans came chugging up the highway. By God, this was luck! A colored chauffeur was at the wheel. Going right into the city. Jedwick's luck was an enchanted affair. When the truck approached he flicked his hand and smiled teethily. The driver jammed his brakes. Didn't he say his luck was magic?

"Sho' nice of you," he said as he skipped up on the seat. He sank into the leather cushion blissfully. "Yassuh."

"Goin' into New York?"

"Yassuh."

"Where you from?"

"Been bummin' my way up from the Districk," said Jedwick. "Ole feller goin' far as the las' town in a little Fo'd brang me thus far."

"I got a samwich I ain't et," said the driver. "You're perfectly welcome to it."

"Sho' nice of you," he repeated. He took the sandwich and swallowed it whole. "My name Jedwick," he grunted past the last mouthful.

At Canal and Sixth Avenue the driver said, "Like you to drop off here, buddy. I get caught ridin' anybody in, it's jes' too bad fo' me."

"Yassuh," said Jedwick gratefully. "Sho' nice of you." He dropped down and the truck turned up Sixth Avenue.

THE BEAUT FROM MONTANA

By FRANK SCULLY

STRIPPED—HER FAVORITE POSE, INCIDENTALLY—SHE WAS A FEATHER-weight, and a fraction under five feet tall. But nobody ever measured her s.a.—in Hollywood or anywhere else.

In Butte, Montana, where she was born and raised, she was known as Sadie Ostromar, but a press agent in Hollywood gave her the nice New England name of Sally Alden. The story was she had seduced her first male in Butte before she was out of pinafores. And whether that's true or not, it's a laughable fact that after she got in pictures every man in Hollywood was scared to death of her. Her five husbands swore to a man that she was *insatiable*, and unfaithful to boot. It is difficult to say which appalled them the more.

While still in Butte, when she was fifteen in fact, she was assigned to the best house in town. No procurer enticed her there. She got in on her own merits. But she was an absolute failure in the business.

When you realize that she was even prettier then than she is now, the thing becomes fantastic. Where now she has a trace of double chin, at that time her features were gently chiseled in Elgin marble. Where now she has to wear an uplift *soutien gorge* to affect a youthful bosom, at that time her body was as firm as an August apple. Today even the cleverest cameramen can't streamline completely her matronly hips, but in those days she was as slender as a birch tree.

From those good old days, however, only her gorgeously slender ankles remain. They're as perfect today as they were twenty years ago. Well, maybe you could add the mass of lovely yellow hair, big blue eyes, uptilted nose and peach-like complexion to her ankles as still being about what they were in Butte.

And yet with all that in her favor she simply couldn't wait to be asked to say yes. The original of the Dorothy Parker girl. "who

85

could speak fourteen languages and couldn't say no in any of them," has always been believed to have been Sally Alden. Nothing could be a greater libel on the Casanova of her sex. It was her impatience and that alone, which caused her to be thrown out of Montana's bawdy houses and into California's picture studios.

From the beginning in Hollywood whenever she came on a set she looked the crew over, and no one from prop-man to producer was safe.

By the time she was forty you'd have expected that sex as a subject would have begun to lose its interest for her, but no victim of Sally's rapacity ever testified privately to that effect. Any of them could show you permanent scars as proof that they had fought for their honor—and lost.

It would not be portraying her fairly at all to call her "vampire," or a "gold-digger," or simply as her discarded lovers did, a "glamorous bitch in ermine." She openly bragged that she had made them all and any man who said anything else was a fairly transparent liar. And you'd be further from truth if you imagined she liked girls. No, her sex-life was conventional enough, except for the *force* behind it.

In the light of all this, can you imagine anything funnier than the story that after the cleanup campaign had driven her out of pictures (she was beginning to skid anyway) and she had decided to try Broadway for a new build-up, she had entered a producer's office and with the terrified eyes of a deer at bay had fought for what the old-fashioned girls used to call something dearer than life?

Why do press agents circulate such yarns? It was, if anything, the producer who put up that old-fashioned fight. I can understand such stories where an old *madame* essays *Little Eva* or *Peter Pan* or the *White Sister*, but Sally was going to play the bag-slinger in a revival of *Rain* and it wouldn't have hurt to let the public know that she had plenty of what it takes, especially since it was true.

It happened in Arch Banton's office. Most chorines who have worked for the oversexed Arch de Triumph will admit that they never were hired without at least a mauling, and any extras waiting in the outer office knew he was through casting when the couch was carried out of his inner office and put back among the props in the wings downstairs.

But in Sally's case they carried Arch out on his own couch like a wounded Spartan warrior being carried home from battle on his shield. Any way you figured it, the scene must have been a howl.

Imagine Arch leering at the sight of a buxom blonde entering his office, licking his thick, loose lips, slyly getting up from his desk so that he could get between her and the door, and then imagine that lecherous look of his turning to terror as he faced a female look more lecherous than his own!

If a bigger belly-laugh could come from mortal man than from the person who might have been privileged to watch Arch hypnotized into a corner—the *couch* corner—gripping his clothes around him, while Sally, the super-sex sensation, started coiling around him like a cobra, I'd like to hear it.

After she had run Arch through the wringer she decided she ought to get a divorce from Stetson Handler, her fifth husband. She decided to do it quietly in Paris if Stetson would take an outright settlment of $25,000 instead of a monthly alimony. Being no fool, Stetson signed for the settlement.

Sally decided she wasn't going to be bothered with husbands any more. As "fronts" they had cost her too much money. Henceforth, she said, she'd live with her men till she tired of them, and then, like a Henrietta the Eighth, toss them aside. Her mother, who had old-fashioned ideas, said that would be her undoing.

"I'll be damned," cried Sally, "if I'll be trapped into marriage any more."

When pressed about "consequences" she replied, "I've had five, and the little bastards can become bank presidents for all I care. I'm through with marrying with an eye to 'consequences'."

When her mother suggested that might be all right for sons, but daughters need society's protection, Sally glared.

"Nuts," was all she would say.

It was really a sore spot with her. Though she was feminine to a fault, it burned her ego to cinders that she couldn't produce a daughter. The one she claimed as her own was a phoney. It was really her maid's. They had gone abroad together, entered a Swiss *clinique*, Sally registering as the maid and the maid as Mme. Sally Alden, and when the baby was born it was officially registered as: *Saline Alden, fille de Mme. Sally Alden de Butte, Montana; père inconnu.* Daughter of Mrs. Sally Alden, father unknown! What malarkey! All hooey, even protected by the official records of a friendly republic.

That, in brief, was Sally's real career up to the time she arrived in Paris to divorce Stetson Handler, America's best-kept gigolo, as the newspaper boys privately called him. Then she learned about Lady Mary Fitton, one of Queen Elizabeth's ladies in waiting, the harlot poor Shakespeare fell for. Somebody talked her into making a picture around the black-eyed "lady" of Shakespeare's sonnets, while waiting for her divorce, and she leaped at the chance. I don't know why. Just to show off her French, probably.

But that was the thing that licked her at last. She brought over a skeleton crew from Hollywood to Joinville, just outside of Paris, and hired some frogs to fill in the frame.

Among these French workers was Henri Dupont. He would have been a Marquis if the Second Empire had survived, and he actually did so title himself, though France had been a Republic for years before he was born. His name oddly, *was* Dupont, though in France that has become a gag name like Jones in America.

Fortunately Sally didn't know that. She didn't even know he was a Marquis. In fact she didn't know anything about him until she walked on the set and saw him moving a "nigger," a sort of black screen they use in studios, further away from the camera on the orders of the cameraman; one of her discarded lovers, incidentally.

"Who's that guy?"

"What?" asked the camerman.

"Who's that guy?" she asked again.

"Just one of the prop-men."

"Make him take my make-up kit to my dressing-room after we knock off for the morning, will you?"

The cameraman saw immediately what was going to happen to Dupont, and though he was an old hand in the picture business and pretty cynical about virtue and all that, something came over him and he decided he had to protect this youth at all costs.

When they had finished shooting the scene and in the general chaos of moving the troupe outdoors for an exterior shot, he told Dupont what he was in for.

"But don't let her do it," he said. "Fight her off. Use every device you can think of and in the end if she has to marry you to get you she'll do it. Whatever you do, don't go in her dressing room. Knock, leave her kit at the door, and scram! That's your only hope. If she gets you as quickly as she wants you, she'll throw you aside in a month like a worn-out glove. I *know*!"

Dupont turned white when he learned the plight he was in, but he had a Frenchman's instinct for self-preservation, and for making money too. For days he played with her and kept slipping in and out of situations that would have hooked even a Cabinet Minister.

It was his cunning against hers, and hers was fortified by a thousand conquests. She was quick enough to see that she could have had him if she proposed marriage, but she was determined not to marry again, and she didn't see why a frog, of all persons, should be so fussy. Wasn't France the "home," if you could call it that, of the *mesalliance*? Why did this kid have to go back of such an established tradition? If she were willing to take up the manners of his country, there was no reason for his going early New England. She said as much to the cameraman, but he only shrugged his shoulders. He had been through all that with her himself.

Oddly, the thing that finally hooked her was a cock-and-bull story the cameraman told Dupont to pass on to her when the occasion arose. The third day on the set she got her first chance to talk to Henri while they were waiting for lights.

"Were you born in Paris, Hank?" she asked familiarly, and with an innocence born of cunning.

"Yes," he said briefly.

"Are you the only child?"

"No."

"I thought the French never had more than one or two children."

"I have five sisters," he said.

That was his cue. The cameraman had told him to say that, and **it** worked like a charm.

"That's a lot of girls," said Sally.

"Yes, *alors*, girls run in our family."

She wanted him now more than ever. That subterfuge by which she got her other daughter may have fooled the world but in her heart it didn't fool her. If this youth, besides being handsome and of good family, could produce a daughter, that would round out her life in the way she wanted it rounded out. And if she couldn't get the guy any other way than by marrying him, well, one more didn't make much difference in her life, she decided. She could get divorced in a couple of months if she tired of him.

She told her mother she was marrying again—"a Marquee this time."

"My God," cried her mother, "not one of those things they hang outside theatres!"

"No, no—a sort of Count," explained Sally.

"Oh," said the mother.

"I can get a divorce in a couple of months if I tire of him."

But she didn't know France as well as she knew men, for France is the easiest country to get a divorce in and the hardest to get married in, and before she was through she realized that anybody who got married there meant it.

"I can understand now," she said, "why all those artists on the left bank live in sin. They haven't the time or money to go through with this ceremony."

She had to get affidavits from the Consul General of the United States, documents from lawyers which the Consul endorsed, certificates of residence from the Chief of Police of Paris, and the manager of the hotel where she stayed and so on. Document on document piled up and even then she was only to first base.

"You now have to stay in the hotel for thirty days," the Chief of the Bureau of Vital Statistics told her, "and then we will have to publish the banns, and after that you can get married."

"How long will that take?" she asked.

"Forty days, Madame."

"Forty days?"

He assured her politely it would take forty days.

"Unless," he added with a pause, "you can get a letter from the Procurer of the Republic waiving the banns, which are not compulsory in your country. As you are a foreigner he might do that for you, but as your *fiancé* is a Frenchman I doubt it."

"Who is this Procurer of the Republic? Does he get Folies Bergère girls for Cabinet Members?"

The Chief of the Bureau of Vital Statistics was visibly shocked.

"No, Madame, he is an officer of the Republic—and a very important one."

"Would 5,000 francs make him forget that ten-day clause?"

The Chief shrugged his shoulders. Since the Stavisky case all of them were wary of bribes.

"You might try, Madame."

But even in this she was unsuccessful and in the end had to wait forty days after Dupont said "Yes" before she could officially cash in on his acquiescence.

What torture she went through during that time even one of the old Amazons never equalled.

She tried to get Dupont to go off on trips, but his mother always went along, and spoiled that.

"How do you know we'll be suited for each other?" she once argued with him. "On principle I never marry a man I haven't slept with before marriage."

"I'm sorry, Sally," he said softly, "but I have my principles, too."

"You're the strangest man I ever met," she said, frustrated, annoyed, but still determined to get him.

In the end she did, of course, but not until they were on their honeymoon, and by then all the fight had been taken out of her and she was a licked woman. To all outward appearances they were a happily married couple, but knowing Sally as you do now, you know that by being brought from the open range of life into its harness room she has been chastened, subdued, defeated.

There was an ironic chuckle in the subdued laughter of her ex-husbands, her ex-lovers and even those who only satisfied her for one night, but to those of us who believe that motherhood is woman's highest purpose in life it would have been a shame if Sally hadn't got her legitimate daughter, and, personally, I was rooting for her.

I don't know if even Sally could have had a greater thrill than I did when the news came from the Montpelier Mountain Lying Inn that an eight-pound daughter had been born to the Marquise Henri Dupont, and that father and child were doing well.

The hospital was proud, too, the Chief Obstetrician saying, "We wanted to keep our record clear. After all, we never lost a father yet."

"Nor an uncle, either," added his assistant.

Sally settled three million francs on Henri for his part in the affair.

"What will you call the baby?" the Bureau of Vital Statistics wanted to know.

"The Beaut of Montana," said Sally, gagging in her ribald way. "*C'est un joli nom,*" the chief said.

"A nice name! You're telling me!" Sally laughed, half pulling him into her bed.

The man wriggled himself free. "*Quelle dame!*" he cried. "In labor pains, even!"

But it really was her last try. After that she settled down in a *château* on the Riviera, curbed her roving eye and soon that look of lust disappeared altogether.

I violate no confidence when I say that once that happened she and Henri and the Little Beaut from Montana lived happily ever after.

GOLD STAR MOTHER

By Philip Stevenson

LADIES: OR SHOULD I SAY FELLOW MEMBERS? I GUESS REALLY IT
doesn't matter, does it. We in our little group understand each
other, I guess. I guess what really matters is my report, and I want
to report we sure did have a morvelous time, and that's what you-all
want to hear about, isn't it.

Maybe some of you'll be sorry too, I mean some of you, that you
wasn't along with us. As I say, we sure had a morvelous time, we
saw everything we was supposed to see and I guess maybe a few
things we wasn't, and . . . really we just—did—ever'thing!

Of course some of it was sort of sad, kind of, and I guess most
of us had sort of the shivers when we saw where Our Boys had
died and blood was actually spilled and all. But then, I guess I can
say that not a one of us forgot she was a Gold Star Mother, we all
just realized that those terrible things have got to be and We
Mothers have just got to be mothers and expect those things because
that's just the way life is, isn't it!

Sad but true, I guess. And so we carried our cross and made the
best of everything, it was hard but we did it and speaking for
myself and I gave nine strapping youngsters to the great cause of
Humanity, speaking just for myself I guess I can say that the Spirit
of Sacrifice was what helped me to get through, I mean the realization that everybody has to carry her cross the best one can because
it's just the way life is, we all have our losses, even the bankers,
don't we.

Well, there we were, I mean Over There, and of course the first
thing was the reception in the Great Gay City, and I just want to
tell you ladies they sure did treat us just morvelous, they couldn't
do enough for us, like Mr. Bramah for instance he was the one
that made the Speech of Welcome. I just want to tell you, ladies,
it was a morvelous speech and Mr. Bramah was sure morvelous
looking too, so big and strong in spite of a slight hump in his back, a

93

regular bull neck and what shoulders, I guess some of us couldn't help making kind of cow eyes at him sort of!

But then! I'm not here to give anybody *away*. I'll just let Mrs. Holstein tell that part in her report, it's really a morvelous story though. Well, anyway, what Mr. Bramah said was that the sight of us Gold Star Mothers made his heart beat faster and his breath come short, I guess you all know how these males are, he would sort of paw the ground kind of while he talked because he said he realized we were the Flower of the Flock, the Blue Ribbon Winner, the very Spirit of Giving, so to speak, and nothing was too good for us, we had Given our All to the cause of Humanity and he just wished he could reward us all like we deserved in the Green Pastures of Eternity, and well, speaking for myself I thought, I said, well, never mind what I *thought* but it was all morvelous and that's the way life in the Great Gay City started that Mrs. Holstein is going to tell you about because she won the toss when we were deciding whom would report on what.

But speaking for myself I can just say this: I can say I promise you we all sure hated parting from Mr. Bramah, and I wondered if I could really go through the terrible part that was coming because you see then we was starting out for the sad part of our Pilgrimage and it was just too awful to think about all the slaughter and the blood and ever'thing. So I just chewed hard on my cud and made up my mind to be a really truly Gold Star Mother and go through with it, but I had a sort of queer little shudder in my udder kind of, and suddenly, I don't know, ladies, I guess I just couldn't help it, I let out one bellow, I didn't think I could go through with it and all. But then Mrs. Guernsey came up to me . . . she's not present, is she? No: well, she tried to be chummy and comforting and so on, and . . . of course I've never drawn the colour line, I just don't have any prejudices, I'm just as democratic as anyone can be, BUT . . . some things are just too much sometimes, I just somehow couldn't stand that great black cow rubbing up against me like that, and so I pretended she had me all wrong, I pretended it was leaving Mr. Bramah that made me so unhappy, and of course she is still just crazy about Mr. Guernsey and so she was shocked to death and so she left me alone and just went off with her tail between her legs! . . .

And now, ladies, this cool sip of water I've just taken has sort of cooled me off and made me realize that I've really kind of exaggerated the terrible part of my report. Because speaking for myself, it wasn't really so awfully terribly terrible. I mean, it was all so morvelously *done*. I thought that really when I saw the place where Our Boys had been struck down in their own blood I would faint dead away. But I didn't, and really I don't believe any of you would have either. What I thought was: How morvelous! I mean, everything about the surroundings. So perfectly suited to the occasion, I mean. Death is clean and kind! I thought. Death is merciful! And for the first time I realized the Great Wisdom behind it all. I saw life was hard and cruel. What did those dear young creatures have ahead of them but sorrow and longing and old age? After all, they couldn't *all* be Bramahs, one Bramah goes a long way, I thought. I thought, Yes! too many are born into this world. Life is the Survival of the Fittest, and Bramah does Fit, doesn't he! And really, isn't it better that one Bramah should live in abundance than that all should survive to know lifelong privation? And if they are to die, isn't it better for them to go like this, quickly and cleanly, than by slow starvation and loneliness?

Ladies, as I stood there those beautiful thoughts just kind of came to me sort of like an Inspiration. I felt like a poit, it was really just a morvelous sensation and I told Mrs. Holstein and Mrs. Jersey and they said, "My dear, it's morvelous, you must remember to put it in your report, it's really just poitry."

Well! After seeing that beautiful spot where Our Boys had fallen and sacrificed their lives for Humanity, I was kind of better prepared for the next part of our Pilgrimage. Maybe you just won't believe it, ladies, but speaking for myself I just want to tell you not one of us cried. It was really morvelous. Not just us, I mean, but the whole thing. "Truly inspiring" is the way Mrs. Jersey put it. "The poitry of death," I think she said. *Was* that what you said, Mrs. ——? Yes, thank you. "The poitry of death." And that's just what it was, too. Oh, I wish I could describe it to you, the beautiful surroundings, and the morvelous way the calves came through the chutes, one after another, Our Dear Boys, with their morvelous big soft eyes, and their sturdy young legs, and their dear little budding horns, and—oh! all the rest of it. But I can't, I just simply can't describe it. They never stopped, but only whimpered a little for their mothers, and marched straight ahead of them, their eyes open, to make the Supreme Sacrifice before their Maker. And when the twenty-pound sledge fell and their front legs collapsed and the blood spurted I thought: How morvelous!

My tears were tears of gladness, tears of joy and gratitude for the privilege of having given nine splendid calves that Humanity might be filled and at peace. It burst upon me as a great truth, that to Give Peace you must Endure Slaughter. And I thought of all the comfort I had created by my act of Sacrifice. I thought of how people all over the world had loosened their belts and grunted with satisfaction and belched from full bellies. And I wept for joy!

Next they took us to the Valley of the Departed, and I just simply can't tell you how inspiring *that* was, too. Thousands of Our Dear Boys, all so clean and pink and white and refrigerated. I was reminded of the words of the great poit of the slaughter:

> "Ribs and shoulders, cold as snow,
> Legs and quarters, row on row—
> In Shambles Fields!"

Never once did I think of Our Boys as dead. Speaking for myself, they seemed as fresh and pink as peppermint candy. And so, ladies, I made a great resolution. I said to myself, "Well, if all the ladies in our little group could see this, they would never again pass resolutions asking to have Their Boys brought home. They'd be delighted with how morvelous everything is done Over There."

And now I've found the word I've been looking for all this time. The very exact word to make you feel what we all felt there in the Valley of the Departed. Morvelous. That's just what it all was: just simply *morvelous*! And so I made my resolution: Never again would I object to having a calf of mine taken away from me in the name of Humanity. No, never, because then I realized: It had all been Well Worth While.

I thankya.

A GOOD JOB GONE

By Langston Hughes

IT WAS A GOOD JOB. BEST I EVER HAD. I GOT IT MY LAST YEAR IN HIGH school and it took me damn near through college. I'm sure sorry it didn't last. I made good money, too. Made so much that I changed from City College to Columbia my Sophomore year. Mr. Lloyd saw to it I got a good education. He had nothing against the Negro race, he said, and I don't believe he did. He certainly treated me swell from the time I met him till that high brown I'm gonna tell you about drove him crazy.

Now, Mr. Lloyd was a man like this: he had plenty of money, he liked his licker, and he liked his women. That was all. A damn nice guy—till he got hold of this jane from Harlem. Or till she got hold of him. My people—they won't do. They'd mess up the Lord if he got too intimate with 'em. Poor Negroes! I guess I was to blame, too. I should of told Mr. Lloyd she didn't mean him no good. But I was minding my own business, and that time I minded it too well.

But that was one of the things Mr. Lloyd told me when I went to work there. He said, "Boy, you're working for me—nobody else. Keep your mouth shut about what goes on here, and I'll look out for you. You're in school, ain't you? Well, you won't want to have to worry about money to buy books and take your girl-friends out—not if you stay with me."

He paid me twenty-two dollars a week, and I ate and slept in. He had a four-room apartment, as cozy a place as you'd want to see, looking right over Riverside Drive. Swell view. In the summer when Mr. Lloyd was in Paris or Berlin, I didn't have a damn thing to do but eat and sleep, and air the furniture. I got so tired, that I went to summer school.

"What you gonna be, boy?" he said.

I said, "A dentist, I reckon."

He said, "Go to it. They make a hell of a lot of money—if they got enough sex appeal."

97

He was always talking about sex-appeal and lovin'. He knew more dirty stories than any man I ever saw, Mr. Lloyd did. And he liked his women young and pretty. That's about all I did, spent my time cleaning up after some woman he'd have around, or makin' sandwiches and drinks in the evenings. When I did something extra, he'd throw me a fiver anytime. I made oodles o' money. Hell of a fine guy, Mr. Lloyd, with his 40-11 pretty gals—right out of the Follies or the Scandals, sweet and willing.

His wife was paralyzed, so I guess he had to have a little outside fun. They lived together in White Plains on a big estate. But he had a suite in the Hotel Stuyvesant, and a office down on Broad. He says, when I got the job, "Boy, no matter what you find out about me, where I live, or where I work, don't *you* connect up with no place but here. No matter what happens on Riverside Drive, don't you take it no further."

"Yes, sir, Mr. Lloyd," I said, because I knew where my bread was buttered. So I never went near the office or saw any of his other help but the chauffeur—and him a Jap.

Only thing I didn't like about the job, he used to bring some awfully cheap women there sometimes—big timers, but cheap inside. Didn't know how to treat a servant. One of 'em used to nigger and darkie me around, but I got her told right quietly one time, and Mr. Lloyd backed me up.

The boss said, "This is no ordinary boy. True, he's my servant, but I got him in Columbia studying to be a dentist, and he's just as white inside as he is black out. Treat him right, or I'll see why." And it wasn't long before this dame was gone, and he had a little Irish girl with blue eyes that he treated mean as hell.

Another thing I didn't like, though. Sometimes I used to have to drink a hell of a lot with him. When there was no women around, and Mr. Lloyd would get one of his blue spells and start talking about his wife, and how she hadn't walked for 18 years, just laying flat on her back. After about an hour of this, he'd want me to start drinking with him. And when he felt good from licker, he'd start talking free about women in general, and he'd ask me what they were like in Harlem. Then he'd tell me what they were like in Montreal and Havana and Honolulu. He'd even had Gypsy women in Spain.

Then he would drink and drink, and make me drink with him

And we'd both be so drunk I couldn't go to classes the next morning, and he wouldn't go to the office maybe all day. About four o'clock he'd send me out for some clam broth and an American Mercury, so he could sober up on Mencken. I'd give him a alcohol rub, then he'd go off to his suite in the Stuyvesant and have dinner with the society folks he knew. I might not see him again for days. But he'd slip me a greenback usually.

"Boy, you'll never lose anything through sticking with me! Here." And it would be a fiver.

Sometimes I wouldn't see Mr. Lloyd for weeks. Then he'd show up late at night with a chippie, and I'd start making drinks and sandwiches and smoothing down the bed. Then there'd be a round o' women, six or eight different ones in a row, for days. And me working my hips off keeping 'em fed and lickered up. This would go on till he got tired and had the blues again. Then he'd beat the hell out of one of his women and send her off. Then we'd get drunk again. When he sobered up he'd telephone for his chauffeur to drive him to White Plains to see his old lady, or down to the hotel where he lived with a private secretary. And that would be that.

He had so damn much money, Mr. Lloyd. I don't see where folks get so much cash. But I don't care so long as they're giving some of it to me. And if it hadn't been for this colored woman, boy, I'd still be sitting pretty.

I don't know where he got her. Out of one of the Harlem night clubs, I guess. They came bustin' in about four o'clock one morning. I heard a woman laughing in the living room, and I knew it was a nigger laugh—one of ours. So deep and pretty, it couldn't have been nothing else. I got up, of course, like I always did when I heard Mr. Lloyd come in. I broke some ice, and took 'em out some drinks.

Yep, she was colored, alright. One of these golden browns, like an Alabama moon. Swell looking kid. She had the old man standing on his ears. I never saw him looking so happy before. She kept him laughing till daylight, and hugging and kissing. She had a hot line, that kid did, without seeming to be serious. But he fell for it. She hadn't worked in Harlem speakeasies for nothing. Jesus! She was like gin and vermouth mixed.

We got on swell, too, that girl and I. "Hy, Pal," she said when she saw me bringing out the drinks. "If it ain't old Harlem, on the

Drive." She wasn't a bit hinkty like so many colored folks when they're light-complexioned and up in the money. If she hadn't been the boss's girl, I might have tried to make her myself. But she had a black boy-friend—a number writer on 135th Street—so she didn't need me. She used to talk to me about him all the time. She was in love with him. Used to call him up as soon as the boss got in the elevator bound for the office.

"Can I use this phone?" she asked me that very morning.

"Sure, Miss," I answered.

"Call me Pauline," she said, "I ain't white." And we got on swell. I cooked her some bacon and eggs while she called up her sweetie. She told him she'd hooked a new butter and egg man with bucks.

Well, the days went on. Everytime, the boss would show up with Pauline. It looked like blondes didn't have a break. A sugar-brown had crowded the white babies out. But it was good for Mr. Lloyd. He didn't have the blues. And he stopped asking me to drink with him, thank God! He was crazy about this Pauline. Didn't want no other woman. She kept him laughing all the time. She used to sing him bad songs that didn't seem bad when she was singing them. Only seemed funny and good-natured. She was nice, that girl. A gorgeous thing to have around the house.

But she knew what it was all about. Don't think she didn't. "You've got to kid white folks along," she said to me. "When you're depending on 'em for a living. Make 'em *think* you like it."

"You said it," I agreed.

And she really put the bee on Mr. Lloyd. He bought her every-thing she wanted, and was as faithful to her as a husband all winter. Used to ask me when she wasn't there, what I thought she wanted. I don't know what got into him. He loved her like a dog.

She used to spend two or three nights a week with him. And the others with her boy-friend in Harlem. And it was a hell of a long time before Mr. Lloyd found out about this colored fellow. When he did, it was a pure accident. He saw Pauline going in the movies at the Roxy one night with him—a tall black good-looking guy with a diamond on his finger. And it made the old man sore.

That same night Mr. Lloyd got a ring-side table at the Cabin Club in Harlem. When Pauline came dancing out in the 2 o'clock revue, he called her, and told her to come there. He looked mad.

Funny, boy, but that rich white man was jealous of the colored guy he had seen her with. Mr. Lloyd, jealous of a jig! Wouldn't that freeze you?

They had a hell of a quarrel that morning when they came to the apartment. First time I ever heard them quarrel. Pauline told him finally he could go to hell. She told him, yes, she loved that black boy, that he was the only boy she loved in the wide world, and the only man she wanted.

They were all drunk, because between words they would drink licker. I'd left two bottles of Haig & Haig on the tray when I went to bed. I thought Pauline was being stupid, talking like that, but I guess she was so drunk she didn't care.

"Yes, I love that colored boy," she hollered. "Yes, I love him. You don't think you're buying my heart, too, do you?"

And that hurt the boss. He'd always thought he was a great lover, and that women liked him for something else besides his money. Because most of them wanted his money, nobody ever told him he wasn't so hot. His girls all swore they loved him, even when he beat them. They all let *him* put *them* out. They hung on till the last dollar.

But that little yellow devil of a Pauline evidently didn't care what she said. She began cussing the boss about dawn. Then Mr. Lloyd slapped her. I could hear it way back in my bedroom where I was sleeping, with one eye open.

In a minute I heard a crash that brought me up on my feet. I ran out, through the kitchen, through the living room, and opened Mr. Lloyd's door. Pauline had thrown one of the whiskey bottles at him. Now they were battling like hell in the middle of the floor.

"Get out of here, boy!" Mr. Lloyd panted. So I got. But I stood outside the door in case I was needed. If she wanted help, I was there. But Pauline was a pretty tough little scrapper herself. It sounded like the boss was getting the worst of it. Finally, the tussling stopped. It was so quiet in there I thought maybe one of them was knocked out, so I cracked the door to see. The boss was kneeling at Pauline's feet, his arms around her knees.

"My God, Pauline, how I love you!" I heard him say. "I want you, child. Don't mind what I've done. Stay here with me. Stay, stay, stay."

"Lemme out of here!" said Pauline, kicking at Mr. Lloyd.

But the boss held her tighter. Then she grabbed the other whiskey bottle and hit him on the head. Of course, he fell out. I got a basin of cold water and put him in bed with a cloth on his dome. Pauline took off all the rings and things he'd given her and threw them at him, laying there on the bed like a ghost.

"A white bastard!" she said. "Just because they pay you, they always think they own you. No white man's gonna own me. I laugh with 'em, and they think I like 'em. Hell, I'm from Arkansas where the crackers lynch niggers in the streets. How could *I* like 'em?" She put on her coat and hat and went away.

When the boss came to, he told me to call his chauffeur. I thought he was going to a doctor, because his head was bleeding. But the chauffeur told me later he spent the whole day driving around Harlem trying to find Pauline. He wanted to bring her back. But he never found her.

He had a lot of trouble with that head, too. Seems like a piece of glass or something stuck in it. I didn't see him for eight weeks. When I did see him, he wasn't the same man. No, sir, boy, something had happened to Mr. Lloyd. He didn't seem quite right in the head. I guess Pauline dazed him for life, made a fool of him. He drank more than ever and had me so high I didn't know B from Bull's Foot. He had his white women around again, but he'd got the idea from somewhere that he was the world's great lover, and that he didn't have to give them anything but himself—which wasn't so forty for the little Broadway gold diggers who wanted diamonds and greenbacks. Women started to clearing out early when they discovered that Mr. Lloyd had gone romantic—and cheap. There were scandals and fights and terrible goings on when the girls didn't get their presents and checks. But Mr. Lloyd just said, "To hell with them," and drank more than ever, and let the pretty girls go. He picked up women off the streets and then wouldn't pay them, cheap as they are. Late in the night he would come in and start drinking and crying about Pauline. The sun would be rising over the Hudson before he'd stop his crazy carryings on—making me drink with him and listen to the nights he'd spent with Pauline.

"I love her, boy! And she thought I was trying to buy her. Some black buck had to come along and cut me out. Fooling her. But I'm just as good a lover as that black boy any day." And he would begin to boast about the white women he could have—without money, too. (Wrong, of course.) But he sent me to Harlem to find Pauline.

I couldn't find her. She'd gone away with her boy-friend. Some said they went to Memphis. Some said Chicago. Some said Los Angeles. Anyway, she was gone—that kid who looked like an Alabama moon.

I told Mr. Lloyd she was gone, so we got drunk again. For almost a week, he made no move to go to the office. I began to be worried, cutting so many classes staying up all night to drink with the old man, and hanging around most of the day. But if I left him alone, he acted like a fool. I was scared. He'd take out women's pictures and beat 'em and stamp on 'em and then make love to 'em, and tear 'em up. Wouldn't eat. Didn't want to see anybody.

Then one night, I knew he was crazy—so it was all up. He grabs the door like it was a woman, and starts to kiss it. I couldn't make him stop, so I telephoned his chauffeur. The chauffeur calls up one of Mr. Lloyd's broker friends. And they take him to the hospital. That was last April. They've had him in the sanatorium ever since. The apartment's closed. His stuff's in storage, and I have no more job than a snake's got hips. Anyway I went through college on it. But I don't know how the hell I'll get to dental school. I just wrote ma down in Atlanta and told her times was hard. Ain't many Mr. Lloyd's, you can bet your life on that.

And the chauffeur told me yesterday he's crazy as a loon now. Sometimes he thinks he's a guy named Don Juan. Again, he thinks he's a stud-horse chasing a mare. Sometimes he's a lion. Poor man! The padded cell! He was a swell guy when he had his right mind. But a yellow woman sure did drive him crazy. As for me, well, it's just one good job gone.

Say, boy, give me a smoke, will you? I hate to talk about it.

WHY I AM FAITHFUL TO MY WIFE

By Thames Williamson

I HAVE BEEN MARRIED TEN YEARS, ALL THIS WHILE FAITHFUL TO MY wife. And lately—reading ultra-modern fiction, listening to people describe their erotic adventures, watching the defections of my men friends—lately I have come to regard myself with wonder.

Not admiration, not smug satisfaction. Wonder. Just why have I remained true to the girl I married, and why doesn't it hurt to be that way?

Because it doesn't. Not really. I have been tempted to go the way of all flesh, a number of times tempted, but thus far I've stayed in line. And this without having to make New Year's resolutions, swear mighty oaths, or tie myself to the mast Ulysses fashion.

How come?

If I were my grandfather, or possibly even my father, it might be explained on moral grounds. The argument would run roughly as follows: I have taken this woman to be my lawful wedded wife. Man's law and the infinitely more powerful law of God constrain me to remain faithful to her now and at all times in the future, forever and ever, until death do us part. This being the case, any act of faithlessness is a sin, too vile and heinous even to contemplate. If I transgress, if I step over the traces into marital infidelity, I shall inevitably be visited with damnation.

It was a good argument, noble and authoritative, but somehow a great deal of water has run under the bridge since then.

Take me, for instance. I consider myself a fairly decent chap, and yet the hell-fire-if-you-do-it theory has lost meaning for me. Meaning and force. It has been outmoded, given way to other sanctions. Alone and unsupported, no such concepts as morality or damnation would keep me faithful to my wife.

Nor am I simply afraid of being caught.

Fear is of course one element in the situation—masculine fear, rooting in a wholesome respect for feminine intuition.

My wife has a goodly supply of intuition; in fact, she is un-canny at divining things which according to the prosier male mind she has no right even to suspect. If I were to bundle up a diamond ring until it resembled a pair of roller skates and give it to the missus for Christmas, she would certainly know, long before she unwrapped it, that it *was* a ring. Did I essay to hide a case of treas-ured Scotch in the garage while my wife was on vacation, she would scarcely have her hat off before she smelled out my secret.

What, then, if I wandered from the path of husbandly virtue? Sooner or later intuition would put my wife on the trail, sooner or later tongues would harry her to the kill. Consider how we rub elbows nowadays. We have innumerable friends, neighbors, ac-quaintances; we are members of a jostling close community; we come and go and eat and laugh and die practically in the public lap. In a net of relationships like this it is devilishly hard to do any-thing odd without attracting the spotlight. Privacy has folded up like an Arab's tent. The slightest irregularities in conduct are noticed, and, if they promise diversion, briskly commented upon. A too-long sojourn on the terrace, a lunch engagement that you fail to report at home—it all tends to get into the record. You fancy no one knows, but at the most inopportune time—at a cosy little dinner party, say—some sweet cat of a Borgia coos across the table:

"Oh, darling, was your hubby in Chicago last week? How *in-teresting*! Harriet Gorse was there, too . . ."

Tough sledding for most married men, doubly tough for me. Because I am the sort of fellow who habitually spends most of his time under ye olde family rooftree. I don't "run the roads," as they say in Maine. I belong to no stag clubs, attend very few purely masculine dinners, play no pool or poker. As a writer who does his typewriter pecking at home, I lack the standard alibi of a sudden business trip to Denver or St. Louis, the excuse of prolonged con-ferences with a big boss in New York. Home body that I am, my absences are rare. Rare and on that account subject to a strong light of wifely interest. Not suspicion—*interest*. A faked trip, a jaunt trumped up for the sake of another woman, would be difficult, if not impossible.

I hope I am not chicken-hearted about it. We men mustn't be that. Feminine intuition is unfair to husbands, organized or disorganized; assisting gossips are an outrage. A man shouldn't be cowed by dastardly opposition of this sort. Stay faithful to my wife merely because I might get caught? Not I. If it were only a question of that particular risk, I'd try my luck in the tournament, fighting single-handed against the odds of feminine wiles and whispering campaigns. I'd do it out of stubbornness and male pride, I'd do it for love of danger and the sake of stolen sweets. Yet I haven't. Beyond fear there are other, more important deterrents.

One of these is the terrific time and energy required to follow up and consummate an illicit amour.

If I were in my twenties it would be different. In such case I'd still revel in an abundance of physical energy, and I could take keen delight in the custom of pursuing love whither it led. I might sneak through dark woods and laugh at thorns and chuck-holes and mosquitoes, I'd wait under a tree that shook delayed raindrops down my neck, I could enthusiastically make love to my inamorata in the confines of a secluded parked automobile. Yes, and count it all a privilege, a glorious opportunity. Lucky, lucky me, and so forth.

The trouble is, however, that I am not in my twenties, and have not been for more than a decade.

Therefore I should not be sustained by the naïve thirsts of the very young. Youth gambols up and down with its tongue hanging out because it is inexperienced, and yearns for conquest and adventure. The boy in his twenties is still intrigued by the mystery that is Woman, the man of forty most often is not. Like other citizens of my age I have long since found out what women look like, act like, and wherein they differ one from another, in intimate as well as superficial particulars. I've had my share of information, my quota of marcelled scalps. Running after further conquests would be an arduous task. Too arduous, considering the returns. The game is no longer worth the candle.

Ah, but doesn't vanity prod me into clandestine love? Vanity is man's weak point, women tell us with scorn; it is our spiritual rickets, a kind of chronic predisposition to horrid disease which every male inherits from his father, back and back to the beginnings of time, when men got their start at playing the twin role of Brute and Beast. Where lives there the husband whose wife has never to him said, "Why, that woman can wrap you right around her finger, just by flattering you!"

No use arguing that we men are not vain, not susceptible to sweet compliments. Me, I am admittedly vain. Women have flattered me and I've loved it, but though I expanded like a toad in the sun and even croaked for more, no smooth gal has yet succeeded in getting me to set up a local Lothario.

I'll tell you why.

Since I am over forty most of the women I know are somewhere in the neighborhood of thirty-five. More than a few of them are the semi-idle wives of successful men and are patently in the market for a romantic diversion. With me or with someone else, it doesn't make a tremendous lot of difference which. Point is, the dears are chiefly seeking relief from ennui, hunting a tonic for self-esteem, planning masculine coups as a means of proving that they are not slipping; or maybe they are simply out to get revenge on an errant husband. It would be no great compliment to be taken to the arms of such a one. Especially since they are no longer young; and a man is never so old that he is not sensitive to lack of youth in women.

It *would* inflate my ego, naturally, if I could captivate a considerably younger woman. Say a girl in her twenties, someone vibrant, fresh, lovely in body and stimulating in mind, and very preferably a girl sought after by men younger than myself. That *would* raise the devil with Mr. Over-Forty!

Yet it is unlikely that this could happen. The reason? My capacity for being mortified is greater than my conceit. Any forty-year-old with a lick of sense must realize that most girls in their twenties look upon him as passé, a has-been well on the road to decrepitude and therefore out of their own gay young race. They would be either disgusted or amused if I attempted to make conquest among their ranks, and on that account I refrain. However much I may admire You Lovely Young Thing, however much I appreciate her riches of flesh and spirit, I confine myself to harmless persiflage. *No fool like an old fool* is a proverb that makes me shudder.

Out with vanity, then. I am vain but not vain enough to make a monkey of myself—I hope.

But are there no women in my set that I might fall for? Certainly there are. Very attractive women, too. And what's more, I now and then get a covert invitation from one of them to take part in the oldest of intrigues. Thrilling, that is—except that I am held back by the realization that we would probably never get to making love expertly, and anything short of expertness would be a humiliating and an unsatisfying experience.

Ponder this for a moment.

Love-making, courtship, the marriage relation, all these things call for practice. Just like a duet, double piano playing, or a set of tennis. The grand passion requires not only two people but two people who are used to each other, who are co-operative in ways bordering upon the artistic. If they are not easily and habitually a team it is impossible to extract the proper satisfaction from what they fondly call their love.

Here, then, is the psychological weakness of the extramarital excursion. No matter how exciting and pleasurable it may be, you cannot escape the fact that the two parties are unused to each other, and—what is even more lamentable—they probably are, or have been, used to someone else. Their habits, methods, technique in general, all are different. They may have danced and played bridge and discussed dahlias for years on end, but when it comes to consummating love they are likely to be maladroit as strangers. Even though they be fundamentally at ease there are subtleties which are off tone, and in so delicate a relationship subtleties can have a most devastating effect. The result can be summed up as interesting—even exciting—but so bungling as to be ruinous to one's self-esteem.

To make matters worse the experience might deprive me of something valuable.

Among my friends is a charming woman whom we shall call Prunella. Prunella is the wife of a rich man; she is witty and vivacious, very good-looking, clever at wearing clothes, and old enough to be sophisticated in the true sense of the word. She is fond of me. Whether this is good taste on her part is beside the point— actually she does like me, very much. By word and gesture I have received this assurance from Prunella. She has got through my skull the information that she would neither swoon, have me arrested, nor shout for her husband if I were to advance our friendship to a warmer phase.

This has been going on for almost a year, and yet except for an occasional kiss—leaving her house or she leaving mine, after dinner —beyond this and a few words of affection, the affair has wilted in the bud. I know Prunella wonders why. With the self-centered yen of her sex she expects me to do something about it. I imagine she has even begun to think me a dud, a stick, a mouse where there ought to be a man. Dreadful image to have rise up in front of me every time I meet her, nevertheless I continue to do nothing. I contemplate it now and then, I even talk to her of ways and means and convenient times, but always vaguely, like a beachcomber who keeps promising the old folks that he'll be coming home—some day.

I'll never do anything about Prunella. For one thing I do not want to ruin my dream of her. To me Prunella has glamor, especially on moonlit terraces and in certain frocks and attitudes. I want her to retain that quality, and intimacy would destroy it. I do not mean that having got her I would on that account spurn her; I mean that her present appeal depends upon a certain aloofness, a certain veiling and artful camouflage; and if she became my mistress she would be stripped of this romantic build-up. Robbed of her aura I should thereafter look upon her with what Jack London referred to as his jaundiced eye. She would never be the same.

That would be bad, very bad. I positively insist upon investing Prunella with glamor, even though it be imaginary glamor. Women of her type I want to admire and yet never possess. Let them be an idyll beyond the horizon, an untouched flower, something delectable and yet harmless, kept at arm's length and so insured against all chance of disillusioning me.

But what of my wife's glamor?

Most of it has thinned away, destroyed by years of intimacy. My better half is, after ten years, not a goddess but merely a woman. No mystery left. I know her physical self; I am as familiar with her methods of dressing and ornamenting herself as I am with my shaving routine. Mentally, too, I understand her; and though she occasionally exhibits an emotional quirk that confounds me I have got into the way of putting this down, not to mystery but to sheer female cussedness. Glamor, no. Never—that is, hardly ever!

Yet she is not spoiled for me. Far from it. Because in the course of our life together she has developed other attractions. Strong and valuable fruits to take the place of her original halo of dream and glamor. Great, fine enduring virtues that she either did not possess when I asked her to marry me, or which I was indifferent to, but for which nevertheless I now thank God. It is partly because of these assets that I cling to my wife; and I look askance at other women because I do not believe that long years with them would develop similar blessings. Certainly no unrelated series of amours could bring them to flower.

My wife's virtues I appreciate, the monotony of married life I appreciate. It's wonderfully pleasant that married life *is* monotonous. Youngsters may thrive, or think they thrive, on a hurly-burly of love and passion, but as a steady diet this is as untenable as an unvarying menu of cake and gin. By the time a man is forty years of age, sex should have become background music, vital and enjoyable, but retired to its proper place as only one ingredient in the feast of marital felicity. Sex becomes a matter of course without becoming the object of careless taking-for-granted. A dozen other satisfactions grow up between a man and a woman, satisfactions requiring order, stability, and the smooth succession of months and years together. So far as I am concerned, nothing could be more appalling than to be forced to go outside my own home on the trail of erotic delights.

All this helps me stay faithful to my wife, and beyond that I am true to her out of a sense of sportsmanship. I have a nice wife. She has never—that I know of, and I think I know—she has never misbehaved. Faults she has, to be sure, but they are clearly outweighed by her good points. She scraped and scrimped when we were poor, she gambled on my unpredictable profession, she put up with the nonsense I used to call temperament. When the children came she took unfailingly good care of them, when any of us falls sick she nurses us and worries and loses her appetite and ten pounds in weight. In a thousand moments of irritability and resentment and despair I have had honest help from my wife. I'd never let her down by having an affair with another woman. I can't see myself subjecting her to the private shame and public humiliation which clandestine affairs almost always bring in their wake. It wouldn't be sporting; it wouldn't be decent.

Besides, there are the children.

Perhaps it is the children that are, to use a German phrase, the *hauptsache*. My mother and father were divorced when I was in my early teens. I grew up and married, and having discovered that it was all a terrible mistake I got a divorce and ultimately married again and had children. Without bothering with the theories of philosophers, or thumbing through the case findings of social workers, I know perfectly well that the children of divorced parents suffer deeply; and understanding my present wife as I do, I realize that infidelity would end in our divorce.

That is unthinkable. Regardless of whether I might prefer another woman to my wife, I recoil from the possibility of harming my children, putting a blight on their budding young lives, robbing them of what I promised by inference in bringing them into the world. When I think of that, when I look upon my fine intelligent son, my adorable lovely small daughter, the mere thought of a broken home fills me with horror. The emotion and joy which my children arouse in me is mighty as the overture to *Tannhäuser*, a crescendo of glorious music beside which the pleasures of infidelity are no more than the quaverings of a tubercular saxophone, trivial and without power.

PART II

PART II

IN THE DOG HOUSE

By JOHN JAY DALY

MY OLD DRINKING COMPANION REMARKED THE OTHER DAY, "YOU haven't been in the dog house for some time, have you?"

Right away I commenced to brag. Fatal: "No, I haven't been in the dog house for quite a spell, and I don't think I'll ever go there again."

That very night I went out and got in the dog house.

Now the dog house is the place in the mind of the little woman where she keeps her man on those occasions when he violates, willy-nilly, the rules of domesticity.

Soon as he steps off the reservation, every married man is a candidate for the dog house. Whenever he leaves the water wagon, goes out on a bat or a bender, coming home three sheets to the wind, the dog catcher is on his trail. Sentence to the dog house is pronounced soon as the culprit staggers through the front door, or is thrown in the vestibule by his companions.

When a woman gets a man in the dog house all hell breaks loose, and the yapping begins.

Off and on, I've been in the dog house so many times I'm all flea-bitten.

In long years of experience, I have discovered all the ways there are to get in the dog house. There is only one way out. The dog house has many entrances but just one exit.

The way out of the dog house leads eventually to the pathway of peace on earth—reconciliation with the little woman.

Just how to bring about this boon is something that comes only with a great deal of experience—and experimentation.

Wives differ in many respects, but they are all alike when they stand as sentinels at the lone door of the dog house. The poor old dog in the manger has a sad look in his eyes. All he wants is a friendly pat on the head. What he gets is a kick in the slats.

Easy to get in the dog house. So hard to get out.

I recall the first time I was there. It came about in a perfectly innocent way. At least I thought it was, but the good wife had other ideas. So she put me in the dog house.

Bill had come to town and dropped into the office. He was anxious to talk over a business deal, so we stepped over to Dinty's Place for a bite. It turned out to be a dog bite.

Along about 6 o'clock the fact dawned upon me that I had a home—and that the bride was waiting for her loved one.

Home was a seven or eight miles out in the suburban country, a good thirty minutes away, dinner was scheduled for 6 o'clock, here it was six, and there were guests.

Bill and I were tossing off a few highballs when I looked at the old timepiece: "Bill," I said quite solemnly, "I'm in dutch."

"Whatdye mean, in dutch?"

"It's six now, I'm due home at six, and there are guests for dinner."

"T'hell with th' guests," Bill drawled. "This is business." He contemplated the bottom of his glass. "Call her up."

So I called her up.

What that gal said to me was plenty:

"Where are you?"

"Where have you been?"

"Why didn't you call before?"

"Why weren't you in your office?"

"Who are you with?"

"Where is all that noise coming from?"

"The next time I have any of your friends out to dinner, you'll know it," and so forth, et cetera, and so on, ad infinitum et gloria patria and nuts to you!

Eventually I got to the little house on the hillside and entered the dog house waiting for the prodigal pup.

The silence of the dog house is intense. It is a cold, frigid affair —even on the hottest nights. No man, whatever his nature, be he the most silent creature in the world, absorbed in his own thoughts, relishes being stared at and not spoken to by the little woman.

That, I believe, is the hardest blow to bear—those silent stares.

If the old gal would only say something—that is, after the first barrage. She says plenty then, but the poor duffer on his way to the dog house would rather not listen. Paradoxically, he would welcome the sweet sound of her voice after he has been in the dog house a day or so—even if it was another good bawling out.

To be in the home and not of the home is the equivalent of being in the dog house.

To sit in a little family gathering, have the good woman talk to all other members of the group, and ignore the old man—that is the pay off. It comes from being a lodger in the dog house.

God help the poor devils in dog houses on occasions like this. There is one other slap that hurts, too. That is to be reminded by innuendo that you are in the dog house—the remark passed along in conversation over the telephone, or to some neighbor over the back fence, or at the side of the house.

"No, we are not going anywhere this week, George was out on a party last night and doesn't feel any too good. Yes, he stayed home from the office today—poor fellow. His head hurts. Yes, I gave him aspirin. What he really needs is a good stiff drink—but he's gone on the water wagon. Yes, he went on this morning. I saw to that. No, there isn't any in the house. While waiting for him last night, I took the last drink in the bottle."

So that's where it went. I had wondered who tapped that till. Curses on forgetfulness. Should have brought home something for the morning after. And the day in the dog house.

Hells bells! This is terrible. If I ever get out of the dog house again I'll never go back.

I can hear loud laughter now, as someone remarks: "That's what they all say!"

Well, so they do. And they mean it, too. But there is an old saying to the effect that boys will be boys. By the same virtue, men will be men—and the man doesn't live who has been in the dog house once and never goes back. They all get there sooner or later, for one reason or another.

Now it may be that looking upon the sherry and port when they are a bit too red or black is one man's method of getting the tag on his neck.

That is not the only way to get in the dog house.

Jim, for instance, tells me he goes to the dog house regularly, every time he and his wife visit the country club for one of those dollar Sunday night dinners.

Invariably, Jim see some woman he knows, renews an old

acquaintance, gets a little too familiar, giving her the old slap-on-the-back stuff and gets sent to the dog house.

Going into the dog house with some men is almost like an actor going into his dance.

Oscar tells me that he goes into the dog house every time his wife's mother comes to town. Now the old lady is all right, y'understand, and she and Oscar get along like a couple of old side kicks —but just the same the old lady has a certain effect on Oscar. He begins to get too mushy when she's around. Helping her with her coat and bonnet. Putting his arms round her shoulder. Squeezing her, calling her mother. Practically makes love to her. But once, years ago, Oscar said something about the old gal that wasn't quite complimentary. Elephant like, the daughter never forgot—and she never forgave. She believes to this day that Oscar hates his mother-in-law, that he is a hypocrite and a liar when he pretends otherwise. So he goes into the dog house whenever the old lady appears on the scene. It's too bad, too, because Oscar is on the level with his admiration of his mother-in-law. When a man actually likes his mother-in-law he shouldn't get punished for it—like Oscar does, being sent to the dog house.

Of course, men have gone to the dog house for less than this; but just the same it isn't right.

As an old inhabitant of the dog house, I'm willing to admit—even to my wife—that there were occasions when I deserved all I got, in and out of the dog house; but I do claim, and I make no bones about it, that Oscar's wife is unjust. If he wants to show the old lady a good time, why send him to the dog house for it? There's a limit to everything. This comes straight from the dog house—and it ain't a fit place for man nor beast.

CHAPTER II

Was a song,

> "I'm bidin' my time,
> That's th' kind-a guy I'm."

It is the theme song of the Dog House Brigade. His period of internment is one of watchful waiting. He must watch and wait for an opportunity to get out. This requires diplomacy and tact.

Repeated trips to the dog house bring out the best in a man. Continued sessions there cultivate latent traits. If further pursued some of these native talents would fit a man for the legal profession; if he were not a lawyer. Legal lights have shone in the dog house, too. It took all the brilliancy they possessed to light their way out.

Even if a man is not a lawyer, once he gets in the dog house he has to present an argument that would convince the judge and jury —the guardian of the dog house—that the time has come for clemency.

On occasion, I personally have delivered masterly orations from the threshold of the dog house—like the old porch philosophers. Also, I have heard friends of mine come across with forensic works that equalled any delivered by Daniel Webster, Patrick Henry, Robert Ingersoll or William Jennings Bryan, with a sprinkling of Father Coughlin and Huey Long.

Many a time have I been surprised at the great gift that is mine, both in rhetoric and oratory. Once, after an outburst, I had the little woman finally wondering in her own mind if she herself should not have been in the dog house, instead of me. There were times, too, when I actually put her in the dog house, by a magnificent display of logic. Aristotle himself could not have done better. She was certainly ashamed of herself, her entire sex, and the way she treated me, after I turned loose the guns of oratory.

There were other times, of course, when all this hidden power was of no avail. Then, the wisdom of Plato, the poetry of Keats and Shelley, and even the argumentative powers of old man Blackstone himself would have been lost. This happens most of the time.

In a long career, I have discovered that the approach is everything when the time comes to get out of the dog house.

As in salesmanship the approach amounts to one-half the victory, so in making the first steps toward a graceful exit from the dog house, the old timer measures his distance carefully before firing the first shot. It must come about naturally or it will prove a dud.

This is where the policy of watchful waiting is developed to its highest degree.

The old woman must be caught unawares—in a moment of weakness. In other words, off guard. Even the best of the vigilantes are sometimes known to sleep. A nod of the head, and the moment has arrived.

As the guardian of a man's morals finds it easier to keep him in the dog house by not remaining for long periods in his presence, but always at a careful distance—usually out of ear-shot—it is no easy matter to make that first advance upon which rests the peace and tranquillity of the American home, and the dog house.

If the little woman has had a hard day, baking a cake or supervising the family wash, she may in the course of the afternoon take herself to the divan and there stretch out—for rest and relaxation.

Here is the quarry.

Now, an old offender always is prepared. When he comes home that afternoon he has under his arm a box of candy—sweets to the sweet. Nuts to the nuts!

Here is his chance. Without a word, he walks to the couch and quietly deposits his precious burden by the side of the lady.

"Just thought you'd enjoy a chocolate snack," he says—and vanishes.

Her first impulse might be to throw the carton to the floor—but candy hath charms to soothe the savage breast.

If she opens that lid she's a gone gosling.

Once she takes the top off a good priced box of bon bons the old battle-axe starts falling from her hands. The man, down on all fours, is on his way out of the dog house. The barking days are over.

He can come back into the room then with a knowledge, born of experience, that there will be no catty remark to greet him.

Instead, he is liable to hear something like this:

"There was a phone call for you awhile ago. I told whoever it was you were busy—at the office. Did you have a hard day?"

The old-timer never answers that question. To say he had a hard day, or a good day, or any other kind of day, is courting disaster. In the first place, the good wife doesn't give a damn what kind of a day the brute had. She knows she had a hard day—one hell of a day, trying to make the hired help wrestle out its wages. That poser on the end of the remark was merely the moment of weakness oozing into the old carcass—the softening of the heart arteries.

When she wants to know if he had a hard day, what your old timer does then is to drop to his knees in front of her, take the hand now holding the candy, kiss the back of it—the hand, not the candy—and blurt out the old formula:

"I'm mighty sorry, Betsy, that I stepped off the reservation," et so forth, et cetera, et tu Brutus!

Two things can happen. First she can pull that old line, "Don't you Betsy me," or she can really capitulate, break down and cry, and ask again the time worn question, "Why did you do it, Reggie —aren't you ever going to have any sense?"

If she says that, and smiles, the chains fall off and the old boy comes out of the dog house. When she says that she's got to smile.

In getting out of the dog house, it's every man for himself.

As an old practitioner, I have perhaps interviewed more fellow offenders than any other inmate of the dog house. An inborn curiosity prompted me to make an exhaustive study, in the hope of finding something worthy of preservation—to be handed down to posterity. For there are puppies today, wagging their tails in glee, who will someday bring down upon them all the wrath of their future keepers of the dog house. Those are the little girls now playing with their dolls—playing mothers they call it, the little dears. You can see them sometimes spank their dolls and put them to bed, for bad behavior. Ah, little boys, in sand-piles and on the sidewalks, beware! Beware of the dog house. Or, as the lawyers say, "Caveat Emptor!"

Was a time when I thought seriously of offering this thesis for my doctorate, having longed in those days to be a doctor of philosophy. Little do the doctors of philosophy, academicians all, know what goes on in the dog house. I doubt if any one of them is aware the place exists.

Later, I learned to my sorrow that colleges and universities, along with other places of higher education, care not one wot—or wot not a care—for the humanities. Still, they are designed primarily to prepare the youngsters for life—and life as it goes on apace, usually lands some of the men folk, even college graduates in the dog house.

All this I pointed out once to a learned professor. He was not fundamentally interested. Nor was his alma mater. The subject could not be included in the curriculum, he said there was no place for it. Not even in those deleterious courses known as domestic economy. Still, those upon whose shoulders some day will fall hardest all the burdens of this so-called domestic economy have a divine right to know what awaits them. . . . Peradventure, most of them will land in the dog house. They have a right to know the low-down.

In squaring all the facts of this old world, it seems to me that those who bury themselves behind pages of books in the shadow of the academic walls, for the purpose of enlightening the race, would do infinitely better by humanity if they sounded the depths of a subject here being treated only casually by a lay-man.

Certainly, the dog house is of interest to most men. Instead of taking it up seriously, most of the professors still ignore it—though, for all I know, some of them even now may be inhabitants of the dog house. Not all the professors are bachelors. Still, they'd rather treat of transcendentalism—which, as I understand it, is the art of living in the cellar and thinking in the attic. There is neither attic or cellar to the dog house. It has four walls, a roof, a hardwood floor—and, that lone way out. That is all. A simple structure, the dog house is one that leads to more complications than all of Euclid's theories, including the simple mental process involved in Pons Asinorum.

Whether a monk read by the aid of candlelight or skylight is of little moment in an age when electricity happens to be the dominant influence of life. A man in the dog house can see sparks flying from his wife's tongue at any time. He gets his shock with the original sentence. After that, the lights go out.

No sir, the monastery blues are nothing compared to the enforced retirement of a good, sound, active, bustling business or professional man to the little kennel provided by his light o' love.

In fact, the only advantage that comes from any prolonged occupancy of the dog house is a meditative process somewhat akin to the monastic life of those who entered the old cloistered orders. It was believed, and it is undoubtedly true, that the monks went into seclusion for their peace of mind. They wanted to get away from the hurly-burly of life. They hoped to find surcease from sorrow by searching the innermost recesses of their souls. A man in the dog house has an opportunity to go and do likewise—though not voluntarily.

A BREAST OF THE TIMES

By Herb Graffis

GENTLEMEN WHO FLIP THROUGH PAGES OF TRADE PAPERS IN THE male-trapping industry, such as *Vogue* and *Harper's Bazaar*, are deterred in this casual practice by the shockingly frank advertising illustrations of intimate items of feminine merchandise. A true gentleman would no more tarry in deliberate inspection of such gems of commercial art than he would pause after blundering accidentally upon an alarmed female stranger partially immersed in a bathtub off the guest room.

This Victorian modesty has preserved a chivalry costly to gentlemen. It has allowed a development of male gullibility to a pathetic degree. Today, even though children are educated in the facts of life and have no longer a prurient curiosity in the lascivious bumble bee on the pollenizing prowl for a trusting virgin rose, millions of males grow to adulthood in the bashful, blind belief that the female form divine is both female and divine. There eventually comes a time when the penalty of this male ignorance must be paid.

Bewildered, disillusioned young men in the darkness sob convulsively, "Why didn't Daddy tell me?" This black sadness has fallen on men before and will fall again. What is Havelock Ellis doing about it; Ellis who has dealt himself a hand in almost everything that used to be strictly the stork's business?

Let us then fend for ourselves. Let us boldly seize this menace of the most virulent boob-bait of modernity, the arch brassieres and/or its companion harnesses, the sinister, sinuous girdles and corsets of the predatory female. There is more than a hunch that these masquerade costumes for the female meat are doing more than any other factors in civilization to destroy man's faith in the finer things of life.

Consider thoughtfully these camouflages from the viewpoints of the anthropologist and sociologist. Be on your guard as you bravely

go after a study of the brazen but insidious advertisements you
hitherto have blushingly skipped. The subject has the alluring
danger of a "wet paint" sign. It's difficult to keep your hands off
despite all warnings.

The far-reaching effect of importance now attached to ladies'
lungs one quickly realizes as he ponders on Bali. Bali, where the
chests of maiden and matron stick out nakedly like a team of firm
generous chunks of chocolate ice-cream cones, has absolutely re-
versed the old-fashioned idea of economics. Bali has become prosperous by going bust. Quite obviously there have been drivelling
tourists who have returned to suggest Bali's economic policy for
our own national adoption, notwithstanding the possibility that
the United States may lack Bali's natural resources.

To remedy the deficiency one corps of our native brain-trusters
have gone thoroughly into the business of busting not from the
economic but from the aesthetic aspect. There are at least two
interesting and apparently opulent scientific journals devoted to
this subject; one, *Corsets and Brassieres, The Foundation Garment
Review,* and the other *Corset and Underwear Review.* It will be
noted that both publications employ meticulously correct use of the
word review. The material in these magazines is such that it is
certain to be not only viewed, but reviewed by the forlorn philosopher who wonders what chance he'll ever have to keep from being
fooled.

About both of these publications there is somewhat the same
atmosphere of the professional military publications dealing calmly
with the heartless problem of most efficiently destroying men.

One advertisement points out, "Summer temperatures send up
the sales of white foundation garments." This cannot be denied
by the susceptible male who feels his temperature mounting to
112° F. because unfair advantage is taken of his credulity by dia-
bolically engineered creations of net, lace, broadcloth, rayon, voile,
mesh, elastic, non-elastic, Lastex and divers other materials. Not
for nix is the leading article in one of these authoritative journals
entitled "Suggestive Selling." No poetic license is employed when
another advertisement in the same publication is headed "You completely eliminate sales resistance."

Now, honestly, what chance has a guy got when he is snatched
almost from innocent boyhood to come face to face with the

Mephistophelian ingenuity of those who plot his downfall with the wily brassiere, bandeaux or whatever trick names happen to be applied to these artful devices? There is little use in the male trying to fight the seductive she-devil with firehose as is being done by valiant cavaliers who swathe themselves with bellybands of elastic mesh. Even a careless female with a naturally lackadaisical contour can don a brassiere and bat over .500 visually, but often the dapper and adipose male encased in a navel-crusher suffers from tallow being squirted in such ridges above the bellyband gunwale that he appears to have been ringed three or four times in a horseshoe game before he put on his shirt and coat.

The utter helplessness of the male, under the circumstances, becomes poignant when one recalls what a fast one was put over on the American male by the eminent Mr. Condé Nast, high priest of the women's fashion journalists.

The Great Conde outdid the Great Ziegfeld as a glorifier by an almost unbelievably great margin. Nast, with his genius in selecting artists and writers and his bravado in turning them loose to do their damnedest, achieved the remarkable success of glorifying the ugly-panned woman.

Women with faces like gargoyles were smarted up in pictures made under the Nast management so even keen-eyed and discriminating men got used to them. These women ultimately shared the destiny of vice according to lines of Mr. Pope:

> "Vice is a monster of so frightful mien,
> As, to be hated, needs but to be seen;
> Yet seen too oft, familiar with her face,
> We first endure, then pity, then embrace."

Now, at the embracing stage of this fantastic development, let us note from the bust-, belly- and behind-casing advertisements what the man gets:

"That graceful uplift, that enchanting silhouette."
"Lines of uninterrupted beauty."
"The ultimate in abbreviation."
"Smooth, slender line of unbroken grace."
"High youthful contour."
"Figure-molding magic."
"Gay bits of witchery."

Those are but a few of the thousands of wily descriptive phrases from the advertisements of the false-front merchants. Is mere man proof against this order of guile? Certainly not! He is soft prey of such phonies.

There is an infernal retribution in the way in which the deceitful business engulfs some of those less cynical males who engage in it. Their progress into the whirlpool is perhaps unwittingly described in the words of an advertising man who murmurs in the first stages of his sweet delirium about a set of dainty buckets that "demurely coaxes the breast into charming young curves." Reveals the bard of his business: ". . . the miracle it performs, coaxing a little, yielding a little, persuading a little . . ." The melancholy layman who is aware of what the hapless victim was up against realizes how irresistibly ruin presented itself to the fellow who should have known better. There are thousands of tabloid newspaper stories compacted in the preceding quotation from a typical brassiere advertisement. "Coaxing . . . yielding . . . persuading," need only "tells all" and "then everything went black" to bind all of life, frustration and stark tragedy, inseparably to the bittersweet story of bust faking.

One who delves into the mysteries of the spurious chests of females begins by suspecting this deceit has become big business only during comparatively recent times. However, one can't be too sure. "The Laws of Solon," quoting a woman's magazine, the *Delineator*, "forbade Greek women to wear more than three garments at a time." This edict, according to current investigation in the form sheets of the bust industry, still allowed leeway for a lively trade in brassieres for such is the ingenuity of the brassiere mechanic that the devices are ofttimes effectively employed with bathing suits and evening dresses of such stunning décolletage a lady can carry a spare packed in the same cartridge as her lipstick. As further period evidence, there are paintings of La Pompadour, exposing in semi-formal attire a resplendently pink team of McCoy honeydews, the budding 90-watt Mazda type lungs of Titian's young Amazons and the pineapple breasts of Pascin and other French artists of that time when la vie Bohème justified its art by making figurative improvements on the current dirty postcards.

However, the scientist can't accept such pictorial evidence as entirely conclusive for after all the artists might have given the models plenty of a break, and a break is literally the genesis of a bust. One of the business magazines in chronicling activities of that commerce which gilds the lily lung and adorns the rosy behind with "beauty molded svelte lines," prints a report of a style show put on by B. Altman & Co., during which "corsetry through the ages" was the theme of a pageant.

The journalist writes: "the blacksmith was the corsetier in the 16th century," but she (or he) also refers to "the magnificent new Charnaux creations of Anotex, significant of 20th century invention and suavity" as being presented. That tribute to the "magnificent new creations" somehow seems to have the same sort of hollow ring to it that technical articles have when they make quick references to the engineering work of the early Chinese, Mayans and other ancients whose unfathomable genius must be dismissed with an "ain't it wonderful?" phrase.

However, it is difficult for the scientist to be quite sure of himself when dealing with the lexicon of the lung and torso traffic. There is what strikes one who is an acolyte in the laboratory, a very careless use of phrases in the bust, belly and behind business ads, but maybe it is all right.

A puzzling instance lauds, as well it may, the merits of detachable brassieres that "let you eat your cake and have it, too!" What leaves the scientist in a fog is who is the "you" of the advertisement and what kind of cake is it? Angel food seems quite a pretty idea in this connection. "Let them eat cake" was the loosely used line that accelerated one revolution. Maybe another revolution is on its way and this "eat your cake" advertisement is a specimen of the skilled and heinous manner in which the propagandists steam up things to get us agreeable to their plans. Well, a fellow can't live forever, and choking to death on cake is 10,000 to one over stopping a hurtling, jagged hunk of shrapnel.

Other advertisements in the magazines for general female public, as well as for the inner circles of the foundation garment trade, are of a character that must be considered entirely blameless, although somewhat disturbing and unique as social documents. No blame attaches to the advertisements because the nature of the business, or the mask of nature in it, permits blanket coverage by that grand old alibi, *honi soit qui mal y pense*.

You bump into an advertisement showing a lady—and there is no mistake about their being ladies in these pictures—attired scantily in a lacy outerhide with more curves than a six-day bike race. This lady is drawing back a curtain and peeking in at a mixed party of people in formal evening wear. Such is one of the popular scenes in the printed annals of the foundation garment business. It has the pleasant, companionable spirit of "company in the parlor, girls."

Should some artist drag a drawing like that around to ESQUIRE, the staff, as dizzy as it is from the painful occupational malady of bust myopia, probably would jump out from ornate padded cells all over the joint and scream, "Scram, you bum, or you'll have the place pinched." But in the underworld of women's apparel advertising such views are very common pictures of practices followed by all the very best figures in this naïve sphere.

Only on rare occasions, however, are the bust, belly and behind business advertisements guilty of rank effrontery and contempt for the man in the street. One such instance is that of a brassiere advertisement headed, "Seeing is Believing" when as a matter of fact, in this affair seeing isn't believing at all. But feeling probably wouldn't be believing either, and as the ad writer evidently wanted to be coldly professional rather than sensual about the affair, he just picked one of the five senses offhand, making the deadline and took a long chance on some fellow finding out that seeing wasn't believing and carrying the case to the Better Business Bureau because of his tragic disappointment.

There is a grave warning to the hitherto unsuspecting male in the very names of the garments in obviously good favor with those who participate as pitchers or catchers in the business of deftly remoulding the female nearer to the heart's desire. There is plenty in a name, when it's applied to a brassiere, girdle or other item of lure harness. Beware, but listen: Popular Thrill, Maiden Form, Her Secret, Myth, Goss-Amour, Fig Leaf, Sho-Form, Sensation, Helen of Troy and Form-O-Uth. Those are some of the tags that tip you off the folks in this trade are playing with 52 spade aces against the normal male, unless all biology textbooks have been revised lately.

Although the major factor in the business is that of conceal-ment, the foundation garment makers' basic sales appeal doesn't go any stronger for protective coloration than do the designers of six-foot stop signs. They are frankly on the make all the time.

The bust barons, in their own devious ways, do a great job of assisting nature in smoothing the way, so to speak, toward nature's ultimate objective. With some cloth, thread and gutta percha, the brassiere and corset mechanics undoubtedly score better for women every ten minutes of the selling day and romantic evenings than Ponce de Leon was able to do plodding many weary months in his futile search for the fountain of youth.

It is due, probably, to the artifice of the bust, belly and behind synthetizers that there are definite, frequent evidences of a complete reversal of form in the employment of the cynical slogan of seduction: "fool 'em and forget 'em." In departed periods that policy was the itinerary of the rake's progress with the pathetic dénouement being that of the maiden sad and alone as the villain resumed his post outside the transfer corner saloon, smirked and roped another female sap by a twirl of his fascinating, sleek black moustachios.

Now it is the female who fools and forgets them. Not with Victorian languor of "that long slanting cascade of bosom—without any apparent relation to the naked body beneath," as Aldous Huxley supplies the description of the "take your time" curves now antiquated. No, the provocative, free-wheeling and impertinent bosoms of contemporaneous models have no delay or indecision about them. They are busts that bust you right in the eye, as the phrase goes. But although the saucy chests of today, terminating in but faintly masked collar-button design papillae may be in only one case in fifty the work of nature, perhaps it is all for the best. Anyway, it can't be helped. Even when the male is beyond the trade territory of the foundation garment business he seems often to be bust-blind, as is attested by such evidence as that of Mahmoud Djelladine Pacha, to wit:

"How beautiful are your breasts with their two russet berries.
At sight of them, stricken, drunken, I cannot make a distinction
Between them and white roses beaten in white snow."

A hundred years later enthusiastic students have the same difficulty making a distinction between Allah's handiwork and the Princess Patticakes, the Nymph Nuggets, the Beautibulbs, or similarly named fabrications of busts, so false and so fair.

So, it all probably ends with the philosophical male concluding that the thoughtful thing for him to do is to keep his mouth shut, as the argot pertinently goes in this case, and be reconciled to the male minding his own business while the female minds hers, part of which plainly is in seeing that her contour is such that the discriminating gentleman is kept ignorantly but aesthetically content with a breast of the times.

AFTER BABY COMES

By DOUGLASS WELCH

THERE HAS BEEN A GREAT DEAL WRITTEN LATELY ABOUT THE CARE of the young mother and about the care and feeding of the newly-born infant. But no one, as far as I can ascertain, has ever bothered his pretty head over an equally important matter, the care and feeding of the young father *after baby comes.*

This is a particularly trying period for the young, inexperienced male. In fact, some authorities hold it to be a particularly trying period for any male, up to and including (but not often) the age of seventy. Indeed, among certain primitive peoples it is the custom for the father, rather than the mother, to go to bed for two weeks and be waited upon when mother and baby arrive home from the hospital. And, on second thought, these people don't appear to be so primitive after all.

Of course, we aren't surprised to find a good many primitive fathers taking advantage of such a custom and there is at least one case on record where a primitive father went to bed and remained in bed with one of the Sunday papers until his child was well through high school. When he finally got up he said he felt fine.

I know a lot of people are going to say I am scarcely qualified to write upon early fatherhood, having been through it only once—even though I came out of that experience with somewhat less hair, a furtive, hunted manner and a curious habit of sitting bolt upright in bed at unpredictable times of the night to cry out, "Was that baby?"

A man doesn't have to become a father more than once to know considerable about fatherhood. You might liken fatherhood to rolling down a mountainside. By the time you've reached the bottom you ought to be able to qualify as an expert on rolling down mountainsides. Subsequent plunges won't much enlarge your experience, merely confirm it. Actually, by the time a man has passed the cigars twice or three times he begins to lose perspective. Things happen around home without being impinged upon his consciousness. He develops a generous negative adaptation toward the very things of which the young father is so painfully aware, things like the rubber ducks and celluloid swans which line the rim of the bathtub (and keep falling in when you're trying to take a bath), and diapers festooned from the backs of the living room chairs, and dozens of bottles on the kitchen sideboards and in the refrigerator, and the horde of female relatives who tramp in and out of the house at all hours.

No, I've seen a three-time loser reading his newspaper, digesting and enjoying every morsel of it, while a small son and daughter fought shrilly over the possession of a drum and another little girl sat in his lap and cut off great chucks of his hair with her play scissors. Subjected to the same conditions, your young father would promptly give himself up to hysterics.

Some people are going to protest, of course, that I had a little *girl* baby and that no one can possibly know much about fatherhood until he has had a little *boy* baby. And, having observed the little boy babies of my friends running berserk and amok through their homes from the age of eight months on, I am willing to concede there is some virtue in the contention. But, as between boy babies and girl babies: while there may be a little more disorder and confusion and a *great deal more noise* in the homes of the former, the fundamental principles of fatherhood are the same. It's a job, anyway you look at it.

I doubt if any man is ever really prepared for fatherhood, or, as I call it, "Man's Valley of the Shadow." He may think he is. His wife may have told him he is. He may have enthused over the layette and the basinette and the bathinette. He may have exclaimed over booties and shirts and bibs and gertrudes and yards upon yards of daisy cloth (do I know my terms!) and he may have spent hours deciding upon the little rascal's name. But when the little rascal arrives, he's due for as rude a shock as he got the first time he caught his wife giving his best ties to her brother ("just a couple of your old ones, Harry"). And if you think it isn't shocking to have your best neckties showing up on your brother-in-law, just drop me a line. I'll be glad to go into details.

From the moment of a man's marriage he is subjected to a

subtle, insidious propaganda designed to put him in the proper frame of mind for parenthood. First thing he knows, some morning his lovely bride is leaning across the breakfast table and looking at him gravely and saying softly, apropos of nothing, "I think you would make a wonderful father." He likes that; he doesn't know why. The idea probably hasn't occurred to him before. Oh, of course, he has vaguely known that a baby or two could be expected as a natural consequence of once having said, "I do," a sort of marital by-product, so to speak. But the way his wife puts it sounds like fun. Maybe he would make a wonderful father! He begins to stand in front of mirrors and imagine himself a wonderful father. He begins to take a subjective interest in the loudest, toughest neighborhood kids. He smiles fondly at songs about the pitter-patter of baby feet (you never hear anything in songs about the *stomping* of baby feet!) and he chuckles at poems about baby's sticky fingerprints on the wall. He pictures himself coming home weary at night and being met at the door by the kiddies, all ready with his slippers and his smoking jacket and pipe. And all this time his young bride is watching him narrowly. And let him nod his head so much as once—she's off to the races. He wakes up some day to learn he IS a father. And then it is the rose dawn of what I call incipient fatherhood dissolves into the gray dawn of practicing parenthood.

Yes, the song writers and the poets and all the other professional Pollyannas have insistently pictured early fatherhood as a blessed domestic trinity in a vine-covered cottage. "Molly and me, and baby makes three, etc." But the young father soon discovers that this doesn't begin to complete the count. His vine-covered cottage will not only house his Molly, his baby and himself but also the inevitable mother-in-law, his wife's aunt Martha (who still thinks Cleveland is president) and a dour, hatchet-faced woman who's been called in to do the first month's washing, and a dozen other obscure female relatives and female sightseers and just plain females who seem to come and go in shifts. I don't know where these women come from. You only find them gathered around the cribs of new-born babies. You never see them in public places. I think they must live out in the woods somewhere, under logs and in caves, and only come to town when they hear someone's had a baby. But, anyway, there they are, making a Roman holiday of it, taking turns at bathing the child and preparing his formula and regaling one another with choice particulars of their own past confinements.

I don't know why it is that married women should let down the conversational bars in front of a young man just because he's become a father, but they do. Overnight they feel free to discuss in his presence topics of the most appalling intimacy. If your young father has come through life with one or two illusions about women still tightly clutched in his chubby little fists, he loses them at this time. When married women get clinical, they're horrid. The discussions I've walked out on!

Subtle changes take place in the young father's diet, particularly with respect to desserts, almost as soon as baby comes. Gradually pie disappears altogether and dishes like soft-boiled custard and tapioca and junket come to take its place. He may inquire about this in time (in fact, he may get quite nasty about it) and he will learn that, inasmuch as baby has to have these foods anyway, it's much simpler to make enough for the entire family. And, for the same reason, he finds himself sitting down to more and more cooked cereal in the morning.

I want to warn young fathers right here that many an unsuspecting husband has been served a dish of cereal at breakfast which the baby had turned down the night before. I know this to be a fact. They tried the trick on me once and they didn't even bother to take the cereal out of baby's dish. When I'd eaten down through it I found myself staring at a rooster sitting on a fence with the words "Cocka Doodle Doo" under it. I didn't comment at the time but I resolved to keep my eyes open. Two nights later I drew a portion of spinach which looked as if it had been squeezed through a jelly bag. A little guarded inquiry confirmed my worst suspicions. The baby had had mashed spinach at noon and hadn't cared for it. A week later two or three large pieces of zwieback showed up in the bread pudding and the night following I was served the left leg of a gingerbread man. I went into a magnificent rage, but it got me exactly nowhere.

I feel very keenly on the subject of zwieback, but I suppose I am one of those many fathers who never can become inured to it. When baby starts eating zwieback, you're likely (no, you're certain) to find bits of sodden zwieback on your chair, in the folds of your newspaper, on the rug, among your neckties in the lower bureau drawer and even in your shaving mug. The way a piece of zwieback can travel through a well-ordered home is a caution.

One ordeal which the young father must inevitably undergo is to see baby munching bacon morning after morning when the family budget allows him, the wage-earner, the bread-winner from whom all blessings flow, bacon only on Sunday mornings. And this also applies to the quarter-inch slice which must come smack out of the middle of the tenderloin every time the family sits down to a steak. One quarter of this slice, carefully chopped, goes into baby's mouth. The rest goes down the front of her dress or is dropped experimentally from the high chair to the floor where the cat, who is nobody's fool, is waiting for it.

Yes, it's a critical period for the young male and I am reminded of one young father who wasn't equal to it. He awoke one morning to startle his family with the announcement that it had been *he* who had had the baby. Some of the best psychologists in the country went to work on the case, but they all got the same response:

"Listen, doc, you can talk all you want to. But *I* know what happened. And, believe me, I never want to go through *that* again!"

And, by the way, as long as we are on the subject, would you like to see a dozen pictures or so of my youngster? It will only take you about twenty minutes.

I MIX THE DRINKS

By W. B. LYTTON

WE HAD NEW NEIGHBORS. TO THOSE OF YOU WHO DWELL IN apartment houses it is just like saying it rained yesterday, or Herbert was drunk again, but to father who went from diapers to long pants; through matrimony and pneumonia and up to my own existence in the same old house it was like saying the Democrats were lousy, or that father was wrong about something. Or as old black William simply put it, new neighbors were just something new. Far away in father's mind was a dim recollection that there was something people ought to do when new neighbors moved in, but he had forgotten the routine. It had been a long time since such a thing had occurred on our block. Father phoned his good friend, Mr. Roach, and asked him what to do about new neighbors. Mr. Roach had spent the greater part of his life moving in and out of apartment houses. He told father to consult a lawyer; to take out liability insurance on the dog, and reinforce the bathroom curtains. Father felt that Mr. Roach had mistaken his good intentions, and phoned a Congressman friend of his for advice. The Congressman replied that new neighbors were perfectly legal and that father couldn't do anything about them. No one seemed to understand father's purpose towards new neighbors. At last, mother told him that it was a custom among nice people to entertain new neighbors. Then it all came back to father in a flash, and one night father phoned them. He invited them to drop over for a few informal cocktails.

The new neighbors were the Albert J. Hawks, and it was rumored around that Mr. Hawks was a shrewd and prosperous mining engineer. As father learned later, Mr. Hawks was a sceptic who believed in no one but himself. He was suspicious of all new inventions and preferred the bath tub to the shower bath. He had a particular dislike for safety razors. He bought Bell Telephone stock because he admired the company for not making radical changes. The telephone was still ugly and clumsy to operate. He liked his wife for the same reason.

Father, on the other hand, liked everything new and modern. And mother liked father to make a good showing with people. She had instructed him carefully not to bore Mr. Hawks with a description of his ulcerated stomach, a possession of which father was rather boastful at times because it had never killed him.

He was to talk only of mining, and poor father knew as little about obstetrics.

Father made the cocktails himself. But because of the limitations of his own diseased stomach he was always inclined to be stingy with his alcoholics. He put them in the new electric ice box to chill. This ice box was the finest and most recent addition to the pantry. Father thought so, anyhow. He had bought it one day when mother was out of town. Life had taught me several things about alcohol and I had always appreciated its ability to make people congenial. Father's cocktails were much too feeble and flaccid, and so with father in the bathroom and William in the cellar I imparted to the drinks the strength and vitality necessary for any diplomatic occasion.

Mr. and Mrs. Hawks arrived promptly at eight o'clock. The business of greeting one another was hurriedly accomplished, and though both parties strove for geniality and informality there was still that touch of stiffness about the whole thing that only alcohol can conquer. Father seemed to feel this and motioned to William for the drinks, and William, with his big white eyes and his small black body, served the first round of cocktails.

Mr. Hawks gave me the impression at first sight that he enjoyed his liquor, probably because it was an ancient drink and there was nothing new or fancy about it. Mrs. Hawks and mother dallied with their glasses until they were sipping half ice water and half fruit juice which was a situation that seemed to play a very minor role in their lives. Both sexes had settled down to their own sphere of conversation, and William hovered about refilling their glasses.

The change in the cocktails had only reached father's stomach and his subconscious mind but he was getting very chatty and open-mouthed. Mr. Hawks perspired about his forehead and became more reticent with each drink. Father had remembered to discuss mining but found difficulty in leading up to the subject. He managed to say something about the fact that we all had to get out and dig for a living. This failed to bring any response about mines out of Mr. Hawks. He just took another drink and looked solemnly at father. But father wasn't easily dampened. He said that all men were essentially miners because they were all digging for something—the sewer digger, the grave digger, the gold digger, doctors digging into people's bellies, farmers digging for potatoes, and that when you dig down to a certain level you suddenly evolute from a common digger to a miner. This bit of conversation brought a sharp glance from mother. Mr. Hawks continued to look silently at father and diddle with his empty glass.

"Have another drink," said father hopefully. Mr. Hawks held out his glass. The change in the cocktails suddenly went from father's subconscious to his conscious mind. He looked incredibly at his glass. It must have been the new electric ice box.

"Wonderful things these electric ice boxes," says father. "They do things to cocktails that's hard to describe logically."

Mr. Hawks said he thought they were excellent drinks. He burped gently.

"Everybody should have electric ice boxes," continued father. "If we had the space, I'd get another one right now," he said emphatically, searching the parlor for a good location. Mr. Hawks said he preferred the old-fashioned ice box. He said that some day father would probably be electrocuted reaching for the lettuce.

This intolerant feeling towards electric ice boxes hurt father deeply. "Maybe you've never taken a real good look at one," suggested father.

"I don't want to look at one," said Mr. Hawks. "They're nothing but regular boxes with a lot of cold air on the inside, and cold air doesn't look any different than any other kind of air."

Mother looked somewhat mortified and I could see she was paying little attention to what Mrs. Hawks was telling her about some new kind of soap. I glanced furtively at father. He was leading Mr. Hawks to the pantry, and Mr. Hawks was following none too steadily through the pantry door. William began to notice things, too, and sniffed suspiciously into the cocktail shaker. I felt that perhaps I should have gone a little easier on the liquor.

"There she is," says father pointing to an ice box that could have easily served a wholesale meat market. "The biggest one they had for eight-hundred dollars delivered. No more ice man, no flirting with the cook, no dirt, no nothing." He slapped the ice box on its bare back. "Let's break the ice with another drink."

Mr. Hawks looked cautiously at father and swallowed his drink. Then he looked haughtily at the ice box. He was in a critical attitude as he stepped up to open one of the doors. He was surprised to find the interior of the box brightly lighted. "Oh ho," said Mr. Hawks, "There's lights on the inside."

"Yep," says father proudly, "Everything's automatic. Open the door and on go the lights. Shut the door and off go the lights."

"How do you know?" asked Mr. Hawks sceptically.

Father looked stupidly at Mr. Hawks. "How do you know what?"

"How do you know the light goes off when you shut the door?" He poured himself another drink.

"Why you just naturally know it," says father, shutting the door to prove it. "See, now the light's off. Very simple."

"You can't see it," said Mr. Hawks. He tried to peek through the crack in the door. "That light is very probably still lit."

Father looked a little bewildered. He got down on his knees and opened the door just a tiny bit. A light shone through the crack.

"What did I tell ya," says Mr. Hawks triumphantly, "She's still lit."

"Listen," says father, speaking just below a shout, "The company that sold me that box said the light goes off automatically. It even says so in the book that comes with the box. That's proof enough, isn't it?"

"You can't believe companies," says Mr. Hawks authoritatively. "Look what the companies say about toothpaste. Then look at what the scientists say about toothpaste. A very deceitful universe," says Mr. Hawks.

Father took another drink and looked intently at his new ice box. Father was thinking fast, but his thoughts were slightly dulled. "Listen," says father, "There's two lights up in the top of that box—one on each side. You stick your head in this side for the vegetables, and watch and see if the light on the other side goes out when I shut the door on that side. That'll prove everything, by God."

"Suppose I get a shock?" asked Mr. Hawks.

"Impossible," says father, "Flies have gotten locked up in there accidentally and come out hours later 'OK'—except of course they were a little chilly."

Mr. Hawks wasn't so sure about the effect of electricity on flies. For all he knew flies might possibly have rubber in them some-place. He was somewhat doubtful but, nevertheless, game.

"All right," said Mr. Hawks, opening the door for the vegetables, "Let's get these tomatoes out of the way and try her out."

One dozen tomatoes rolled on the pantry floor. Mr. Hawks inserted his bald head through the aperture while father closed the door gently on his neck. "OK," says Mr. Hawks from the inside of the ice box, "Shut the other door now."

Father shut the door on his side and waited breathlessly. It was at this point that mother saw a tomato rolling aimlessly into the dining room. Occasionally the dog got as far as the dining room, but so far, the tomatoes in our house had always kept their place. They never came into the dining room unless they were accompanied by lettuce and a little salad dressing. Mother excused herself and went cautiously out to the pantry door. She opened it gently just enough to see Mr. Hawks bent at a right angle with his south end sticking out of the vegetable side of her ice box.

"Still lit, Albert?" asked father in a tone of suspense.

"Still lit," says Albert Hawks.

Mother returned somehow to the parlor. She looked old. But her expression was indecipherable. I remembered once before when she had returned from the pantry with that same expression. It seemed that father had been showing a new dance step to Martha, a pretty young kid, who up until that time had been our maid. But now I could tell that mother was pretty near her boiling point when she whispered to me that father had Mr. Hawks in the ice box and that Mr. Hawks was lit and even admitted it. "And above everything else," said mother, "Your father is calling him Albert."

I found both gentlemen in the pantry looking at each other silently and sipping their cocktails. The doors of the ice box hung open.

"Well, what do you say now?" asks Mr. Hawks.

"It don't prove a thing," answers father. "All of the doors have to be completely shut before that light goes off. It says so on page three of this pamphlet." He shoved the book at Mr. Hawks.

"Well, Mr. Hawks," I broke in, "is father showing you through the new ice box?" It was a great relief to my conscience to see that mother had evidently misinterpreted the situation.

"Yes," said Mr. Hawks, "Your gullible father has been tricked. He thinks the lights in this fancy ice box of his go out when you close the doors. And of course they don't go out. They stay lit."

"Call up the company," says father, "And tell them to send a man out here. Tell them right away."

I tried to explain to father that the ice box company had gone home to bed hours ago and that, furthermore, to actually prove anything on the lights a person would have to be on the inside of the box when the doors were closed. Father just looked at the box and called it names.

I returned to mother and attempted to restore her youth and composure.

William's curiosity had also led him to the pantry. He had never seen father under the influence of spirits nor the pantry spotted with tomatoes.

He sniffed the cocktail shaker once more, and then with a look of determination held it under the water faucet.

"What the hell are you doing?" shouted father.

"Diluting dee drinks," says William. "They's power stricken. Ya sir, they's no good fer ulceration of dee stomick."

"You get away from that," says father. "Here," he says, pointing to the ice box, "empty everything out of that box and remove all the shelves."

"Wait a minute," interrupts Mr. Hawks and eyeing father anxiously, "What are your plans?"

"I'm getting inside that box," says father.

"He's gettin' drunk," says William to himself.

William slowly emptied the box, distributing its varied contents all over the pantry and keeping one eye on the door and one eye on the shaker. He removed all the shelves and looked foolishly at father.

The light of respect had begun to fade. Father put down his

glass and prepared to enter the ice box. He squeezed his head and shoulders through the large door while Mr. Hawks leaned against the sink and sipped his cocktail. It looked unpromising.

"Listen, Mr. Houdini," says Mr. Hawks, "I can tell already you're not going to make it. You simply weren't made for ice boxes. Now, if you were a banana or somethin'—."

"Push," commanded father.

Mr. Hawks pushed but nothing happened. "Maybe if you took your clothes off you'd slide in better," he suggested.

William looked maliciously at Mr. Hawks. "He's goin' to citch cold enough as it is," says William.

Father sneezed from inside the box. He gave one or two feeble wiggles which reminded Mr. Hawks of a bug stuck in the radiator of an automobile.

"Coming out," says father.

The score was one to nothing in favor of Mr. Hawks. Father was desperate and ideation was slow.

Unexpectedly Mr. Hawks announced that he would like to go upstairs and wash his hands.

"You can wash 'em right here in the sink," said father.

"I said I had to wash my hands," repeated Mr. Hawks, looking rather worried. "And I don't think I ought to use the pantry sink."

"Oh," said father, "Just follow me. We can go up the back stairs." He steered Mr. Hawks to the second floor.

While father waited at the bathroom door he happened to glance into the back bedroom. At that very moment a brilliant idea struck the gong of father's mental clock.

Anyway *HE* thought it was a good idea and told Mr. Hawks it was as he led him into the bedroom. My little five-year-old brother lay snugly in his bed. Little Henry had always been undernourished.

"What the hell?" inquired Mr. Hawks.

"Shh," says father, going to the bedside in his most gentle manner. "I think he'll fit in the ice box. He's sort of a runt anyhow." He poked little Henry in the ribs. Henry responded sluggishly to the stimulus.

"Want to come and play with Daddy?"

Little Henry stared crossly at father through the slits of his optics.

"Go away," he said flatly.

"Come, come," returned father. "We're going down in the kitchen and play Eskimo."

"Mamma going to play, too?" asked Henry, showing some interest.

"She'll play hell if she finds him," said Mr. Hawks.

"We're all going to play," explained father, "And you'll be the Eskimo who lives in an ice house." And, so saying, he lifted little Henry out of bed. Father felt right proud of himself, but as he said several years later, the alcohol probably altered his judgment.

He gave Mr. Hawks a superior smile and told him the controversy would soon be settled.

And so it was Henry who was going to solve the question of the light in the ice box.

Little Henry was led quietly through the kitchen, and into the pantry where stood the confused William in front of the empty ice box.

William tried to be cheerful about the whole affair. "Well, Masta Henry, sho enough," he said gayly, "What brought you all down here?"

"His father," said Mr. Hawks.

"Aren't we goin' to play nothing?" inquired little Henry. "Where's mamma?" Henry would have felt better if his mother were in the game.

"Not so loud," cautioned father. "We're going to play Eskimo. You'll be the Eskimo and hide in your ice house. I'll be an arctic explorer and William will be a polar bear."

At this point William informed father that all the polar bears he knew of were white.

"Keep quiet," father told him. "They can get dirty, can't they?"

Mr. Hawks was feeling technical again. "How could a polar bear get dirty with nothing but snow, ice, and the ocean under him?" he asked father.

"OK," says father. "OK, we won't have a polar bear. We'll have a monkey," and he looked pointedly at William.

Mr. Hawks was about to give a lecture on the habitat of the

primates, but on second thought let the matter drop. He suggested that he be the polar bear and William be an Eskimo bootlegger and give the explorers another drink.

Father was showing little Henry his ice house. Henry was rather sceptical. He had been taught to stay out of the ice box and couldn't adjust himself to this new school of thought. There was a question of treachery about the whole business and his father seemed suddenly and oddly different. He even smelled different. He looked hopefully towards William who apparently hadn't changed with the night. "Are you going to play, too, William?" he asked.

"Ya suh," said William weakly as he poured Mr. Hawks another drink. "I'se already began." His tone was anything but enthusiastic but his affirmation washed the doubt from little Henry's mind.

"See," says father, "we're playing right now. I'm an arctic explorer coming over a cake of ice." Father put several ice cubes on the pantry floor. "Now run and hide in your ice house," says father.

"I don't want to hide," said Henry proudly, "I'm not afraid of any explorer man."

Father hadn't planned on anything like this, and for a minute he just looked stupidly at little Henry.

"Well hide anyway," said father, "I'm a very dangerous man." Mr. Hawks was beginning to think so himself.

"You told me never to hide from anybody," said Henry.

"Listen," explained father, "This is just a game. You only pretend you're afraid. See?"

Little Henry looked solemnly at father. He walked over to the ice box and stood reluctant before the door.

"Go ahead," coaxed father, "Open her up and climb in."

Henry opened the door and with a good amount of effort slowly wedged his little body along the floor of the box. Father stood by giving directions and helped Henry maneuver his head under the refrigeration chamber. Henry doubled up his legs and father shoved them in the box.

"That's fine," says father pleasantly.

"It's cold," says Henry. "I don't want to play Eskimo. I want to come out!"

Father quickly shut the door. Mr. Hawks thought of the days when he used to catch rabbits in wooden traps.

"Now then," says father, "When he comes out we'll simply ask him about the lights and then we'll know the answer to this thing." He looked carefully to see that all the doors were shut tightly. William shot a cautious look at the pantry door. He wasn't so sure mother would appreciate finding her son on ice.

There was a faint and muffled scream inside the ice box followed by vigorous thumps against the doors.

"The little fellow don't like it," said Mr. Hawks with a touch of emotion. "He's crying like hell."

"Ah, ha," says father, "That proves definitely that the light is out. He's afraid of the dark."

"Wait a minute," said Mr. Hawks, "I suppose he starts crying at sunset? No sir, that's no proof at all. We'll ask him whether it was dark or not."

Father opened the door cautiously and was rewarded with the left foot of Henry in his ulcerated stomach.

"Let me outa here," cried Henry, "Let me out!" He wiggled frantically and slid out on the floor. He stood up before the two arctic explorers and shivered and bawled.

"Listen," says father, "Was it dark in there or was it light?"

"It was cold," whimpered Henry, the tears dripping off his cheeks.

"But the light," pleaded father, "Was it on or off?"

Little Henry rubbed the top of his head tenderly. He sneezed and cried louder. "I don't want to play Eskimo. It's cold! I want mamma."

Father looked helplessly at Mr. Hawks who had somewhat of a futile expression himself. "Don't cry so loud," snapped father.

"Tell your father, why dontcha," says Mr. Hawks. "Tell him if it was the dark that made you cry."

"It was the cold!" bawled little Henry. He touched the surface of his head carefully.

"But if it hadn't been cold," continued Mr. Hawks, "Would you have cried because the light was out?"

"But it *was* cold," replied Henry stubbornly. "I want mamma!"

Father wore a belligerent look. There was the answer right in front of him and yet he couldn't reach it. "You answer my question," said father. "Was it light or dark in that ice box?"

Little Henry sobbed and put his hand gently to his head again. "It's busted," he cried.

"Your head's all right," says father looking carelessly at its surface. "It's just cold."

"The light," says little Henry, "The light is busted. I bumped my head on it and it exploded. I want mamma!" he screamed.

And he got mamma.

CAFETERIA COMPLEX

By Fred S. Tobey

"I GUESS YOU DIDN'T GET ME THE FIRST TIME," SAID THE CHAP behind the cafeteria counter, genially enough. "I asked if you wanted hard rolls or soft." For emphasis, he held up a hard roll in one hand, and a soft roll in the other. I nodded to show comprehension.

"I don't want any rolls at all," said I.

Grinning broadly, he loaded my platter with Broiled Sdfsh, Fr. Fr. Pot., Cup Coffee.

"Now, Sir," said he cajolingly, "will you have hard rolls or soft?"

I think I had a premonitory sense of what was ahead. Nevertheless I took the bit in my teeth.

"I really don't want any rolls at all," said I, enunciating clearly. "I really don't. Now if you'll just punch my check, I'll be taking this tray along to the table."

A look of amazement suffused the chap's countenance. Gone was the happy, carefree grin.

"Are you quite serious about this, Sir?" said he, searching my face for a sign of mirth.

"Quite."

"But the special you ordered includes rolls, Sir, so you must have one sort or another."

"That," I replied, "is an underhanded attack upon individualism, and cannot be countenanced by thinking persons."

The chap seemed impressed with this, and turned to a companion, who was busily loading a tray.

"What do you do, Joe," he whispered, "when a gentleman don't want no rolls?"

"There ain't no gentlemen don't want no rolls," said Joe. "Ask him does he want hard rolls or soft rolls."

"Says he doesn't want either."

"Then he's kidding you. Make him take 'em."

"Look here," said the chap nervously, coming back to me, "even if you don't want any rolls, why don't you have one—just one— to straighten the thing out. Just say 'hard' or 'soft'—like that—and everything will be all right."

"No," I repeated, kindly yet without yielding my position, "I do not want them and it would be economically unsound to take them."

"All right then," said the chap. "All right then, I'll call the manager." He called the manager.

"And what is the trouble?" asked that functionary, very pleasantly indeed, as he bustled up in response to the call. Can we do something for one of our patrons?"

"The gentleman won't have any rolls with his special," said the chap, plaintively.

"Now, now!" said the manager, patting him on the shoulder with a friendly hand, "surely a little tact would straighten matters out. Did you ask him what *kind* of rolls he would like?"

"Yes, Sir." Plainly, he was on the verge of tears.

"And he said ——?"

"Said he wouldn't have any at all, Sir," sobbed the chap.

Executives are far-seeing people. The manager turned to me gravely.

"Sir," said he, "this cafeteria is but one of a great chain. Though I am manager here I cannot initiate any policy which might seem to set a precedent for the entire organization. If you persist in your stand I shall be forced to take the matter to headquarters. The very structural core of the nation may quiver. What is your reply, Sir?"

We stood silently a moment, he with his piercing eyes fixed upon my face; I thoughtfully considering every phase of the situation.

My decision was made at last.

"Nuts," said I, politely but firmly.

"In that case, Sir," said the manager, "I will ask you to have a seat in my office while I wire the district supervisor."

Half an hour later he handed me a telegram from the district office in New Jersey. It read as follows:

AM AT LOSS SOLVE PROBLEM IN YOUR UNIT STOP CIRCUMSTANCES
NEW MY EXPERIENCE STOP AM FLYING DETROIT WITHIN HOUR TO
TAKE UP WITH CENTRAL OFFICE STOP WAIT INSTRUCTIONS

L X JONQUIL DIST SUPER

The manager was apologetic, and very nice about everything.
Said he was having the Gimmer Furniture Company bring in a
studio couch for me, in case the central office might be a bit slow
reaching an agreement. Sometimes had an awful lot on their minds,
he said.

I spent a restless night on the studio couch, biting my finger
nails, while the manager sat at his desk and did cross-word puzzles.
By the time morning came—and another wire—we both were
pretty well on edge.

OFFICIALS DEADLOCKED YOUR CASE STOP HESITATE ACT WITHOUT AD-
VICE PRESIDENT OF CORPORATION WHO IS CRUISING IN PACIFIC STOP
EXPECT REACH HIM BY RADIO PHONE THIS MORNING

L X JONQUIL DIST SUPER

The next telegram sent a thrill through the manager, and I must
admit to having taken a little pride in it myself.

PRESIDENT OF CORPORATION INTERESTED YOUR CASE STOP HE WILL
TAKE PLANE AT LOS ANGELES ARRIVING NEW YORK TOMORROW NIGHT
STOP WATCH YOUR LINEN

L X JONQUIL DIST SUPER

The Gimmer Furniture truck rolled up with another studio
couch, and the manager and I both bit our finger nails the second
night.

Somehow or other the newspapers got hold of the thing. By
next evening four theatrical companies had offered me sums of
money to make a stage tour and six nationally advertised products
had sought my testimonials at $100 a word. The Betty's Bigger
Buns Company wanted me to say the trouble was all because
the cafeteria didn't serve Betty's Bigger Buns. I turned them all
down. I am in the hot water bottle business and believe a man
should stick to what he knows.

At 5:45 a boy rushed in with a tabloid showing the President
of the Corporation stepping from a plane and into a high-powered

car at the airport. He was saying, "Never put off till tomorrow what you can do today. That motto is as good here and now as it was when Abraham Lincoln first said it!"

At 5:55 a boy rushed in with another tabloid, showing the President of the Corporation flashing past the Empire State Building with four motorcycle officers front and rear.

"That's only a few blocks from here," said I. "He ought to be here any minute."

Sure enough, scarcely were the words out of my mouth than there appeared in the doorway the President of the Corporation.

"Good day, Sir!" said he abruptly to the manager. "I am the President of the Cross-Country Cafeteria Corporation!"

"Yes, Sir," said the manager.

"You have a customer here who has ordered our Special Broiled Sdfsh., Fr. Fr. Pot., Cup Coffee, Rolls, 35 Cents—and who will not take the rolls with the order?"

"Yes, Sir."

The President of the Cross-Country Cafeteria Corporation turned his head and bored me with a gimlet eye.

"And is this the gentleman?" he asked. I brushed my hair back, self-consciously.

"Yes, Sir," said the manager.

"Why damme," went on the gimlet-eyed President, peering at me closely, "Isn't your name Locomovich?"

"As a matter of fact," said I, shuffling my feet nervously, "my name is J. Perry Locomovich."

"Didn't you row for Harvard back in '99?"

"As a matter of fact," said I, "I did."

"Well, you old son-of-a-gun!" cried the President of the Cross-Country Cafeteria Corporation. "I was the fellow whose oar was always splashing water in your eye!"

"Well, you old son-of-a-gun!" said I. We embraced.

"If this gentleman wants his lunch without rolls," said he, turning to the manager, "let him have it. Goodbye. I have an appointment in California."

He was gone.

"Oh, by the way," I shouted after him, "that one about putting things off till tomorrow—that was Franklin, you know, not Lincoln—Ben Franklin."

"Twaddle!" he snapped, putting his head back through the door. "Popular superstition. Like many of Franklin's sayings, it was lifted from the Greek. A. Lincoln had the first copyright on it, way back in 1865. Saw the papers myself. Goodbye."

He was gone again.

"That man is a veritable storehouse of human knowledge," said the manager. "I never suspected Lincoln was a Greek."

It seemed to me there was something funny about the date, too, but I was too hungry to worry over it. I stumbled out into the dining room clutching a slip on which was scrawled, "O.K. No rolls. Manager." Sure enough, there was my order just as I had left it. It was cold and it was stale, but it was the first food I had tasted in three days, so I consumed it with relish.

Stepping into a telegraph office fifteen minutes later to let my company know why the hot water bottles were behind schedule, I found a line of angry people waiting to file telegrams.

"Can't get a word over the wires for half an hour," growled one of them. "Some damned cafeteria outfit has every telegraph line in the country tied up, sending messages to its managers. Something about changing one of their specials. Something about rolls."

THE MARTYR

By Newman Levy

BEFORE HIS EXCURSION INTO HOMICIDE TIM BRENNECKE'S CAREER HAD
been mild and unadventurous. The various jobs that he had adorned
at one time or another, delivery boy, shipping clerk, truck driver
and more recently, beverage dispenser at the fountain of a popular
drug store, seemed hardly an appropriate prelude to what com-
mentators were later to describe as "the crime of the century." Nor
did his appearance suggest any of the stigmata of crime so dear to
the hearts of certain criminologists. Tall and slightly emaciated, a
shock of sandy hair which was usually tousled—except during his
soda water period when it was kept sleek and glossy by the diligent
application of unguents—weak watery eyes that peered earnestly
from behind gold rimmed spectacles, he looked more like a down
at the heels philosophy student than the principal actor in a *cause
célèbre*.

In fact, the crime itself in the beginning scarcely appeared to be
fraught with earth shaking possibilities. On the surface it seemed
to be merely the tragic conclusion of a sordid speakeasy brawl. The
morning after it happened a few of the newspapers gave it two or
three obscure inches of space; most of them ignored it completely.
For a shot that was destined to be heard round the world, it sounded
at first, ridiculously like the explosion of a toy pop gun. In like
fashion, did the assassination at Sarajevo break unheralded upon
an unaware world.

Tim sat moodily at a table in the basement of Tony's, one of
those dingy emancipated speakeasies in the West Forties that contributed so much to the conviviality of those arid times, now happily past. Mike Angelo, swarthy and eager eyed, sat opposite him.
Each had before him a pale amber fluid, described by the management in a magnificent burst of metaphor as Scotch Whiskey, a
potent decoction that possessed the combined stimulative and
health giving properties of bichloride of mercury, arsenic and dyna-

mite. The affairs of the universe were being settled with earnest alcoholic finality; the discussion was profound and philosophical.

"This country's run by the capitalists—the Wall Street Crowd," said Tim morosely. "It's a helova note. Here we are, slavin'——"

"What's the matter with this country?" retorted Angelo, with the natural indignation of the proprietor of a prosperous fruit stand.

"Just a bunch of suckers," said Tim. "Now look at Russia, f'rinstance."

"Yeah," said Mike. "*Look* at Russia. A lot o' Bolsheviks and—and Russians. Look at it!" He laughed sarcastically.

"What's matter with Russia?" said Tim with dignity. "Here Tony. Two more o' these."

He reached into his trousers pocket as Tony came from behind the bar with the drinks.

"No, this is on me," insisted Mike.

"Nothing doing," said Tim. "You paid last time."

That was settled and they drank in silence.

"What's matter with Russia?" Tim repeated. "Look at that guy Lenin."

"Lot o' hooey," said Angelo.

"Look at what he done for Russia," said Tim. "Lenin was a great little feller. Look what he done for Russia."

"Lot o' hooey," said Angelo.

"He was a great little feller."

"What's matter with Roosevelt?" declared Mike.

"What Roosevelt?"

"Franklin Roosevelt," said Mike.

"What's Roosevelt ever done for Russia?" Tim demanded. "Look what Lenin done for Russia. What's Roosevelt ever done for Russia?"

"Lot o' hooey," said Mike. "If you don't like it in this country why don't you go back where you came from?"

Tim looked at his companion in pained surprise.

"Say that again, you fat wop!" he said.

"You heard me," said Mike.

"Say that again," Tim insisted.

"Lot o' hooey," Mike repeated.

There seemed to be but one logical retort to this remark. Tim seized the glass of water, known technically as a chaser, and with an accuracy surprising in one so completely alcoholized, hurled the contents in Mike's face.

There was a crash of overturning chairs; Mike advanced belligerently towards Tim who backed unsteadily up against the bar. "Here! Cut that!" exclaimed Tony in a panic. Mike swung wildly. Tim reached for the whiskey bottle that stood near at hand on the bar, and brought it down with conclusive force upon Mike's head. The Italian toppled over and lay motionless on the ground.

There were shrieks and a scuffle of excitement. The fashionably dressed patrons in the front room slipped silently out. Policemen and white coated internes appeared suddenly and miraculously. Mike Angelo, his skull crushed in, died in the ambulance on the way to the hospital. Tim stupefied and manacled was deposited in a cell at police headquarters charged with murder, and Tony, the proprietor of the restaurant, was held as a material witness.

And there the matter might have rested had it not been for the fortuitous arrival of Miss Irma Lubetkin upon the scene. Miss Lubetkin was a student of journalism. At night she took courses in dramatic criticism at N.Y.U. and in the daytime she worked as reporter on *The Daily Clarion*, the somewhat vociferous organ of the downtrodden working classes. Miss Lubetkin took her journalistic activities seriously. She reported the happening of a one alarm fire on Forsythe Street with the same passionate fervor that she might have felt in describing the San Francisco earthquake. A taxicab collision was to her a matter of cosmic importance.

She sat, notebook in hand, at the reporter's table in the Homicide Court when Tim Brennecke was brought in for arraignment. Some of his sleekness had departed; his hair no longer bore evidence of the faithful application of his favorite widely advertised cosmetic; he had a three day growth of beard—perhaps the most disreputable period in a man's hirsute development; his collar was torn and he was bedraggled and dirty.

"What's it all about?" said the magistrate.

"A row in a dump over on Fortieth Street," said Detective Riley who had Tim in custody. "This lad and the deceased got into a scrap about Lenin and Trotsky and the Bolsheviks and this defendant tells the deceased that Lenin's a better man than Roosevelt and that's how it started. He crowned the deceased with a bottle of hooch."

"Suppose we put it over for a couple of days," suggested the assistant district attorney. "He'll probably be indicted this week."

Tim, tightly handcuffed, was led from the room. Miss Lubetkin sat trembling with excitement. This was indeed a story! Lenin—Trotsky—Bolshevism—Murder! None of the daily papers had mentioned it. It was what they called at the N. Y. U. School of Journalism "a scoop." She rushed with eager haste from the courtroom clutching her pencil and notebook, and headed up Mulberry Street to the offices of the *Clarion* in Union Square.

She found the editorial office of *The Daily Clarion*, upon her arrival, in a curious state of lassitude. There had been no flagrant violation of the rights of the proletariat for several days. True there were the usual textile strikes somewhere in New England, but the state constabulary had inconsiderately refrained from shooting anybody; no injunctions worth speaking about had been issued by a venal and class-conscious judiciary. To put it in a word, civil liberties were in a distressing state of equilibrium, and things were dull around the *Clarion* office. Sig Goldberg, the swarthy bearded editor, whose secret vanity was that he looked like Karl Marx, sat in his shirt sleeves matching pennies with Barney McCormick, the *Clarion* columnist as Irma burst in breathlessly, her fuzzy tam o'-shanter awry, and with excitement flashing from behind her bone rimmed spectacles.

"I've got a great story!" she exclaimed.

"Huh," said Sig Goldberg.

"Am I matching you or are you matching me?" said Barney McCormick.

"Listen," said Irma. "It's—it's a scoop—I'm not kidding."

"Horse ran away on Grand Street, I suppose," said Sig. "You're matching me."

"No. Listen. It's a murder. A political murder. A fellow named Tim Brennecke—a communist. He was attacked last night for defending Lenin and Trotsky, and in the row some Italian was killed. Brennecke is held for murder without bail. I've just come from the court ——"

At the mention of the word "communist" the two men desisted from their game and listened attentively.

"It sounds like maybe the kid's got something," said Goldberg.

"Sounds like something to me," said McCormick. "Tell me that again."

Irma repeated her story with added details.

"Did he have a lawyer?" McCormick asked.

"No—I don't think so," said Irma. "He's just a poor soda clerk. They're hounding him because he's a communist. You should of heard that judge!"

"He's got to have a lawyer," said Sig. "You'd better run up there, Barney, and get the dope. I'll call a committee meeting for this evening ——"

"Committee?" asked Irma.

"Sure. A defense committee. We're not going to let this kid be persecuted for his political opinions. Call up Wilfred Beecher, Aaron Federblum ——"

"Rev. Dr. Peters," suggested Barney.

"Sure. He'll serve. Frank Leary ——"

The Defense Committee met at eight o'clock that evening at the *Clarion* office. Wilfred Beecher, the radical novelist, suave and shrewd behind a deceptive Harvard accent, was in the chair.

"The first thing I'd suggest," said Aaron Federblum, the labor leader, "is about raising funds—what I call the sinews of war. You can't fight a battle like this without money." He rose and addressed the chair oratorically. "If J. P. Morgan and Andrew Mellon want to send that boy to the electric chair we've got to ——"

"We'll come to that," said the chairman. "The first thing now is to get our committee organized. We've got fifty names suggested so far—clergymen, editors, college presidents and men of importance. Now the next thing is to get a paid secretary to handle the correspondence and the publicity."

"How about Mary Larkin?" suggested Frank Leary. "She did a swell job with that strike case out in Idaho ——"

"Fine," said Beecher. "Wire Mary to come on at seventy-five a week. Later when we get going, maybe we'll be able to pay her more."

Federblum adjusted his eye glasses and again attempted to launch into an oration.

"Where's it coming from?" he said. "A case like this takes money ——"

"Don't worry about that," said Dr. Peters. "It'll come."

"The Reverend is right," said Leary. "We'll get up mass meetings and dances and raffles—the usual stuff. But meantime, how about gettin the kid a lawyer?"

"How about Darrow?" suggested Beecher. "This is his kind of case."

"I don't think he can come," said Sig Goldberg. "He's out west somewhere lecturing. But Bob Thayer is in town."

"Nothing doing," said Federblum. "I don't like these road company Darrows ——"

"Well we've got to take what we can get in these radical cases," said Beecher. "You can't expect those bar association lawyers to fight the Morgan crowd. Let's get in touch with Thayer just so the boy's taken care of now. Later on ——"

The following day the *Clarion* scored a beat on all its local contemporaries. By startling headlines across its front page a palpitating world—or so much of it as read the *Clarion*—was informed that the octopuses, tigers, hyenas and such like fauna of Wall Street had conspired to send one Tim Brennecke to the electric chair for daring to defend unorthodox views on economics and government. A committee of distinguished citizens, the *Clarion* readers were further advised, had been formed to combat this sinister plot. Mr. Robert Thayer, the well known leader of the bar, had generously consented to act as defense counsel. Mr. Thayer also generously consented to give a two column interview to Miss Lubetkin, the *Clarion's* star reporter, together with selected portions from the unabridged history of his life. Barney McCormick's column bristled with epigrams calculated to throw terror into the combined houses of Morgan and Kuhn and Loeb.

And then the laggard editors of the less altruistic journals woke up, rubbed their eyes, and wondered what it was all about. By the afternoon the camera men of the tabloid press were besieging the Tombs to obtain portraits of Tim Brennecke, the communist martyr—the man who was willing to give his life that the struggling workers of the world might be free.

Tim Brennecke, in a strange state of bewilderment, sat in his cell in the Tombs reading the newspapers and playing solitaire. The case was only two weeks old but he had already acquired quite a respectable collection of clippings. When his desire for solitaire lagged he amused himself by pasting them in a large scrap book.

It was all extremely confusing; particularly the story he had just read in the morning paper about the picketers who had been arrested the day before for parading in front of the Standard Oil Building as a protest against his arrest. They had carried banners bearing such legends as "Brennecke Must Be Free," and "Socrates—Dreyfus—Brennecke, Martyrs of Freedom." He wondered vaguely who Socrates and Dreyfus were, and whom they had killed, and whether they had been drunk on bootleg hooch when it happened. He wondered, too, why the Standard Oil Crowd should be as bitter against him as the newspapers led him to believe. So far as he could remember he had never done anything to them.

Each day he was called down to the squalid, iron barred counsel room to confer with his attorney.

"Well Tim," exclaimed Mr. Thayer with professional heartiness. "The old machine's running along grand—hitting on all four. We're getting your defense whipped into shape."

"Yeah?" said Tim apathetically.

"The money's coming in fine. We've got three girls working now —sending out letters and pamphlets and that sort of thing."

"That's swell," said Tim unenthusiastically. "When do I get out o' here?"

"We've got to go slow," said Mr. Thayer. "We can't rush this sort of thing. Did you read Irma Smedly Van Heusen's poem today?"

"I couldn't understand it," said Tim.

"Well that's the kind of propaganda we need," said Thayer. "She's one of the best poets in the country. She's going down to Washington next week with a bunch of authors to picket the White House."

"What good'll that do?" Tim asked.

"What good?" Mr. Thayer exclaimed in surprise. "Why they may be arrested!"

"And when do I get out o' here?" Tim asked.

"Take it easy," said the lawyer, calling the uniformed attendant over to let him out of the cage. "You're going to have one of the best defenses any defendant ever had."

Mr. Thayer's prediction concerning the defense was soon to be verified. The following week a crushing blow was struck in the battle to free Tim Brennecke from the toils of capitalism. Fifty ardent devotees of liberty marched on to the American Embassy in London. His Excellency, the Ambassador, looked out from behind the curtains as the delegation paused to sing *The Internationale*.

"Can you make out those banners?" he said to his secretary who stood beside him.

"As near as I can make out," said the secretary peering through the window, "it has something to do with someone named Brennecke."

"Never heard of him," said the Ambassador.

"That banner says that you're trying to electrocute him," said the secretary.

"Possibly," said his Excellency. "It must have slipped my mind."

He left the window and returned to his desk and the contemplation of more ponderous diplomatic affairs. Three débutantes were to be presented at court that night.

To Mr. Tim Brennecke languishing in durance vile all this was not so bad as it might have been. True, he would rather have been out; the opportunities for diversion in the Tombs were circumscribed. He missed his gay debonair companions of the drug store; the jolly care free life of the soda fountain. But there were compensations. His cell was amply decorated with flowers—the daily tribute of the Ladies' Auxiliary of the Soda Dispensers Union, Local No. 18; there were books aplenty, the devoted gifts of various libertarian organizations—and although the titles were largely communistic and unintelligible to him, they added quite a cozy touch to his cell. But best of all was the kick he got out of being a celebrity—of seeing his picture spread across the pages of daily papers, of reading the glowing tributes to his martyrdom, of the illustrious names that were increasingly added to his list of champions, and of all the baskets full of sympathetic letters that poured in each day from all parts of the world.

Tim Brennecke awoke one morning with a feeling that all was not quite well with the world. He had been feeling that way a lot lately. Even the attack upon the American Embassy in Madrid—an occurrence that might have delighted his soul a month or two before—left him strangely unmoved. His literary labors into which he had plunged with so much verve—he was writing the story of his life for the *Evening Tabloid*—no longer thrilled him with that rare glow of creativeness that comes with the first adventure into authorship. Even the announcement that a committee of prominent European composers, authors, and sculptors was about to embark for the United States to protest to the President in his behalf was so much dead sea fruit in his mouth.

Vaguely he sensed the reason. It was springtime, and once again the vernal syrups were coursing riotously through the silvered taps of the soda fountains; sundaes, marshmallow floats, frosted chocolates, harbingers of the ever recurring miracle of the springtide were heaped in gay profusion upon the marble topped counters, beautiful maidens perched on tall stools sipped fragrant iced drinks through straws; while behind the counter tall, dapper Ganymedes, his erstwhile companions, performed their immemorial rites. It was springtime in the great outside world and Tim Brennecke, glum and disconsolate, lay a prisoner in his dungeon cell.

A keeper appeared at the door to inform him that his lawyer was downstairs. He descended the iron steps and found Bob Thayer waiting for him in the counsel room. Mr. Thayer was jubilant.

"Well we've got 'em on the run," he exclaimed.

"I suppose Irma Smedly Van Heusen's written another poem," said Tim.

"Better than that. They've fixed the date for your trial—October 5th."

"Do you mean I gotta stay here all summer?" Tim demanded.

"Why not?" said the lawyer. "Think of the propaganda we can put over in that time. Time is of the essence, as we lawyers say. We'll keep this thing going all summer and we'll have your case in great shape. It's the greatest blow that's been struck for liberalism since ——"

"An' when do I get out?" said Tim.

"You'll have the most sensational trial in the annals of jurisprudence. They're altering the basement of the court house to make room for the telegraphers and newspaper men. They're even talking of broadcasting the trial."

"That's just fine and dandy," said Tim. "That gets me a lot. An' then what?" Mr. Thayer looked sadly at his client.

"I sometimes wonder, Tim," he said, "whether you're really big enough for the rôle you're playing—whether you actually are worthy of your good fortune. All over the world the downtrodden masses are looking to you as a symbol of their emancipation—as a torch to light the pathway to freedom. Your grave will be a shrine of liberty, your blood will baptize ——"

"My blood?" Tim exclaimed. "Wait a minute! Let me get this straight. Whaddye mean, my blood?"

"I'm speaking figuratively, of course," said Thayer. "Electrocution, as you know, is—er—unsanguinary."

Tim sank back limply.

"Electrocution," he whispered. "Do you mean there's a chance I'll get the chair?"

"Chance?" said the lawyer. "Chance isn't the word. It's an opportunity. It's a priceless privilege to die that freedom might live. You might make a note of that. It'll sound good in your farewell message."

"But my defense?" Tim gasped.

"Your defense is that you slew the Italian in vindication of the priceless heritage of mankind. No jury will believe you; the Wall Street crowd will see to that. But what of it? Your name will be blazoned among the immortals."

He signalled to the attendant that the interview was at an end, and hurried out of the Tombs to attend the weekly meeting of the defense committee.

That afternoon Tim interrupted his literary activities long enough to write a letter to the District Attorney.

"Dear Mr. District Attorney (he wrote).

My lawyer is a sap and he says I got to be a marter. I don't want to be a marter. I'm sick and tired of the whole business and I want to get out of jail. I hit that wop just for the sake of argument and not because I want to be a marter. A fellow on my tier says if I cop a plea maybe you'll give me the pen. I've been in this dump six mos. already and if it's all the same to you I'd like to drop the whole affair.
                    Respectfully
                              TIMOTHY BRENNECKE."

The District Attorney of New York County sat in his office discussing the letter with his assistant Mr. Couzens.

"If we give him the penitentiary that means three years," he said. "I don't like to do it. There'd be a howl in the press. It was a clear case of murder ——"

"We'd never convict him of murder. He was pie eyed," said the assistant. "That would probably take the question of premeditation out of the case and reduce it to murder in the second, or, more likely, manslaughter."

"I guess you're right," said the district attorney. "Besides, I'm getting fed up on all this newspaper stuff. You never can tell what sort of turn one of these radical cases will take. I'm for getting rid of it at any price."

"My opinion exactly," said his assistant. "One nut on the jury may tie up the whole works. I suppose I ought to get in touch with his lawyer."

"Sure," said the district attorney. "Professional etiquette, and all that sore of thing."

To say that the information conveyed by Assistant District Attorney Couzens over the telephone was a bombshell in the defense camp is an understatement. An earthquake would be somewhat nearer the truth. Sig Goldberg and Wilfred Beecher gazed at each other in consternation as Bob Thayer broke the news to the defense committee. Barney McCormick groped helplessly for a wise crack.

"So he sold us out to the Wall Street Crowd—the rat!" Aaron Federblum murmured.

"They got to him at last," said Frank Leary.

"We've got to stop him," Sig Goldberg exclaimed. "We can't let him throw us like this—after all we've done for him. Think of the time we've spent on this case! Think of the preparations! You've got to make him go to trial Bob!"

Counselor Thayer puffed sadly upon his pipe.

"I can't make a man stand trial if he wants to plead guilty," he said. "The judge wouldn't stand for it."

"How are finances?" Federblum asked.

"We're in a hole," Sig Goldberg replied. "Rent for the headquarters, postage, stenographers, all that sort of thing. We figured on making a big drive for contributions on the eve of the trial. That's when they always come across. We're in a fine mess."

Then Reverend Dr. Peters spoke.

"The fight will go on. This is not the first time the Cause has been betrayed. The fight will go on. Brennecke was not deserving of his martyrdom. I move that we adjourn. I'm getting hungry."

When Tim Brennecke stood up in court the following week and heard himself sentenced to the penitentiary "to be dealt with according to law," there were few in the courtroom to witness his tragic act of betrayal. Judas like he slunk down into the detention pen and away into oblivion. The *Clarion* had dismissed his perfidy with a scathing editorial; the capitalistic press had glossed over the affair lightly and unobtrusively.

In all the great city there was only one so poor to do him reverence. In the rear of the court room sat a young girl in a fuzzy tam o'shanter. She chewed on her pencil as she crowded back the tears that clouded with mist the lenses of her bone rimmed spectacles.

Then Miss Irma Lubetkin left the court, and since it was lunch time, she went across the street to a drug store to order a marshmallow nut sundae.

DON'T LAUGH NOW

By J. C. FURNAS

THE MAJORITY OF ANY GIVEN GROUP OF PEOPLE ARE PROBABLY ALL too sane. One of the more sporting ways of finding out which ones are not is to try shaggy-dog stories on them. Take the story of the cake as a sample:

One morning a morning-coated, top-hatted man came into a famous New York confectioner's, ordered a special cake to be made in the shape of an S—and said he would call in to inspect it the next day. Expense was obviously no object, so the confectioner had a special S-shaped pan made up at the tinsmith's and baked a beautiful cake, lavishly decorated. When the customer arrived next morning, however, he was not at all satisfied: "This is a block S," he said; "I wanted a script S." The confectioner apologized, ordered another pan and baked another cake. In the morning the customer was still unhappy about it: "No, this won't do," he said. "The curlicue is cut off. I want a large and graceful curlicue, do you understand?" The confectioner, tactful and patient through it all, ordered another pan with an elaborate curlicue and baked another cake. This time the customer was delighted—the cake was perfect. "I'm so glad, sir," said the confectioner. "Where shall we send it, sir?" "Never mind," said the customer, "I'll eat it here."

When confronted with that one, two of a job lot of listeners will laugh hollowly and briefly, unmistakably bewildered and yet trying to be polite. Two more, probably forthright young women, will say, frowning attractively: "But I don't see anything to laugh at." Certain kinds of middle-aged men will turn away in silent contempt. But those members of the party who are sufficiently matured spiritually to be slightly nuts will double up and whoop, regardless of the feelings of the uninitiate.

So, if you don't think the story of the cake is funny, you might as well congratulate yourself on being thoroughly well-balanced mentally and stop reading here, because there's more and giddier underneath. This tradition has something in common with a certain kind of revue blackout, a little of the screwily logical Alice-in-Wonderland dream quality, a good deal of the modern tradition in comic cartooning. If you liked James Thurber's story of the horse who had gone to college with the narrator, you are probably fair game. About the best of them, however, there is concision, a sudden flicker of comic lightning with no apparent right to be comic, which puts them in a separate class. The closest cousins crop up in the Marx Brothers' high spots. When Groucho and Chico in *Animal Crackers* were discussing the whereabouts of the missing painting, guessing that it was probably in the house next door, remembering that there was no house next door and deciding: "Then we'll have to build one," they were getting very warm indeed.

The story of the brass cannon is, in fact, almost pure Marx. In a park on top of a high bluff in a certain small town was a brass cannon as a decorative relic. The town paid a small salary to one of its citizens to climb the bluff every day and polish the cannon. After forty years on the job, the polisher returned home one day and told his wife he was going to quit. When she asked why: "I can't see any future in it," he said, "I've got a little money saved up—I'm going to take it and buy another cannon and go in business for myself."

Perhaps the core of it is this kind of success in suddenly slapping you in the face with a strict application of an outlandish premise. That element comes out very clearly in the briefer specimens, which are often little more than momentary flashes of lunacy:

The old gentleman who advertised for a young man with a college education to accompany him on a European tour and was called to the phone at 5 a.m. to hear: "My name is Robinson and I'm a Yale graduate—I thought I'd better call and tell you I'm very sorry, but I won't be able to go to Europe with you." . . . The tourist guide who explained to the returning vacationist that nobody had fallen over Lover's Leap since they put up a "Danger" sign, so they took it down as useless . . . The well-known soda-jerker who, faced with an order for a banana split without the chopped walnuts, said he was out of walnuts so he'd have to make it without chopped peanuts . . . The harassed mother who dressed her little girl up in her best white dress and let her go out to play, saying: "Now if you come home with your dress dirty, I'll strangle you." The little girl fell in a puddle and came home very dirty indeed, so her mother strangled her . . .

But there are meatier items, foursquare classics which, once heard, stick in the mind like taffy in a dog's jaws and are beautifully calculated to outrage people who can see nothing funny in them at all. When General Tom Thumb, Barnum's famous dwarf, was playing a certain town, the local paper sent a reporter around to his hotel to interview him. The reporter got the room number and knocked at the right door. It was opened by a towering giant, who filled the doorway from threshold to lintel and jamb to jamb. "I'm from the *Argus*," says the reporter, "I want to interview General Tom Thumb." "Glad to see you," says the giant, "I'm General Tom Thumb. Come right in." "You're crazy," says the reporter, peering up at the giant, "General Tom Thumb's a dwarf." "Well," says the giant, "this is my day off."

Although that has every earmark of antiquity, the writer has never yet found a victim who had ever heard it before. The mongoose story is another item from the dim past which has been neglected in modern times. The mongoose probably needs a couple of good vaudeville character actors to do it justice, but the dialogue without the business is still first-class. There is a sour-faced old farmer in a day coach with an animal-box on the seat beside him, obviously containing something alive. The traditionally flashy drummer, incurably loquacious and inquisitive as usual, gets in and sits down opposite. After studying the box for a while he leans over and asks: "What you got in that box, stranger?" "Mongoose," says the farmer, tersely enough to close the conversation. The traveling man shuts up for ten minutes or so, then: "Say, what's a mongoose?" "Little animal that kills snakes." The traveling man ponders that one for a few minutes, "Whatcha want to kill snakes for?" . . . "I got a brother . . ." "What's your brother got to do with snakes?" . . . "Wal, he drinks . . ." "But those ain't real snakes, brother." . . . "This ain't a real mongoose."

Matters can get screwier at will. There is always the horse that sat on grapefruit. At this point the listener is apt to say that you might as well stop right there, and there's probably something to it. This is a matter of a man's going to a county fair to look for a good horse, finding one at a ridiculously low price and asking suspiciously what's wrong with him: "Well, we never could break him of one bad habit," says the dealer. "He sits on grapefruit. Whenever he sees a grapefruit he sits on it and won't get up." The man figures that isn't much of a drawback in an otherwise valuable animal, so he pays the price and starts to ride the new horse home by a road which crosses a ford. Right in the middle of the ford the horse sits down, and refuses to budge. The man gets off his back, looks round carefully for grapefruit, finds none, wades ashore and goes back to the fair to protest to the dealer: "Hay," he says, "that horse you sold me sat down in the middle of the river and he's still there and there weren't any grapefruit around either." "Oh, hell," says the dealer, "I guess I forgot to tell you. He sits on fish, too."

The nub in that one may well consist in the sudden introduction of a new set of lunacies after the listener has already survived the first set, a kind of intellectual one-two rabbit punch. Curiously the story of the whole lot which is most likely to be greeted with "I've heard that before" is another in the same class: A guest at dinner is served with creamed cauliflower. Instead of spooning it out, he dips in both his hands and rubs a double-handful of creamed cauliflower into his scalp with great care and thoroughness. His hostess stares for a moment or two in speechless horror and finally gasps: "Mr. Smith, do you realize that is creamed cauliflower?" "Cauliflower!" says Mr. Smith, apparently taken aback. "Why, I thought it was parsnips."

You will often find that people try to palm off on you stories which are silly enough, but fail to achieve the crisp clean irresponsibility which is the earmark of the true breed. Drunk stories come in that class—the drunk who asks the other drunk the time in the Pullman washroom—it was used in an old Harold Lloyd comedy—the two drunks in the saloon who turn out to be father and son—the drunk clutching the tree and complaining that he's walled in—the drunk who misses the train while the two friends who came to see him off just make it—and so forth. The point is that drunks are loony by definition and, although funny, cannot produce the required effect of looniness suddenly intruding into a cold sober situation.

They say they are known as shaggy-dog stories because the

story of the shaggy dog was the first of the lot to become popular. That can't be true, since the shaggy dog, besides being a poor specimen, seems to have appeared fairly recently and, to the writer's certain knowledge, a couple of the classic examples go much farther back. But "shaggy-dog" will have to do because there is no other label which fits at all neatly. "Goofy" is disparagingly broad. Many a goofy story, told to make people look ridiculous in laughing out of politeness, is a dull, dirty trick. "Pointless" is too derogatory, since these stories have their own kind of point. Just what it is may well be inscrutable but the outraged hilarity which greets them when tested on the right sense of humor demonstrates that a perversely back-handed point is there.

Addicts sometimes express a fondness for the shaggy-dog story, however, so it should probably be included as clinical datum. An advertisement appears in a New York paper offering a £500 reward for the return of a certain large, white shaggy dog, marked thus and so, to an address in a London suburb. A New Yorker who has just picked up a big white shaggy stray with the indicated markings, immediately takes ship for England with the dog, goes to the advertised address and rings the doorbell. A man opens the door. "You advertised about a lost dog," says the American, "a shaggy dog." "Oh," says the Englishman coldly, "not so damn shaggy" and slams the door in the American's face.

The values in that are highly esoteric but a thorough-going addict can detect them. As a matter of fact, the classic type of the whole tradition may well be one of the worst overworked gags of the vaudeville stage. Think back to the time you first heard it, if memory goes back that far, scrape away the crusted remains of irritation at hearing it too often repeated and ponder the simple, lucid virtues of the old line about "it must have been two other fellows." The shaggy dog cannot be tolerated in the same country.

But then, most people find these stories pretty hard to tolerate anyway.

AUTHOR's NOTE:

Readers who have seen Max Eastman's *Enjoyment of Laughter* will recognize this story as a compressed version of one of Mr. Eastman's examples of nonsense. To the present writer it seems rather unfortunate to lump this sort of thing as nonsense along with Edward Lear's pure Lunacies or Lewis Carroll's intellectual irresponsibility. The point in

Shaggy-Dog stories may well be that, although heedless of sense, they are not nonsense. Instead they insist on making the logic of a situation impose itself ruthlessly on the hearer, who tricked himself into being surprised by making normal reflex shortcuts between an opening situation and the sort of conclusion o 1e would expect in normal life.

All that is pretty solemn, however, and, if anybody feels cheated by finding one of Mr. Eastman's stories here, this is a grisly substitute: A reasonably prosperous looking man standing by the rail between horse races is approached by a sad looking creature huddled into a long overcoat which he holds tightly round his neck. Figuring that this is a probable touch, the prosperous spectator tries to turn away but the other man stops him. "I don't want anything from you, Mister," he says, "I just want to tell you. Listen. I've been here all week. The first day I bet thirty bucks, and that was all I had, on a two-to-one shot and I won. The next day I put that sixty bucks on a four-to-one shot and I won again. And yesterday I put my $480 on a long shot and the long shot came home at fifty to one and today I put all my $24,000 on the favorite and he lost. Now what would you do in a case like that?" The prosperous spectator, still suspecting a touch, answers gruffly: "Well, I guess I'd just cut my throat." "I thought of that," says the shabby man, suddenly opening his coat collar. "Looka here."

YOU CAN'T SLEEP WITH WOMEN

By ALAN MacDONALD

MOST MEN FIND SOONER OR LATER THAT SLEEPING WITH WOMEN IS one of the arts—the art of self-defense. Totally unprepared for what happens to them, they are plunged by tradition into the un-heralded Battle of the Bedroom, armed only with the most meager previous experience. Their struggle for sleep is immediate and un-ending. It covers a period of twelve or fourteen night-years spent with women in unstrategic horizontal position. They may fight valiantly at the beginning but eventually one and all find themselves weakened refugees from the coveted regions of rest—for they just can't sleep.

When we say sleeping, we mean simply that. The writer-wrought credo of the predatory male is pure bunk. Men are mere babes in a bedroom. The story-tellers usually have conventions of men chasing one woman but even the wily widows will tell you the exact reverse is true in non-fiction existence. It is entirely plausi-ble, then, to assume that the sleep-killing tactics of women is purely force of habit, a carry-over from constant pursuit routine.

Not having the background of a Casanova or a Cellini, we are devoting this short treatise to the morphetic rather than the erotic antics of our feminine sleeping companions. Millions of words have been written and spoken on human love caperings. But the wealth of information stops right there. No diagnostic panacea has ever been offered for that age-old cry of a man in the night: "My God, I've gotta get some sleep."

Our findings have been based upon numerous unexpected and unplanned observations over a period of years, and upon unwilling complaints of fatigue-racked friends during their frantic search for surcease. So, in order to promote a more general discussion of this universal and too long soft-pedaled subject, let us enter the bedroom.

Passing quickly over the more commonly recognized disturbers of masculine sleep—the Cover Pullers, the Snorers and Groaners, the Window Arguers, the Get Up and Goers, the Food Munchers, the Arm Huggers, the Wheezers and Grunters, the Leg Tossers, the Medicine Takers, and the Which Side of the Bed Janglers— we will attempt to classify the Nine Major Invincibles.

1. THE NECK NOSERS. Of all sleeping companions, these are the most irritating and hardest to curb. They cleave to conquer. Their devilish artistry begins with the slipping of a casual arm over the chest of the unfortunate clunk who happens to be at their side. This is usually accompanied by a sleepy sigh indicating that they are not clearly conscious of what they are doing. Within the next few moments, the Barnacle Beautiful has settled a soft chin quite definitely upon the man's weary shoulder. When this is accomplished, he finds he is securely anchored on the lee-side. If he offers no resistance at this stage, her final gesture is a short upward tug accompanied by a slight inward heave—and a face rests in the hollow of his unwilling neck. Wisps of stray hair begin to tickle his nostrils with deadly insistence. The annihilation of his rest has now been completed to the last bitter detail.

2. THE INCHING ROLLERS. Closely allied to the Neck Nosers, this group is larger in point of numbers and individual silhouette. Their size range varies from 44 to 52, since they are effective only in these dimensions. They are the Big-Way sleep dispatchers. A series of fitful rolls in conjunction with an inch by inch crowding method constitutes their slumber disturbing tactics. They can be elbowed, shouted at, kicked, but they keep on inching with unabated vigor and remarkable placidity. When their victims find themselves poised at the edge of the bed, they may make a resolute struggle while the final inching goes on. Ultimately they must choose between yelling like a lumberjack or walking stealthily around to the lately departed other side. Relief through the latter course is, at the best, only temporary. The vanquished ones find that their own body-heat or slightest movement acts like a magnet to their pursuers who seem able to reverse themselves automatically. No matter how active they have been during the day, these sufferers must keep on traveling unmeasured distances throughout the night.

3. THE BRIDES OF FRANKENSTEIN. These are the gals who inspired that classic query: "When in hell are you going to get into bed?" Their annoying prelude to sleep involves long intervals in

front of the bathroom mirror and the dressing table. Face creams are rubbed on, then rubbed off. Yards of cleansing tissue are used. Lotions, astringents, hair fixing contraptions, and sometimes head caps or chin guards, must be put on before they can lie down to rest. Lights glare long and grievously into the eyes of their male bed partners. When the buttery apparition that has been a healthy flesh and blood woman finally approaches the bed, her companion views her with unfailing amazement not unmixed with distrust. The fright-mask never looks the same twice in succession and he is unable to acclimate himself to these multitudinous identities. The disturbances caused by this group, once they have arranged themselves rigidly in bed, changes from optical to olfactory. Conglomerate odors ride the air. In gaseous stupor, their fagged victims sometimes make incoherent outbursts about "the good old soap and water days." But the Frankensteiners regard these demonstrations as inconsistent, irrelevant, and unimportant.

4. THE ETERNAL GLAMORISTS. Diametrically opposed to the Butter Belles of Group 3 are the Glamorists. They never give up. Going to bed is to them a ceremony and they go through their adroit devices with a gusto that is astonishing. They have a flair for good-looking night gowns, pajamas, lounging robes, and negligees. No oily creams or headgears for them. They always look their best. They can toss a robe over a chair with the grace of a movie siren or strike an informal pose with pointed carelessness. They are cozy. They like to sit on the edge of the bed for a last cigarette or trail around the room talking brightly about very little. A lot of attention-compelling gadgets are strewn by them within easy reach—smart magazines, modern poetry volumes, cigarette accessories, and sometimes a bedside radio, or a miniature bar for a chatty cocktail. Their main contributing annoyance, according to irritated consorts, is that they can't or won't relax—even in bed. They go right on posturing, talking, and glamoring with fatiguing intensity—and the older they get the more hectic they become.

5. THE MATTRESS FIGHTERS. These are the Can't Get Set-ers. No matter in what position they try to find sleep, that position seems uncomfortable. They continually "wrassle" the mattress. When they first get into bed, they'll stretch quietly at full length for a moment. Suddenly they'll hurtle sideways twisting themselves into an acute letter S. They'll rear up and pound the pillows

repeatedly. Emitting spasmodic yawns and little grunting noises, they'll tuck the covers around their shoulders a hundred different ways. They are the main springs on an inner-spring mattress. They can heave from flat-back to stomach with the agility of a leaping salmon, or spread themselves over the bed in a confusion of arms and legs that would put an octopus to shame. The masculine bed-mate hangs on to the pitching bed desperately, wondering how long it will hold together under these onslaughts. Each night to him is like a cruise on a choppy sea, but not in the Slumber Boat of song and story. There's no retiring lullaby corner on his precarious raft.

6. THE MUSH BOILERS. This unique type of female sleep-destroyer must not be confused with the more common respiratory annoyers such as the Wheezers, Snorers, and Groaners. The Boilers have a style all their own. Their breath is inhaled through the nose, then exhaled into the mouth with a slight puffing of the cheeks. As the pressure increases, the outgoing air bubbles through the lips with a noise like a muted Roman candle. Viewed in early daylight the entire sequence is reminiscent of a pot of boiling mush. Sometimes the exhalation is accompanied by a faint whistling sound. Other times there is a double-bubble effect. It is the uncertainty of the whole thing which keeps the listener on edge. As long as the Musher keeps an even rhythm, her male bedfellow can make his adjustment. But let an off-beat or an overtone creep into her "phouf-f-fing" and he is wide awake—and swearing.

7. THE TWITCHERS. It takes the ordinary man years to become inured to these "jerky" ones. A woman may be the picture of physical health and mental serenity yet, at the slightest touch or noise, she'll twitch in her sleep. No man's relaxation can be quite complete if he knows that his every unconscious move in bed is to be followed by a temblor of no mean proportions. Many of the Twitchers are addicted to dealing out short rabbit kicks in conjunction with their jerking. Or they'll sit suddenly straight up in bed, taking the covers with them. This type, too, is prone to argue if they are awakened by their own gymnastics. Seldom will they admit that the basis of the dual irritation lies in their own touch-and-jump mechanisms.

8. THE BED READERS. To have the light on or off, that is the question. Whether 'tis better for the suffering male to take it in the

eyes like a gentleman or, with the light cord, to throttle the book-clutching female at his side. To sleep—perchance, to dream. Ah, there's the rub, for there is no sleep and there are no dreams. The sharp thudding of a book to the floor at any time in the night, the rustle of a sheaf of magazines if he moves any part of his tired anatomy, the ready-for-debate attitude of his companion—these things encompass the sufferer roundabout. For him to cite the statistical fact that every train into Reno carries at least one Bed Reader is an unfailing signal for verbal combat. If he succeeds in delivering a speech on the deplorable state of his union, he finds upon concluding that—(1) the light is still on, (2) his companion is still talking, and (3) the book has again been opened to the place where she left off.

9. THE PILLOW LOOKERS. The ones in this final group, while rare, belong among the major classifications since the effect of their doings is so profound and lasting. It is alleged by those who have experienced it that there is nothing more disturbing than to realize that the woman lying beside you in the darkness is fully awake and looking in your direction. Why is she looking at you? What is she thinking? A thousand doubts assail you and a thousand answers come crowding into your mind. And in the broad morning light, if a man awakens suddenly to meet a wide-eyed gaze from the adjoining pillow, the effect is doubly disconcerting. How long has this been going on? Has his mouth been hanging open? This gaze business is something about which a man knows nothing. He is suspicious because he does not understand it. He is afraid of a question in that intent, but somehow detached, look and his normal ego is scattered in all directions. An immediate freezing undercurrent seizes him which no amount of subsequent conversation can dispel.

And there, gents, are your gals. If this broad classification of Rest Assassins helps to pave the way to a more clinical research into a grievous male predicament, this article will not have been written in vain. And so to bed—but not to sleep.

YONDER'S HENRY

By THORNE SMITH

HIS QUESTION SO UPSET ME I PUT DOWN MY DRINK UNTASTED. Albert was like that. Upsetting. Years ago I had gone to school with Albert. He had been upsetting then—a sort of experimental liar indefatigable in his efforts to plumb the depths of human credulity. Fifteen years in the discard that had been. Now fate had returned Albert—Albert Green—to my side. In a little bar in a little town in the large state of Texas we had been celebrating all morning. I now wonder why. In his charmingly casual manner Albert had just inquired if I cared to go fox hunting. He had added modestly that he lived in this state of Texas together with a population composed almost entirely of foxes. The first part of this statement might just possibly be true. I'm inclined to believe it is. He seemed to be living in Texas. It would take a big, strong state like Texas to stand for Albert. He would have upset any normal state just as he upset me. At the moment he was more interested in upsetting a lot of foxes.

I asked him a frank question. "Albert," I asked him, "do I bear on my face the stamp of a man consumed with a secret passion for foxes?"

"Don't have to be passionate about foxes, just to hunt 'em," he replied. "In fact, you can hate foxes."

I stopped to consider exactly where I stood about foxes. It surprised me to discover that I had no strong feelings either for or against foxes. Years ago I had heard something about a fox mentioned in connection with a bunch of grapes. Since that time, however, foxes had gone their way and I had gone mine. Our paths had never crossed. I saw no reason why they should.

"We'll waive that part of it," I said with befitting dignity. "What do you know about fox-hunting anyway?"

Albert indulged in a tragic laugh. "Every possible thing," he asserted. "Own the finest pack of hounds in Texas. You'd think they

175

were on tracks the way they follow foxes. Wonderful dogs. And Henry! What a hound. Man! Man! Oh, I know all about foxes. Recognize one at a glance."

"To recognize a fox is one thing," I told him, "but to chase him over the landscape is an elk of another burrow."

"Come on down to my place and I'll show you," urged Albert. "We'll do more than just hunt foxes. Henry'll juggle some for you. It's his way."

Precocious dogs, like precocious children, had always been one of my pet aversions, but the picture of a noble hound juggling a number of foxes fired my imagination. I accepted Albert's invitation, which goes to prove that one should never talk with Albert in a barroom.

On further consideration I am inclined to believe one should never talk with Albert at all.

II

After sleeping through numerous miles of Texas scenery while Albert sat alone with his God and his automobile, I found myself gazing miserably into the grim but good looking face of Mrs. Albert across the sparkling reaches of her luncheon table.

"The trouble with you boys," she said, "is that you don't drink enough."

Suiting her action to her words she replenished our glasses with what she was pleased to call real Texas mule, adding that it was something like the hair of the dog that had so brutally and recently mutilated us.

"My dear," remarked Albert, accepting the drink, but ignoring the remark that went with it, "I've decided to hold the fox hunt tomorrow—you know, the regular weekly fox hunt."

"Yes," I added. "He wants to show me Henry in action. I can see him now at the head of your splendid pack of hounds."

Mrs. Albert considered the suggestion. She poured out a drink for herself and tossed it off with professional detachment.

"Can you?" she asked in level tones. "You must have a remarkable imagination. Most northerners would not even believe it."

"My wife is a little touchy about Henry," Albert hastened to explain. "I brag so much about him. Might as well hold the hunt tomorrow at the usual time."

"Oh, certainly," replied Mrs. Albert. "Why not?" As she rose from the table she added, "Did I hear a door slam?"

"That's difficult to say," said Albert.

"Correct. It's almost impossible to tell whether a door has slammed or not after it's once slammed," Mrs. Albert continued thoughtfully. "It leaves no tracks behind."

"Not like Henry," I said to Albert. "He must fairly scoop up the earth when he once gets started."

I thought I saw Albert flinch. "Of course," he agreed quite seriously. "Fairly excavates it, that dog."

"Come, Albert," said his wife. "We must see about that door . . . and make some arrangements for tomorrow."

"May I stroll out and take a look at the pack?" I inquired.

"I'd hardly advise it," observed Albert. "Not just before a hunt."

"No, don't do that," put in his wife. "Henry does much better after he's been lonely a spell."

Later that afternoon I inadvertently overheard Mrs. Albert at the telephone.

"Certainly," she was saying, "Bring your guests right along. We have an alcoholic with us who doesn't know the first thing about fox-hunting. Doubt if he knows one end of a horse from the other." She must have suspected my presence for she went on in an altered voice, "Oh, yes, he's quite charming, this guest of ours. You must meet him. And tell the others not to dress formally, you know. Cut out the red coats for a change. He hasn't an outfit with him. Neither have your guests, I reckon." When she had hung up she turned to me.

"Did you hear?" she asked.

"No," I replied gallantly. "A door slammed. But I gathered I won't be alone in my misery."

"No," said Mrs. Albert. "There will be several other novices."

That night Albert, weak from the lack of liquor, came into my room and deposited a bundle of clothing on a chair.

"For tomorrow," he explained, eyeing the garments with disfavor. "The hunt, you know."

"Oh, I don't care what I look like," I assured the dispirited man. "What I'm interested in is what Henry looks like. Does he usually juggle the foxes before or after the hunt?"

"It makes no difference to Henry," said Albert brightening. "Whenever he gets a fox. Some call it brutal."

"Nonsense," I replied heartily.

Albert went away.

III

When I looked out of my window the next morning I received a decided shock. For a moment I feared that Albert had gotten himself into some trouble. His ancestral home seemed to have become entirely surrounded either by bandits or deputies. I was not sure which. Anyway, they were rough looking men, most of them carrying shot guns and rifles while others were swinging large, ugly looking clubs. There were many women also. They had the rough and ready appearance of experienced camp followers.

"The hunt breakfast," Albert murmured over my shoulder. I gave a slight start. He had made his appearance so quietly. "The regular hunt breakfast," he repeated.

"Why, there's hardly a red coat in the lot," I complained. "Albert, I feel cheated."

"Seldom wear red coats except on formal occasions," said Albert. "Thought you knew that."

"What does it matter?" I said philosophically. "We're chiefly interested in foxes, after all."

"So we are," replied Albert simply. "What's the sense in a lot of red coats, anyway? I don't think the dogs like 'em or the foxes either."

"Don't see why they should," I told him. "But I will ask you this. Do you use clubs and rifles and machine guns on your damn Texas foxes?"

"Not machine guns," said Albert gently. "We use the others for hand to hand fighting. Texas foxes are often violent. They don't seem to understand."

"Neither do I, quite," I admitted. "Why don't you bomb the foxes and save yourself a lot of trouble?"

"That wouldn't be sporting," said Albert blandly. "And anyway, we like it. Then again, there's Henry to consider. He must have his foxes."

"That's so too," I replied. "I guess that great beast would die unless he had his foxes."

"Those clubs and guns are brought along just in case," he informed me.

"In case of what?" I asked.

"Of wild turkeys," he answered without cracking a smile.

When I had finished dressing I was nearly as funny looking as Albert, but not quite. However, I was funny looking enough. I was exactly as funny looking as an oversized pair of plus fours, a checked flannel shirt, high boots and a campaign hat could make me. Albert was a little funnier because he was wearing a pair of white duck trousers encased in knee-length leggins. His nautical appearance was somewhat nullified by the presence of a large floppy straw hat on the back of his head. A corduroy hunting jacket alone suggested the general nature of Albert's intentions. There was a colored shirt also which I find it pleasanter not to write about.

"The foxes are going to have the laugh of their lives today," I remarked when I had acclimated myself to Albert. "They'll be too weak to run."

"Come," said Albert with dignity. "The hunt breakfast is on. There is drink."

"Let's abandon this incessant fox hunting," I suggested, "and make millions on the stage. We wouldn't have to do much, Albert. One look would drive 'em frantic."

"Later, perhaps," replied Albert a little moodily. "We have to go through with this fox hunt first. Come on."

I was introduced to a series of majors, doctors and judges. All men over thirty seemed automatically to come into a title. Whether they were merely hunt breakfast titles or not I never learned. There was one rotund colonel, authentic in every detail, and upon him was bestowed all the honor and glory due to his colorful record of violent and abrupt endings. He was the Colonel. Fat was this gentleman, fat, pompous and over-blooded, but a life-loving soul withal. In his youth he had been the life of all the local lynching parties, and now, in his declining years, he had acquired the reputation of an implacable hunter. He was wearing a Prince Albert coat and highly polished boots which lent the only touch of distinction to this nondescript gathering.

After being properly introduced to the ladies, all of whom seemed to be guarding some shameful secret the full significance of which they failed to grasp themselves, I was placed by the side of my hostess, and urged to drink. She subjected me to one swift scrutiny, then quickly dropped her eyes.

"Pardon me," she said in a strained voice. "I think I heard a door slam."

The next moment she rose hastily and walked unsteadily toward the house. With pained eyes I followed her retreating figure.

Down the line a lady showing no end of well turned southern legs as she sat on the grass was speaking in an excited voice and waving a cocktail glass in the air.

"What a lark," she proclaimed. "John's never so much as seen a fox and he can't stand the sight of horses. They give him a violent rash, do horses."

I turned and regarded my host inquiringly.

"Is he one of the initiates like myself at this ceremony?" I asked.

"Yes," he answered. "There are several others—lots of new faces, in fact. You won't be alone. Drink up."

A man on my right leaned confidentially over and made helpless, little motions with his hands.

"Pardon me," he said incredulously, "but do I understand we're actually going fox hunting?"

I told him that that was about the size of it.

"Fancy that," he observed musingly. "Of all things, fox hunting. Wonder where Mr. Green caught the beast. Haven't seen a fox in years. I'll ask him."

To my great delight he leaned over and made some more motions at Albert.

"Mr. Green," he whispered piercingly, "where in the world did you get this fox?"

"What fox?" exclaimed Albert in a startled voice, looking quickly about as if he feared a fox was creeping up behind him.

"You know," said the man mysteriously. "This fox we're supposed to hunt."

"Certainly," I put in. "The fox Henry's going to juggle together with several others."

"Who's Henry?" asked the man innocently.

"Why don't you know, Henry?" I replied in some amazement. "He's the greatest foxer in the state of Texas, that dog."

"Strange," muttered the man. "Don't know him—but I'm a stranger to these parts."

"We raise many of our foxes in England," Albert explained.

"And ruin them in Texas," said the stranger.

Albert's answer was cut short by a sudden shout winging across the lawn from the direction of the outhouses. I looked up and saw a negro, running with great concentration, coming in our direction. He was leaning so far over in his efforts to separate himself from some still unrevealed peril that he gave the impression of a six-day bicycle racer. Then something happened which I am sure must have come upon everybody as a complete surprise to put it mildly. Before our astonished eyes the negro was borne down and blotted out beneath an onrushing avalanche of dogs. The air was disturbed by eager yelpings and churned by innumerable jauntily waving tails. In another moment the hunt breakfast had been reduced to a shambles. One imperishable vision of our colonel staunchly defending a chunk of fried chicken was vouchsafed me. Then he, too, disappeared, emulating the negro, as the dogs danced giddily over his recumbent form. After that my impressions became somewhat clouded I remember a large dog neatly removing a sandwich from my fingers and breathing appreciatively in my face. Sandwiches seemed to be moving through the air like things of life. The once spotless table cloth was leaping weirdly under the stress of greedily searching muzzles. Figures of men and women as they rolled and struggled on the grass were caught in the most undignified, not to say compromising positions. The element of surprise was all in favor of the raiders. The famous hunt breakfast was theirs without a struggle. I remember hearing quite distinctly Mrs. Albert as if lost to decency, ironically cheering the pack on to still greater endeavors. From their utter disregard of all those little niceties of deportment that give life its subtle fragrance I decided that it had been many a long day since those dogs had enjoyed a square meal.

Then, above the din and the barking, the cries of the insulted and injured and—I regret to say—the shocking blasphemy of our colonel, my host, Albert, who should have been the master of this hunt, lifted up his voice in command.

"Grab sticks!" he shouted. "Grab anything and beat 'em off."

Then began a grim struggle, man facing defiant beast, for the honor and supremacy of the human race. We fought those dogs bitterly and oftentimes unfairly. For example, I saw one gentleman deliberately enticing one of the enemy to accept a peace offering of chicken—a delicious bit it looked—and then when the poor animal had been betrayed by its own greed this man, this southern gentleman, squared off and kicked the dog quite severely in the rump. Foot by foot the dogs yielded and were driven back in the direction whence they came. One inspired sportsman accelerated their departure by firing off a shotgun. This horrid noise entirely demoralized the dogs, all of whom must have been born gun shy. With yelps of nervous alarm they sheathed their once valiant tails and deployed in the direction of the barn.

Mrs. Albert was sitting calmly on the grass. Her husband was rushing from one guest to another, assuring everyone that everything was all right, and begging them not to let this slight interruption mar the pleasure of the hunt.

"Pleasure?" one forthright gentleman—obviously a novice—demanded indignantly. "How do you get that way? You mean the horror of the hunt."

"What's the matter with you?" Mrs. Albert asked defensively before I had opened my lips. "There's nothing unusual about this hunt breakfast. Only last week the dogs broke loose and one of the fresh things had the nerve to snatch a cocktail right out of my hand. Think of that."

I did. I looked steadily at Mrs. Albert's innocently upturned face and thought of that as well as of other things. This made me think of Albert, the last person in the world I wanted to think about at that moment.

IV

I was being introduced by Albert to the mount upon which I was to pursue foxes for the remainder of the day.

"This is Molly," he said with Jeffersonian simplicity. "Your horse."

It had to be my horse because most certainly no one else would have taken Molly as a gift. As I studied the disillusioned features of this venerable wreck I feared that she was going to take advantage of her sex and weep on my shoulder. Nevertheless, I mounted to her back and awaited with closed eyes the inevitable crash.

Molly braced herself, quivered along her keel, but managed to remain erect.

The lawn now became the scene of fresh activity. The colonel, still dazed, with the help of three strong men was being elevated to the top of his horse, an operation in which neither the colonel nor the horse seemed to be the least bit interested. Presently the sweating huntsmen were safely if not securely installed in their saddles while the women stood about and made unhelpful but irritating suggestions, as women always do and always will when men are striving to maintain their dignity in the face of overwhelming odds.

Once more the pack appeared. Its mood had now shifted from one of famished activity to satiated greed. Leisurely the hounds ambled across the lawn and slipped past us with many a furtive backward glance, as if expecting a sudden kick. Their respective rumps were guiltily shrunken. Once safely out of reach they broke into a run and speedily absorbed themselves into the landscape, several secretly amused negroes pretending to pursue them.

"Are you all ready?" cried Albert, holding up his hand. "If you are, let's go."

"Just a minute now," came the querulous voice of the stranger. "Go where, Mr. Green? I've gotten me up on the top of this dumb beast like you said but damned if I enjoy the prospect of jouncing all over the countryside on it without any idea where I'm going or when I'm coming back."

In the face of this reasonable question the hunting party fell into a depressed silence. Obviously many of its members were asking themselves the same thing. Albert rushed gamely into the breach.

"We go wherever the fox goes," he explained.

"What fox?" demanded the man.

"I don't know what fox," said Albert. "Just any fox—the fox we're after."

"What's this fox gone and done, Albert?" another unknown inquired mildly.

"He hasn't done anything," said my host.

"Then why are we after him?" continued the voice.

"Well, you can't very well have a fox hunt without some sort of fox, can you?" asked Albert bitterly. "It's all very simple. We just sit on our horses and go where the fox goes."

"If you think it's so simple sitting on this animated file," someone indignantly observed, "I'd like you to change places with me and let him chafe you for awhile. I'm two-thirds ruined already and we haven't even started yet."

"Let's hope this old fox goes to bed, then we can all do likewise," the weary stranger offered hopefully.

As the company straggled through the gate, a sudden cry of warning brought us to a stop. It seems that our colonel with the aid of a low-hanging limb had somehow managed to unhorse himself. Turning quickly, I caught a momentary glimpse of that stout gentleman descending earthward with terrific speed where he landed in a sitting posture and remained as if atrophied. Horses and riders alike gazed down at him with concentrated attention as if wondering why their colonel had taken it into his head to act in such a peculiar manner.

"What's the meaning of all this?" asked Albert, pushing his horse through the circle.

The colonel regarded him balefully.

"What the hell do you think it means?" he demanded in a high, thin voice. "That I'm playing mud pies? Young man, it means foul play. I was struck from behind."

"Well," said Albert at last, "we can't very well leave him sitting there like that all day. Get him back on his horse again and we'll make a fresh start."

The colonel accepted a drink and once more allowed himself to be heaved into the saddle, where he sat in stunned silence.

"I say, Mr. Green," a third stranger to Albert cried out, "What are we supposed to do with this fox once we catch him?"

"Which is very doubtful," the first one added.

Albert laughed with false heartiness. "Have your little joke,"

"It's no joke," said the other earnestly. "Swear to God I wouldn't know how to act with a real live fox."

"Cut off his brush," grated Albert.

"His what?" came the startled rejoinder in a shocked voice. "Oh, Mr. Green."

"You know as well as I do," replied Albert.

"Oh," exclaimed the other. "You don't like to talk about it. I think I know now."

Albert flushed furiously.

"Say, Mr. Green," asked a rider rather plaintively. "Why are you so mean to foxes, anyway? You certainly must hate 'em to do a thing to 'em—you know—like you said."

At this moment I reminded Albert that unless we looked for the dogs we might lose them forever, not that I greatly cared. A startled expression added to the unhappiness of his features. He held up a hand and listened.

"Now where do you reckon those dogs could have gotten themselves to?" he asked at last.

"Let's make it a dog hunt instead of a fox hunt," a bright young man suggested.

Albert winced, then suddenly his face cleared. From far down the road came an awful sound, the deep baying of a great hound. I had begun to doubt the existence of Henry, but now I changed my mind.

"Yonder's Henry!" exclaimed the delighted Albert with as much pride as if he were emitting all those terrible sounds himself. "Hear him!"

We did. Henry had a shocking voice.

"Glad I'm not a fox," someone piously observed. "I'm a'scared even to hunt with that dog loose."

"Henry's giving tongue," exclaimed Albert.

"Giving!" exclaimed the accurate rider. "Henry's doing heaps more than that. He's fairly tossing tongue away—lavishing tongue on the countryside."

When finally we found the dogs they were lying round a tree in various reposeful attitudes while they idly watched one of their members trying to get at a negro clinging to the topmost limb. This dog was beyond description. Canine obscenities gushed from its throat. Its fangs were bared and foam flecked its lips. Henry, without a doubt. Upon seeing Albert, the negro in the tree let out a yell.

"Fo' Gawd's sake, Mr. Albert, take dat dawg away or I'se a gone nigger."

Albert looked up at the negro, then transferred his attention to the frantic beast.

"Josh," he said at last, "that dog isn't Henry. Where do you suppose he came from?"

"I don't care who the hell he is," one of our little group complained, "if he doesn't stop making those awful noises I'll climb one of those trees myself."

"No, suh," responded Josh. "Dat dawg sho ain't Henry. Dat dawg's Fanny. Mr. Albert, Fanny's by way of being a bloodhound. We sort of invited her over last night just to fancy up the pack a bit."

"A charming piece of garnishing, Fanny," remarked a gentleman on my left.

"Well, Josh," said Albert wearily, "I reckon you'd better get Fanny home or she'll be treeing every damn nigger in the countryside and then we'll never get any foxes."

"Foxes?" I quietly inquired.

"Certainly," shot back Albert. "I said foxes. Henry must be looking for some now."

The subject was changed by a sudden groan from our colonel.

"Gentlemen," he announced, "I can stand it no longer. I fear I'm bleeding to death."

"Where?" demanded Albert, turning to cope with this new disaster.

The colonel seemed reluctant to take us into his confidence concerning the exact location of his mortal wound.

"I must have sat on my flask," he replied after some hesitation. "When I fell, you know. I've been sitting on the pieces ever since."

"My God," breathed Albert. "What next? Help the colonel down, some of you, and I'll see what I can do about it."

Our colonel and Albert, now assuming the role of glass picker, retired among the bushes with old fashioned southern modesty. Presently Albert reappeared.

"I am happy to announce," he said, "that the colonel's injuries were more demeaning to a gentleman of his high spirit than serious to his person. He has decided to continue with us. Let us hope and pray that this will be the last interruption. We must now find Henry, the leader of the pack."

An ironical cheer greeted this fine speech. The colonel was placed delicately on his horse. The negro attendants beat the dogs into a reluctant state of activity. Once more the hunt was in motion. For an hour or more we cantered along the roads pleasantly enough, stopping occasionally to let the pack catch up with us. The dogs were friendly, courteous and even playful. They seemed to nourish no grudge against us, but it was plain to see that no one had taken the trouble to tell them what it was all about. To the pack it was merely an outing—a casually informal affair.

"Just wait till they catch up with Henry," Albert kept assuring us. "Then just watch 'em go."

We did. From somewhere far down the road the earnest ravings of a mad dog were borne to us. Albert's face became radiant.

"Yonder's Henry!" he shouted. "Hear him!"

The dogs, exerting their last ounce of energy, broke into a run and sped down the road. Fresh hope returned to our hearts as we thundered after. Perhaps there might be something in this fox-hunting business after all. The pack was now in full cry. We rounded a curve and saw the dogs streaming across an open field in the direction of some woods. A large and elated rabbit was cutting insulting capers in their faces. Albert's own face looked a trifle dismayed.

"Shucks," he said, "that fool rabbit just crossed the fox's trail, but he won't put Henry off. Follow on."

Follow on we did, and in a short time crashed into the woods. Then consternation reigned. Close to my ear a shotgun suddenly exploded. It exploded very close to my ear.

"Moonshiners!" someone shouted, and the effect was electrifying.

From behind the most innocent looking trees bearded faces appeared. In a methodical manner the owners of these faces began to discharge lead into the ranks of the disorganized hunt. In an instant dogs, horses and men were fighting democratically together for mere survival. There was a great thrashing of branches and a complicated entangling of man and beast. The moonshiners seemingly had an inexhaustible supply of ammunition and a passionate desire to use it. I now saw the reasonableness of our clubs and guns, although our party used neither.

Personally, I sustained no loss other than Molly and a large quantity of breath. From the safety of a slight elevation I observed the component parts of the hunt break from the woods and dash across the field. Men who had known each other for years passed without the slightest sign of recognition, so occupied were they with their own thoughts. The field was dotted with horses, dogs and men, some of the men in their impatience even pushing horses out of their way. I felt that I was looking at an old English hunt-

ing print suddenly thrown into reverse. Some of those dogs, I
dare say, are still running.

The last to withdraw from the woods were our colonel, Albert
and my Molly. The colonel was leaning on Albert's arm. Molly
appeared to be trying to hold his other hand. I was joined by this
little group and with Albert's help put our colonel on to Molly.
He sat well forward and practiced soul stirring groans. Foxes would
have little to fear from our colonel for many days to come. Very
little was said. There was hardly anything either fit or safe to be
said unless we talked about the weather. Albert steadily refused
to meet my eyes.

After an interminable walk we at last approached the smooth
green lawn of my host's home. Several members of the hunt were
grouped round the rumpled tablecloth. They were looking down
sadly on a large inert body. Mrs. Albert was saying things. We
listened.

"Would you believe it?" she was saying. "Ever since you all got
out of sight he's been sleeping there just like a lamb. Must have
eaten too much hunt breakfast. Isn't he sweet?"

We, too, gazed down at the slumbering figure. The expression in
Albert's eyes was too terrible for man to behold. I felt inclined
to withdraw quietly—to leave him alone with his sorrow. The
figure, as if feeling our eyes upon it feebly attempted to raise its
head. Slumber overcame it. A gnawed chicken bone slipped from
its mouth as it drifted off to sleep. A tail moved with propitiatory
intentions. A gentle sigh fell upon the still evening air.

Then our colonel lifted up his voice.

"Yonder's Henry!" he howled, and there was a touch of mad·
ness in his eyes. "Hear him!" He paused, squared his shoulders
then confronted Albert.

The rest is silence . . .

I SAY IT'S FALSE!

By PARKE CUMMINGS

ALMOST ALL OF THE NEWSPAPERS I READ, AND A GOOD MANY OF THE magazines, contain information tests, and I am never the one to pass these up. And I take pride in reporting that on those questions of the true-or-false variety I am nothing short of a bearcat. I practically never miss.

It isn't that I'm well-informed or smart; it's simply that, from study, I've evolved an almost foolproof system, one that is simplicity itself.

If I am asked to determine the truth or the falsity of any commonly accepted generality, any statement that seems reasonable and sensible, I simply say "False!" and I'm invariably right.

I never bother to study the question on its merits. That's a waste of time, and it may prompt me to go wrong. These fellows who make up the questions seem to have a knack of picking holes in all the established beliefs of humanity. "Blondes are more emotional than brunettes." False, of course. "Cats can see in the dark." We've all been brought up to believe that they can, so the statement is obviously wrong. "Women are worse drivers than men." You'd think they are, so obviously they aren't. See how simple it is?

I have taken so many of these tests, that I do them in my sleep now. In my mind I see the questions, the answers (always "false," remember), and the detailed explanations of how mankind happened to become seized with the particular delusion that is now being exploded before my eyes. A sample true-or-false test, as my impressions form it, runs about like this:

Q: *Horses have four legs. True or false?*

A: False! Horses have three legs. Scientific tests have determined that the so-called left fore-"leg" of a horse is not a leg at all. Study of its cellular structure shows that it is in reality merely an extension of the equine breastbone, and hence cannot qualify technically as being a leg. The popular belief that horses have four legs accordingly has no basis in scientific fact.

Q: Washington was the first president of the United States. True or false?

A: False! There have never been any presidents of the United States. In the Federal Convention of 1783, a man named Scopesby was assigned to incorporate provisions for the election of a president into the Constitution, but he was suddenly stricken with appenditicis, and, without the consent of the assembly, turned the task over to a compatriot, John Wade. It was Wade who unconstitutionally worked up the provisions which thereby have no legal standing whatsoever. The error still persists to this day, and the American populace still believes that the men it elects to office are presidents in good constitutional standing.

Q: Blind people cannot see. True or false?

A: False! Blind people *can* see. Careful study of the derivation of the word "see" reveals that it springs from the old Anglo-Saxon word *se* (Dutch: *ze*) which means, as nearly as it can be translated: "to get a general hazy idea of things." It is obvious that the impressions that blind people get of their surroundings either by touch and smell or from the information relayed to them by people with normal eyesight, qualify under this definition.

Q: You can sleep better in a comfortable bed than on a hard floor. True or false?

A: False as usual! Recent tests at the University of Chicago revealed the opposite. Ten subjects slept in comfortable beds for seven nights after which they were assigned various tasks. They were then ordered to sleep on hardwood floors for another period of seven nights. There were complaints for the first two nights, but after that, every subject slept like a baby. Moreover, the subjects accomplished nothing unusual after sleeping on beds, but after the floor tests, here is what the group did: Wrote two symphonies. Placed in the semi-finals of the intercollegiate boxing tournament. Discovered a cure for whooping cough. Painted a picture which compared favorably with the *Mona Lisa.* Cornered U. S. Steel. Received a total of 742 proposals of marriage. The explanation lies in the fact that the fabular muscles (the ones that make people accomplish unusual things) are given beneficial stimulation by contact with hard materials where lying in soft beds simply tends to atrophy them.

Q: Fat people weigh more than thin people. How about it?

A: Not on your life! All wrong as usual. Fat people have greater volume than thin people, and this extra volume causes more air resistance to their susceptibility to gravity. In other words, fat people only *appear* to weigh more than thin people because our present-day scales are not correctly graduated to deduct properly for this additional air-resistance. If they were, it would be found that all people weigh exactly the same.

Q: Dogs cannot climb trees. True or false?

A:False! All dogs are perfectly capable of climbing trees. The reason they do not do so is because of an element in the bark of trees (scennic acid) which is injurious to their feet. If it were not for that, as tests with trees from which that acid has been removed prove, dogs would climb trees just as eagerly as cats.

Q: It is colder in winter than in summer. True or false?

A: Not on your tintype! The common custom of wearing heavy clothing in wintertime has caused this popular misconception. Heavy clothing impedes the circulation and hence leads to the erroneous belief that one is "cold." The so-called "evidence" of the thermometer also adds to the misconception. Actually the mercury in thermometers does not sink lower on account of the colder weather but because there is a different chemical make-up in the air during the winter season. The proof of this whole matter lies in the fact that certain animals that do not wear binding clothes and never look at thermometers, get along all right.

Q: Skunks smell terrible. True or false?

A: False! It is not the skunk that smells terrible, but the air surrounding him. Therefore skunks do *not* smell terrible.

Q: Fish suffocate if they are removed from water. How about it?

A: No sir! This delusion belongs strictly in the realm of folklore and superstition. Fish, it is true, die when taken out of their native element, but they only *appear* to suffocate. Actually the reason for their demise is due to the fact that fish cannot stand the intense light that pervades the atmosphere. Their eyes suffer so severely from it, that they die for this reason.

Q: Wellington defeated Napoleon at the Battle of Waterloo. True or false?

A: False! Neither of them was at the scene of battle, recently-disclosed records prove. Napoleon was killed in the retreat from Moscow, and a French sergeant named Duprois, who resembled him closely, was chosen to take command of the armies so that the enemy should never become aware of the truth. As for Wellington, documentary evidence proves that he was on leave of absence in England at the time.

Q: *Two and two are four. Yes or no?*

A: No! Careful study of history shows that prior to 1363, the word "four" was used to connote the number currently known as "five." A monk, named Groschius, in adding a simple sum, inadvertently put down "five" as the total of three added to two, and future scholars who got hold of his work moved the number "four" back a notch. The error was not discovered until recently.

Q: *New York is north of Miami. True or false?*

A: False. Medieval map makers, unaware that the world is round, started drawing their maps upside down, and all subsequent mapmakers followed them. The terms "North" and "South" were first invented by Askaran, an Egyptian philosopher, and careful reading of his treatise, *Boundaries of the Earth;* will convince anybody that he intended North to be what we now consider South, and vice versa. Hence, in the only true sense, New York is *South* of Miami.

Q: *It is better to be healthy than sick. Is that right?*

A: It *is* not. On the contrary, it is better to be sick than healthy. "Healthy," correctly defined, means to be without any ailments whatsoever. This would even mean being devoid of such common physiological symptoms as aging through the process of time, running low on energy due to exercise, suffering brain-fatigue or sleepiness from being awake, etc., etc. Thus, no living mechanism can exist without suffering ailments of one sort or another, and the only truly "healthy" person is a dead one. What we *really* mean is that it is better to be sick than to be *very* sick.

Q: *It is lighter in the daytime than at night. True or false?*

A: False. A moment's thought should convince us that all the light we get on this planet comes from the sun. The sun gives just as much light all the time—at night just as much as in the daytime. It is really just as light at night, accordingly, but we just don't see it.

Q: *Ducks like the water. How about it?*

A: Not a bit of it. This is another example of the common habit of arriving at foolish beliefs through improper observation and faulty inferences. The fact that ducks are frequently seen in water has led to this delusion. Laboratory experiments have disclosed the fact that ducks don't like *anything*, and that they go in the water purely to get away from land which they dislike even more intensely than water. This disclosure has led some scientists to believe the duck's lack of sympathy with his surroundings. (*her* surroundings, to be accurate) will lead to her extinction in another century or two. And the drake's also.

Q: Vienna is the capital of Austria. True or false?

A: Oh, let's not go into *that* again.

LITTLE AUGIE AND THE DAVIS CUP

By ROBERT H. BUCKNER

EVERY SUNDAY AFTERNOON FROM THREE UNTIL FIVE O'CLOCK throughout the summer of '32, Monsieur Bondidier, Frank Beals and myself, played tennis at the Peugeot factory. The courts, which are on the roof, command a grand view of the Seine, the Isle des Cygnes and the Eiffel Tower. Here even on the sultriest day in August there was a light breeze from the Bois, and after our game the three of us would sit in the shade of the toy pavilion, talking and rattling the ice in the tall glasses.

In most matters we three were as different as sunrise, noon and evening, but we did have in common a love for tennis. Beals, of course, had been born to the game, and played it with the most discouraging skill and nonchalance. For years he had served at Auteuil as an official in the Davis Cup matches, and he knew everything and everybody connected with the sport, for sooner or later all the international players dropped into his famous bar in the Rue Castiglione, where he presided as the undisputed umpire for two grinny negro waiters, Slew-foot and Sam, whom he had rescued from a stranded jazz-band.

Our companion, M. August Felix Xupery Bondidier (*Little Augie* to Beals), was short and fat, with a moustache far less mature than his wife's. Really, he resembled nothing on earth so closely as one of the butterballs from his own kitchen, to which a faint strand of hair had become accidentally atttached. He had, so far as we could ever discover, only two passions in life—food and tennis. The first he had inherited and naturally from a Lyonnaise father, and the second he had acquired recently from myself and Beals. In his zeal he had once attempted to combine the two in a most amazing dish of his own invention, which consisted of boiled potatoes served upon a network of spaghetti in an oval platter, and which he called *pommes de terre au tennis*.

As you know, every good Frenchman must have some definite

194

objective for his years of retirement, and the twin goals of Monsieur Bondidier's life were, to perfect the cuisine of his neat little hotel in the Rue d'Anjou, and to become a member of the exclusive sporting set at the Pistolet Club. He said as much often, brightly and frankly.

Frank Beals and I spoke only a fair French and *Little Augie's* English consisted of only six words—*yes, so sorry and come back again*—so that we depended largely in our conversations upon the odd pictures we drew on the backs of envelopes and passed around amid shouts of laughter. It was one of these pictures (and I still have it), idly sketched by Beals on a Sunday that August, which began the whole farce; a business which, before it was over, had upset the sacred sanctum of the Pistolet Club more than anything since the Dreyfus Affair.

This drawing, like all of them, was an extraordinary creation. It depicted a huge bowl, the two handles of which were clutched by naked men with feathers in their hair. Frank told me later that he had meant them to represent the Spirits of Lafayette and Light Wines, but unfortunately he gave another explanation at the time. At any rate, Bondidier took the envelope, turned it around and gazed at it for a while with an uncertain smile.

"Ah, c'est une salade Americaine, n'est ce pas?" he asked.

I took a look, hitched up my verbs and vowels and hazarded a guess. "No, that's no salad bowl," I replied. "Why, it's that old hokum bucket, The Davis Cup!"

This meant practically nothing to M. Bondidier. So far as he knew, tennis was a game which Beals and I might have invented. We proceeded to explain about the Cup, and suggested to him that he accompany us to Auteuil to watch the final-round matches between France and America.

Little Augie's round face flushed with sudden pleasure. But why not? He would go with us, his very good friends. We would take a lunch perhaps, and make it an occasion, a *peeknic*! So the French were the champions of the tennis? That was interesting, indeed a great honor. And this salad bowl it was *theirs*, eh? Service for the service, wasn't it? And Bondidier chuckled at his pun. He retrieved the drawing and looked at it again with an enlightened expression which was shadowed however by a single flicker of uncertainty.

The two gentlemen, he inquired, pointing with a stubby fore-finger, they were without doubt les messieurs Davis, no?

I said I hardly thought so, and looked across at Frank. The peculiar glint of fiendish glee in his eyes and in the arched eyebrow gave me a sudden cold sweat, for I knew that look of old, and what it meant. Before I could stop him he had pulled his chair closer to Bondidier and reached for the drawing. He looked all around us suspiciously, hesitated a moment, and then, leaning forward, whispered confidentially:

"You are our good friend, are you not, monsieur?"

Bondidier nodded vigorously.

"Then I can speak freely," Frank continued, and pointed at the envelope. "These two men are *not* les messieurs Davis. They are the talk of the entire tennis underworld. *They are, monsieur, the true Men of Mystery!* Everywhere, on every tongue, one meets this question: 'Who are they and where do they practice?'"

Bondidier's eyes were black beads of excitement, for he thrived upon gossip of any sort, and mystery was his special dish.

"Don't ask me who they are," Frank warned him with upraised finger. "I only know their names and that they are really red Indians from the Arizona desert, trained in secret by 'le Beeg Bill' himself, and that they are the secret stars of the American team."

Little Augie's mouth was now a funnel of astonishment upon which his twig of moustache teetered nervously.

"Les Indiens *rouge!*" he whispered in horror.

"Red as radishes!" I chimed in, plunging headforemost into the crime. "I have seen them myself, August, once when I drove out from New York to Arizona for the week-end. *Caphars!* What speed! What ferocity! What craftiness! If it were really these two . . ." I shrugged and smiled wanly.

Bondidier was fairly bouncing in his chair. He set his glass upon the iron table with a bang, so that he might have both hands free. "But this is terrible! It is *incredible!*" he cried. "The journals the authorities, the Pistolet, do they not know this thing? Are they then deaf and blind?"

Beals flicked a speck of dust from his blazer and smiled indulgently. "Ah, *there* you have it. They do not know, those worthies. If they did, then it would be no secret. It will be one rarc treat, Monsieur Bondidier, to watch their faces when *Sock-in-the-*

Wash and *Lob-in-the-Alley* run out on the courts, screaming their Navajo war-cry. That is something we will not want to miss, eh?"

This was pure, unadulterated torture, and my toes curled in their sneakers for *Little Augie*. His fingers drummed a swift tattoo upon the chair-arms and in his eyes was the look which Saint Joan must have worn before Orleans, and Papa Joffre at the Marne.

"Rouge . . . Messieurs Soak-eny-Warsh et Lowb-eny-Yallee . . ." he repeated, as if memorizing the words. He jumped up, bowed to us both, murmured his *plaisirs* and hurried off to the dressing-room.

I pretended to be looking for my coat until Bondidier was well out of sight, and when I straightened up there was Beals chuckling into his glass with a most unholy glee.

"Look here, Frank," I said seriously. "You can't go through with it. The fellow's ready for the Sante now!"

"Sure I can. Why not?" he replied. "Say, I even know where I can dig up two Injuns—Slew-foot and Sam! Though how I can spring 'em on him is something you'll have to figure out. Son, this is going to be *rich*, colossal! Come on, grab your racket."

"They ought to slap you into jail for this," I grinned.

"We've certainly started something," he admitted generously. "And speaking of jails, if your *Little Augie* doesn't have the whole Surete on the trail by midnight I'll stand you my lone bottle of '12 Verzenay—in the silver bucket."

Back at the hotel I saw nothing of my host for several days. In fact, it was not until Friday that he appeared at all during the waking hours of his guests—extraordinary behavior for a man of his hospitable nature. Every morning when I descended for breakfast Madame Bondidier, whose figure was modelled after a Benedictine bottle, smiled politely and spoke, though there was a vaguely distrustful glint in her sharp gray eyes. In the evenings after dinner I either retired to my room to read or else went out to visit friends, so that I had no idea when M. Bondidier returned or where he had been.

On Friday morning while I was shaving and listening with one ear to the chefs' discussion of a fish in the courtyard below, there came a knock at my door, and I opened to Bondidier himself. His usually cheery face, of the type rounded by nature and the Rhone sun for laughter, had that peaked look of a man's who had been up all night for a week with a sick relative. He barely answered my greeting and sat heavily upon the bed with a deep sigh of resignation and despair.

"Well, my old one," I began, "you have failed us recently."

His eyes rolled to meet mine with a burden of utter misery. "Yes, I know," he replied. "I have failed France also."

I turned back from the mirror and pointed my razor at him. "*You*, Bondidier, fail France! Why, in all Paris there is no fiercer patriot!"

He nodded faintly in agreement, and there was a momentary flicker in his eyes. "Nevertheless," he said, "I have damn few balls of fire to spit now."

I drew myself up to full height and, mustering as much dignity as a face-towel and a pair of shorts could support, I said in a deep voice. "Tell me, Bondidier, what has happened?"

He studied the tips of his shoes for a moment, then spread his hands and looked up at me.

"I will tell you everything, monsieur, for anyway now it is too late. I have done my best, but I have failed. It cannot be helped. . . . You remember the red Indians, the secret Americans about whom you and M. Beals spoke last Sunday?"

I sat down in relief and covered a grin with the towel.

"I cannot find them!" he continued heatedly. "*We* cannot find them! The Pistolet cannot find them! We have scoured Paris from Neuilly to Pantin, from Passy to the Porte de Vitry, but without effect. Hindus we have found, yes. And some few Senegalese. But Indians?—not so much as one red hair!"

"The Pistolet!" I exclaimed. "You went to *them*?"

Bondidier flushed and looked away. "You do not blame me, my friend? Surely you would have done as much for your country. Yes, I went to them with the whole story. 'Alors, we must find them!' they cried. 'Alors, it is for France!' I said. 'Alors, you shall lead the search!' they said. And so I did. But—" and he dropped his voice to a dramatic whisper, "in going to them I risked all my pride, my business, even my ——"

"Scalp!" I supplied, in the same voice "Ah, Bondidier, you are indeed a brave man."

"I am a Frenchman," he answered simply.

We bowed.

"And the gentlemen at the Pistolet, they were amazed, eh?"

"They were undone completely," he replied with new enthusiasm. "I had to repeat the story three times; once for Count Clary himself, once for M. Henri Bourdelle, and again for M. Georges d'Arcy." The name of his gods rolled upon *Little Augie's* tongue in a bath of ecstacy. "We decided to tell no one, but to solve the mystery for the further glory of the Pistolet, and to submit a complete report of the Indian technique to the French Tennis Federation before next Tuesday's match. We then divided all Paris into eight parts and began the search. Every club, every court, every *hotel* . . . for four days we have searched and what have we found? *Nothing*, precisely and exactly." He hesitated, cocked his head to one side, and continued archly: "I wonder really if they *are* in Paris?"

I turned my back abruptly and lathered, for a while in silence. "I have seen them," I said finally.

Bondidier scrambled to his feet and clasped both hands to his breast. "Helas for France!" he cried. "Then it is true! I have failed!"

"Somebody wins, somebody loses," I said brightly. "Anyway, you are not disgraced."

"At the Pistolet," replied *Little Augie* slowly, "I am worse than disgraced. I am just a 'gorgonzola detective,' and perhaps even a liar. My chances of membership now are—*pfft*" and he snapped a pair of pudgy fingers.

Just at that exact second The Idea popped into my head, the plan whereby Beals and I might have a little harmless fun and also make up to Bondidier for his week of work and worry.

"Come now, August," I said, placing a hand on his shoulder. "Show yourself a good loser and I will have Monsieur Beals bring Messieurs *Sock-in-the-Wash* and *Lob-in-the-Alley* here for dinner Monday, so that you may meet them."

He sat forward suddenly, his eyes blinking. "Here to the hotel?"

"But yes. Why not? Are we not all sportsmen, brothers in the racquet? You, Bondidier, will be the one host whom they shall honor with their presence."

"And I shall serve the *pommes de terre au tennis!*" he exclaimed.

"With the strings," I added.

"*With the strings!*" he cried, and shot through the doorway.

It is for just such occasions as this that Beals lives. When finally

I found him poring over accounts in the room behind his bar and told him the news he slammed close the ledger and gave two shouts —one for pure joy, the other for Slew-foot and Sam. Almost instantly the two black boys shuffled in and stood nervously grinning and twisting their aprons while Frank handed them enough of the facts. Their shiny faces were two perfect masks of misgivings, and I knew it was a doubt well-founded upon past escapades, but they had no choice. In the chest under his bed Frank kept a certain brass cornet and a less certain nickel trombone, twin swords of Damocles over those ebony heads. It was a plain case of be Indians or else . . .

On Monday from the crack of dawn our little hotel was a storm-center of furious activity. At dinner the regular guests were rushed politely but firmly through their meal, and the space cleared for the elaborate table set for five with the best of the Bondidier family silver, linen and glassware. When all else was to his taste, *Little Augie* dragged out a stepladder and proceeded to drape the flags of France and America in a funereal bow over the entrance to the dining-room. As the final artistic touch he tacked above the center of the bow his third-best racquet, as completely unstrung as himself.

Sharply at eight the taxi arrived and disgorged the guests of dishonor. Frank was in tails and shook hands with much dignity, but Sam and Slew-foot I barely recognized, for they were truly works of art. Their faces had been rouged to a tone somewhere between a mouldy copper and the color of a sick salmon's belly, and around their necks hung several strings of bright dime-store beads. They had both been terrified into the solemnity of owls, and neither showed me the slightest sign of recognition. In appropriate Indian file we trouped through the lobby to our table, with Bondidier trotting fussily around and in front of us, filled with pride and gurgling grunts.

Now in my time I have witnessed some weird meals and survived the shocks of many an odd table-mate, from Neo-Soofist lady poets to amateur cannibals, but never have I spilt salt at a dinner quite like this one. Certainly nobody could deny its success. M. Bondidier tucked a colossal napkin under his chin, carved, mixed the salad, told stories and poured the champagne in a state of purest bliss. Probably nowhere in France on that evening was there a happier man. He was radiant, He was brilliant. And if he burped a bit along towards the coffee it was due more to an excess of eclat than of eclairs.

The high point of the dinner was, of course, the *pommes de terre au tennis*, served in a great platter by the head chef. There was one awkward moment when Sam exclaimed, at the sight of the dish: "Gawd, Cap'n Frank, wha's '*at*?" Beals arose to the occasion however with a free translation: "Monsieur *Sock-in-the-Wash* is overcome with emotion; he says that as a work of art it can be compared only to a Navajo rug." Whereupon *Little Augie* wriggled in delight as he received the dish with loving hands, served us two balls apiece and a spoonful of string.

The best key to the precise mood of the party lies perhaps in a sample of our table-talk. Unfortunately, only snatches of it occur to my memory, but it went along these lines.

Frank (from the corner of his mouth, to the Navajos): "Say something, you two; say *anything*!"

Slew-foot: "B-boy, he sho' do know how to th'ow a party!"

Frank (smilingly to Bondidier): "Monsieur *Lob-in-the-Alley* hopes that some day you can visit the reservation. He wishes to decorate you with the order of the Ring-Tailed Howler of the Panhandle, Second Class."

Bondidier: "Echanté! Avec plaisir!" And *Little Augie* stood up, bowed, sat down and poured Slew-foot another bumper of Pol Roger.

By midnight we were all five comfortably tight and mutually delighted. Bondidier toasted us with a long rambling speech in which comments upon Columbus, Camembert, tennis and General Pershing mixed in glorious confusion; and Frank I responded in the same mood, even adding Free Silver and the Monroe Doctrine as final fillips of international amity. But it was Slew-foot and Sam who carried off the honors of the evening by rendering with intense emotion upon combs and tissuepaper *My Man, Louisville Lou* and *Come to Me, You Beautiful Thing*. "Old tribal chants," Frank explained in a whisper to our host.

It was not until the last great chieftain had been poured into the taxi and *Little Augie* and I stood there on the sidewalk of the quiet, deserted street that I realized fully the charming simplicity which was the fellow's strength, and I felt a sudden uneasiness in the lower chest which might well have been a twinging conscience.

Hadn't we perhaps put him through one hoop too many? We had given him a week of utter anguish and lost him his slim chance for the Pistolet Club, but in spite of all this his spirits remained undaunted. Somehow, someday, I vowed as I turned into bed, we would have to make it up to him; an opportunity which, luckily, came sooner than I had any reason to expect.

The following afternoon we arrived at Auteuil with the tickets and a small picnic basket. Bondidier made a valiant effort to be cheerful, but the sight of the crowds streaming into the stadium obviously depressed him with a renewed sense of his "failure." I was frankly worried as to how the rather delicate question of the missing Navajos would be met, but I put full faith in Frank Beals' ingenuity, and sure enough, when we met him at the entrance to the south stands his usually pleasant expression was replaced by one of worry and seriousness, almost pain.

"It's all up. We're licked," he said. "The story's all around that *Sock-in-the-Wash* and *Lob-in-the-Alley* are out. Sudden attack of acute indigestion and they're both flat on their backs, with lumps in their gullets like . . . well, like *tennis balls*, exactly!"

Bondidier's eyes opened wide, and he set the basket upon the ground. "Indigestion?" he asked in a rising contralto. "They cannot play?"

Frank nodded, looking him squarely in the eyes, while I stood by speechless with admiration and relief.

"I wonder . . . could it *possibly* have been those *pommes de terre au tennis*?" Frank mused aloud, stroking his infernal cheek.

Little Augie quivered erect, his every Latin ligament twitching in indignation. "But no!" he cried. "The *pommes de terre au tennis*? That is hardly possible! I ate two, you ate two, and *you* Monsieur Beals, ate six . . . strings and all, and yet here we are. Voila!"

"Well whatever it was," Frank replied, "it certainly saved old France's neck. O God, O Montreal, O Navajos!" and he turned away, his shoulders slouched like the Second Grave-digger's, and one hand clasped Duse-like to his heaving chest.

Bondidier puzzled at that deceitful back until it rounded a corner, then he picked up his basket, looked at me and shrugged. "Cuckoo," he observed darkly, while we mounted the steps.

Just as we stepped through the south portal into the sun-flooded square, an elderly distinguished gentleman, dashing madly along with his white "official's" badge flapping at his shoulder, bumped full-force into August and spun him around until the lunch basket stood out at arm's length, like the airplane-swings at the fair.

The two little Frenchmen, recovering their winds and balances at the same time, stood facing each other like a pair of game-cocks until a slow glow of recognition spread over their faces.

Then the stranger stepped forward until his grand moustache bristled within inches of *Little Augie's* modest wisp.

"Head of a Swiss cabbage!" he exploded. "You and your 'red Indians'! *Pooh!* and a *Bah!* So . . . where are they, then?"

"Count Clary . . ." Bondidier gaped for a second at his god of the Pistolet before he snapped his heels together, bowed, and, moving closer, stood on his toes to whisper into the other's ear.

I was rooted to the spot. Now Bondidier's back was to me, and Count Clary's eyes, staring directly ahead of him, fixed me through as he listened to my companion in rapt attention. Finally he nodded slowly, then rapidly, until finally he turned and kissed Bondidier on both cheeks; after which extraordinary behavior he dashed back through the gate by which he had entered.

Little Augie stood there, basket in hand, the other clenched tight, his eyes closed and his snubby nose gently quirking. I had to shake him before he would move.

"August," I said in real alarm, "what did you tell Count Clary? About the . . ."

He nodded, his eyes still blissfully shut.

"About the . . . gullet lumps?" I finally managed.

The near eye opened and surveyed me coolly.

"What lumps?" he asked, with immense dignity. "You do not, by any chance, refer to my *pommes de terre au tennis*? 'Lumps' indeed!"

KEEPING COOL AT CONNEAUT

By Paul Gallico

WE HAD COME TO CONNEAUT LAKE PARK, PENNSYLVANIA, IN THE
wake of a terrible June heat wave and on the heels of the then
heavyweight champion of the world, Max Schmeling. Max had
set up his training camp on the shores of Lake Conneaut, and was
preparing to defend his title against Young Stribling in Cleveland.
A group of sports writers, boxing experts and columnists found
ourselves living in one end of the rambling, three-story wooden
hotel that sprawled truculently between the shores of the Lake
and the fringes of a frowsy and ramshackle amusement park.

The hotel had all of the inconveniences of a cheap summer resort, including tissue paper walls, bad service and cold running
water. Two rambling wings stretched out from a central lobby.
The corridors were cavernous, the sitting rooms that opened off
them musty and depressing, the "crystal ball room" a tawdry barn,
and the rooms that led from them at the end of the wings, dark
and hot.

When we arrived at Conneaut, the Veterans of Foreign Wars
were still in convention. They overflowed the resort and cluttered
up the hotel. Sleep was impossible. The temperature stood around
102 and the noise of nocturnal parading, not only inside the hotel,
but from all quarters of the town, was unrelenting.

There was nothing for us to do but seek company in misery,
gather in one of the crowd's room, and sit up all night drinking
warm beer. There were about five of us. Sometimes we could persuade Edgar, the bellhop, to make an excursion for ice. Edgar had
to time his trips to avoid the V. F. W., who took it away from
him. When we got the ice we put it inside the beer. It was too
precious to wrap around the bottles. The monotonous blare of the
trumpets burst around the corner again. Bra! Bra! Bra-bra-bra!

"God God," moaned the man from the *Times-Eagle*. "How long
is this going to last? I gotta get some sleep. How long are these

bastards booked up for?" He glared at Edgar, who had just slipped inside with another pitcher, locking the door behind him.

"Three days, mister," said Edgar. "How long you stayin' here?"

"July 2nd," said the man from the *Times-Eagle*. "It might as well be the rest of my life. Can't something be done about that? Get hold of the manager."

Edgar sniggered. "You ain't seen nuthin' yet," he said—"Wait 'til the undertakers gits in next week. Nobody ever gets to bed at all. Boy, they're bad."

"The what?" said Curley, spilling his beer on the bed.

"The undertakers," repeated Edgar, showing his gums. "They're booked in here next week. Boy, that's something. Wait 'til *them* guys get drunk and take to carrying on. I guess you'll all be here yet?

"Boy, that'll be something. Wait 'til they all get rolling around in their own coffins. It scares you awhile 'til you get used to it. See a guy sittin' up in a coffin hollerin' to beat all get out. It scared me, first time."

"Good God," said Curley, "do you mean to say they bring *coffins* into this joint? I thought this was a summer hotel!"

"That ain't all," Edgar said, eyeing a bottle of beer. Somebody handed it to him and when he uncapped it it spurted over his chest. He got his mouth on the neck, and went pop-eyed for a few moments, drinking. "They sure do get drunk. One year they rolled a feller dead drunk in a big iron coffin down the hall and she took off'n to the left and lit into a parlor where they had a lot of them bottles of colored embalming stuff standing up on tables, and right kersmack into 'em and they all busted and ran all over the feller and he wakes up with one of them wax ears they use to fix up corpses in his hand and thinks he's killed. Boy, that stuff in the bottles sure does stink."

"Do you mean to tell me," said the man from the *Times-Eagle*, "that for the next week I am to live in the midst of a mortuary exhibit? Why they can't do that in a place like this."

"They come in every year," Edgar insisted. "I guess this place needs the money. You wait and see. They fix it up real nice. What the hell, when they're all in here there ain't much room for anybody else. Boy, them undertakers are just like a lot of kids, no kiddin'. There was a feller last year got knockin' the necks off some of the bottles of stuff they was exhibiting—and drinking the stuff, and I guess he got pretty sick. I guess they thought he was gonna die. So they was talkin' about what a bang up job they would do on him if he did die."

"What?" said the man from the *Sun-Herald*, "right here in the hotel?"

"Oh God," said Curley.

The parade drew near again. "Bra! Bra! Bra-bra-bra!"

The mortuary exhibits set up to tempt the convening undertakers began with a row of caskets in one corner of the dining hall. From there the exhibits spread through the lobby, down the hallway through the reception rooms, downstairs into the night club and out onto the verandah overflowing upon the lawn surrounding the hotel. Here, eight or nine sparkling and immaculate hearses were collected in eager poses, their rear or side doors yawning hopefully.

At lunch the waitress who brought our order hesitated for a moment as she passed a bronze casket. The casket had fluted columns topped with scrolls and graceful, hand-tooled handles. The lid was thrown back temptingly to show the quilted lilac satin interior. She looked at it for a few seconds and then brought the tray over and set it down. She wasn't bad looking. The boys watched her as she bent over the food.

"Picked yours out yet, baby?" inquired Curley. "That's our Al Capone model. I think you'd take about a Number 3. May we show you our Thursday specials on the second floor?"

"Boy," said the waitress and began slinging dishes onto the table, "ain't that some kimono? I wisht I could spend one night in a bed like that. Them beds they give upstairs is awful. I ain't had a night's sleep yet. I betcha it would even be cool. Was yours the fish, sir?"

"You eat that fish in weather like this, Curley, my boy, and you'll be picking one out," said Dan, who was covering for a Cleveland paper.

"Go ahead," advised the man from the *Times-Eagle*, "Osmotone will make you look natural again. I think you'd take about a Number 4 skin bleach. I was talking to an undertaker from Wilkes-

Barre last night, and he told me that he got some very good results with ptomaine cases."

"There he is in the doorway now, waitin' for you, Curley," suggested Lawson of the *Post*.

A stout, jolly looking fellow stood perspiring in the entrance to the dining room. He looked us over, and measured us, automatically. We were beginning to get used to that.

"As a consequence of using Osmotone," droned the *Times-Eagle* man, who had stolen a book on embalming from one of the exhibits, "the complexion shows precisely as in life."

"Oh, Jesus," said Curley, and pushed the fish away from him.

"I don't blame you," said the waitress. "It don't look very good. Wanna try the barbecued ham?"

"Three parts Osmotone with a dash of skin bleach is very fine on barbecued ham," continued the *Times-Eagle* man, cheerfully.

In the first parlor opening off the lobby, the cosmetic displays were pyramided on tables against a tasteful background of potted palms, and rubber flowers. All the paraphernalia for the last makeup.

On the center table in a glass-covered blue velvet lined box, rested the Derma-Surgery outfit, with the white wax contents listed on a white card—12 ears, 6 noses, 2 masks, 1 extra cake molding wax, 1 bottle blendine, 4 tubes Creme de Paris cosmetic enamel, 1 jar ruby red for the lips, 1 tinting brush, 2 powder brushes, 2 cans silk face powder, 7 shades hair for scalp, mustache and eyebrows, 1 set embalmer's flesh tints, 4 nickel plated plastic instruments, 1 bottle Fleshine, eye brow pencils, 1 tube lid lip for cementing hair. Two white face masks lay in separate compartments, and around them the ears and noses were alternated in a pleasing design. $25.00 complete.

"For God's sake," said Curley, shoving his hands deep in his pockets, "what the hell is *that* for?"

"Eh?" said the salesman in charge. He came over to the table mopping his brow with a blue handkerchief. He was a tall, sallow man with large bony hands. His coat, vest, collar and tie were off and the shirt was turned in at the neckband. "Them? My boy, was you ever in a real serious accident, because if you was you wouldn't ask. You get smashed up serious in a automobile and get brought home with a nose or an ear missin', your family don't want to see you that way, do they?"

"The man's right, Curley," said Lawson—"this number three nose is just about your style if you ever get smashed up serious."

"You boys ain't in the trade, are you? Like to demonstrate our line if you are."

"You know what I hope," said Curley, as we wandered into the writing room which had been turned into a clothing store, "I hope that Schmeling gets his brains knocked out for training in a place like this."

There was a woman in charge of a display of burial clothing which hung dispiritedly on racks as though the garments themselves knew that no living form would ever fill them. She was a stout, hot female with an enormous bust. She wore a white dress that looked like some of the numbers on the rack. She was fanning herself with a copy of *The Casket and Sunnyside*. She said, "Can I show you anything?" but made no attempt to get up from the rocker in which she sat. Nobody said anything.

"We got real classy styles this year," she said, waving the magazine in front of her broad face. "Folks want class nowadays. We have to keep up with the styles. Mosta this stuff comes from Chicago. You can looka those dresses. Some of them are the very latest styles."

"Looka the size of those dogs," said Dan, pointing to a row of slippers. "Must be all western trade."

The woman blew some stray hairs off her face by jutting out her lower lip. She nodded. "A lotta times the feet swells," she said. "Those are all the latest styles. It don't show when they're on. You boys going to the dance later?"

The portable organ in the exhibit in the grill room on the floor below began to whine *Nearer My God to Thee* again. It had been playing that tune off and on all day long. Curley fidgetted and even Lawson looked nervous. The stout lady began to fan herself and nod her head in time to the thin, reedy complaint of the organ.

We went on down the hall; we passed the portable bronze "Funeral, No Parking" signs. Curley said, "I'd like to know what son-of-a-bitch put that sign out in front of my door last night."

Lawson's laugh clattered down the corridor again. "Ho ho ho! You'd like to know . . . *you'd* like to know. *I'd* like to know who the guy was sneaked into my room last night. I wake up this morning and there's one of those wax wreaths on the end of my bed with 'Rest in Peace' on it."

"Nuts," said Charley. "Let's go across the way to the Beetle Inn." This was the title given, in the natural course of events, to press headquarters, a frowsy cottage opposite the hotel. "Maybe Sam's got some more beer up from Cleveland."

Rounding the corner of the corridor we ran smack into a half dozen little dancing girls wearing lavender fleshings, short spangled skirts and pink bonnets perched on the sides of their heads. They had been brought over from Pittsburgh for the "Entertainment, Cabaret Show and Dancing in the Crystal Room." With them were two musicians in rustic costume. One had an accordion slung from his shoulders and a wire contraption which fitted around his neck holding a mouth organ in front of his face, so that he could play both instruments at once. The other had a fiddle and a ukulele. The one with the accordion began to wheeze *Turkey in the Straw.* A red-faced man, quite drunk, stuck his head out the door of a room labelled "New Little Giant Morgue Table" and yelled "Wow, wow, wow, Yahoooo!" The door of the Crane Breed Casket Company's room was open, and caskets glinted dully in the shadow. The dancing girls looked frightened. Their rouge stood out like fever spots. Curley looked the girls over and brightened up.

The convention's attractions were announced on the huge bulletin board that stood in the lobby.

Curley on his way back from Schmeling's cottage stopped at the board.

"Jesus," he said, reading over my shoulder, "there's the prize." He pointed to an item for Thursday at 8:30. It read: "Visit the displays and find the Lucky Numbers."

Curley began to curse. "Find the lucky numbers! Can you tie that? They probably got 'em hidden in a can of emblaming fluid, or inside one of those God damn suits with the dickey shirts and collars that lace up the back. How can a guy ever be lucky again after living in this cemetery for three days? Jesus, can you imagine playing hunt the slipper down among that layout of fancy iron boxes they got in the grill room? This afternoon a guy comes up to me and wants to sell me a bronze tube to stick in my coffin. Called it a Memo roll. It looks like one of those things relay racers hand each other. So I says 'What the hell is that for'. So he unscrews the top and says—'There you are. You write out your complete record and put it in here. Your name, address, birthday, occupation, lodges you belong to, any remarks you want to make, stick it in here, seal it up and it keeps forever. A thousand years from now someone opening this will be able to read all about you.' So I says, 'So *what*? . . .' These guys think of the God damnedest things."

The undertakers got drunk according to schedule. They didn't look or act like undertakers, but just like a lot of guys named Joe who are drunk. They attached themselves to the hick character who played the ukulele and went whooping and singing through the corridors like the V.F.W. It was so hot the men danced in their shirts and the women's light dresses clung to them before the evening was half through. The "Crystal Ball Room" was jammed and airless. It smelled of powder, cheap perfume and hot bodies. The noise of the crowd, the crash of the roller coaster behind the hotel, and the creaking of the Aeroplane Whirl drowned out five pieces of the six-piece orchestra and let nothing through but the "boomp-boomp-boomp-boomp" of the bass drum worked by the drummer's foot pedal. Occasionally a man whooped or a woman screamed, but mostly they shuffled, shuffled, shuffled to the beat of the tomtom, and then went out among the exhibits during intermission to drink and cool off.

A group sat around in their shirt sleeves on gilt funeral chairs in the exhibition space of the R. and F. Casket Company. A pint of Four Aces and three bottles of dry ginger ale, a pitcher of ice and some glasses stood on the silvery lid of a large aluminum casket. One of them told about a job that his partner had done on a jaundice case in Allentown, and another mentioned with pride the job *his* firm had done on a 460 pound man who died during a hot spell worse than this. A third said that his wife had been disappointed at not being able to come. She had been looking forward to it all year, especially the parading at night. He didn't think he'd parade without her. He added that some of those cabaret girls were pretty cute. A chunky little fellow asked if anyone wanted to shoot some golf in the morning, but they all said it was too God damn hot. The rye vanished. Their glasses left wet circles on the casket top.

An undertaker in a pair of pants and his B.V.D. top went tearing down the hall to the rear of the hotel with two girls chasing him. He had a woman's hat on his head. His convention badge was pinned to his back, and stood out behind him.

A thin bald-headed man and a stoutish woman wearing eyeglasses sat locked in a damp embrace in one corner of the display room, in front of a portable stained glass window representing, on one panel, the Virgin Mary and on the other Madonna and Child. They were a little drunk and kissed with loud smacks.

We were gathered in Curley's room. There were Dan, Lawson, Farrell, a couple of boxing writers from Chicago, one from Pittsburgh and three girls who had been sent down from Cleveland. Lawson was over by the window banging out an overnight story on his portable typewriter, quite oblivious to everyone else in the room. Suddenly from down the hall came strains of "Turkey in the Straw," whoops, catcalls and the sound of feet.

"Oh Christ," moaned Curley. He was in his pyjamas with the top unbuttoned. "Here they come again."

The music rendered on the accordion, banjo and mouth organ changed to *There's A Long Long Trail A-Winding*. Mixed voices began to sing it lustily, marching feet beat the time and many hands clapped a further rhythm. The parade drew nearer.

"They'll keep that up all night," said Curley. Lawson's typewriter went "clackety-clack clack, clack-clack-clack, clickety clack, ding." "What the hell are you writing, an epic?" asked Curley, irritably.

"A classic, my boy, just a classic," replied Lawson, cheerfully slamming the carriage back. "I am reserving my epic for the evening of the combat. If my constituents could see in what vulgar surroundings their literature is prepared . . ."

"Where's the beer?" said Dan.

Somebody said "Tony's bringing it over." There was a kick on the door, and Tony, the boy of all work at the training camp, came in with two heavy packages wrapped in brown paper under his arms. As he did so the undertakers, snake-dancing in lockstep, went by. They were now chanting *Pack Up Your Troubles In Your Old Kit Bag*.

"Christ," shouted Curley, "shut the door."

"I got a couple of stink bombs," volunteered Tony, "why don't you throw 'em among 'em?"

"You'd be doing the bastards a favor," said Lawson without looking up from his typewriter.

The noise of the parade began to fade. "Get Edgar to bring us some ice." One of the Chicago reporters reached over and pushed the button. There was a silence through which the keys of Lawson's typewriter sounded like triphammers. Lawson looked around and said—"For Pete's sake, somebody say something. I can't work when it's quiet."

"Who shall I bet on in the fight?" asked a blonde and giggled.

"The Dutchman'll knock him out," said Dan.

"He will in a—" began Curley when Edgar kicked open the door.

"Ice," said Curley. "A couple-abuckets full and make it snappy. Madame due Barry over here has a great thirst."

Edgar grinned. "There ain't any."

"Isn't any what?"

"Ice. We're all out of it."

"You're all out of it? A hotel running short of ice in this weather? Holy . . ."

"They hadda use it up this afternoon. They got more coming in the morning. They hadda use it on account of it bein' so awful hot for them two stiffs they had sent over from the penitentiary. This is the hottest I can remember around here."

"Jesus!" said Curley. Lawson's big laugh filled the room. "Ho ho ho ho! Can you beat that? Nobody can get a drink around here because they've used up the ice keeping a couple of *dead* guys cool when everybody who's still alive is dying of heat? Ho, ho ho!"

Curley uncapped a bottle of beer savagely and the warm liquid shot up like a geyser, hitting the ceiling and leaving a yellow stain. Curley looked up at the mark while the beer continued to foam over the bottle neck. "I hope," he said, and his face was composed for prayer, "I hope that Dutch bastard gets killed when he gets in the ring, for bringing us to a joint like this to train!"

"I'll drink it warm," said one of the girls, and reached out her hand for a bottle. "Gimme."

THE RESURRECTION OF SOLLY MOON

By WALTER D. EDMONDS

WE STOOD IN THE DOOR OF THE BARN WHERE JOHN WAS SPLITTING a load of stove wood, and across the valley we could hear the chug-chug of Brown's tractor; they were threshing there, or bringing in the corn. John leaned on his axe with both hands and lifted his good eye to look over the river-bottom. Even in the barn it was a hot day to split wood.

He lifted his head. The chug-chug of the tractor across the valley struck the air like steady mallet strokes.

"Times change," said John, "you remember how there weren't any tractors and a thresher used to come through the country with his machine and engine? Sure, I remember working here when you was small. Solly Moon used to come around this valley with his two boys, Pete and Georgey, and that old steam engine. There was not any gasoline engine those days with the grit to cut your Pa's Eureka Corn, and he advertised around till he found Solly Moon's old steamer. We all had him down the valley. That old engine certainly did have the power. Once it got to going it could put an iron crowbar through the cutter. Did I ever tell you how we threshed through Solly Moon? No?"

John sat down and brought out a chew.

"That year was a great year for crops and Moon went right down the valley as far as Hearn's big barn. There was three thousand bushel there to thresh in that big barn and a lot of us hired out to help. I never see such oats and rye. The old machine would very nearly lift herself up by her wheels if you put in more than two bundles at once. Even that old engine would get sort of breathless after a good chew of those white charters.

"It was a temperance farm; but it was most way through October and the weather was cold and we enjoyed it. It was the last threshing of the year. We went down with Solly and the machines, a wagon load of us, Pete and Leo, me, and Jarvis, he's dead now:

and Jarvis took along three jugs he'd manufactured with his own hands.

"We helped Solly Moon set up the rigging. You remember him. He was a little twerp with a back end that filled his pants right out and a shiny red face that always got a sweat on, even setting in the shade of a tree. He used to run around the whole darn time, talking funny as a Dutchman, and bossing to beat the cars. I never see him do a stroke of work but once, and that's what I'm telling you about. He had a drink that day.

"Either one of those two boys of his could have picked him up by the ear and throwed him across the river. And the other one could have set him up on a piece of dirt and kicked him back again. But he had them buffaloed. They was twins and going onto thirty when I knowed them, and they was still working for the old man, paying off their keep till they was twenty-one. Solly said when they was forty-two he'd begin giving them a wage. I don't know how he done it. I guess he never give them a chance to say a word. They certainly didn't say anything to anybody all the time I knew them.

"He was always a-running here and there, bossing them. 'Hey-hey!' he'd holler. 'This ain't a picnic, Georgey! Get up there and lay out that carrier. God damn!' He had a little high voice you could hear right through the engine noises. 'Hey-hey! God damn!' He bossed them around everywhere.

"That engine was a funny contraption. It had a big box at the back end with a furnace door you put the wood into and a smoke pipe over it and the fly wheels looked as if they'd been taken off a locomotive engine. You could get up steam in fifteen minutes with it and it would come out of the boiler in a dozen places, but it delivered the power all right. It had a whistle on it they used to blow for knocking off. I guess that was the only fun those two boys of Moon's ever got out of life. It made him screech like a burnt Jack, but with that whistle going you couldn't hear him. And they'd keep on blowing it until he'd find his whip and come down hopping after them."

John chuckled.

"I remember just as if it happened last week how we threshed through three days. The food was all right. But some of us boys were getting pretty dry. We was thinking about getting into the woods for a week to get some meat. I was always a timber-beast, and so was Jarvis, and once a year we'd get meat-hungry and have to get away.

"Well, noon of the last day, we come out from eating to set in the barn, and Jarvis said, 'Let's get out some of that oil I brought down with me.' He went and got it. Solly was close by, sweating out his dinner and picking his teeth with half a straw and he says, 'Oil?' 'Sure,' says Leo. 'Oil. It keeps a man from sweating.' 'Hey-hey!' says Solly. 'I'll have a try at it.'

"I don't believe that little twerp had ever took a snort. Too mean to pay for it, and too much work for him to make him some. He set there sucking his teeth till Jarvis come back with those three jugs.

"Old man Hearn was temperance and nasty about it, too, so we took the jugs up in the loft, me and Jarvis and Pete and Leo, and Solly he turned on his two boys and says: 'God damn! Go down and get up steam. This is oil for men that have to sweat, hey-hey!'

"Georgey he got down and him and his brother went down by the engine and begun stuffing in the wood. They'd used up all the wood but some pine, knotty pieces, and the old engine liked the taste of that and started spitting through her valve in no time. But Solly didn't notice. He had a suck at a jug that dang near collared him and he held up his mustache with one hand and had to cough. 'God damn!' he says. 'What kind of oil is it, Jarvis?' Jarvis told him it was home made oil. Moon sat there, the little twerp, holding on to his stummick, and his fat face getting red, until the heat caught him.

" 'It feels like a good digester,' he says. 'Hey-hey!' And we passed him another jug. He took it onto his lap like a baby and from time to time he had a suck. I don't remember what we got to talking of. We all of us forgot about Solly for a while, until our jugs was getting low, and then we found the little twerp holding his jug and sort of crooning over it. By cripus! He was a sight. His face was all lit up like a full moon and his mustache looked as if it was sticking straight out of his lip, and he was looking down at the machine.

" 'My God!' says Leo, pointing with his wooden leg, 'look at

that!' Solly had the jug upside down and there wasn't a drop left.
It was dry as the inside of a five weeks' drought and all the wet
was inside Solly and was just commencing to percolate out. He
says, 'God damn! Those boys have got some steam in the old
engine.' Then he turns to Jarvis. 'I thought this oil kept a man
from sweating. I feel warm. I don't know if I'm sweating. But I
feel kind of warm.' 'It works like that,' says Jarvis, looking at me,
'if a man ain't accustomed to it, he has to work the sweat out.'
That idea puzzled Moon. 'Work?' he says. 'Hey-hey! I've got
two boys. Georgey, is there a good head on?' Georgey looks at
the gauge and says there was a good head on. The old engine was
just shaking in its shoes. Solly says, 'Then we'd better commence.
I got them two boys to sweat for me.'

  " 'That won't do no good,' says Jarvis. 'A man has to do his own
sweating.' 'Is that right?' says Solly. 'But if I done that those boys
would get a bad idea.' 'Did you ever work?' asks Leo, looking at
him. 'Sure,' says Solly. 'Who do you think run this machine before them boys got big enough?' 'I thought mybe the missus did
that?' 'God damn!' says Solly. 'She carried the watter to the
engine.' 'Then,' says Leo, 'you'd better feed that thresher. 'What
for, hey-hey?' 'Solly, did you ever see a engine get up steam without no safety-valve?' 'Once, God damn!' 'That,' says Leo, 'is what
this here oil does to a man that don't work.' 'Hey-hey!' says Solly.
But he was scared. In two shakes he was down on the apron. 'Make
quick-hurry-up,' he says to us. 'Gimme some bundles.' He yells
like a screech owl to those boys to start the engine. He was scared."

  John listened. Across the valley we could hear the chug-chug of
the tractor working at Brown's.

  "Solly Moon looked so queer standing ready to work that the
rest of us laid right hold. That Jarvis dope was powerful all right.
In two shakes we was feeding down the buckwheat. And the old
thresher was humming, and the engine was rocking it was so full
of steam let loose. Them two boys was setting there feeding in
those pine knots and just grinning. I never see two boys grin so
hard. They didn't say nothing, but they kept the door open and
stuffed the old girl like a roasted chicken. The skin was peeling
right off of them but they didn't care. They had their Pa working
for the first time in history, and they aimed to make things hum.

  "I don't remember much. But I never fed down bundles the way

I did to that sweaty little twerp. I never see a man's hands travel the way his did. He'd ketch the bundle with his knife and have it cut in one wipe and feed it in with the other hand. He was leaning right down over the machine, his face all full of chaff, and the sweat just running off his mustache like rain off eaves-troughs.

"I sweated, too. I had to hump to keep ahead of that lousy little bum. And Leo, who was bagging the grain because he couldn't make no progress in a straw mow with that wooden leg, he had to hop, yes sir! He certainly had to hop. I could hear him pegging back and forth over the floor right through the ructions that old thresher was making.

"The dust was too heavy for the flue to carry. It came out like poison over everything. You couldn't hardly see. And it built up on my neck faster than the sweat could clean it down. The straw went up the carrier just like a river. That engine was doing double speed and the way that thresher took the works was wonderful to see.

"In half an hour we found out we'd finish in half time if the machine held together and the bearings in that little twerp didn't burn out entirely. But that didn't seem likely. All the time we could hear him screeching, 'Hey-hey!' or 'Make more quick-hurry-up!' or 'God damn!' "

John himself was almost sweating at his recollections.

His eye came round at me.

"Well, none of us never knew rightly how it happened. We was all too busy keeping time. But all to oncet that engine sort of sighed and set its teeth, and the thresher give itself an extra shake, and the whole barn rumbled. And then things commenced taking place. First there come a hiss from the dust flue, just the way spit sounds on a hot flat-iron. Then Pete who was gathering the straw from the carrier let out a holler. I took one look and seen him wrapped about the head with a pair of pants, a shirt and an old hat, and while I looked there come out a dirty set of underwear and a pair of boots and then a lot of white things like a skeleton hit him in the stummick and he yelled and went down.

"But the engine kept on whirling and I looked down and seen Leo bent over the basket letting the oats run through his fingers. And all at once his face got kind of sober, and he was peering down at something in his paw and I seen it was a heart beating.

Yes sir! Just as plain as day, right through the dust I seen a beating heart! But just for a minute. A lot of other things kept coming after.

"And then by holy crinkus! I looked at the apron and seen that Solly Moon was gone!"

John wiped his brow.

"I hollered to them two boys and I seen they had seen. They was grinning like two black devils. But when I hollered they turned off the power and a little at a time, that machine slowed down and the noise got less and the dust rose and everything was still. I took my hat off and climbed down the ladder. The others come down too. The machine was quiet when we gathered round Leo and looked down at the basket, Jarvis holding the clothes and the skeleton of little Solly Moon. We felt kind of mean, then, I guess, having built him up like that with likker. He was all there. And Leo just looked down with his hat in his hand and puzzled at that basket. He always puzzled over things like that. And pretty soon he said, 'I never thought a little man like him could carry such a lot of lights and liver.'

"Well, I tell you we felt pretty bad, and even them two boys looked sort of unhappy, like they didn't know what to do next. I guess they'd always been bossed so they couldn't get along without their Paw.

"We sat down and had a chew, and pretty soon, Jarvis asked, 'Where's the buttons?' and he held up the pants. Yes sir, even the buttons was sifted off him! We looked around and after a while we found them in the sifter. Yes sir, in the sifter, lying in among the dirty buckwheat.

"But we left them there and sat down again and wondered what to do, and Jarvis said, 'I'm sorry for it. He was a little twerp, but he was all right.'"

John turned to me with utmost seriousness.

"Maybe you won't believe this. But here's what happened. Leo, the old bezabor, thought it out. He said, 'I don't know what this machine looks like inside, but I think we ought to make a try at saving poor old Solly Moon!'

"We said that that was right.

"He said that maybe if we put the little twerp in just as he come out and put the engine in reverse, something would happen.

"Pete said, 'But the little twerp is dead.' 'No,' says Leo, 'I been looking.' He was setting with that bushel basket in between his leg and his wooden stump and he held aside the stuff for us to see, and there, in the bottom of the basket, was the heart. Yes, sir, it was still beating. I don't know if it was that manufactured stuff of Jarvises, or if it was just natural. But there it was, beating to beat the cars. And while we looked at it it gave two little hops.

"That got us proper. It was just as if each one of us together had heard that lousy little twerp holler, 'Hey-hey!'"

"So we figured. There was a reverse all right. And Jarvis he took the stuff up that had been delivered at the carrier, and Leo he set the basket under the grain feeder, and the boys went back to the engine. Just then Pete said. 'I heard a hiss in the dust flue.' 'So did I,' I says. 'What was it?' 'Sweat,' says one of the boys, 'I seen it drip off Pa and it's been coming out since dinner time.'

"Leo says, 'Then how are we going to put that back. We can't bring him out all dry.' 'Water,' says Jarvis. 'And I'll get some stable salt and mix a brine.' Well he fixed three buckets full which was just about the right amount as near as we could figure without paper; and then we took our places. I had to pour the brine into the flue. The boys was at the engine. Pete was helping Jarvis with the skeleton and underwear and clothes. Leo was at the basket. He had the hardest job. I could see it bothered him. 'I don't know how man's lights go—backwards,' he says, scratching his head, 'it would be kind of hard to get him out of order all his life. But I'll do the best I can. I'll feed them just the way they lay.'

"He give the word and the engine let out a sight of steam and got to going. 'Run it fast,' hollered Leo. And when it was rattling pretty smart he took hold of an end and stuck it in.

"Well it was hot work while it lasted. I had to toss them buckets in and Jarvis and Pete got a little ruffled up about the bones, but the engine smashed along, and all to once, yes sir, all to once, there come a kind of pop, and we all jumped to catch that little twerp for fear he would fall in again.

"There he come! There was his boots and his feet and his little round legs, and his pants, and all to once, there he was. 'Hey hey! God damn! Where's that bundle, John?' and he made a swipe with his hand.

"Yes sir! It was all right. But he was sober as a judge. And then he looked around and says, 'Georgey, get up here! God damn! Ain't you shamed to see your old Pa sweating here, hey-hey?'

"He made a wipe at Georgey with his foot, but as he did so, his boot fell off and his pants come down. That danged machine had done the job but it hadn't been able to tie his shoe or sew his buttons on.

"We had to send him in to be repaired and all the way his boys kept laughing at him. It was the only time I ever see them laugh."

John examined my face gravely.

"Solly Moon never knowed what had happened. He hadn't felt a thing. It must have been that manufactured oil that Jarvis brought along."

He paused.

"But just the same, if you had seen him in that basket, you would feel the way I feel. It was a lucky thing that that old bezabor, Leo, kept things straight."

GREEK TRAGEDY

By RING LARDNER

THE LARGEST CROWD OF THE WRESTLING SEASON GAVE GREEK ALEXIS
and Big Bill Buell a loud and joyous welcome as they climbed into
the ring for their fifth meeting in two years. Because they entered
almost simultaneously, it was hard to judge from the cheering
which man was better liked; there was a possibility, too, that
some of the noise was a demonstration of relief that there would
be no more preliminaries, the ones on this evening's program having proved unusually dull and meaningless.

The main bout was one of the most important in wrestling history. For one thing each of the contestants was heavyweight
champion of the world, the Greek being recognized as such in
the New England states, in New York, New Jersey and Delaware,
and in the Dakotas, Nebraska, Kansas, Oklahoma, Utah, Washington, Oregon and California, and Buell holding the title in the
District of Columbia, the Solid South, Minnesota, Colorado, Idaho
and Montana. For another thing, the winner was promised a match
for the world's championship with Legs Lamont, wearer of the
crown in Pennsylvania, Maryland, West Virginia, Ohio, Indiana,
Illinois, Michigan, Wisconsin, New Mexico, Arizona, Wyoming,
the Philippines, Hawaii, Porto Rico, Alaska and the Canal Zone,
as well as a battle with Chesty Leach, official mat king of the
Universe by ruling of the Athletic Commissions of Arkansas and
Guam. Besides, it might settle the question of supremacy between
the two gladiators themselves, each of whom had been credited
with two victories in four bouts so bitterly and brutally con-
tested that no wrestling fan could doubt the existence of a private
grudge, rumors of which had been printed right after the pair's
first encounter and not denied by either man.

Complaints of unnecessary roughness had never been lodged
against Buell or Alexis in their matches with other foeman, but
when they met, they slugged, bit, gouged, scratched, pinched and

pulled hair, paying no attention to protests or threats from the referee, who could do nothing save threaten or protest because both were equally guilty. Also worthy of note was that while they were on the mat, they did a lot of talking in tones so low as to be inaudible to the nearby newspaper men, and made faces at each other in a manner childish even for champion wrestlers.

Fred Hoffmann, who was refereeing tonight and had officiated for the pair twice before, knew no Greek and very little of the language of his forbears' Vaterland, but could tell, he said, that the conversation was just an exchange of horrible insults.

Rumors of the grudge were of mysterious origin and in the beginning there had been no hint of a reason for its existence. Then some irreverent writer for the Daily Dispatch ventured the guess, in print, that Big Bill, winner of the first match, had won in a fit of absent-mindedness, a fit costly to several friends, including his own manager, who had bet a tidy sum on the Greek. The manager, Ike Morris, and the Greek's manager, Lou Schwartz, said that if the Dispatch did not retract, they would sue for libel.

But as a matter of fact, the Dispatch writer had guessed wrong. Ike Morris had not bet against his own man in that initial bout, which was almost on the level. The arrangement had been that the man who won the first fall should win the match, but only after losing the second. It was true that Big Bill Buell had become absent-minded and won in straight falls, taking the second rather easily because the Greek, not being absent-minded, was surprised. They pacified him with profuse apologies and gave Big Bill a good bawling out.

A more serious double-cross, such as the Dispatch charged, would have explained the grudge, but the Messrs. Morris and Schwartz were not pleased with an explanation based on perfidy, which, as everybody knows, is virtually obsolete in the wrestling game. Not strong on invention themselves, they had long been hoping that some bright young writer would think up a plausible and interesting excuse for the bad blood between their two champs. A suggestion of rivalry for the affections of any of the Joans and Jeans of Hollywood was not to be considered. In a love interest plot involving this pair of baboons, the girl would have to be blind. A hint that the quarrel was over financial matters would indicate dishonesty on one side or the other and neither man wanted te be cast in the rôle of victim, knowing that the other, credited with having cheated successfully, would monopolize popular esteem. Religious and national differences were discarded as unintelligible to the average wrestling fan, who was not sure whether Greece was a suburb of Berlin or an Asiatic monarchy and would believe, if you told him so, that Helen of Troy, in private life, was Mrs. Martin Luther.

Jack Wells, wrestling expert on the Record, had finally justified the faith of Morris and Schwartz and solved the problem, inspiration coming to him during the second Buell-Alexis match. He had for weeks been aware that Alexis would triumph in that second encounter and that it would go three falls, and this uncanny expertness had made it difficult for him to grow excited over what transpired up there in the ring. But on one of the occasions when his eyes focused on the combatants, it had suddenly struck him that never in the world were two homelier men engaged in one show. A committee of artists would have given either man at least a draw with Bull Montana, but there had never been two Bull Montanas in the same ring at the same time.

Jack was not long in evolving a use for his discovery and his idea was received with acclaim when he sprang it next day on Doc Bishop, Lou Schwartz and Ike Morris. Lou and Ike assured him that their meal tickets had no vanity and he was free to go the limit on the subject of their looks. So the secret of the grudge had been revealed in the following Sunday's papers, in a story to this effect:

After the Greek and the German and their managers and Doc Bishop had assembled for the first time, to talk terms and be photographed and so on, a "friend" of Buell's had asked him what he thought of his new rival. Big Bill had replied in broken English that of course, he had been unable to form an opinion of the Greek's skill by merely seeing him. "But," he had said, "he looks like a gargoyle." And the "friend," naturally, had repeated this remark to an acquaintance who turned out to be a "friend" of the Greek's and who repeated it to Alexis in a spirit of true friendship.

"That Dutchman says you look like a gargoyle."

"Wait till I get a hold of him," Alexis had retorted in broken something, "and we'll see which is the sissy."

Whereupon it had been explained that the word did not imply

effeminancy, but sheer ugliness, and at this, Alexis had gone into a terrifying rage, not, he swore, because he was proud of his looks, but because the comment had come from a man who would appear perfectly at home walking on all fours.

This, duly reported to Buell, had called forth the remark that the latter would rather wrestle Alexis free than not at all, because just being close to the Greek made him (Big Bill) feel like Gary Cooper.

The first and second matches had drawn sizable crowds. The third had been a sell-out and none of the insiders doubted that Jack Wells' story was largely responsible. Opinion was about evenly divided on the merits of the case, but the public clearly relished a feud based on an argument between two self-confessed eyesores as to which was the more unsightly.

The third match had resulted in a second victory for the Greek (this having been decided previously by the toss of a coin) and the papers had said it would entitle him to a bout with Legs Lamont. But that big crowd and its wild enthusiasm (for Buell and Alexis were good entertainers) caused a change in plans. Ike Morris' plea for another chance was granted, there was another packed house and the German had won and evened the score. So here we are, where we were hundreds of words ago, with two of Darwin's best witnesses ready to wrestle for the fifth time, the biggest crowd of the season cheering them, three or four morbid camera men getting fresh material with which to frighten children, and Referee Fred Hoffmann showing more signs of nervousness than anyone else in sight.

The referee called the athletes together for a special instruction:

"Listen, youse! I don't know and don't care whose turn it is, but will you be good guys and snap it up? Every one of them two-dollar prelims went full time. They wasn't a lousy bum in the whole gang that could of throwed J. P. Morgan's midget. I've got a gal in that Harris show and she's out at eleven-twenty and if I ain't there, I'm out for life."

As you may observe, this speech was made in the purest English, and though no one translated it into Greek or German or both, the parties addressed seemed to understand it perfectly.

"My women wait," said Alexis.

"Yes," said Hoffmann. "They'd wait up in the top of a tree

as long as you was at the bottom. But let's get going. And listen: Does it have to be three falls?"

"Three is right," said Alexis, "and the last two pretty near an hour apiece. So you better wire the dame good-bye and congratulations."

"Come on. Let's get started. I'm in a hurry, too," said Big Bill Buell, and drawing closer to his rival, he shook his fist in the Greek's face and added: "Ike wants me to open with a Savoldi. Take it like you was surprised, and flop. I've got to talk to you."

"All right," said the Greek, "but be sure and get high enough. You kicked me in the stomach last time and I was sick for a week."

The match was on and the Savoldi, beautifully executed on this occasion, came as a big surprise to the crowd and threw it into a furor. The German was on top of his man and Hoffmann, praying for a quick fall, hovered too near them to suit Buell's taste.

"Move off a ways, Fred," he ordered, without taking his eyes from his opponent's face. "This is just a conference and you ain't in on it."

"You've almost got him," said the referee, disappointed.

"Well, now I ain't," said Buell as he relaxed his hold sufficiently to render the Greek's position less precarious, to the vociferous delight of Alexis' supporters, who credited him with one more of his famous displays of superhuman resourcefulness in a pinch.

As if angered by the cheering for his antagonist, Big Bill doubled up his right fist and punched the Greek on the left side of the jaw.

"Lay off that side of my face," he gasped. "I forgot to warn you. I got an infested tooth. Can't you see how it's swole?"

"I'll tell you some news that'll make you forget your toothache," said Big Bill. "Who do you think I seen today?"

"Somebody from home?"

"Yeah."

"Not Harry Marsh!"

"Somebody a whole lot more dangerous than a blind old bat of a sheriff. It was the Clayton boy, young Roy Clayton."

"Did he see you?"

"Yeah, and you can thank me that he ain't here tonight."

"He wouldn't reco'nize me."

"He reco'nized me without no trouble."

"But when he seen me last, I had a mustache and my head wasn't shaved."

"Listen, Miss America: You couldn't disguise that pan of yours if you wored it inside out. I'll tell you the rest in a few minutes. Right now you got to throw me off or they'll know we're stalling, and when you get me down, never mind that toe-hold. You hurt me the last time."

There was another wild outburst of enthusiasm by the Greek's admirers when he deftly freed himself from Buell's grasp and almost before the two regained their feet, had the German down on hands and knees and was straddling him. Said Big Bill:

"You ain't heard the worst yet, I'll make it short, but remember, while I'm talking, that this is supposed to be a wrestling match."

"It was around five o'clock and I'd been for a walk," said Buell, "and I run into the fella right outside the hotel. The people at home, they're sore at me because I ain't wrote to nobody since I win the title. I told him I didn't write to nobody before I win the title neither because they's nobody there can read. So he says he can read and Old Man Richards gets a Phoenix paper and when my name is mentioned, reads it out loud in the store and that's how they follow my career. And a couple times my picture was in after I win a match from 'the Greek,' and it's just luck that 'the Greek's' picture wasn't in, too."

"The way I've changed myself," said Alexis, "nobody would know me, let alone a picture."

"The quicker you get that idear out of your head, you're better off," said Buell.

"Well, then," said Alexis, "I can lay low for a few days, till this little rat goes home."

"That's the tough part of it, Tom," said Buell. "The little rat ain't going home. Hey! Watch yourself! I could of got up and sat on you then if I'd wanted to."

Big Bill's last bit of news had shocked the Greek into utter insensibility of where he was and why he was there. Mechanically he resumed operations while the referee cursed both men.

"He's got a job, is why he's here," Buell continued, "and it ain't going to make you no happier when I tell you what the job is. He's going to write up sports for the Dispatch; maybe wrestling, too. How he landed it was through some radio contest. I don't understand it, but as I understand it, this young Clayton boy, he win."

"Sure!" said Alexis. "That's just like him, the dirty little rat!"

"Well, I tried to phone you by phone, to tip you off, but they tell me you're out."

"I was to the dentist with this tooth. It's infested. You can see how it's swole."

"You better forget your tooth and think about young Clayton, because he's thinking about you."

"What do you mean? How can he? He don't know who I am."

"He knows who you was, and that's who he's thinking about. He says—Let's see what he did say. He ast if I had ever ran acrost any traces of Tom Mcyers."

"Lay off that name!"

"I says no, and he spoke of how you and me always used to be wrestling and he says you might of turned out as good as me only for—you know. And he says he would certainly like to run acrost you and grab that two thousand reward."

"The dirty little rat!"

"So I says that was a lousy way to make money, and I says if I ever run acrost you I would keep my mouth shut, providing you was reasonably yourself and slipped me, say, a thousand or fifteen hundred."

"What did he think of that?"

"He didn't think nothing of it. He says it wouldn't be honest and if it was ever found out, the guy that done it would land in a cell next door to yours. So I says, even if you was living in America, you'd be disguised so as nobody could reco'nize you. But he says he would know you in a minute even if you had a complete, entire new set of features, by the shape of your head."

"I'll have to lay low. I won't dast show myself nowheres."

"And some of the papers is sure to have your picture tomorrow. Some of them always has a picture of which of us win."

"Yes, and that dirty little rat will reco'nize me, and then I'm gone! What can I do!"

Referee Hoffmann was speaking to them sharply:

"What's the matter with youse bums? Are you deaf? Can't you hear Schwartz and Morris? The crowd's been booing you for a week! Now one of you get a fall in the next half minute or I swear I'll call it no contest. You ain't going to make a sucker out of me!"

"All right, Fred," said Big Bill. "We haven't seen each other in two months and we had a lot to talk over. We forgot you was in a hurry. Come on, Alexis; take me. Anything but a toe-hold."

So the Greek, spurred to action once more, won the first fall with a body scissors and double wristlock, or whatever it was, and went to his corner looking thoroughly licked.

He seemed not to listen while Lou Schwartz scolded, though ordinarily he was inclined to talk back.

"What got into you?" Schwartz demanded. "What was he doing to you, reciting poetry? That was supposed to be a quick one and you was out there pretty near half an hour. Even the crowd seen you wasn't trying. They never rode you like that before. When Buell wins this fall, he'll have everybody with him. And tonight I wanted you to look good on account of Jack Wells. A swell write-up he'll give you for this exhibition, after me turning him down cold. Ike Morris is laughing and you must be the joke."

Ike was laughing all right, and the cause of his amusement was Big Bill's description of the piteous manner in which the Greek kept asking, "What can I do!"

"He'll faint away when you pull the rest of it," said Ike. "Look at Schwartz. He's bawling him out plenty and the Greek ain't even listening. It was a great idear! And what's twenty-five dollars a week? Chicken's food!"

At the resumption of hostilities, the men remained on their feet only long enough to exchange punches, and I regret to report that the absent-minded Buell's punch landed on the sore side of the Greek's jaw. Alexis was still moaning when Big Bill brought him to the mat, but before he had a chance to mention the ailing molar, Buell ignited the fuse of his final bomb.

"Did you see him?" he asked in excited tremolo.

"Who?" demanded the Greek, the ugliness of his face enhanced by the panic that seized him.

"Young Clayton," said Buell, speaking rapidly. "He's here, eight or nine rows up that aisle, right over Jack Wells' head. I happened to see him and he waved to me and then pointed at you. I don't know what he meant."

"He's reco'nized me, the dirty little rat!"

"I don't know, but if I was you, I wouldn't look in his direction."

"What can I do? What can I do? Listen, Bill, you got to help me!"

"Sure, I'll help you, but how?"

"The first thing is to throw me and throw me quick. That'll give me a chance to think up something. Wait! I got an idear. You win this fall and the next one, too. I'll flop to you. Then I'll be out of it. But I got to have money and Schwartz won't give me none. Will you give me twenty-five hundred if I flop? You'll get the match with Leach and Lamont both and that means twenty or thirty thousand to you, maybe more than that."

"It wouldn't be honest," said Buell. "I've always played square with Doc Bishop and everybody. And Schwartz would never stop squawking. He'd tell the whole gang that I and you and Ike Morris had give him the works, and he'd be right. I can't do nothing crooked. I got a future to think of."

"My God, ain't I!" groaned Alexis, and groaned it so loudly that he drew a warning from the referee.

"Pipe down, you sap!" said Hoffmann. "If it wasn't for the crowd making so much noise, people could of heard that in Europe, and it wouldn't of been Greek to them, neither."

"Get it over with, Bill," said Alexis. "Use a toe-hold and hurry it up."

"How about a split?" said Buell.

"You don't do it good."

"I may hurt you more with a toe-hold."

"I don't care."

Eighty per cent of the sweet-natured customers yelled in delighted anticipation as they saw the German reach for his adversary's foot. Alexis undoubtedly had lost friends. This particular toe-hold will go down in wrestling history as a record-breaker for the speed with which it got results and the queer sort of results it got. Scarcely a minute after Big Bill had grasped Alexis' foot, Fred Hoffmann was patting the German's back in token that he had achieved a fall and squared the match. The crowd, surprised into silence at first, soon was cheering Big Bill with more unanimity and volume than he had ever been cheered in his life. Then the cheering ceased as suddenly as it had begun, for the Greek did not get up, but lay there apparently dead to the world.

Big Bill and the referee dropped to their knees beside him, one feeling for his pulse, the other listening for his heart. They were joined by the Commission's doctor and the rival managers, Schwartz and Morris, the doctor looking important, the managers anxious.

"He's all right," said the doctor, after a hurried examination. "What's the matter, Alexis?"

Alexis, forgetting that he could neither understand nor speak English, was about to reply when Lou Schwartz forestalled him and asked the doctor's question in good Brooklyn Greek. The recumbent wrestler grunted briefly and too softly for his manager to hear. He beckoned Schwartz to come within whispering distance.

"He says," translated the manager, "that he's unconscious and his ankle's sprained."

"Which ankle?" demanded the doctor.

There was more whispering.

"The one that hurts," translated the manager.

The doctor roughly squeezed both ankles. The Greek howled and pointed to the left one.

"There's no sprain; there's nothing," said the doctor. "Tell him to quit stalling and get up."

This order, relayed in Greek, brought only a shake of the head, whereupon, at the doctor's suggestion, the other members of the group helped him to his feet. But no sooner had they withdrawn their support than he regained unconsciousness and fell on the floor as earnestly as he had ever been thrown there.

It is for fear of boring you stiff that I refrain from itemizing the result of the evening's events, which included two or three exchanges of blows between the Greek and his manager, and at length the definite announcement that the contest had been awarded to Big Bill Buell by forfeit or default; wherefore Big Bill Buell would be given the coveted match with Legs Lamont for the championship of all the states and territories save Arkansas and Guam.

Besides, it is perhaps more important for you to know that young Mr. Wells had called on Schwartz and hinted that for twenty-five dollars a week, he could do him a lot of good in a publicity way. Mr. Schwartz had replied: "Maybe later on. Just now we don't need you." Mr. Wells had never liked the Schwartz-Alexis crowd anyway. Mr. Wells had then called on Ike Morris, and though there was no immediate prospect of a match for Buell, Ike had said all right, because he knew that Mr. Wells was on Doc Bishop's payroll and Doc Bishop's judgment was pretty good.

Mr. Wells got it into his head that Buell ought to have the Lamont match; that the Greek was unworthy. And he knew that Buell and Alexis had come from the same Arizona town, if you could call it a town. So he prodded Buell with questions about the Greek's past until Buell had told him the whole story.

Now there actually was a young fellow named Roy Clayton in Alexis' and Buell's home town. Whether he ever left there or not, I don't know. I do know, as does every other ardent wrestling fan, that the Greek, sprained ankle and all, left Lou Schwartz, wrestling and probably the United States right after this fifth match with Big Bill Buell.

AS FAR AS WE GOT

By PARKE CUMMINGS

THIS IS A COLLECTION OF ASSORTED ARTICLES, SQUIBS, STORIES, POEMS, novels and what have you that we started but never finished due to the inexorable march of events, weariness, the interruption of vacuum cleaner salesmen, the decision to go out and play golf, lack of inspiration, wet grounds and various other causes.

I

A HOUSE DIVIDED

When this appears, the election of 1936 will be history, but the fate of this nation will be something that only God can foretell. One thing is certain: President Roosevelt will have to deal with a senate and a house of representatives where the Democratic majorities will have been appreciably reduced. Of course I am assuming that the President *will* be re-elected, although his victory will not be as one-sided as many so-called experts seem to take for granted.

However, assuming that the Roosevelt forces are able, by hook or by crook, to gather the requisite number of electoral votes.

II

IF GEORGE WASHINGTON HAD MET A TRAFFIC COP

"Hey you, pull over! Say, how fast was you going?"

"About twenty-five, officer."

"Twenty-five, my eyeball. I clocked you at fifty-three. Hey, what's your name anyhow?"

"George Washington."

"Washington, eh? That's a laugh. The guy who can't tell a lie. O.K. Why did you go through that light?"

"That light? I didn't see any light."

"Oh yeah? I've heard that one too. All right. Answer me this:

III

DUST TO DUST

Chapter One

The sun beat down mercilessly on the fields of stubble. There wouldn't be any crop this year. There was no crop last year, either. They could starve, thought Hilda, as she put the things on the table. Just as Mary had starved when the drought had come before. They'd all starve this time, damn them. Hilda became conscious of someone in her presence. It was Olaf, the new hired man. She could feel his presence. He was there, in the room, with her. She could feel his maleness. He was going to say something. She could feel it. Damn it, why didn't he speak instead of standing there— always standing there with his dirty hands and the grime on his overalls? He came towards her,

IV

ROMANCE IN THE RAIN

It was just like George Varick to run smack into her without looking where he was going. George had always been like that— like a planet whirling through space. He stooped down and picked up her pocketbook. When he handed it to her, he saw that she was pretty—Pretty in a quaint timid sort of way. Her eyes, he noticed, were the color of

V

When autumn decks the countryside
And Nature bursts with glowing pride,
  When crimson hues bedeck the trees,
And perfume's in the rushing breeze,
When limpid ponds are gleaming silver,
And

VI

HOME COOKING

A Play in Three Acts

Act I

The curtain goes up on the living room dining room of the Morrisons, a typical middle-class New York family.

There is a table, center, set for six people. Backstage, right, is a divan, a cabinet radio to the left of it. There are several family portraits on the walls, and also a large framed copy of Greuze's *Innocence*.

One large chair nestles backstage, left, a small table with a lamp on it by its side.

All the other available chairs, a nondescript collection, are pulled up to the dinner table.

Mrs. Morrison, a blowsy woman in her middle forties, stands back of the table, and Nellie, a colored maid of ample proportions, has just made her entrance from the right.

Mrs. Morrison: Nellie, is the roast done?

Nellie: Yes mam, ah done put it in de oven.

Mrs. Morrison: Oh Nellie, you'll be the death of me yet. I mean is it cooked?

Nellie: Well, mam, ah always says if yo put a roast in de oben for three hours, den if it ain't cooked, it oughter be.

(A bell rings)

Mrs. Morrison: Oh dear, I'll bet that's the Walkers now, and I'm not nearly ready.

(She goes to the door)

VII

What this country needs is

VIII

YOU TELL 'EM

'Twas the night before Christmas, and all through the flat
Not a creature was stirring, not even a rat
The children were

IX

UP TO DATE

He: I think I'm going to kiss you.
She:

X

SWEEPING THE COUNTRY

Well, soaks—I mean folks, this here Tom Thumb golf craze sure
is the latest rage.—Especially for them guys that don't make good
scores, eh? I mean putting them in a rage. Yes sirree. A coupla hundred years ago, everywhere you looked there was guys swinging
tomahawks. Today you look, and they're swinging golf clubs at a
little round ball. Did you hear the one about the guy who was a
champ at midget golf, so finally he retired to write short short short
short stories. Back in seventeen our boys was all going over the
top. Now they're aiming at golf balls, and topping it over. Maybe
that wasn't so good. Well, it sure gives me a laugh to park my car
and see these blokes pushing away at them little pills when it's about
a hundred and eight in the shade, and no shade around—like that
weather we been having lately. After some of these fellas have
been doing that a while, they're hotter than a

XI

ENGLAND SHOULD RETAIN DAVIS CUP

Already optimistic sports writers, of which there seems to be a
plethora in this country, are predicting that 1937 is going to be
Uncle Sam's year in tennis, and that next summer is going to see
the United States lift the Davis Cup from Great Britain. My an-

swer is: I hope so, but I doubt it very much. Fred Perry has just beaten Donald Budge in our national championships, and it is my belief that he will continue to do so as long as he chooses. The California redhead is a capable young player, but he has gone as far as he ever will, and I cannot see him as a world's champion. Baron Von Cramm, the great German player, is also capable of defeating Budge at least seventy-five per cent of the time.

However, there are some who predict that Great Britain will be a pushover because Fred Perry will turn professional. This is sheer nonsense. There is not the slightest prospect of Perry turning professional either now or at any subsequent time. Too much pressure will be brought to bear on him by the British authorities. Moreover, Perry would have little to gain by such a move. He would have no chance at all against Ellsworth Vines, and after a few meetings between them, tennis fans would refuse to patronize such hopelessly one-sided exhibitions.

Now let us analyze

XII

WILL EDWARD MARRY?

One of the most fantastic rumors to which your correspondent has listened in many long years is the one about King Edward's supposed infatuation with a certain lady who hails from the Southern section of the U. S. A. Not only is the monarch reputed to have a yen for her, but he actually hopes to marry the gal. This is just another confirmation of the old gag that people will believe anything if you tell them often enough and loud enough. There is about as much chance of a confirmed bachelor like Edward

XIII

THE HOWITZER MURDERS

I opened the door to Jonathan Glade's studio, stepped inside, and then stopped in horror. There, on the floor, in a pool of blood, lay the decapitated body of John Glade.

"Inspector Griswold!" I called.

In an instant the Inspector was by my side. "What do you make of this?" I asked.

Inspector Griswold's practiced eye roved around the studio. "Just murder," he said grimly. "That's all."

"His head's been completely severed from his body," I said. It was then that the full import of what had taken place dawned on me. "Where *is* his head?" I inquired. "I don't see it anywhere."

The Inspector nodded sagely. "Exactly," he said. "Because it isn't anywhere around."

"You mean the murderer took his head—I mean Glade's head—with him?—I mean with the murderer?"

"No," said Griswold in that calm impersonal voice I had come to know so well, "I do not mean that. John Glade's head was shot off by a howitzer."

"You mean a big cannon?" I demanded incredulously.

The Inspector nodded.

"But that's inconceivable!" I exclaimed. "Look at this studio. The windows are all tightly shut. There's no hole in the walls.—Not even a scratch. How could an enormous shell have entered this studio, decapitated John Glade, and then gone out again without leaving the slightest trace. It's inconceivable," I repeated.

"It may be inconceivable," retorted Griswold, "but that is what happened."

"But how?" I insisted.

"I'm hungry," said Griswold, "and there is a restaurant around the corner that serves the finest ragout of mutton in the city. I suggest that we adjourn there for culinary repairs."

XIV

SCRIPT FOR RADIO

Announcer: Introducing ——————, radio's king of laughs!

(Short music and fanfare)

Straight Man: Well, Joe, it's nice to see you here. How are things going?

Comic: Like a thirty-cent steak, Harry.

Straight Man: Like a thirty-cent steak, Joe? How do you mean?

Comic: Pretty tough.

(Pause for laughs)

Straight Man: Joe, you slay me.
Comic: All right, give me a gun.

(Pause for laughs)

Straight Man: Joe, I understand your girl stood you up last night.
Comic: Yeah, she said

I DRINK AMERICAN

By DONALD HOUGH

I DO NOT LIKE TO SIT DOWN AND DRINK LIKE A GENTLEMAN. NEITHER do I like to stop drinking because I can feel my liquor, as gentlemen do in England, or anyway in English books.

I am an American and I drink American.

I do not understand this constant bickering about drinks and gentlemen. A man who drinks like a gentleman is, it is popularly supposed, one who sips his liquor sitting down, looks straight ahead with dignity, drinks with all the gusto and expression of an Indian taking his balsam tea against the evil spirits, and ends by rising slowly to his feet and saying, "Well, old fellow, I'll toddle up to bed."

And then he really does toddle up to bed.

This is a waste of time, a waste of liquor, and a waste of gentleman.

It makes it difficult for the layman to discover why Englishmen and others who drink like gentlemen drink at all. Drinking, throughout America excepting the Harvard Club, and among non-gentlemen the world over, is an adventure, not a heathen ritual. It springs from an understandable and, so far as I am concerned, a laudable, curiosity as to what will happen if, just about the time the gentlemanly drinker is toddling up to bed, you shake your head vigorously and start walking in a northeasterly direction.

It is at this point that the spirit of the pioneers in the American bloodstream comes bounding to the surface, and the American steps forth. He is unafraid. The impenetrable night lies just ahead, holding dangers that are exceeded in magnitude only by the rewards that are possible. Where the Englishman knows he's going to end up in bed, the American likes to think he may end up in Bali. Frequently he ends up in jail, but, incredible as it may seem, he often does get to Bali. It's worth trying for.

There is a basic difference, it seems to me, between a man who drinks like a gentleman and a really and truly gentleman. A genuine gentleman often takes to drink because he is infernally tired of being a gentleman and wishes, for the time being, to get away from it all.

It is important to remember that gentlemen sometimes get drunk. It's all right to carry on the tradition among the lads in prep school that gentlemen never get drunk—especially English gentlemen, from whom all gentlemen the world over are said to stem —but the real truth is that a large percentage of the gentlemen who drink, drink like gentlemanly fish. I have seen some splendid gentlemen get very stiff. Not only very stiff but very ungentlemanly and often in everybody's hair and on everybody's hands.

Looking at the other side of it, I have seen many people, strictly non-gentlemen, become wonderful gentlemen the minute they reach the proper solution. They are polite, considerate, and polished. They take their hats off constantly, bow every few minutes, murmur the most charming phrases, help ladies in distress and even ladies who are not in distress. They are democratic and magnanimous, equally at home in the lodgings of the poor and beneath the tables of the very rich.

They are no bargain in any language. Examined closely, they usually are cads escaping from the boredom of being cads by going out and drinking like gentlemen.

Personally, I do not know whether I am a gentleman or not, but the reports that keep coming in to my wife all the next day following a little drinking on my part indicate vividly that I do not drink like one. This is all right with me. It is the only indication I have that I may be a gentleman after all. The reports vary as to detail, but on one point they are unanimous: When out drinking, I'm a cad. I'm no weakly, part-time cad, either. I'm the real article. I'm a cad you may hate, but whose steadfast purpose and workmanlike job you can't help but respect.

All right. If I can't be a cad, I won't play. I care nothing whatever about sitting down and sipping a drink, and I do not like the kind of parties where some nice person with an imitation Oxford accent keeps looking me firmly in the eye and saying, "Don't you think you've had enough, old man?"

The answer is no.

I am out to drink enough to make it pay. Lots of people think this is not well-bred. I think it is very genteel. I am out to get rid of a lot of inhibitions, including myself, with which I am bored, and the idea that I am a gentleman, which gets in my hair. I also want to get rid of the haunting fear that some day I may take a few drinks and begin to get real polished, Oxford style.

Once I saw a concrete example of the difference, both in approach and results, between American and English style drinking. I was invited to hear Bruce Lockhart, author of *British Agent*, give his first lecture in the United States, at the Harvard Club of New York. Of course the idea of anybody entering this country by way of the Harvard Club is slightly confusing. The Harvard Club is American soil only through courtesy and inescapable geographical considerations.

With my host, I had the usual two whiskeys-and-soda before dinner, and brandy at the end. I then thought it would be fine if we had quite a few more drinks. I never had heard Mr. Lockhart, but during my days as a newspaper reporter I had heard quite a few lectures and I felt I was on firm ground when I suggested that we hurry to the bar and get ready for the evening.

I thought the lecture was more or less an excuse, a kind of rallying point, to be used next morning as circumstances might require. I had looked forward to the evening for a couple of days, but the thought that we would have to take time out to listen to the lecture never had entered my thick skull. I had reckoned without the Harvard Club. At the Harvard Club you listen to the lectures.

So we sat in the game room and discussed English literature until it was time for the lecture, at which time we went into the auditorium as cold as a couple of herring.

We went into a large and impressive hall. It rose in smoky, black walnut grandeur some three or four stories, so that the upper timbers were lost in aristocratic gloom. Portraits in oil—representing, I was told, past presidents of the club—hung at well-bred intervals on the walls, each with its individual electric light. These august gents, each sitting in one of the three poses permitted Harvard Club presidents, dominated the scene: looking at it, for some reason I could not fathom right at first, in extreme disapproval.

Our seats were along the wall, up front, flanking the speaker's rostrum, giving us a side view of Mr. Lockhart, when he should appear, but affording us a splendid front view of the entire assem-

blage. The entry of the guests into the hall was all but impercepti-
ble. They came singly and in pairs, sat down quietly and
unobtrusively by bending the hip and knee joints, and froze solid in
place.

The Committee, in tails, anticipated the entrance of Mr. Lockhart when they paraded into the hall and filed into their seats,
which were separated from the hoi polloi by pieces of string and a
sign which said, "For The Committee." This section used up one-
quarter of the entire seating capacity. The Committee was a wow.

The Committee got seated and arranged their beards across their
beautiful shirt fronts, Mr. Lockhart and all the chairmen arrived,
and we were ready to proceed, or rather to listen to Mr. Lockhart
proceed. Mr. Lockhart stepped to the rostrum as soon as the
various chairmen had introduced him, and commenced his address.

To get to the point quickly and impolitely, Mr. Lockhart, at
the time of his first American, or Harvard, appearance, was not a
blood-stirring elocutionist. He seemed distinctly impressed by the
past presidents on the wall, and spoke with a great deal of defer-
ence and in a genteel monotone. He occasionally interrupted himself to mop his brow with his pocket handkerchief, and gave me,
at least, the impression that he wished to heaven this really was
London, instead of the Harvard Club version thereof, so he could
toss the whole evening into the laps of his audience and tell them
what to do with it.

He was three-quarters through, and well into the intricacies of
the financial situation in the Balkans, when the entire occasion
suddenly went straight American on him.

The door in the rear of the hall opened and a drunk walked
unsteadily down the broad center aisle.

He was a plain drunk, American style. He had his hat and overcoat on, and he kept them on. His overcoat was unbuttoned and
it flopped around like the wings of a cockeyed bat. He wanted
to sit down and hear the lecture, or anyway he wanted to sit down,
and he searched for an empty place. His system was simplicity
itself. He would stop at each row, spread his legs apart for support,
and ask the person on the aisle if there was a seat vacant. Nobody
answered him.

Slowly, inexorably, he came to the Committee.

Here, he thought was something classy. This was his style. He nudged the first Member of the Committee he came to. The Member, in common with everybody else in the place, gazed stonily ahead. Maybe, thought the drunk, he's deaf. He looks deaf. He nudged harder, and repeated his request in a voice he evidently had been saving for the Committee.

No soap. The drunk looked hurt. He tried a few other rows but met only chagrin and defeat.

All right, if everybody wanted to be so damned impolite, he could be impolite, too. He stepped back, took good aim, and rushed the nearest Member on the aisle. But he had overlooked the string. The string tossed him into the Member's lap.

Our friend recovered himself, got out of the beard that was enveloping him, and regained the aisle. He looked around in horrible uncertainty. Not a face, not an eye, was turned in his direction, save only the faces and eyes of the past presidents on the wall, which were turned in everybody's direction with what, as I have mentioned, was an expression of permanent disapproval.

The poor fellow felt this. A hopeless look came over his face. Maybe, he thought, this is all just a terrible dream. He looked as though he were about to flee, and Mr. Thomas Lamont, the head chairman, took a deep breath. I mean, I suppose he took a deep breath. You couldn't tell.

But the drunk did not flee. He wanted to find out about the financial situation in the Balkans. He steered himself carefully down the front of the aisle, some fifteen feet in front of Mr. Lockhart, and, after turning around a few times to trample down the long grass as his ancestors had done, sat down on the floor and crossed his legs Indian fashion. He did not bother to remove his hat.

But our drunk was not entirely without manners. Having lit a cigarette, he looked around and noticed nobody else was smoking. His better nature rose to the surface. He tossed the cigarette to the carpet directly in front of him. He now proposed to step on it.

Had he been a student of the human body, he would have realized in the first place that from his position it is impossible to step on anything without breaking the ankle. He tried one foot, then the other, laboriously untangling them before each trial. It seemed to him, from where he sat, that he was stepping on the cigarette, but each time he withdrew his foot, the cigarette still was burning. Despair plainly was written on his face.

Finally, after a period spent in deep thought, sitting there look-ing at the wisp of smoke curling up between him and Mr. Lock-hart, he got to his feet after much trouble and fuss, and stepped squarely on the damned thing, ground it beneath his heel, resumed his seat and heard the lecture through to the end.

During all this time, not an eye in the place was turned toward this common American drunk. The feeling seemed to be that if no-body looked at him, Mr. Lockhart would not see him, either. Or, if he saw him, he would think it was just somebody from the Balkans.

What is even more remarkable, while we were walking out of the hall, while we were moving around the club afterward, I never heard the presence of the drunk so much as hinted at by anybody. He had not existed. He was a ghost.

We went up to Hugh Leonard's house and discussed the lecture at some length. I guess Hugh noticed that I looked rather glum. Perhaps he felt I had the drunk on my mind and was disappointed with the whole evening. He said, "Well, I'm sorry about that—interruption down at the Club."

The subject having thus been brought up and thoroughly aired, it was dropped—forever.

Hugh had been right about my thoughts. I did have the drunk on my mind. I was regretting that I had not thought of it first. Our man evidently had started his evening on the American plan—take a few drinks, shake your head and follow all hunches. As hunches go, he had come up with a superepic. Since that night I have had a Goal. I never have attained it. I have tried. But in the circles in which I move, I am not appreciated. They have bouncers. It never ends in the way I had planned.

The lone drunk, of course, is an American institution. This type of sport seldom is practiced in foreign lands.

In fact, a fine British stigma has come to be associated with the individual who takes his spirits without benefit of companions. There is no sense to this, but there is a great deal to be said for the American point of view. If a person is tired of his routine, tired of himself, tired of being a gentleman, why should he not be equally—or more—tired of his friends? In many cases, this is easily the No. 1 reason for the bender.

A person on a tear with his usual companions is progressing

vertically, but he is standing still horizontally. Only when he has broken away from all things familiar does his binge begin to pay dividends.

New scenes, new people, new policemen, fill his life—into and out of bars, into and out of the lives of innumerable people, into and out of love, into and out of magnificent business deals, great adventures, dazzling projects.

He drinks, not sitting down, but standing gloriously at the bar, facing half toward the door, poised for the leap into the Unknown, on and ever on, to greater and ever greater things.

That is the American way, and it is mine.

So let my companion finish his gentlemanly drink and toddle up to bed or toddle over to the lake and jump into it. Let him, and be damned. I get up from the table with him, but I do no toddling.

I walk with brisk, elastic step to the main entrance, and look eagerly into the black night.

I am ready to plow a white furrow through the darkness, leaving in my turbulent wake a growing accumulation of insults, lost friends, dropped acquaintances, indignant waiters, discouraged cops, people named Marie, disregarded phone calls, promissory notes, and a lot of miscellaneous seaweed, all churned up into a phosphorescent glow.

I now am on the threshold of high adventure, and I take my first step firmly, realizing that some place, far off on the horizon, is the only certainty that awaits me—the dawn.

TAKE ALONG THE LITTLE PAL!

By Donald Hough

UNDER THE GENERAL HEADING OF LITTLE PALS COME THOSE WOMEN— newly married, as a rule—who can hike as far as any man, shoot ducks with the best of them, carry a full pack over the portages, whip a stream with an iron wrist, and for whom the lash of storm, cold of winter, heat and flies of summer, hardships of the wilderness, hold no terrors: little rays of sunshine in any man's life: the life, that is to say, of any man's party. Little Pals, in fact, get into my hair. My hair is full of Little Pals. They have been put there by Big Pals, those self-assured grooms who think they have married, not a wife for their own private use, but a Pal for mankind.

Big Pal's wedding present to his squaw-woman consists of a fly rod, a set of golf clubs, some hiking boots, a neat toy shotgun, a shooting jacket, some hipboots, a pair of skis and a stack of poker chips.

"But of course," says Big Pal when his companions indicate that the old crowd will try to get along without him, "my Little Pal will go right along with us. She's just one of the gang, from now on. You fellows don't know that girl. She's an outdoor *man*, if you know what I mean."

(*We know exactly what you mean. You mean we've got to take turns carrying her.*)

"She can stand right up to me any old day, doing anything. She'll take her turn just like the rest of us—you fellows won't have to give her anything. You won't have to worry about *her*. For example, she never gets tired.

"She's a he-man, that girl. She don't care what happens. The more it rains the better she likes it. And she sleeps right smack on the bare ground."

(*Of course she does, Oscar. We've lugged enough spruce boughs for Little Pals-Who-Sleep-On-The-Ground to float the Queen Mary. We ought to know.*)

"Say, she loves the old outdoor life. Shoot? She'll knock mallards that you and I'll miss.

"Another thing, she can paddle a canoe like an Indian—I often call her 'Squaw'—and she can pitch a tent, make a fire, and hit the trail like a veteran. She's a born woodsman. She knows what it's all about. You can't lose that girl in the woods. I've tried it and I know."

(*You didn't try hard enough, maybe.*)

"You ought to see her fish. Boy! She can lay that fly on a dime. She's a better little old fisherman than I am, any day. Her fishing's like her golf game: hits from the men's tees. None of that washwoman swing. She clicks 'em, that girl. On the stream it's the same way. Just let her whip that stream beside you for one day, and you'll know what I mean. When evening comes you'll know that you been up against something.

"Another thing you fellows don't want to forget. The cooking." (This is Big Pal's ace. He plays it.) "She can do all the cooking. All we have to do is loaf around: shooting, fishing, any old thing we want to. When meal time comes all we have to do is listen for the old dinner bell."

(*With our hearts in our mouths.*)

But you can't down Big Pal. Having played his ace, he tosses in the joker. He draws himself slightly up: "Well, anyway, she's good enough for me. Where I go, she goes. The way I figure it, any place a man goes, he shouldn't be afraid to take his wife."

Now this is subject to so many wise cracks we won't put any in italics. Make up your own. Go easy. After all, Big Pal has been through hell and highwater with you. He's regular. This temporary illness of his won't last. Let him bring along the little dumpling. Some of the boys may object, they may think good God what are we up against now, but Big Pal can count on me for one. You might as well plunge in, Oscar, all of us might as well plunge in, Little Pal included, and have done. It won't last. One bright day you'll show up alone, as of yore. It seems that Little Pal—just for this once—has to stay home to put up some preserves, something she couldn't let go, and so on. That's all. That's all. (Maybe you ought to hurry home, Oscar.)

As for me, I've waded through many a Little Pal in my day. I've seen them come and I've seen them go. The little he-man comes out for the first outing all dolled up in her new pants. She's one of the crowd: you can tell by the way she puts her hands in her new pockets and whistles through her new lips. Go ahead, fellows, swear if you want to, I'm just one of the gang. God damn it.

She wields her fly rod with a magnificent, careless flourish, and Big Pal climbs out on a limb to untangle the fly with many a robust joke on his lips, lips that heretofore registered nothing but contempt for any fly-hanger. "Hell," says he, his eyes in a mute plea to the rest of us, "you ought to be ashamed of yourself, Squaw, getting your fly up in a tree like this, the very first thing." He chuckles, shakes his head. "Old timer like you! Getting your fly up in a tree! Good joke on you, Mate: good joke on you. Ha, ha, ha!"

(*Ha, ha, ha! Good joke on you, Mate, ha, ha, ha!*)

And on the golf course, where, so Oscar has assured us, you don't have to give her any handicap, you don't have to give her anything, she clicks three or four balls over the fence at the right of the first tee, and does Big Pal rise to the occasion and laugh it off. "Why, darling, that isn't like you, not a bit like you, you usually straighten them out a couple hundred yards or more darling, gosh, darling, you better look out the fellows here'll get to thinking you don't play a very good game, darling." (*§-!!-?¶&! Darling*)

Down at the shooting lodge our friend Oscar loudly proclaims Little Pal's determination to relieve everybody of the kitchen drudgery. What a comfort she turns out to be: scooting around under everybody's feet and managing to monopolize the space around the door to the gent's toilet just at a time when some old wool underwear is the best you can scrape up in the way of a company negligee. In the kitchen she's a dream. She can't find things, she isn't used to this kind of stove, how can she be expected to make coffee in this old tin thing, and in the end she is down with a headache and Big Pal is assuring us all that he never saw her this way before, usually she's the life of the party, like the time down in Florida . . .

On a camping trip Little Pal is virtually indispensable. She takes things so easy! What does she care? Oh, hell, she left her manicure set back at the last camp site! Big Pal laughingly lets us draw straws to see who has the honor of going back after it. Hell of a swell joke!

Little Pal turns out to be a great he-man, but as her hands get blistered and she gives up paddling just for today (and the discovery is made that her idea of cooking is to open a jar of potato salad), Big Pal swings into lusty action and thrashes to the rescue: "Bill," he calls her, and "Old Man," and "Partner," and "Squaw," in a desperate effort to lift her up by his own boot straps into full membership in the gang. "It's your turn to get water, Bill," he says heartily. "No favorites in the Big Woods, you know."

He slaps a paddle into her hands with great gusto. "Dig into the water there, Squaw woman. We're on the old trail you know, where every man does his day's work or goes hungry." In the morning he asks her, "Well, how's the old partner today?" and slaps her on the back so hard it splits her shoes. This keeps up until Little Pal, trying her best to fall into the spirit of Nature, takes a sun bath and gets so nicely sunburned she can't even sit on a canoe seat, and she's finally given up, even by the Old Man, and tossed into the hold and carried across the portages with the rest of the baggage.

In my long experience with Little Pals I have discovered three distinct groupings of the species. The first group has been reading advice columns in the ladies' magazines and is now holding the Master's love by taking an interest in his work, his hobbies, everything he does. She has set out on a serious career as a True Helpmeet, and in every possible way makes a damned bother of herself.

The next group of Pals are those who have no idea of staying home and wondering if her male really went out fishing this weekend, or whether, as she suspects, he started toward the lake and as soon as he was out of sight veered well around to the left. She's going to be on hand, is this little gem.

Most numerous of them all are those who have been dragged in by the hair. They have run afoul of the big, tweedy outdoor male who has no intention of merging his big brown October life with that of any woman, but who has married to add another convert to his ideas. The things he likes are the Only Things in Life.

This last Little Pal puts on her pants like a good little girl, and she pretends to enjoy baiting her own hook, but usually she has private plans of her own, once the excitement is over.

I remember one member of a group I used to go hunting with who brought out his Squaw Woman with a broader flourish than most. Just a little Danny Boone, he called her—and as for her, she seconded the motion with a cheer. There's nothing, says she, like the great outdoors: she loved it. Why, she even liked to be bitten by mosquitoes; she thought it was fun, really.

But one of the boys made a horrible mistake. We were duck shooting, and the day was cold and raw. Nothing goes better on such a day than a touch of spirits—in this case, gin. In a burst of generosity he gave a drink to Little Pal. She seemed to take her dose with a distinctly professional air. She wanted more.

By the time she felt she'd had enough to ward off the chills, she was looking around with queer little jerks of her head. During one of these she focused on her Big Pal. She wanted to know who the hell he thought he was, and all she wanted was a nice warm room and a thick steak and a flock of cocktails and she wanted to get into her lace panties and go out dancing. And he could take his damned old ducks and his dirty grub and he knew what he could God damn well do with them, and she didn't want any more pioneering in her life, her ancestors had taken care of that for her, and please take her home. And the same went for fishing. She could buy all the fish she ever wanted, with tartar sauce on the side, long before she met him, and besides her boots made her feet hurt and look at her nails, and from now on, in her life, a tent was something a circus came in.

Then off came the boots to whistle past Big Pal's startled ears, and she gave a fine old Bronx cheer and started, bravely but with lack of finesse, up the road toward the railroad station, followed by the cheers of all except Big Pal, who ran after her crying, "Wait a minute, Dear, you're not yourself, dear!" The last we saw of them he was carrying her and she was kicking her legs. He was trying to carry her toward the lodge, but she was kicking toward the railroad station, and we all knew that we had lost another Little Pal, and the world had lost another he-man camper, another Partner, another Bill, another Old Man, another Squaw, another hiker with the best of us, shooter beside any·man, caster of flies on any stream, and nuisance in anybody's language.

PART III

THE SNOWS OF KILIMANJARO

By ERNEST HEMINGWAY

Kilimanjaro is a snow covered mountain 19,710 feet high, and is said to be the highest mountain in Africa. Its western summit is called by the Masai "Ngàje Ngài," the House of God. Close to the western summit there is the dried and frozen carcass of a leopard. No one has explained what the leopard was seeking at that altitude.

"THE MARVELLOUS THING IS THAT IT'S PAINLESS," HE SAID. "THAT'S how you know when it starts."

"Is it really?"

"Absolutely. I'm awfully sorry about the odor though. That must bother you."

"Don't! Please don't."

"Look at them," he said. "Now is it sight or is it scent that brings them like that?"

The cot the man lay on was in the wide shade of a mimosa tree and as he looked out past the shade onto the glare of the plain there were three of the big birds squatted obscenely, while in the sky a dozen more sailed, making quick-moving shadows as they passed.

"They've been there since the day the truck broke down," he said. "Today's the first time any have lit on the ground. I watched the way they sailed very carefully at first in case I ever wanted to use them in a story. That's funny now."

"I wish you wouldn't," she said.

"I'm only talking," he said. "It's much easier if I talk. But I don't want to bother you."

"You know it doesn't bother me," she said. "It's that I've gotten so very nervous not being able to do anything. I think we might make it as easy as we can until the plane comes."

"Or until the plane doesn't come."

"Please tell me what I can do. There must be something I can do."

"You can take the leg off and that might stop it, though I doubt it. Or you can shoot me. You're a good shot now. I taught you to shoot didn't I?"

"Please don't talk that way. Couldn't I read to you?"

"Read what?"

"Anything in the book bag that we haven't read."

"I can't listen to it," he said. "Talking is the easiest. We quarrel and that makes the time pass."

"I don't quarrel. I never want to quarrel. Let's not quarrel any more. No matter how nervous we get. Maybe they will be back with another truck today. Maybe the plane will come."

"I don't want to move," the man said. "There is no sense in moving now except to make it easier for you."

"That's cowardly."

"Can't you let a man die as comfortably as he can without calling him names? What's the use of slanging me?"

"You're not going to die."

"Don't be silly. I'm dying now. Ask those bastards." He looked over to where the huge, filthy birds sat, their naked heads sunk in the bunched feathers. A fourth planed down, to run quick-legged and then waddle slowly toward the others.

"They are around every camp. You never notice them. You can't die if you don't give up."

"Where did you read that? You're such a bloody fool."

"You might think about someone else."

"For Christ's sake," he said. "That's been my trade." He lay then and was quiet for a while and looked across the heat shimmer of the plain to the edge of the bush. There were a few Tommies that showed minute and white against the yellow and, far off, he saw a herd of zebra, white against the green of the bush. This was a pleasant camp under big trees against a hill, with good water, and, close by, a nearly dry water hole where sand grouse flighted in the mornings.

"Wouldn't you like me to read?" she asked. She was sitting on a canvas chair beside his cot. "There's a breeze coming up."

"No thanks."

"Maybe the truck will come."

"I don't give a damn about the truck."

"I do."

"You give a damn about so many things that I don't."

"Not so many, Harry."

"What about a drink?"

"It's supposed to be bad for you. It said in Black's to avoid all alcohol. You shouldn't drink."

"Molo!" he shouted.

"Yes Bwana."

"Bring whiskey-soda."

"Yes Bwana."

"You shouldn't," she said. "That's what I mean by giving up. It says it's bad for you. I know it's bad for you."

"No," he said. "It's good for me."

So now it was all over, he thought. So now he would never have a chance to finish it. So this was the way it ended in a bickering over a drink. Since the gangrene started in his right leg he had no pain and with the pain the horror had gone and all he felt now was a great tiredness and anger that this was the end of it. For this, that now was coming, he had very little curiosity. For years it had obsessed him; but now it meant nothing in itself. It was strange how easy being tired enough made it.

Now he would never write the things that he had saved to write until he knew enough to write them well. Well, he would not have to fail at trying to write them either. Maybe you could never write them, and that was why you put them off and delayed the starting. Well he would never know, now.

"I wish we'd never come," the woman said. She was looking at him holding the glass and biting her lip. "You never would have gotten anything like this in Paris. You always said you loved Paris. We could have stayed in Paris or gone anywhere. I'd have gone anywhere. I said I'd go anywhere you wanted. If you wanted to shoot we could have gone shooting in Hungary and been comfortable."

"Your bloody money," he said.

"That's not fair," she said. "It was always yours as much as mine. I left everything and I went wherever you wanted to go and I've done what you wanted to do. But I wish we'd never come here."

"You said you loved it."

"I did when you were all right. But now I hate it. I don't see why that had to happen to your leg. What have we done to have that happen to us?"

"I suppose what I did was to forget to put iodine on it when I first scratched it. Then I didn't pay any attention to it because I never infect. Then, later, when it got bad, it was probably using that weak carbolic solution when the other antiseptics ran out that paralyzed the minute blood vessels and started the gangrene." He looked at her, "What else?"

"I don't mean that."

"If we would have hired a good mechanic instead of a half baked kikuyu driver, he would have checked the oil and never burned out that bearing in the truck."

"I don't mean that."

"If you hadn't left your own people, your goddamned old Westbury, Saratoga, Palm Beach people to take me on ——"

"Why I loved you. That's not fair. I love you now. I'll always love you. Don't you love me?"

"No," said the man. "I don't think so. I never have."

"Harry, what are you saying? You're out of your head."

"No. I haven't any head to go out of."

"Don't drink that," she said. "Darling, please don't drink that. We have to do everything we can."

"You do it," he said. "I'm tired."

Now in his mind he saw a railway station at Karagatch and he was standing with his pack and that was the headlight of the Simplon-Orient cutting the dark now and he was leaving Thrace then after the retreat. That was one of the things he had saved to write, with, in the morning at breakfast, looking out the window and seeing snow on the mountains in Bulgaria and Nansen's Secretary asking the old man if it were snow and the old man looking at it and saying, No, that's not snow. It's too early for snow. And the Secretary repeating to the other girls, No, you see. It's not snow and them all saying, It's not snow we were mistaken. But it was the snow all right and he sent them on into it when he evolved exchange of populations. And it was snow they tramped along in until they died that winter.

It was snow too that fell all Christmas week that year up in the Gauertal, that year they lived in the woodcutter's house with the big square porcelain stove that filled half the room, and they slept on mattresses filled with beech leaves, the time the deserter came with his feet bloody in the snow. He said the police were right behind him and they gave him woolen socks and held the gendarmes talking until the tracks had drifted over. In Schruns, on Christmas day, the snow was so bright it hurt your eyes when you looked out from the weinstub and saw everyone coming home from church. That was where they walked up the sleigh-smoothed urine-yellowed road along the river with the steep pine hills, skis heavy on the shoulder, and where they ran that great run down the glacier above the Madlener-haus, the snow as smooth to see as cake frosting and as light as powder and he remembered the noiseless rush the speed made as you dropped down like a bird. They were snowbound a week in the Madlener-haus that time in the blizzard playing cards in the smoke by the lantern light and the stakes were higher all the time as Herr Lent lost more. Finally he lost it all. Everything, the ski-schule money and all the season's profit and then his capital. He could see him with his long nose, picking up the cards and then opening, "Sans Voir." There was always gambling then. When there was no snow you gambled and when there was too much you gambled. He thought of all the time in his life he had spent gambling. But he had never written a line of that, nor of that cold, bright Christmas day with the mountains showing across the plain that Barker had flown across the lines to bomb the Austrian officers' leave train, machine-gunning them as they scattered and ran. He remembered Barker afterwards coming into the mess and starting to tell about it. And how quiet it got and then somebody saying, "You bloody, murderous bastard." Those were the same Austrians they killed then that he skied with later. No not the same. Hans, that he skied with all that year, had been in the Kaiser-Jägers and when they went hunting hares together up the little valley above the saw-mill they had talked of the fighting on Pasubio and of the attack on Pertica and Asalone and he had never written a word of that. Nor of Monte Corno, nor the Siete Commuti, nor of Arsiero. How many winters had he lived in the Vorarlberg and the Arlberg? It was four and then he remembered the man who had the fox to sell when they had walked into Bludenz, that time to buy presents, and the cherry pit taste of good kirsch, the fast-slipping rush of running powder-snow on crust, singing "Hi Ho said Rolly!" as you ran down the last stretch to the steep drop, taking it straight,

*then running the orchard in three turns and out across the ditch
and onto the icy road behind the inn. Knocking your bindings
loose, kicking the skis free and leaning them up against the wooden
wall of the inn, the lamplight coming from the window where inside, in the smoky, new-wine smelling warmth, they were playing
the accordion.*

"Where did we stay in Paris?" he asked the woman who was
sitting by him in a canvas chair, now, in Africa.

"At the Crillon. You know that."

"Why do I know that?"

"That's where we always stayed."

"No. Not always."

"There and at the Pavillion Henri-Quatre in St. Germain. You
said you loved it there."

"Love is a dunghill," said Harry. "And I'm the cock that gets
on it to crow."

"If you have to go away," she said, "is it absolutely necessary to
kill off everything you leave behind? I mean do you have to take
away everything? Do you have to kill your horse, and your wife
and burn your saddle and your armour?"

"Yes," he said. "You're damned money was my armour. My
Swift and My Armour."

"Don't."

"All right. I'll stop that. I don't want to hurt you."

"It's a little bit late now."

"All right then. I'll go on hurting you. It's more amusing. The
only thing I ever really liked to do with you I can't do now."

"No, that's not true. You liked to do many things and everything you wanted to do I did."

"Oh for Christ sake stop bragging will you?"

He looked at her and saw her crying.

"Listen," he said. "Do you think that it is fun to do this? I don't
know why I'm doing it. It's trying to kill to keep yourself alive I
imagine. I was all right when we started talking. I didn't mean to
start this, and now I'm crazy as a coot and being as cruel to you
as I can be. Don't pay any attention, darling, to what I say. I love
you, really. You know I love you. I've never loved anyone else the
way I love you." He slipped into the familiar lie he made his bread
and butter by.

"You're sweet to me."

"You bitch," he said. "You rich bitch. That's poetry. I'm full of poetry now. Rot and poetry. Rotten poetry."

"Stop it. Harry, why do you have to turn into a devil now?"

"I don't like to leave anything," the man said. "I don't like to leave things behind."

*   *   *

It was evening now and he had been asleep. The sun was gone behind the hill and there was a shadow all across the plain and the small animals were feeding close to camp; quick dropping heads and switching tails, he watched them keeping well out away from the bush now. The birds no longer waited on the ground. They were all perched heavily in a tree. There were many more of them. His personal boy was sitting by the bed.

"Memsahib's gone to shoot," the boy said. "Does Bwana want?"

"Nothing."

She had gone to kill a piece of meat and, knowing how he liked to watch the game, she had gone well away so she would not disturb this little pocket of the plain that he could see. She was always thoughtful, he thought. On anything she knew about, or had read, or that she had ever heard.

It was not her fault that when he went to her he was already over. How could a woman know that you meant nothing that you said; that you spoke only from habit and to be comfortable. After he no longer meant what he said, his lies were more successful with women than when he had told them the truth.

It was not that he lied as that there was no truth to tell. He had had his life and it was over and then he went on living it again with different people and more money, with the best of the same places, and some new ones. You kept from thinking and it was all marvellous. You were equipped with good insides so that you did not go to pieces that way, the way most of them had, and you made an attitude that you cared nothing for the work you used to do, now that you could no longer do it. But, in yourself, you said that you would write about these people; about the very rich; that you were really not of them but a spy in their country; that you would leave it and write of it and for once it would be written by someone who knew what he was writing of. But he would never do it, because each day of not writing, of comfort, of being that which he despised, dulled his ability and softened his will to work so that, finally, he did no work at all. The people he knew now were all much more comfortable when he did not work. Africa was where he had been happiest in the good time of his life so he had come out here to start again. They had made this safari with the minimum of comfort. There was no hardship; but there was no luxury and he had thought that he could get back into training that way. That in some way he could work the fat off his soul the way a fighter went into the mountains to work and train in order to burn it out of his body.

She had liked it. She said she loved it. She loved anything that was exciting, that involved a change of scene, where there were new people and where things were pleasant. And he had felt the illusion of returning strength of will to work. Now if this was how it ended, and he knew it was, he must not turn like some snake biting itself because its back was broken. It wasn't this woman's fault. If it had not been she it would have been another. If he lived by a lie he should try to die by it. He heard a shot beyond the hill.

She shot very well this good, this rich bitch, this kindly caretaker and destroyer of his talent. Nonsense. He had destroyed his talent himself. Why should he blame this woman because she kept him well? He had destroyed his talent by not using it, by betrayals of himself and what he believed in, by drinking so much that he blunted the edge of his perceptions, by laziness, by sloth, and by snobbery, by pride and by prejudice, by hook and by crook. What was this? A catalogue of old books? What was his talent anyway? It was a talent all right but instead of using it, he had traded on it. It was never what he had done, but always what he could do. And he had chosen to make his living with something else instead of a pen or a pencil. It was strange too, wasn't it, that when he fell in love with another woman, that woman should always have more money than the last one? But when he no longer was in love, when he was only lying, as to this woman, now, who had the most money of all, who had all the money there was, who had had a husband and children, who had taken lovers and been dissatisfied with them, and who loved him dearly as a writer, as a man, as a companion and as a proud possession; it was strange that when he did not love her at all and was lying, that he should be able to give her more for her money than when he had really loved. We must all be cut out for what we do, he thought. However you make your living is where your talent lies. He had sold vitality, in one form or another, all his life and when your affections are not too involved you give much better value for the money. He had found that out but he would never write that, now, either. No, he would not write that, although it was well worth writing.

Now she came in sight, walking across the open toward the camp. She was wearing jodphurs and carrying her rifle. The two boys had a Tommie slung and they were coming along behind her. She was still a good looking woman, he thought, and she had a pleasant body. She had a great talent and appreciation for the bed, she was not pretty, but he liked her face, she read enormously, liked to ride and shoot and, certainly, she drank too much. Her husband had died when she was still a comparatively young woman and for a while she had devoted herself to her two just-grown children, who did not need her and were embarrassed at having her about, to her stable of horses, to books, and to bottles. She liked to read in the evening before dinner and she drank scotch and soda while she read. By dinner she was fairly drunk and after a bottle of wine at dinner she was usually drunk enough to sleep.

That was before the lovers. After she had the lovers she did not drink so much because she did not have to be drunk to sleep. But the lovers bored her. She had been married to a man who had never bored her and these people bored her very much.

Then one of her two children was killed in a plane crash and after that was over she did not want the lovers, and drink being no anaesthetic she had to make another life. Suddenly she had been acutely frightened of being alone. But she wanted someone that she respected with her.

It had begun very simply. She liked what he wrote and she had always envied the life he led. She thought he did exactly what he wanted to. The steps by which she had acquired him and the way in which she had finally fallen in love with him were all part of a regular progression in which she had built herself a new life and he had traded away what remained of his old life. He had traded it for security, for comfort too, there was no denying that, and for what else? He did not know. She would have bought him anything he wanted. He knew that. She was a damned nice woman too. He would as soon be in bed with her as anyone; rather with her, because she was richer, because she was very pleasant and appreciative and because she never made scenes. And now this life that she had built again was coming to a term because he had not used iodine two weeks ago when a thorn had scratched his knee as they moved forward trying to photograph a herd of waterbuck standing, their heads up, peering while their nostrils searched the air, their ears spread wide to hear the first noise that would send them rushing into the bush. They had bolted, too, before he got the picture.

Here she came now.

He turned his head on the cot to look toward her. "Hello," he said.

"I shot a Tommy ram," she told him. "He'll make you a good broth and I'll have them mash some potatoes with the Klim. How do you feel?"

"Much better."

"Isn't that lovely. You know I thought perhaps you would. You were sleeping when I left."

"I had a good sleep. Did you walk far?"

"No. Just around behind the hill. I made quite a good shot on the Tommy."

"You shoot marvellously you know."

"I love it. I've loved Africa. Really. If *you're* all right it's the most fun that I've ever had. You don't know the fun it's been to shoot with you. I've loved the country."

"I love it too."

"Darling you don't know how marvellous it is to see you feeling better. I couldn't stand it when you felt that way. You won't talk to me like that again, will you? Promise me?"

"No," he said. "I don't remember what I said."

"You don't have to destroy me. Do you? I'm only a middle-aged woman who loves you and wants to do what you want to do. I've been destroyed two or three times already. You wouldn't want to destroy me again, would you?"

"I'd like to destroy you a few times in bed," he said.

"Yes. That's the good destruction. That's the way we're made to be destroyed. The plane will be here tomorrow."

"How do you know?"

"I'm sure. It's bound to come. The boys have the wood all ready and the grass to make the smudge. I went down and looked at it again today. There's plenty of room to land and we have the smudges ready at both ends."

"What makes you think it will come tomorrow?"

"I'm sure it will. It's overdue now. Then, in town, they will fix up your leg and then we will have some good destruction. Not that dreadful talking kind."

"Should we have a drink? The sun is down."

"Do you think you should?"

"I'm having one."

"We'll have one together. *Molo, letti dui whiskey-soda!*" she called.

"You'd better put on your mosquito boots," he told her.

"I'll wait till I bathe . . ."

While it grew dark they drank and just before it was dark and there was no longer enough light to shoot, a hyena crossed the open on his way around the hill.

"That bastard crosses there every night," the man said. "Every night for two weeks."

"He's the one makes the noise at night. I don't mind it. They're a filthy animal though."

Drinking together, with no pain now except the discomfort of lying in the one position, the boys lighting a fire, its shadow jumping on the tents, he could feel the return of acquiescence in this life of pleasant surrender. She *was* very good to him. He had been cruel and unjust in the afternoon. She was a fine woman, marvellous really. And just then it occurred to him that he was going to die.

It came with a rush; not as a rush of water nor of wind; but of a sudden evil smelling emptiness and the odd thing was that the hyena slipped lightly along the edge of it.

"What is it, Harry?" she asked him.

"Nothing," he said. "You had better move over to the other side. To windward."

"Did Molo change the dressing?"

"Yes. I'm just using the boric now."

"How do you feel?"

"A little wobbly."

"I'm going in to bathe," she said. "I'll be right out. I'll eat with you and then we'll put the cot in."

So, he said to himself, we did well to stop the quarreling. He had never quarreled much with this woman, while with the women that he loved he had quarreled so much they had finally, always, with the corrosion of the quarreling, killed what they had together. He had loved too much, demanded too much, and he wore it all out.

*He thought about alone in Constantinople that time, having quarreled in Paris before he had gone out. He had whored the whole time and then, when that was over, and he had failed to kill his loneliness, but only made it worse, he had written her, the first one, the one who left him, a letter telling her how he had never been able to kill it. . . . How when he thought he saw her outside the Re-*gence *one time it made him go all faint and sick inside, and that he would follow a woman who looked like her in some way, along the Boulevard, afraid to see it was not she, afraid to lose the feeling it gave him. How everyone he had slept with had only made him miss her more. How what she had done could never matter since he knew he could not cure himself of loving her. He wrote this letter at the Club, cold sober, and mailed it to New York asking her to write him at the office in Paris. That seemed safe. And that night missing her so much it made him feel hollow sick inside, he wandered up past Taxim's, picked a girl up and took her out to supper. He had gone to a place to dance with her afterward, she danced badly, and left her for a hot Armenian slut, that swung her belly against him so it almost scalded. He took her away from a British gunner subaltern after a row. The gunner asked him outside and they fought in the street on the cobbles in the dark. He'd hit him twice, hard, on the side of the jaw and when he didn't go down he knew he was in for a fight. The gunner hit him in the body, then beside his eye. He swung with his left again and landed and the gunner fell on him and grabbed his coat and tore the sleeve off and he clubbed him twice behind the ear and then smashed him with his right as he pushed him away. When the gunner went down his head hit first and he ran with the girl because they heard the M. P.'s coming. They got into a taxi and drove out to Rimmily Hissa along the Bosphorus, and around, and back in the cool night and went to bed and she felt as over-ripe as she looked but smooth, rose-petal, syrupy, smooth-bellied, big-breasted and needed no pillow under her, and he left her before she was awake looking blousy enough in the first daylight and turned up at the Pera Palace with a black eye, car-*

*rying his coat because one sleeve was missing. That same night he
left for Anatolia and he remembered, later on that trip, riding all
day through fields of the poppies that they raised for opium and
how strange it made you feel finally and all the distances seemed
wrong, to where they had made the attack with the newly arrived
Constantine officers, that did not know a goddamned thing, and the
artillery had fired into the troops and the British observer had cried
like a child. That was the day he'd first seen dead men wearing
white ballet skirts and upturned shoes with pompons on them. The
Turks had come steadily and lumpily and he had seen the skirted
men running and the officers shooting into them and running then
themselves and he and the British observer had run too until his
lungs ached and his mouth was full of the taste of pennies and they
stopped behind some rocks and there were the Turks coming as
lumpily as ever. Later he had seen the things that he could never
think of and later still he had seen much worse. So when he got back
to Paris that time he could not talk about it or stand to have it mentioned. And there in the café as he passed was that American poet
with a pile of saucers in front of him and a stupid look on his potato
face talking about the Dada movement with a Roumanian who said
his name was Tristan Tzara, who always wore a monocle and had
a headache, and, back at the apartment with his wife that now he
loved again, the quarrel all over, the madness all over, glad to be
home, the office sent his mail up to the flat. So then the letter in answer to the one he'd written came in on a platter one morning and
when he saw the handwriting he went cold all over and tried to slip
the letter underneath another. But his wife said, "Who is that letter
from, dear?" and that was the end of the beginning of that. He remembered the good times with them all, and the quarrels. They always picked the finest places to have the quarrels. And why had
they always quarreled when he was feeling best? He had never written any of that because, at first, he never wanted to hurt anyone and
then it seemed as though there was enough to write without it. But
he had always thought that he would write it finally. There was so
much to write. He had seen the world change; not just the events;
although he had seen many of them and had watched the people,
but he had seen the subtler change and he could remember how the
people were at different times. He had been in it and he had watched
it and it was his duty to write of it; but now he never would.*

"How do you feel?" she said. She had come out from the tent now after her bath.

"All right."

"Could you eat now?" He saw Molo behind her with the folding table and the other boy with the dishes.

"I want to write," he said.

"You ought to take some broth to keep your strength up."

"I'm going to die tonight," he said. "I don't need my strength up."

"Don't be melodramatic, Harry, please," she said.

"Why don't you use your nose? I'm rotted half way up my thigh now. What the hell should I fool with broth for? Molo bring whiskey-soda."

"Please take the broth," she said gently.

"All right."

The broth was too hot. He had to hold it in the cup until it cooled enough to take it and then he just got it down without gagging.

"You're a fine woman," he said. "Don't pay any attention to me."

She looked at him with her well known, well loved face from *Spur* and *Town and Country*, only a little the worse for drink, only a little the worse for bed, but *Town and Country* never showed those good breasts and those useful thighs and those lightly small-of-back-caressing hands, and as he looked and saw her well known pleasant smile, he felt death come again. This time there was no rush. It was a puff, as of a wind that makes a candle flicker and the flame go tall.

"They can bring my net out later and hang it from the tree and build the fire up. I'm not going in the tent tonight. It's not worth moving. It's a clear night. There won't be any rain."

So this was how you died, in whispers that you did not hear. Well, there would be no more quarreling. He could promise that. The one experience that he had never had he was not going to spoil now. He probably would. You spoiled everything. But perhaps he wouldn't.

"You can't take dictation, can you?"

"I never learned," she told him.

"That's all right."

There wasn't time, of course, although it seemed as though it telescoped so that you might put it all into one paragraph if you could get it right.

There was a log house, chinked white with mortar, on a hill above the lake. There was a bell on a pole by the door to call the people in to meals. Behind the house were fields and behind the fields was the timber. A line of lombardy poplars ran from the house to the dock. Other poplars ran along the point. A road went up to the hills along the edge of the timber and along that road he picked blackberries. Then that log house was burned down and all the guns that had been on deer foot racks above the open fire place were burned and afterwards their barrels, with the lead melted in the magazines, and the stocks burned away, lay out on the heap of ashes that were used to make lye for the big iron soap kettles, and you asked Grandfather if you could have them to play with, and he said, no. You see they were his guns still and he never bought any others. Nor did he hunt any more. The house was rebuilt in the same place out of lumber now and painted white and from its porch you saw the poplars and the lake beyond; but there were never any more guns. The barrels of the guns that had hung on the deer feet on the wall of the log house lay out there on the heap of ashes and no one ever touched them.

In the Black Forest, after the war, we rented a trout stream and there were two ways to walk to it. One was down the valley from Triberg and around the valley road in the shade of the trees that bordered the white road, and then up a side road that went up through the hills past many small farms, with the big Schwartzwald houses, until that road crossed the stream. That was where our fishing began. The other way was to climb steeply up to the edge of the woods and then go across the top of the hills through the pine woods, and then out to the edge of a meadow and down across this meadow to the bridge. There were birches along the stream and it was not big, but narrow, clear and fast, with pools where it had cut under the roots of the birches. At the Hotel in Triberg the proprietor had a fine season. It was very pleasant and we were all great friends. The next year came the inflation and the money he had made the year before was not enough to buy supplies to open the hotel and he hanged himself.

You could dictate that, but you could not dictate the Place Contrescarpe where the flower sellers dyed their flowers in the street and the dye ran over the paving where the autobus started and the old men and the women, always drunk on wine and bad marc; and the children with their noses running in the cold; the smell of dirty sweat and poverty and drunkenness at the Café des Amateurs and the whores at the Bal Musette they lived above. The Concierge who entertained the trooper of the Garde Republicaine in her loge, his horsehair plumed helmet on a chair. The locataire across the hall whose husband was a bicycle racer and her joy that morning at the Cremerie when she had opened L'Auto and seen where he placed third in Paris-Tours, his first big race. She had blushed and laughed and then gone upstairs crying with the yellow sporting paper in her hand. The husband of the woman who ran the Bal Musette drove a taxi and when he, Harry, had to take an early plane the husband knocked upon the door to wake him and they each drank a glass of white wine at the Zinc of the bar before they started. He knew his neighbors in that quarter then because they all were poor. Around that Place there were two kinds; the drunkards and the sportifs. The drunkards killed their poverty that way; the sportifs took it out in exercise. They were the descendants of the Communards and it was no struggle for them to know their politics. They knew who had shot their fathers, their relatives, their brothers, and their friends when the Versailles troops came in and took the town after the Commune and executed any one they could catch with calloused hands, or who wore a cap, or carried any other sign he was a working man. And in that poverty, and in that quarter across the street from a Boucherie Chevaline and a wine co-operative he had written the start of all he was to do. There never was another part of Paris that he loved like that, the sprawling trees, the old white plastered houses painted brown below, the long green of the auto-bus in that round square, the purple flower dye upon the paving, the sudden drop down the hill of the rue Cardinal Lemoine to the River, and the other way the narrow crowded world of the rue Mouffetard. The street that ran up toward the Pantheon and the other that he always took with the bicycle, the only asphalted street in all that quarter, smooth under the tires, with the high narrow houses and the cheap tall hotel where Paul Verlaine had died. There were only two rooms in the apartment where they lived and he had a room on the top floor of that hotel that cost him sixty francs a month where he did his writing, and from it he could see the roofs and chimney pots and all the hills of Paris.

From the apartment you could only see the wood and coal man's

place. He sold wine too, bad wine. The golden horse's head out-
side the Boucherie Chevaline where the carcasses hung yellow gold
and red in the open window, and the green painted co-operative
where they bought their wine; good wine and cheap. The rest was
plaster walls and the windows of the neighbors. The neighbors who,
at night, when someone lay drunk in the street, moaning and groan-
ing in that typical French ivresse that you were propaganded to be-
lieve did not exist, would open their windows and then the murmur
of talk.

"Where is the policeman? When you don't want him the bugger
is always there. He's sleeping with some concierge. Get the Agent."
Till someone threw a bucket of water from a window and the moan-
ing stopped. "What's that? Water. Ah, that's intelligent." And the
windows shutting. Marie, his femme de menage, protesting against
the eight hour day saying, "If a husband works until six he gets only
a little drunk on the way home and does not waste too much. If he
works only until five he is drunk every night and one has no money.
It is the wife of the working man who suffers from this shortening
of hours."

"Wouldn't you like some more broth?" the woman asked him
now.

"No thank you very much. It is awfully good."

"Try just a little."

"I would like a whiskey-soda."

"It's not good for you."

"No. It's bad for me. Cole Porter wrote the words and the music.
This knowledge that you're going mad for me."

"You know I like you to drink."

"Oh yes. Only it's bad for me."

When she goes, he thought. I'll have all I want. Not all I want
but all there is. Ayee he was tired. Too tired. He was going to sleep
a little while. He lay still and death was not there. It must have
gone around another street. It went in pairs, on bicycles, and moved
absolutely silently on the pavements.

No, he had never written about Paris. Not the Paris that he cared
about. But what about the rest that he had never written?

What about the ranch and the silvered gray of the sage brush, the
quick, clear water in the irrigation ditches, and the heavy green of
the alfalfa. The trail went up into the hills and the cattle in the

summer were shy as deer. The bawling and the steady noise and slow moving mass raising a dust as you brought them down in the fall. And behind the mountains, the clear sharpness of the peak in the evening light and, riding down along the trail in the moonlight, bright across the valley. Now he remembered coming down through the timber in the dark holding the horse's tail when you could not see and all the stories that he meant to write.

About the half-wit chore boy who was left at the ranch that time and told not to let anyone get any hay, and that old bastard from the Forks who had beaten the boy when he had worked for him stopping to get some feed. The boy refusing and the old man saying he would beat him again. The boy got the rifle from the kitchen and shot him when he tried to come into the barn and when they came back to the ranch he'd been dead a week, frozen in the corrall, and the dogs had eaten a big part of him. But what was left you packed on a sled wrapped in a blanket and roped on and you got the boy to help you haul it, and the two of you took it out over the road on skis, and sixty miles down to town to turn the boy over. He having no idea that he would be arrested. Thinking he had done his duty and that you were his friend and he would be rewarded. He'd helped to haul the old man in so everybody could know how bad the old man had been and how he'd tried to steal some feed that didn't belong to him, and when the sheriff put the handcuffs on the boy he couldn't believe it. Then he'd started to cry. That was one story he had saved to write. He knew at least twenty good stories from out there and he had never written one. Why?

"You tell them why," he said.

"Why what, dear?"

"Why nothing."

She didn't drink so much, now, since she had him. But if he lived he would never write about her, he knew that now. Nor about any of them. The rich were dull and they drank too much, or they played too much backgammon. They were dull and they were repetitious. He remembered poor Scott Fitzgerald and his romantic awe of them and how he had started a story once that began, 'The very rich are different from you and me.' And how someone had said to Scott, Yes they have more money. But that was not humorous to Scott. He thought they were a special glamorous race and when he found they weren't it wrecked him just as much as any other thing that wrecked him.

He had been contemptuous of those who wrecked. You did not have to like it because you understood it. He could beat anything, he thought, because no thing could hurt him if he did not care.

All right. Now he would not care for death. One thing he had always dreaded was the pain. He could stand pain as well as any man, until it went on too long, and wore him out, but here he had something that had hurt frightfully and just when he had felt it breaking him, the pain had stopped.

He remembered long ago when Williamson, the bombing officer, had been hit by a stick bomb someone in a German patrol had thrown as he was coming in through the wire that night and, screaming, had begged everyone to kill him. He was a fat man, very brave, and a good officer, although addicted to fantastic shows. But that night he was caught in the wire, with a flare lighting him up and his bowels spilled out into the wire, so when they brought him in, alive, they had to cut him loose. Shoot me, Harry. For Christ sake shoot me. They had had an argument one time about our Lord never sending you anything you could not bear and someone's theory had been that meant that at a certain time the pain passed you out automatically. But he had always remembered Williamson that night. Nothing passed out Williamson until he gave him all his morphine tablets that he had always saved to use himself and then they did not work right away.

Still this now, that he had, was very easy; and if it was no worse as it went on there was nothing to worry about. Except that he would rather be in better company.

He thought a little about the company that he would like to have.

No, he thought, when everything you do, you do too long, and do too late, you can't expect to find the people still there. The people all are gone. The party's over and you are with your hostess now.

I'm getting as bored with dying as with everything else, he thought.

"It's a bore," he said out loud.

"What is, my dear?"

"Anything you do too bloody long."

He looked at her face between him and the fire. She was leaning back in the chair and the firelight shone on her pleasantly lined face and he could see that she was sleepy. He heard the hyena make a noise just outside the range of the fire.

"I've been writing," he said. "But I got tired."

"Do you think you will be able to sleep?"

"Pretty sure. Why don't you turn in?"

"I like to sit here with you."

"Do you feel anything strange?" he asked her.

"No. Just a little sleepy."

"I do," he said.

He had just felt death come by again.

"You know the only thing I've never lost is curiosity," he said to her.

"You've never lost anything. You're the most complete man I've ever known."

"Christ," he said. "How little a woman knows. What is that? Your intuition?"

Because, just then, death had come and rested its head on the foot of the cot and he could smell its breath.

"Never believe any of that about a scythe and a skull," he told her. "It can be two bicycle policemen as easily, or be a bird. Or it can have a wide snout like a hyena."

It had moved up on him now, but it had no shape anymore. It simply occupied space.

"Tell it to go away."

It did not go away but moved a little closer.

"You've got a hell of a breath," he told it. "You stinking bastard."

It moved up closer to him still and now he could not speak to it, and when it saw he could not speak it came a little closer, and now he tried to send it away without speaking, but it moved in on him so its weight was all upon his chest, and while it crouched there and he could not move, or speak, he heard the woman say, "Bwana is asleep now. Take the cot up very gently and carry it into the tent."

He could not speak to tell her to make it go away and it crouched now, heavier, so he could not breathe. And then, while they lifted the cot, suddenly it was all right and the weight went from his chest.

* * *

It was morning and had been morning for some time and he heard the plane. It showed very tiny and then made a wide circle and the boys ran out and lit the fires, using kerosene, and piled on grass so there were two big smudges at each end of the level place and the morning breeze blew them toward the camp and the plane circled twice more, low this time, and then glided down and leveled off and landed smoothly and, coming walking toward him, was old Compton in slacks, a tweed jacket and a brown felt hat.

"What's the matter, old cock?" Compton said.

"Bad leg," he told him. "Will you have some breakfast?"

"Thanks. I'll just have some tea. It's the Puss Moth you know. I won't be able to take the Memsahib. There's only room for one. Your lorry is on the way."

Helen had taken Compton aside and was speaking to him. Compton came back more cheery than ever.

"We'll get you right in," he said. "I'll be back for the Mem. Now I'm afraid I'll have to stop at Arusha to refuel. We'd better get going."

"What about the tea?"

"I don't really care about it you know."

The boys had picked up the cot and carried it around the green tents and down along the rock and out onto the plain and along past the smudges that were burning brightly now, the grass all consumed, and the wind fanning the fire, to the little plane. It was difficult getting him in, but once in he lay back in the leather seat, and the leg was stuck straight out to one side of the seat where Compton sat. Compton started the motor and got in. He waved to Helen and to the boys and, as the clatter moved into the old familiar roar, they swung around with Compie watching for wart-hog holes and roared, bumping, along the stretch between the fires and with the last bump rose and he saw them all standing below, waving, and the camp beside the hill, flattening now, and the plain spreading, clumps of trees, and the bush flattening, while the game trails ran now smoothly to the dry waterholes, and there was a new water that he had never known of. The zebra, small rounded backs now, and the wildebeeste, big headed dots seeming to climb as they moved in long fingers across the plain, now scattering as the shadow came toward them, they were tiny now, and the movement had no gallop, and the plain as far as you could see, gray-yellow now and ahead old Compie's tweed back and the brown felt hat. Then they were over the first hills and the wildebeeste were trailing up them, and then they were over mountains with sudden depths of green-rising forest and the solid bamboo slopes, and then the heavy forest again, sculptured into peaks and hollows until they crossed, and hills sloped down and then another plain, hot now, and purple brown, bumpy, with heat and Compie looking back to see how he was riding. Then there were other mountains dark ahead. And then instead of going on to Arusha they turned left, he evidently figured that they had the gas, and looking down he saw a pink sifting cloud, moving over the ground, and in the air, like the first snow in a blizzard, that comes from nowhere, and he knew the locusts were coming up from the South. Then they began to climb and they were going to the East it seemed, and then it darkened and they were in a storm, the rain so thick it seemed like flying through a waterfall, and then they were out and Compie turned his head and grinned and pointed and there, ahead, all he could see, as wide as all the world, great, high, and unbelievably white in the sun, was the square top of Kilimanjaro. And then he knew that there was where he was going.

* * *

Just then the hyena stopped whimpering in the night and started to make a strange, human, almost crying sound. The woman heard it and stirred uneasily. She did not wake. In her dream she was at the house on Long Island and it was the night before her daughter's début. Somehow her father was there and he had been very rude. Then the noise the hyena made was so loud she woke and for a moment she did not know where she was and she was very afraid. Then she took the flashlight and shone it on the other cot that they had carried in after Harry had gone to sleep. She could see his bulk under the mosquito bar but somehow he had gotten his leg out and it hung down alongside the cot. The dressings had all come down and she could not look at it.

"Molo," she called. "Molo! Molo!"

Then she said, "Harry, Harry!" Then her voice rising, "Harry! Please, Oh Harry!"

There was no answer and she could not hear him breathing.

Outside the tent the hyena made the same strange noise that had awakened her. But she did not hear him for the beating of her heart.

UNCLE FONSE LAUGHED

By Jesse Stuart

HE WASN'T NO AKIN TO US. HE WAS JUST A GOOD FRIEND TO PA. I remember when Pa would say to Ma: "Get every big pot on today, every little pot, every dirty pot—every clean pot. Fonse and Effie's coming over and bringing all the youngins." Then I'd see Pa just tickled to death—a smile on his thin brown lips from ear to ear. He would grab the ax and start to the woodyard. He would get a pole of wood and put it on a block. He would whack off a stick at a lick. He would cut two arm loads of dry stovewood. Mom would take a chair with her apron full of soupbeans. She would lift them from her apron and blow the chaff from them as she let them fall from her hand into a crock. It took plenty of beans when Uncle Fonse brought the family over to see us.

I can remember seeing the mule straining at the Tillman family express right down at the yellow bank below our house. He would stop, pant, wiggle his ears—then try again. He would pull the express about two cornrows wide at a time coming up the bank slonchways. Uncle Fonse would holler at Pa: "Good a mule, Mick, as ever was hooked in the harness. Never have to touch this mule with the withe." Pa would say: "Fonse, you old lazy devil you—why don't you get out and walk up the bank."

Then Fonse would laugh and Pa would laugh and slap his knees. And the mule would pull again up the bank—the yellow clods of dirt a-flying from the hoofs—the foam spattering from the nostrils— white breaths of air going from the nostrils and spreading out thin on the blue air.

When the mule would make it with his heavy load to our yard, Fonse would get out and he'd slap Pa on the back and Pa would slap Fonse. They would go around and around: Pa would say: "How are you, you old turkey buzzard you?" And Fonse would slap Pa on the back hard enough to scare us children for Fonse was so much bigger than Pa. Fonse would say: "How are you—you little game

275

rooster you?" And they would laugh—Uncle Fonse's red face beaming in the sun—his blue eyes twinkling—his heavy jaws bobbing up and down on his wattled neck. Pa would say: "You're getting dough-bellied Fonse. You ain't doing enough running up and down the hills. Maybe you're getting more to eat than I'm getting. My old woman won't feed me only when I got company. That's why I wanted you over here today." Then Uncle Fonse would hit Pa on the shoulder and Pa would laugh.

Aunt Effie would start in the house with all seven of the children. Pa would say: "Finn, you take your Uncle Fonse's mule out to the barn and give him seven ears of that good white corn and some of the clover hay." Well, I would unhook the traces, and do up the lines on the hames—take the mule from between the shafts and feed him hay and corn that our mules couldn't get. We were saving it for tougher plowing days. But Pa didn't have anything that was too good for Uncle Fonse's mule. Finn and me we had fists that made his boys stand around. Pa said once: "Why don't you call his boys Cousin Bill, Cousin Charlie, Cousin Henry and the girls: Cousin Effie, Cousin Martha, Cousin Grace and Cousin Fleece."

We never said anything to Pa but we thought he was better to Uncle Fonse's boys than he was to us. We didn't like it. We put the rocks to Bill a couple o' times out in the cowpasture. Brother Finn peeled a pine tree right above Bill's head when he was running toward the house. Uncle Fonse's boys were afraid of us. We couldn't get 'em into the woods to play with us. Finn would say: "Them boys ain't no kin to me. I don't like 'em. Pa can't make me like 'em. I'll peel the bark off 'n one's head with a rock when I get a chance."

Aunt Effie would go in the kitchen where Mom was. She would say: "Now let me help you right along with the dinner Mrs. Powderjay. Let me blow the chaff out'n the beans. Let me peel the taters. Let me do something." Mom would let her peel the taters. She was so fat and to stir around in the kitchen between the stove, the safe and the kitchen table and the woodbox, she'd get to wheezing a getting her breath. Mom would tell Pop when she left: "I just can't stand that wheezing. It is like catching a young mouse in a trap. It run all through me. I can't stand a mouse screak in the kitchen. So, I put Effie to peeling taters. She's so fat. She can't hardly get around in her fat. I don't see how she can cook for seven brats that eat as much as hers eat. Pon my words—I thought mine could eat. But it's just a drop in the bucket the way her youngins eat."

We would get Uncle Fonse's boys out as far as the smoke-house to play with us. We would play fox and dog. We kindly liked the little girls—they wasn't our cousins and we didn't want them to be. We helped them make playhouses behind the smoke-house. Sister Clara, Belle, and Sophie wouldn't like to see us play with Uncle Fonse's girls all the time—carry them the biggest arm loads of moss and broken dishes—but we did. We were the men and we watched over the house and kept away the Indians that were hiding behind the trees out in the pasture—out there among the pines.

Before dinner was ready—Pa and Uncle Fonse would sprawl down in the floor. They would wallow on the floor and talk. Pa would say: "Fonse what makes me and you such big fools. We aint no kin are we?" Uncle Fonse would say: "We got good fences between our farms Mick. We pay our debts. We take time off to go and see one another like them old folks used to do when we was boys back in Flint County . . . We aint no akin unless Pa's fox hound run a fox across the creek back yander on Gimpson creek in Flint County and your Pa drunk of the waters below." Then Pa would laugh and laugh. He would say: "Drunk of the waters below," and slap Uncle Fonse on the shoulder.

Pa would say: "Something I'm forgetting Fonse . . ." He would get up and bring a couple of tastebud cigars rolled out'n home-made tobacco by Pa's own hands. Uncle Fonse would lay there in the floor and look to the ceiling and laugh. He would say: "W'y you'd forget your head Mick if it was loose." And he would laugh. He would lay there in the floor with Pa. They would smoke their long cigars and look to the loft and blow smoke at a spider on a web. "Make that sucker sick up there Fonse. A dime you can't do it." Uncle Fonse would blow smoke toward the spider on the low loft. It would fidget around on the little white strands of the web. It looked like it was looking over the edges of its mountain at the deep canyon below—at the big devils on the floor where the clouds of strong smoke were coming from.

Pa and Uncle Fonse would talk about farming. Pa would say: "I'll raise the best corn in the country over there in that new ground. Awful freeze we had this winter will make the ground meller as meal. I'll get some good taters out'n that ground too. You watch me this year. I'll raise more corn than you—you old pup. You beat me last year. But I'm going to lower the boom on you this year." Uncle Fonse would say: "You ain't going to beat nobody. Your wife might." And he would laugh and Pa would laugh. Uncle Fonse's neck wattles would shake like a turkey gobbler's red wattles.

Mom would come to the door. She would say: "Dinner is ready Mick. Call the youngins." Pa and Uncle Fonse would jump up from the floor and Pa would go out and holler like he was blowing a foxhorn: "Dinner youngins—come to it. Yaho! Yaho! Dinner is ready! Come to it youngins if you want any." Well, we'd come running from behind the smoke-house and from the woods like chickens coming to the corncrib of a morning for corn. We would run in to get dinner. It would be late on Sunday when Mom and Aunt Effie would get dinner.

We didn't have to wait for a second table. Mom would say: "Put two tables together so everybody can eat." And we'd all eat together.

Uncle Fonse would say: "Pass me a little sugar for my coffee please." Pa would hand him the salt. Uncle Fonse would be busy. He wouldn't notice. Uncle Fonse would say: "Three spoonsful of sugar to my coffee and if it ain't sweet enough I have Effie to dip her little finger in it." Pa would be trying to hold back a laugh so Uncle Fonse wouldn't catch on. And when Uncle Fonse would take the drink of coffee, Pa would stand up at the table and laugh at Uncle Fonse running to the door. All of us children would laugh at Pa and Uncle Fonse. Mom would say: "Pon my soul Effie, I do believe there is two of the craziest men in this country. I believe we got 'em." Mom would laugh. Aunt Effie would shake in her fat and laugh. Then Uncle Fonse would say: "I take better care of my woman than you do though, Mick. I feed her better. Your woman is poor as a snake. She don't get nothing to eat only when I come over." Then Uncle Fonse and Pa would start laughing again.

"We got the two craziest men in the world," Aunt Effie would say to Mom. "Fonse just plagues me to death. When we go down the road in the express to town, Fonse hollers something at everybody. They stop and look at us in that old express setting upon that little hug-me-tight seat till we get out of sight." Aunt Effie would shake in her fat laughing at Pa and Uncle Fonse. Pa would say: "Want so-more sugar for your coffee, Fonse? You'd better let Effie stick her little finger in it the next time." Then Mom would start laughing.

After dinner Pa and Uncle Fonse would light their tastebud cigars. Mom and Aunt Effie would get their long-stemmed clay pipes. They would get homemade tobacco out'n the oatbox where Mom always kept her tobacco. They would fill their pipes—shove the tobacco down with a forefinger—light their pipes with a piece of rich pine kindling. I'd take it to the stove and light the kindling from the kitchen stove fire. And big clouds of smoke would go up from our table. It would be hard for us to get our breath around the table. I would say: "Bet I never smoke when I grow up. I hate the old stinking stuff." Pa would say: "Got the bluff on our youngins, ain't we Fonse?" And Fonse would say: "That boy ain't no Powderjay if he don't smoke the blessed weed when he grows up. Comes by it honest you know—his Ma, his Pa and all his Uncles and Aunts on both side used the fragrant weed—a blessing to all mankind."

After Pa and Uncle Fonse would smoke, they would walk out in the pasture. Mom and Aunt Effie would put my sisters and Uncle Fonse's pretty little girls in the kitchen to washing the dishes. I would come in and offer to dry the dishes. Mom would try to get me to help my sisters. But I never would do it. I'd say: "I ain't going to do no girl's work. I'm going to work outside with Pa. Ain't getting me in no kitchen." Mom and Aunt Effie would take their chairs out in the yard and put them under the peach tree. They would smoke their pipes and blow the blue smoke into the pretty spring wind. I can see it going to the sky in tiny swirls. I can see Pa and Uncle Fonse—Pa, little and spry—Uncle Fonse, big, square shouldered and fat—walking slowly out the pasture path—talking, laughing, whittling.

We would play fox and dog over the hills. We would forget about Uncle Fonse's boys liking Pa and him liking them. We would forget all our troubles and play. We would quit throwing rocks at each other. Uncle Fonse's boys liked my sisters and I liked their sisters and Finn did too. We got along all right—running in the sunlight—jumping over the creeks—laughing, playing, shouting, screaming under the sun. It just seemed like the time was too short.

Uncle Fonse and Pa would come back around through the pasture—
around the path under the pines by the hog-pen. Pa so little and
thin—Uncle Fonse so short and heavy. They would come whittling,
laughing, talking. I could see Pa slap Uncle Fonse on the shoulder.
Pa would say: "Fine day this has been Fonse. Come again and see
me." And Uncle Fonse would say: "I ain't never coming to see you
again till you bring Sall and all the kids and come to see me, Mick.
Now this has been twice on the straight I have been to see you.
You got to come to see me next time."

Well Brother Finn and Uncle Fonse's boy Bill would have the
mule out and hooked to the express. I can see the mule standing in
the blue wind by the hollyhocks—switching his tail in the bright
blue wind at the flies. I can see the sun the way it went down over
Lonesome ridge dragging a patch of red clouds behind it. I can see
Pa and Uncle Fonse and Mom helping Aunt Effie into the express.
They would put a chair by the express stirrup. Aunt Effie would
step on a rock—from that up in the chair—from the chair to the
stirrup and from the stirrup to the express bed. And when she got
up to the chair, Pa, Uncle Fonse and Mom would all be ahold of
her to keep her from falling. "I don't want to break a bone at my
age," Aunt Effie would say. "And if my wife gets any more
pounds," Uncle Fonse would say, "she going to break a seat. I'm
going to put a good hickory chair up there in the front for myself."
And Uncle Fonse would laugh again and say: "I feed my wife.
Now look at your wife there Mick—thin as a beanpole." Uncle
Fonse would slap the mule's back lightly with the lines and say:
"Get up! Get up there boy! Guess I got all the youngins."

"Come back again," Pa would say.

After they would leave Pa would say: "I tell you Sall, they
don't make a better neighbor than old Fonse. Of course, he don't
belong to my Party nor my church. I can't help that. He can't
help it. He's just what he is and I am just what I am. But he's a
good neighbor as a body ever lived by. It's good fences that we got
between our places that make us good neighbors. You remember
we couldn't get along with that hirm-skirm piece of a man that
used to live over there. I built my part of the line fence and
couldn't get him to build his. He would just brush it—keep throwing more brush on it. Cattle is smart these days on them brush fences
after they've been used to barbwire. So his cattle kept getting in

and eating up devilish nigh everything I had planted in the ground. Since Fonse has moved over there and bought that place we don't have any more trouble."

"But you all are the craziest acting men I ever saw get together," Mom would say. "I don't care if he does belong to the Forty Gallon Baptis and you are a Slab Baptis and you belong to one Party and he belongs to the other. You all just plague women folks to death the way you lay around in the floor and go on about this and that." Pa would say: "I popped it to him out there in the pasture when we's out there a looking at my cattle. I ast him some questions he couldn't answer about Resurrection. They've got some funny beliefs in his church. Them Forty Gallon Baptis is a funny church. And I sure did get him about his Party. Then he popped it to me about my Party and the Slab Baptis. Even jumped on me about my fox hound. He said the night out there when old Gun Powder led that pack of hounds that I put moonshine in sweet milk and give it to him. He'll have that going all over the country. Devil can't uptrip that man."

"You beat all men I ever saw," Mom would say.

"Something heavy in my coat pocket."

And when Pop pulled it out it was a tack hammer Uncle Fonse had made for Pop and slipped it in his pocket. "What do you know about that, Sall. Look here what old Fonse has made for me. He heard me say I needed a tack hammer and he made me one. He can make anything in the world he wants to make in a blacksmith shop and just to think what I used to slip in old Fonse's pocket. I used to slip a dead bird in his pocket every week. I'd do it and he'd come to me and he'd say: 'Funny thing, Mick. I find a dead bird in my left coat pocket every week. It is some kind of a token.' I would laugh and say: 'You are just a dreaming. You don't find no bird in your pocket.' He would say: 'Oh, yes, I do. I know I ain't that crazy. I remember what happens to me. I remember too, that I don't put the bird in my own pocket. I reach down in my pocket. It is there—a dead bird. There's something strange about a dead bird. It is a strange token of some kind.' Yes, I put the birds in his pocket—and he gives me this fine tack hammer—big enough to draw nails with from the old planks."

Time will go on as time will. New people will be born into the world. The old people go from the world and give place to the new. Children grow up and babies are born. And the world goes on. There is not any turning back the hand on the clock. Time is in a swift race—it keeps running and running and it never gets anyplace. I could see the gray hairs come to Pop's head. He was getting older. Uncle Fonse was getting older. I remember when we made the blackberry wine and had it in a churn in the smokehouse, how Pop and Uncle Fonse went into the smokehouse. They walked in straight as sourwood saplings. They come out bent over and swaying like windblown willows by the creek. Uncle Fonse wasn't laughing when he said to Pa: "Mick, we ain't young as we used to be. But this old heart is young, Mick even if the old body is getting old." Uncle Fonse was holding to the corner logs of the smokehouse and helping Pa around by the shoulder . . . No, time is a thief that comes in the daylight, the moonlight—sunlight. He steals what that can never be brought back. He is a thief that cannot be jailed. There is not a jail big enough to hold him, nor money enough in the world to bribe him. But, not a thief of time, could keep Pa and Uncle Fonse from bringing the families together for a big dinner once and twice sometimes each week. Not even a thief of time could stop them from laughing and argying—They were against time. It didn't matter. They went laughing freely with the wind. Growing older had made them younger in a world where one sees joy, sorrow, has music, life, love, tears—where life is before one— life so big, so great—high as the skies are high—deep as the earth is deep.

I remember how Pa laughed at the table that morning. He said to Mom: "Pour me another cup of coffee, Sall. You remember how I got the salt in old Fonse's coffee that day for dinner here. Well, he tried to get a good one on me yesterday. I went over there to see him about my boy Finn and his boy Bill—You know how they are since they got to running together. He can't get no work out'n Bill and I can't get no work out'n Finn. I heard they'd been plum up there at that bad dance hall where them Perkins boys got cut the other night. So I says to Fonse: 'Fonse, ain't they something we can do about our boys running around together the way they do.' Fonse was getting in the express then. Had the mule all trigged up. Had red tassels on the bridle. Had brass rings on the hames for the check lines to run through and snap into brass rings on the bristle bitts. So, Fonse says to me: 'You take care of the boys, Mick.

I won't be here to take care of them after tomorrow night.' And I says: 'Why Fonse—you're not skipping the country are you? Ain't stole no sheep—broke no bank—shot no man have you?' And Fonse says: 'No, I ain't done nothing I'm ashamed of. I am just going to die. It's my heart. The whole thing was pictured to me in bed last night. I saw the whole thing.' And Fonse, he just laughed and laughed. He thinks he's got a good 'n on me. And when he started driving off, I says: 'Where are you going Fonse?' 'Going to town to have the James boys to make my coffin tomorrow.' And he drove off down the road. He was laughing. And I was laughing. You know how Fonse acts. I can see old Fonse going yet—the mule trotting down that piece of sandy road by the pear trees. I can hear the creaking of the buggy wheels. And it all just kindly went through my mind that I'd have to slip another bird in the old boy's pocket. But instead of a bird this time I got a ground mole with baby hands. I'm going to slip it in his pocket. I'll pull a rich 'n on old Fonse . . ."

Finn went to town the next day. I remember when he came in he said to Pa: "You know I believe Uncle Fonse is going crazy. I was over to see Bill awhile ago and Uncle Fonse was upon the hill cutting briars and sprouts off a little knoll. He said he was going to die tonight. Had the James boys to make him a coffin out 'n planks he's had seasoning in the barn for ten years. He's said he didn't want no undertaker's fancy-coffin. Said he wanted a coffin made out'n them oaks back of the barn. That's where he got them planks from ten years ago when Ben Ulling had that mill back there in the head of the hollow. He had a couple of trees cut and sawed into heavy planks. He had his coffin made out'n them very boards. While I was over there he got down in his coffin and tried it out. 'It is just a fit,' he said. Bill is a laughing at his Pa. Aunt Effie is a crying. The girls are crying. Aunt Effie said: 'He is either telling the truth or he is going crazy. And they ain't never been a Tillman gone crazy to the extent of my knowings-yet.' He don't act to me like a man that is going to die. He won't tell how he knows."

I remember how Pa laughed. He said: "He's pulling a good one this time. He's got it up his sleeve to have some fun. If he's going to die, old Fonse would make his own coffin. He can make a hammer, make nails, wagon wheels, guns, smoothing irons. He can make anything he wants to make. He surely can make a coffin."

Pa went to bed that night. The wind howled through the green hickories at the end of the porch by Pa's bed. I remember seeing Pa get out of the bed in a night shirt. He looked at the moon and the stars in the heavens. He walked across the dewy grass barefooted. That was strange for Pa. Pa is a solid man. He is hard to move to tears. But Pa was in trouble. I heard him come to the bed. He got Mom up from sleep. He said: "Sall, I am troubled about Fonse. I can't sleep. I hear the death-bells ringing in my ears. I have tried to sleep. But I can see a wooden box in front of me. Get out of the bed and make a biler of strong coffee."

Pa put on his clothes. He walked to the barn and to the pigpen while Mom was making the coffee. I know he went to the pigpen for the shoats squealed when Pa went past. The cows mooed when he passed them sleeping in the dewy grass by the barn-gate. Pa was in trouble. I never saw him act like this only once before in my life. That was the night Brother Finn got cut at the square dance and they brought him home all slashed up with a hawk-billed barlow knife. I heard Mom call him to get his coffee. And I heard Pa lumber through the house. I heard him pull his chair up to the table. I heard him say to Mom: "I am going over to Fonse's place just as soon as I've got light to travel by. I know something has happened. I have seen Fonse. I have heard him laugh. I know what I am saying is true. You know he said to me once when we's out in the pasture: 'Mick, you ought to be in my church. To prove to you we are right, if I die first you'll hear me laugh out there in the little pine grove where we always went on Sundays to talk and whittle by that salt-trough. If you die first I'll go out there and see if I can hear you laugh or speak to me first. And we'll see who's right—the Slabs or the Forty Gallons—' And I says to Fonse: 'It's a go Fonse. You laugh to me. I'll know that old crow laugh you got.' And I would know it in Halifax too if I was to hear it there. So, I went out to the pine grove this morning. I've just come from there. I heard old Fonse laugh. I know it was his voice. Lord, I know his voice. I know that laugh. I know it was his laugh. It wasn't the wind. It wasn't the rustle of the green leaves. It was his laugh. I am trembling like a leaf in the wind."

I saw Pa cross the hill. It wasn't good day. He told me to feed the hogs and not harness the mules till he come back. I saw him going up the path to the top of the hill. He walked beside of the good barbwire fence Uncle Fonse and Pa built. I saw him go between the wires and disappear among the green sassafras sprouts—wet with dew. They would soak Pa but he didn't care. Mom said: "It is a funny thing the way them men act. Maybe they're both going crazy. Your Pa is about crazy this morning. He drunk six cups of strong coffee. He says that something has happened to your Uncle Fonse. He says he knows that something has happened. Said he heard Fonse speak to him from the pine grove out there where they go on Sundays to talk and whittle. He said it wasn't the wind. He said it was Fonse. But wonder if it wasn't the wind in the pine needles? Wonder if it wasn't something besides Fonse? How could it be Fonse there so soon?" And Mom went to looking off into space. It kindly scared me. And I said: "Mom there is something funny about the whole thing. I know I am right. I saw Uncle Fonse cutting the sprouts off a place to bury him on yesterday. He was having the James boys to make his coffin. He got down in it and tried it out. He said: 'It's just a fit.' I remember it well. I know that I am not dreaming. I come on up the road. I met Ben Ulling and I told him about it. Ben said: 'He's either got a communication with the sperit or he's losing his mind, I-jacks, one.' I come on up there at that sweet apple tree below Aimes' barnlot and frailed me some sweet apples with a crooked limb. I remember it as if it had just happened. I was not dreaming."

When Pa walked down the hill, Mom run out to meet him: "What has happened to Fonse," Mom said. Pa just walked right down to the porch. He almost fell on the edge of the porch. He was quivering like a leaf in the wind. "Fonse is dead as a piece of dirt," said Pa. "He died last night sometime. I was there just a few minutes ago. I took the mole along to slip in his pocket. But he was dead. The family is all crying and going on something awful. I didn't stay. I couldn't stay. Fonse, there so quiet—not laughing! W'y he laughed when he was going to have the James boys to make his coffin. I thought he was joking. He didn't care to die. He laughed quietly into the arms of Death. I've always thought God would want a man that could laugh no matter what church he belonged to . . . Fonse there so quiet, so silent. He didn't speak to me. I couldn't stand it."

Mom shed tears. "What will Effie do now," Mom said, "with all that family of children? She can't keep 'em in grub the way they eat. Place not paid for with all them good fences around it. One thing Fonse believed in was a good fence between him and his neighbors . . . Poor Effie. No way to turn back time. It just keeps slipping up on a body like it slips up on the flower and a stalk of corn. Everything has a season—even to man. God wanted Fonse to do something else—maybe to make fences in Heaven. Maybe, God wanted to hear him laugh."

Pa went about silently all day. He would walk to the pinegrove, then to the house. He would watch a crow fly over. He would look at the growing corn. He would watch the white clouds float over. Pa would not turn his hand to work. He would not let us work. He did not go back to Tillman's house. Pa stayed at home all day. He was nervous as a shoemake leaf in the wind.

"Just to think about it all is a funny thing," said Pa, "life is so strange. To think about it all the time would make a man lose his mind. Fonse has left the earth. He was a good man—tended to his own business. He owned his land. He took care of his family and sent his children to school. He went to church. He believed in God's workings through the sperits. He didn't belong to the right Party but he belonged to the one he thought was right. Fonse Tillman was the kind of a man the country is built on. Yet, God called him out of this life. He left men in it not worth powder and lead to kill 'em. I just don't understand it. And tomorrow!"

"Yes, tomorrow, at two o'clock," said Mom, "right back of the house on that old poor point up there where the blackberry briars and the sawbriars take the place. That is where they will plant Fonse. That is where he wanted to be planted—up there where he used to tend corn. I remember seeing him go around that hill behind the mules. I can't forget it."

I remember the day at two o'clock. Yesterday never caught up with tomorrow. We were there. The crowd was there. The hill was lined with people. Pa said to Mom: "See what the people think of Fonse. Respected in life. Respected in death. Look at this crowd here. It's the biggest funeral I've ever seen among these hills. I have to help carry him up the hill to the grave. I don't know whether I can make it or not." I remember seeing Pa. He walked over the old corn rows—puffing and blowing under the corn of the heavy box. The crowd followed up the hill. We passed under Fonse's heavy fruited apple trees.

The crowd stood there with heads bowed and heads bare. The checklines were slipped under the box—the heavy box was lowered into the earth and the check lines slipped from beneath it. I remember the tears that flowed down Pa's brown cheeks. I remember the cries of Uncle Fonse's children and Aunt Effie. I remembered they were not my real aunt and uncle but Pop and Mom taught us to call them uncle and aunt and they taught their children to call Pop and Mom uncle and aunt.

I remember the farm that Uncle Fonse owned. I remember the roses in bloom in the woods not far from where Uncle Fonse was buried. I remember how they waved in the wind—how the mountain daisy gently swayed on the hill where Uncle Fonse would sleep—the old furrows where he had plowed that time would soon blot out and leave the land level as a yard. I remember the silent crowd that left the hill—the wind overhead in the apple tree leaves.

Before my eyes were the eternal Kentucky hills. The crow flew over them. The buzzard sailed high above them. Among them men and women worked for their bread—knew the change of season. They saw life ripen sweetly and sourly with the years. They saw the flowers bloom in their season—die in their season. But even among these hills eternal in their great beauty of lilting green leaves in the wind—no one could stop time. No one could deny Uncle Fonse knew he was going to die. He had his coffin made himself. He cleared off his ground to sleep upon. Now he rests in that vast silence—under the sighing of the wind—the passing of the white cloud in the heavens—under the bloom of the rose and the mountain daisy and the swift wing of the crow. He lies in eternal Kentucky hills that if they were alive and could speak they could tell greater stories than any man of life, love, death, darkness, gloom, despair, the communion of the spirits. They could tell stories of many a carcass that does not sleep in a grave. They could tell unbelievable stories to make a book stalwart as a mountain.

A DUEL BY CANDLELIGHT

By ANDREAS LATZKO

THE BARONIAL CASTLE OF GYOROKY, IN TRANSYLVANIA, WAS DESTROYED at the end of the XVth century by a passing horde of Turks. For centuries its moss-grown ruins had no other inhabitants than a few emaciated goats, and the descendants of the lords of Gyoroky, who in the days of old had plundered every convoy of merchandise that passed near their stronghold, and were now but a modest family of Austrian officers.

Within the memory of these survivors, no Baron Gyoroky had known what it was to eat and drink to his heart's content; all were giants in limb and muscle, but their portion of the good things of life was no more than that of ordinary men. Reduced circumstances had tamed their spirit, and the feudal brigands of yore passed from the severe routine of the Cadets' school to the barrack-square, where they were limited to bullying young recruits.

At last rescue came.

A little German professor of geology visited Gyoroky on holiday. His idea had been to hunt for traces of Saxon elements there, tossed by a historic tempest as far as Transylvania. Instead, he went up hill and down dale, tapping with his little hammer all the bits of rock he found, sounding them like a physician. Finally he carried off two sacks full of stones.

To the general surprise, he returned some months later, accompanied by an imposing procession of motor cars.

Included in this escort was the last scion of the house of Gyoroky. Laced into the uniform of an infantry officer, the lieutenant sulkily strode into the smoky parlor of the village inn, openly distrustful of the mad professor and the whole company of financiers and lawyers. He sat inattentively through a tedious discussion, supporting himself with copious draughts of the familiar sour wine of the district. The wine and the monotonous murmur of the speeches, which conveyed nothing at all to him, made him so sleepy that he thought he was dreaming in good earnest when he heard his own name, and found himself appointed chairman.

His distrust increased as he looked at the imposing document which he was asked to sign in connection with the issue of shares numbered 1 to 100,000. The lieutenant's experience of papers with large figures above and his signature below had not been happy. And the unencumbered portion of his meagre pay did not admit of any further signatures.

In vain did the others try to explain to the officer the difference between a promissory note and a share; a baron of Gyoroky was above these Jewish subtleties, and he was on the point of exploding when the magic word "advance" promptly dissipated both his annoyance and the effects of the wine. After much hesitation, scared at his own effrontery, and mainly in order to get rid of the fellows, he asked for 10,000 Austrian crowns—say £400. When no one demurred he was confirmed in his suspicion, and when he placed ten irreproachable 1000-crown notes in his worn pocket-book he felt sure that he was dealing with a band of brigands. Anyhow, for once he had got some money out of the Jews without any prospect of its return. For it would have been quite impossible to produce ten thousand crowns out of what was still assignable of his pay, even though he lived to the age of Methuselah. That was the end of that.

He soon learned better. The counterfoils of his check-book taught the chairman of the new mining company the value of his signature. Instead of reducing the worth of the paper on which he placed it, as had happened sometimes in the past, his scrawl now transformed every sheet into money. The lord of Gyoroky was not a man to disdain this magic power. On the contrary, the vague fear of seeing the beautiful dream end in a painful awakening urged him to put his power to the test. He indulged his most extravagant desires—and still the enchantment lasted.

Then the ancestral itch for authority, so long repressed, awoke in its primitive force. The feudal pride, humiliated for centuries, welled up, bursting the frail barrier of the codes of what is called civilization. Rich and powerful, Baron Gyoroky saw no reason for repressing his natural instincts. What if he had been born some centuries too late? He resumed the life of the lords of Gyoroky at the point at which his ancestors had had to abandon it.

From the open flanks of the old mountain there flowed inexhaustible dividends. On a neighboring summit the ancient fortress rose again, exact at all points to the descriptions and engravings of the family chronicle, with its wide moat filled with water, its drawbridge and its keep. But instead of the ancient bombards, long-range guns of the most modern type showed their muzzles, and machine guns lurked behind the ramparts. The garrison, however, wore the livery of the house of Gyoroky, and, before the gates, men-at-arms mounted guard with halberds, though the men thus attired were the best non-commissioned officers in the country, picked by the experienced baron from among his former subordinates.

With this bodyguard, his fortress, and his riches, the baron was a power in the State. He requisitioned what he fancied, and imprisoned anyone who disobeyed him. A person who was simpleton enough to try to prosecute him received from the authorities a reply to this effect: "Let the plaintiff himself serve the writ on the lord of the manor, and justice will take its course!" In fact, since the baron, putting threats into effect, had received writ-servers with machine-gun fire, there was no longer a magistrate sitting in Transylvania within range of New Gyoroky.

In the capital, the extravagances of the brigand baron were treated with amused indulgence. He became the hero of musical comedies. Picture-postcard factories and illustrated papers sent their photographers to Gyoroky, the latest arrival in the news. A reporter succeeded in getting engaged as a man-at-arms, and his description of the life of the castle was "splashed" in every popular newspaper in the whole world.

In time, however, the authorities began to tire of the complaints of the baron's behavior. The joke had lasted long enough, and it was decided, in principle, to put an end to it. In practice, there was hesitation in mobilizing the forces of the State against a single citizen; it might excite ridicule abroad. Even when the baron virtually invested the churches and carried off such brides as he fancied, on the strength of the *jus primae noctis* of his ancestors, it was preferred to turn a blind eye to his excesses, and the scandal was hushed up. Indiscreet journalists were taken to task for publishing objectionable reports, but the ogre was able to keep the young brides captive in his fortress, without fear of justice or of the vengeance of the outraged husbands. The wisest of these made no boast of their predicament, and thus avoided adding mockery to misfortune.

However, the urgency of the prelates at last persuaded the State to act. A lien was placed on all the bank accounts of the lord of Gyoroky, and he was threatened with the blockade of his castle. The baron replied by levelling all his guns at the neighboring mine-workings, threatening to reduce to atoms the property of his fellow shareholders unless they did something to protect him from the attacks of the Church.

In this fight between big capital and the high clergy, it was the worldly power that won. The severest sanctions were discussed, but once more the affair was allowed to drop, since a few injured husbands could not outweigh the social significance of an enterprise capitalized at millions. The public was informed that in view of the necessity of protecting the miners' families from the disaster of unemployment nothing more could be done.

So the laugh was once more on the baron's side, and the only practical result of this affair of state was to demonstrate to the lord of Gyoroky the necessity of insuring against the danger of a siege. The national canning factories received an order on a scale that startled them.

After this decisive victory, the baron threw off all restraint. There was a regular *sauve qui peut* in the neighborhood; officials who had pretty wives asked to be transferred, landowners sold their estates at a loss, no sacrifice was too great to make for escape from the neighborhood of the lion's den. Those who were unavoidably retained in the vicinity of New Gyoroky made the best of a bad job, and discreetly went away on an alleged business journey when it came to the turn of their wives to make a more or less prolonged stay in the sumptuous private apartments of the castle. The reign of the Iron King was absolute. Villagers far around hid when, by the light of torches and to the beat of drums, the garrison of New Gyoroky passed by. The police set a good example, as was their duty; at the first sound of a raiding party they became completely invisible.

* * *

One day, when riding at no great distance from the castle, the baron discovered a delicious little person, with hair like a raven's wing; a surprising spectacle, as he supposed all this district to have been long exhausted. Inquiries revealed a simple explanation: the young woman with the dark eyes was the wife of Rabbi Samuel Levi, and the baron, now that he had money, had given up all intercourse with Jews. But Mrs. Levi was different. Here was an amorous domain beyond his ken. He embarked excitedly upon the exotic adventure.

Rabbi Samuel Levi was a delicate little man, with a thin pointed beard and twinkling eyes. His co-religionists considered him the cutest of them all. He noticed the baron's frequent torchlight rides past his house, and he was not wholly unprepared when one night, on his return home from officiating in a neighboring village, he found the nest empty. The flowers in the garden had been trampled by horses' hooves, the walls of his house blackened by torches; the furniture was in disorder as if there had been a raid, and the weeping servant related the unheard-of brutality with which her poor mistress had been carried off. But Samuel Levi glanced at the open wardrobe. He saw that the finest dresses and the best linen had vanished, and the gap helped him to bear his loss with manly composure.

Pronouncing the prescribed ritual curse against the "seduced" wife, he put on his silk cap and set off at once along the road to the fortress. Trotting as fast as his short legs would carry him, and murmuring his prayers as he went, he was barely two hours in reaching the castle. But he found the drawbridge raised and the gates barred. In answer to his shouts, the laughing guards, with mocking courtesy, begged him to be good enough to wait a little: the baron was too pleasantly occupied just then to receive visitors.

The Rabbi nodded to signify that he quite understood. He sat down on a moss-covered slab, opened his prayer book, and waited patiently. At last, toward sunset, the drawbridge was lowered with a thunderous rattling, the massive gates slowly opened, and a halberdier actually approached him and bade him welcome in the name of his master.

Little Samuel Levi, deaf to the tittering around him, gravely entered the imposing vault.

The lord of Gyoroky received the little man in the huge ancestral hall, his enormous body stretched in a gigantic armchair; from the magnificently chased golden cup that stood before him was wafted the aroma of a very old Tokay. He was in an excellent humor.

"And what can I do for you, Mr. Levi?" he asked, patronizingly.

The rabbi bowed humbly, rubbed the palms of his hands together, and, after a moment's hesitation, declared with firmness:

"I have come to demand reparation from you, My Lord."

The baron jumped out of his chair in astonishment. Then he burst into a roar of laughter, and, producing his pocket-book, enquired:

"How much do you want, Mr. Levi?"

The shrewd eyes flashed for a moment. But the rabbi recovered his imperturbability. He replied, with due respect:

"Your lordship is pleased to jest. I know how fastidious are the lords of Gyoroky on a point of honor. You will not refuse me due reparation."

The baron's mouthful of Tokay nearly choked him. But with an effort he checked his laughter. He bowed low and replied:

"Very well, then! We will fight, little rabbi. I leave you the choice of weapons. It is for you, the injured party, to dictate the conditions of the duel. I undertake to respect them. As you see, there are rapiers and yataghans on the walls here. Perhaps you prefer the heavy cavalry saber. There are plenty in my armory, with a first-class edge on them. Or pistols, rifles, guns, mortars—anything you like."

Samuel Levi raised his thin hands in a gesture of refusal.

"Why all this profusion, My Lord? You know well enough that I have no skill in the use of your lethal weapons. I have not come to challenge you in order to give myself up to be helplessly slaughtered. If you intend to give me satisfaction, you must leave it to me to state the conditions."

The baron bowed to the ground.

"And your conditions are—?" he asked.

The rabbi took two or three little steps forward.

"In the first place, your lordship will be so kind as to have yourself firmly tied to that armchair with stout ropes."

"Tied? I—tied?" cried the baron, indignantly. "Not I!"

Levi made a hurried deprecating gesture.

"Pardon, pardon, My Lord, I shall merely see that it has been properly done, and then I will have myself similarly tied in this other chair. Your lordship can trust your men to make sure that they will bind me no less securely."

"What is the game?" said the baron, grudgingly giving way: "Let myself be bound! Get that out of your head, Jew!"

The rabbi spoke up with decision:

"Your lordship has yourself said that it is for me, as the injured party, to determine the conditions of the duel. Nobody will seriously suggest that a baron of Gyoroky would decline to keep his word. As I said, your servants will bind me with equally strong ropes. Just look at my arm, and you will agree that the condition cannot be prejudicial to you. Is it conceivable that a bound Jew should cause more fear to a baron of Gyoroky than *vice versa?*"

The baron flushed.

"Fear is a Hebrew word, Mr. Levi; excuse me for not understanding that language."

"Quite so! So there we are," said the rabbi, with satisfaction. "I am forced to insist on this condition, because I hope to wound you, My Lord, and you have a way of hitting out if one comes too close ——"

"Faint heart!" laughed the baron. "If I fight with you, you are free to wound me as much as you can. But in your own interest, little man, I advise you to do without ropes. How can you talk with your hands tied? I give you my word of honor that, even without ropes, I will keep entirely to your conditions, and my word protects you better than the most powerful hawsers could."

"Surely, surely, My Lord! I know that is so, but you are reckoning without a force stronger than any word of honor, the force of habit. You would regret it, of course—you would be ready to cut off the arm that had made you break your word. But that would not help me. Unless I am mistaken, the windows of this hall look out over the great moat, with deep water in it ——"

The baron burst out laughing:

"That's so. The windows are a hundred feet and more above the moat; you have the bump of locality, old chap. Well, now, this is a good joke. I'll agree to deliver myself to you bound hand and foot. I make only one condition: our duel must not last too long. No doubt you know there is better fun awaiting me than a *tête à tête* with a trussed Jew!"

Nothing in the rabbi's bony face revealed that he understood the allusion. The baron put a heavy hand on his shoulder, and gave him a confiding wink:

"You will allow me, Mr. Levi, to drink one more cup of Tokay, to give me courage before the duel. Perhaps you too will accept a cup?"

"I thank you, My Lord; but I prefer water. Will you, however, do me the honor of drinking both glasses?"

"With the greatest of pleasure, good rabbi. While I am about it, give your orders. I don't think we shall need a surgeon under your prudent system of trussed duellists?"

The rabbi discreetly left this question unanswered, only smiling faintly with satisfaction as the lord of the manor had his enormous goblet filled twice to the brim, and swallowed the heavy Tokay like so much water. After that, Samuel Levi carefully superintended the work of the servants. The baron's arms were securely bound with three turns of rope to the arms of his chair, and his whole body, from chest to ankles, to the back, seat, and legs of the heavy piece of oak furniture. Levi tested the ropes, found here and there a knot insufficiently tight—and finally sat down exactly three paces away, opposite the baron, and was bound with equally strong ropes to a similar armchair. He himself warned the servants to draw the bonds round his skinny arms no less tightly than round the bulging muscles of their master's. Everything must be done with rigorous correctness. He fully appreciated the honor of measuring himself against a Baron Gyoroky!

Lastly, fresh candles were placed in the great candelabra, and, at the request of the rabbi, the baron formally prohibited anyone from entering the hall until daybreak, whatever noise might be heard. The servants obediently withdrew, the doors were closed, the footsteps died away; the duellers were alone.

*　　*　　*

Then an extraordinary thing happened.

The mighty lord of New Gyoroky, who had never before known fear, had the impression of being suddenly crippled and cast upon a desert island, abandoned by the whole world, and struck off the roll of living men. The slight spluttering of the candles in the deep silence called up memories of a night spent on guard at a lying-in-state; the enforced immobility, the loss of power over his muscles, suggested the immobility of the corpse in its coffin. A cold shiver ran down the baron's spine.

He pulled himself together and looked across with a mocking smile at the little Jew, prepared to laugh at his ridiculous appearance.

But the sight of the little man sitting trussed up opposite to him froze his blood, just as if he had seen Satan himself in the chair.

Every trace of inferiority, every sign of respect had vanished from Samuel Levi's face. A disquieting and inexorable assurance shone from his little eyes, while his glance measured the powerful frame of this baron of Gyoroky. He looked as sure of victory as a practised duellist about to use his deadliest thrust to transfix his adversary.

The baron was very near calling for his servants.

"Come, come, little man!" he burst out, chaffingly, but grimacing as though every word had to be dragged from his mouth like a tooth. "I feel very like going to sleep, and then all the guns in the castle could not wake me. So hurry up with your 'wounding.'"

"I'm just going to!" replied the rabbi, cheerfully, and his face showed how much at ease he felt in his bonds. At the first considered words that he spoke, the last traces of uncertainty disappeared, and he seemed like a man set free.

"So, you have—as your friends would put it—seduced my wife, and you are very proud of your success? I wonder why. If I were a Baron Gyoroky I should have begun by looking for a pretty young maid, and only afterwards, when I was tired of her, should I have married her to Rabbi Levi. For Rabbi Levi that, I must say, would have been a bitter pill. But, thank goodness, you are content to have it the other way round. You say 'After you, Mr. Levi!' Well, I reply 'With pleasure!' If you are so modest as to take my leavings, it is a matter of taste. You may keep your bit of fluff."

The baron smiled sourly:

"Thank you, rabbi. It is not a bad bit of fluff; the only thing is to know how to get hold of it."

Samuel Levi bowed approvingly:

"Quite so, My Lord, quite so. We others go and find ourselves wives, young and virgin, in their parents' homes, without serenading or seduction nonsense. It is only then that your sort comes along, with your flowers and chocolates, even jewellery, and set out to conquer women who are deflowered and out of currency. It mystifies me. Is it your modesty or your stupidity?"

The baron paled:

"None of your insolence, Jew! Don't forget that my word of honor protects you only until dawn!"

"Are you hurt already?" said the rabbi. "I thought I was free to do my worst to wound you. Are you straining at your bonds so soon? It seems as if you are the one that needs his hands to talk with."

"Cowardly dog!" growled the baron. "How you would beg for mercy if only I had my right arm free!"

Samuel Levi's face shone. His voice grew hard and grating. He hacked at his adversary as though with the beak of a vulture:

"Why do you call me coward? Am I not tied to my chair just like you, and telling you the truth to your face? Is that cowardly? As for cowardice, what of yourself? As far back as your family chronicle goes, no Gyoroky has ever refrained from insulting and beating men who were defenceless, men in chains. Did you not torment your soldiers because discipline forbade them to retaliate? You—Gyorokys, did you not whip your serfs, and rob your merchants? Did you not squander their substance in drinking dens and gaming hells, always yourselves armed and surrounded by armed men, armed against trembling and helpless victims? That is the sort of cowardly dogs your ancestors were—and you yourself ——"

"Another word about my ancestors, and I will kill you, Jew!" roared the baron in his fury.

"When?" laughed the rabbi, contemptuously. "Tomorrow morning, perhaps? I can believe it. Tomorrow morning, when I am once more the weak and defenceless little Jew, and you are lord of the manor of New Gyoroky, with all your men. But why are you helpless now, when we are equals? I am using no arms against you, I have no servants at my back, and yet here you are squirming and grinding your teeth like a caged gorilla. Do you see now what a miserable coward you are?"

The words died on the rabbi's paling lips, for Baron Gyoroky, with a terrific heave, brought his seat so far forward that the arms of the two chairs touched. Levi shrank back in mortal fear; he could feel the baron's panting breath on his face, as though his head were now in the jaws of a wild beast. In terrified fascination he watched the powerful arms twisting in their bonds, like harpooned sharks.

But the knots held.

The rabbi breathed again. He shouted into his adversary's purple face:

"You brute beast! I will suffocate you with your own rage!"

The baron managed to regain command of himself. Quietly, almost inaudibly, he whispered between his clenched teeth:

"I am sorry for you, Jew. You have no notion of what is in store for you in the morning!"

"Don't worry about me," Levi jeered. "Unless I greatly overestimate my powers, you will have a stroke before midnight."

"Murder! Help!" gasped the other. The affront was beyond bearing. This worm, this louse—and he could not move two fingers to smash it! Raving fury clutched at his throat, hammered at his temples, set the blood surging through his swelling veins. The giant whimpered like a child, quelled by the malevolently grinning face bent over his own.

"Well, who is the cowardly dog?" shouted the rabbi in his ear. "Now do you know how good it is to be bound hand and foot? Can you feel what it means to be gagged and helpless? Wasn't it fine fun to chain men to a bench and whip them until they began to whimper like children? . . . Squeal away! You yourself, you fool, gave orders that nobody was to enter. I shall let you suffocate . . . trample on you . . . not a soldier, not a gun: on equal terms. Ha! You are blue already. Keep it up! . . ."

The baron made a supreme, superhuman effort to burst his bonds.

Then, suddenly, with a deafening crash, the back of the armchair broke in two, the arms came asunder, and the lord of the manor of Gyoroky was on his feet, with the pieces of the broken chair clinging to him like fragments of a shattered coat of mail.

Samuel Levi raised a piercing shriek to his God, and, with his head shrunk between his shoulders, waited for death.

But the blow did not fall. The baron swung round, made a few queer dance-like steps, clutched the air as if in search of a hold—and crumpled up, half buried under the heavy timbers of the broken chair.

Outside, the tower clock chimed the last quarter before midnight.

When, hours later, after vainly knocking and listening at the door, the servants at last ventured into the hall, they found the candles burnt down, and little Samuel Levi snoring loudly in his armchair, his weedy beard fluttering in the morning breeze.

At his feet the lord of Gyoroky, nicknamed the Iron King, lay stretched out, stone dead.

THE TALL COORTER

By SEAN O'FAOLAIN

IF YOU WENT TODAY INTO BALLINDORE MADHOUSE AND ASKED FOR the matron you would meet a woman tall as a candle, dark-eyed, with a wide, merry laugh. She walks like Pride. Her nickname is The Coorter.

They gave her that name when she was a young probationer in the Madhouse because she alone, of all the nurses there, was willing to coort (or court, or flirt, or make love, or whatever bad or good meaning you like to put into the word by the way you say it), within the precincts of the House. All the other nurses, male and female, did their courting in the town whose turf-tang sometimes came to them on the wind from the clustered cabins a mile away. For though they might be, all of them, and mostly were, a bit soft in the head, from so long attending on people who were a small bit softer, they were none of them so daft as to think of marrying another like themselves—unless perhaps, when they were getting on in years, one pension might think of marrying another pension. But that was not courting, only sound common-sense.

The Coorter was tall, then as now, so very tall that she seemed to sway like bullrush; but she was strong, and when any man felt her waist in the crook of his arm it was firm as a bullrush pith. She had hair that was black as night and her eyes were like two holes burned in a blanket—she was tawny-skinned. Her mouth was wide and loose and it quivered like water under wind. Her name was Sheila Considine—as it still is, for she never married—and she came from a parish in East Galway where, if the truth were told, there are a great many people who should long since have been put into the grey, damp building where she has spent her life tending many like them.

Not that she would "coort" everybody, even in her flightiest days. The male for "coorter" in that Madhouse is "bruiser," but no "bruiser," except two men only, ever dared touch her. The first was Jim Motherway, an early flame, a six-footer from near her own townland: a fisherman's son, a Gaelic speaker, a wild colt with curls on his brow and two bright bull's eyes. He had been a bit too wild, however, and while she was still a bit of a girl he had left the place suddenly for America—it had something to do with a knifing affair in one of the town pubs and she had not heard from him for years after. Then she had flirted one summer with the young doctor who came as deputy for old Jollop-and-Wather, the Resident Medical Superintendent: after him she did a strong "line" with Mousey Murphy, the clerk of the stores, until, true to the traditions of the place, he jilted her for a midwife. Then came the years of The Troubles and with them her best and gayest days; that was when it was dangerous to as much as walk the roads, what with ambushes and Black and Tans firing wildly over the hedges, and the "boys" taking refuge in the asylum, and the nurses hiding them during raids. She knew everybody, then, and everybody said she was the pluckiest girl in the place, and it was like her to fall madly in love with a young Sinn Fein councillor who always stayed the night whenever there was a Board Meeting. She lost him, too: he was brought into the mortuary one day with a couple of .45's through the forehead.

After that she quietened down, content to do her courting with another attendant in the asylum—Frankie Leydon, a soft, quiet lad from the town, a millionaire every first of the month, all-in-all with his fellow-nurses, and a pauper, avoided by them and cursing them, to the next payday. When the "bruisers" saw them together they smiled mockingly. "That's the wild goat," they said, "spancelled to the tame goat." Or they said, "Milady must be near the end of her tether when she's taking up with Milord." Or they said, looking at the wrinkles around her mouth, "Ah, well—maybe she has her eye on his pension!"

During those years she and Frankie Leydon so arranged their duties that they were together at work, and together when they were free; though it was she who arranged it, because if he was too easy-going to arrange anything she liked it in him that he was gentle and quiet, not like the rest of them, and she was able to help him at his duties. He was not strong; he had the gentle blush of a consumptive; big bright eyes; febrile hands. She would sit beside him on the bench up in Ballarat—their name for the high open yard where the better-behaved lunatics took the air—and, ignoring the babbling and screaming and mad laughter around them, she would talk and talk, and he would listen.

Far away a little spire broke the emptiness of the rock-greyed plain: it wavered a little in the miasma of heat and distance. Farther still the peaks of the West Connaught ranges might be fogged with summer rain, always passing across them like steam. In the lulls of the gabbling about them, he would hear over the wall the houghing of a ploughman or the swish of his share, or the squawk of far-flown gulls. A boat like a speck on one of the lakes. Her voice, heard in snatches. He would have a newspaper spread on the ground between his feet, and a cigarette in his palm that dangled between his knees for fear Jollop-and-Wather should take them by surprise. One day she snatched the paper and let it fly with the spring wind. She laughed and chucked him under the chin. "Well, Frankie, you ould slow-bags," she cried at him, "don't you agree with me?"

He had not heard what she said so he let his eyes rove slowly along the back-wall where on one vast bench a row of old women clicked their needles over socks whose tops were already yards long. A young woman rose from the bench, took one step forward and screamed with delight—"I'm Mary Molo-o-oney from half-way to Ballinro-o-be, Whoop, Ho-o-o-o!" Then stepping back like a soldier she sat down again: she had never been known to say anything else. Another ancient woman was striding up and down, saying in a low, sad voice, without rest, "The cake is baking, the cake is baking, the cake is baking. . . ."

"Aye, sure," he said.

"But amn't I right to go away?" she challenged.

He rubbed his palms together painfully.

"Where did you say, this time?" he asked.

"London."

"To see the Queen?" he teased.

"Oh, God, I *am* right!" she started off again. "They'd get on anyone's nerves. There's not a man among 'em. Not a man. Is there one solitary man, I ask you, with a bit of go in him? One solitary soul in the place I can talk to but yourself?"

"Aye, sure," he said, with content.

"A lot of clod-hoppers!" She put on a whining voice and imitated their western drawl. "Waiting for their *bit of a pinsion*. Looking for *a nice little wife* in Ballindore—*with a little purseen of money for my old age*. Ssah! So I'm going," she cried, and in the turn of a second she was in her merry mood. "In fact I'm gone. It's only my spirit that's talking to you."

"You have enough of it," he flattered.

"I'd need it," she said proudly, and as she smiled with vanity her big mouth ran like silk and the wrinkles shot in and out of her cheeks. "There's not enough spirit here to fill a thimble."

"Have you the job got?" he asked anxiously.

"I wrote this morning to a Mental Home outside London."

"I thought they said they had nothing?"

"This is a different one."

"Well," he said, more at his ease, "they might have something suitable. You never know."

He jumped up quickly. The wicket-gate had opened and old Jollop-and-Wather appeared. But he did not come in. He just put his pince-nez to his nose and waved the way to a stranger. Sheila billowed away to the top of the hill where she put her hands on her greyhound waist and faced the smoking thatch of the little town. She was a lighthouse.

"Hello, Frankie boy!" shouted the stranger.

Not until the lunatics drove left and right of the advancing bruiser did Leydon recognize Jim Motherway. He wore a soft, light-grey hat, light-grey clothes, yellow boots, a light-grey coat was slung over his shoulder like a matador's cloak, a speckled yellow handkerchief flowed out of his breast-pocket. He had gold eye-teeth.

"Bejaney!" said Leydon with a slow, warm grin. "It's Jim Motherway. You're looking prosperous," he said as they shook hands.

Motherway laughed and calmly turned Leydon round and round, chewing easily as he did so. Then he looked him up and down like a horse, and laughed.

"Boy!" he said. "There's not a bleeding change in one inch of the lot of you. Does nothing ever happen here?"

"Not *now*," winked Frankie, with a gentle thrust.

Motherway laughed again: he was a little vain about that old knifing affair.

"Made good?" asked Frankie, with an effort at a man-of-the-world air.

"Tell the world, boy! I've come straight from Buenos Aires—or as straight as half-way round the world. Money? Foo! I've made oodles of money. Yessir, I've hit the bell." He added a bit patronizingly:—"You should have cleared outa here when I did Frankie boy. That was the time for it. There was money for nothing in America during the war. And after it. And I made it."

"Aye, sure," said Frankie easily. "One of these days too, I'll shake a leg."

"Nah!" said Motherway in scorn. "Too late. The whole caboose is a mess-up in a dixie now. I caught it on the hop. Say, how's Sheila? Same old angel-in-the-street-devil-in-the-home, eh?"

"Sheila's alright," Frankie was beginning to protest, half-turning to look at her when Motherway swept past him, halloing up the hill. Then for the rest of the hour those two talked and laughed on the hill-top while Frankie watched them idly. At the sound of the bell she went in with Motherway, arm-in-arm, and he was left alone, as he had never before been left alone, to shepherd in both his babblers and her's.

II

He was left alone that night, too. She went into town with Motherway, and Frankie dawdled at the gate-lodge waiting for her return. The bruisers passed out and then they began to pass in, their usual few oranges or sweets, penny-worths of cautious pleasure in little paper-bags, clutched tightly in their great fists. As they passed in for the night they saluted him elaborately, and Fat Micky, the lodge-keeper winked at the gaslight to show that he understood the joke. Still Leydon hung on, and by his gossip he managed to keep the gate open for her. She swept by him up the drive, in Motherway's great scarlet saloon-car, waving her hand to him as she whirled by. Only then did he go indoors, followed by Fat Micky's suggestive coughing.

He joined her at the long enamel-topped supper table. They had the room to themselves.

"He's turned out to be a grand fellow," she assured him, while he sipped at his cold milk. She smoked with bravado.

"Mind the cigarette," he warned.

"What the hell?" she cried and he knew who she was imitating. She gabbled on: "He's been all over the world. He has pots of money."

"Oh, so? And what is his job?" he asked, trying to keep his voice down from the key of envy.

"Everything! Investments? I think he's nearly a millionaire. You never saw the like of it. Splashing it all over the hotel. He has influence, too. He knows all sorts of people. He's going to get me a job in London, or maybe New York, I don't care. Oh, Frankie, he's an awfully decent fellow, really, and when he was here in the old days he was nothing to me no more than any other fellow. But," she laughed with excitement, and with pride, "I know how to handle him. I always did. He has a great regard for me."

Again she laughed with pleasure at some little incident of the evening out.

"By God," she cried, "we cut a hell of a dash, the pair of us, in the hotel. He's a divil," she said admiringly. "Oh, a proper hard chaw. By God, he has *go* in him!"

Frankie sipped his milk slowly.

"Yes, he nearly went to prison for knifing that poor Englishman. It wasn't right either. If it was one of our own you wouldn't mind."

She explained eagerly.

"I got it all out of him. He didn't want to talk, but I knew how to handle him. He didn't really do it at all. It was put over on him. He was mixed up with the others and blamed in the wrong."

"Then why did he run away?"

"I tell you, he was blamed in the wrong."

"The Board thought different."

"They had to find a scapegoat."

"You're very fond of him all of a sudden?"

Sullenly she stabbed her cigarette into her plate.

"Aren't you?" he prodded.

Her mouth was sheet-lightning. Her eyes were restless with the memory of the night. His envy broke through him. He had no money. He remembered the smiles and the winks.

"He didn't do it," she said to her plate.

"Bejay," he sneered, "any fellow with a bit of money nowadays can get a girl to . . ."

She tore up her cap and gloves and strode out, banging the door.

For a week Motherway almost lived in the House. He flirted with every girl in the place he had a mind for. Every morning his big scarlet car was at the door and he was off with one or other of them, splashing his money on them like a Rajah. But Sheila Considine never had an hour free that he wasn't with her; and twice he begged a special leave for her from Jollop-and-Wather, bribing him with a salmon from the lakes or a woodcock from the islands. Sheila would laugh at the laughing impudence of him, race upstairs to get out of her uniform, and red with pleasure at the show of it race down to be curled and wrapped into her corner and whirled off amid the cheers of the nurses. Then the grounds would become silent again, except for that ceaseless babble of the lunatics from the barred windows—so often heard as to be un-heeded—and in the rarefied air of oncoming Autumn the whirr of the car would die away slowly, into the miles of distance. Frankie would turn back to the screaming and the babbling, showing only by the way he sucked deep at his cigarette what heavings were going on inside him. He would never look at the others. Yet would never fail to be there to see her go.

At night she was the center of the table. They liked her in her triumph and they loved to hear how he did fifty miles an hour to the sea, or to the Spa, or even as far as Galway for an afternoon dance.

Once she handed around a gold bangle. It came to Frankie. He turned it over and over as if he were mesmerised by it: suddenly he passed it on, saying:

"Yes. Very nice. Very nice. A long time before any of ye will get anything like that."

But somehow or other the way he said it was belittling to her and she hated him for it.

She did not tell them everything that happened—she could not—it was not to be put into words. Only Jim could do that, she felt; his way of talk, how he made her see a new world by simply mentioning the names of towns and places, saying: "One time, Sheila, in Santa Felicitas . . ." or, "So then I blew into Cordoba. . . ."

"Oh, God, Jim!" she said once to him. "You've had a gay time, surely."

"Ah!" he had laughed. "Too hot, girl! A bit too hot."

"Is it as warm as all that?" she had said in her innocence.

"Warm? North of Santiago, it's warm. But, I mean in other ways, Sheila." He touched her arm and knee. "I've seen things in Buenos Aires, Sheila, that'd make your hair go like that."

Fingers outspread.

"Yes, and nothing cheap or bum about it either. Not that I haven't seen the other side, too. Now take Africa. I came back that way. I had a pal in Capetown with a diamond mine to sell. I have another friend in Angola wants me to come in on a gold-mine. But I won't bother about that—not enough money in it. Well, take a town like Beira, port of Angola. A small place. As a matter of fact I own the blessed place, took it over from a syndicate. A white elephant. I wish I never bought it. You couldn't live in that place. All dust and sand and wind and muck and sweat."

In a rising inflection: "No, sir! Look, Sheila, you go into a café there. You see the grey walls. You go to hang up your hat. And the damn wall moves. Moves, I tell you! Flies and beetles solid on it. And then the women—you know what I mean. Every prostitute from the East finishes up there, down from Cairo, India, Arabia, stranded for the rest of their lives. Foo! The sight of them drove me out my last day to the foreshore for a breath of clean air. Well, honest to God, girl, and you can laugh if you like, I thought I had the rats that time. That beach was red. I thought it looked nice. But do you know what made it red? Soldier-crabs. I raised my hand and they suddenly took a pace to the left and a pace to the right. That shore *stirred*. I ran back to town and I got blind drunk and I jumped on a boat. The fellow who owned it was a Liberian nigger. 'Here, bozo,' says I, 'take me up to Aden to hell out of this.' He didn't want to, but I bought the whole damn boat and crew off him. I own it still. It's somewhere around the Red Sea. No, I'm telling a lie. I gave it, to be frank, to a poor kid of a girl I wanted to do a good turn to—an English girl. I tell you, Sheila, I was glad to get a clean hotel in Cairo."

"Heavens, Jim!"

So, on and on, while the September breathed its early frost on the little lake by which they sat and the patriarch goats bent their horns over the lava rocks. Across the steel of the water they could see and hear a man swishing the ferns with his scythe. Hearing that sound, so familiar to his youth, so suggestive of the brown heap that would be fed into the fire by some little girl in red petticoats sitting by the hob, he sang her a love-song in Gaelic. And he took her hand in his and looked gently at her. He said:

> O. Ero. My bright one.
> O. Ero. Bright girl. . . .
> It's long since the dark night
> When we kissed with our mouths. . . .

"Ah, Sheileen," he sighed. "I need somebody to look after me. I've burned the candle at both ends—and in the bloody middle, too."

"Sing it, Jim. It's lovely."

To the rhythm of the scything he crooned it:

> Your mother was from home,
> And your brothers were in bed.
> We sat by the fire
> And the *daradaoil* crept by us
> While I nestled your dark head.
> My heart is like a nut
> That hangs withered on the bough. . . ."

Of such things she did not speak when she came back of nights to the Madhouse; nor how he began to cry and said he would give all his millions to be young again, to have a little whitewashed cottage, to be cutting the ferns, to be seeing his little child poking them idly into the turf-fire.

"And why can't you, Jim?" she said.

He looked at her. He jumped up, dragged her to the car, and he drove like a madman to the asylum, singing wildly all the way.

III

She came back one night with the ring on her finger. Jim was there, and what with the nurses running to their duties, their keys rattling, and stopping to congratulate her, and more coming off duty to drag her aside and hear how he proposed, bells clanging, doors banging and echoing, and Jim Motherway telling the men the life they were going to have when they were married—it was no wonder Frankie Leydon said the place was "like a madhouse."

Some of them said afterwards that when he said that, he suddenly went white. But he did manage to go up to Sheila and say that he hoped she would always be happy. She took his good wishes with a smile, too happy at that moment to bear any grudge.

Then he said something in a whisper to Motherway, and he went out into the grounds.

Motherway went out soon after. It was cold and a wind swayed the cypresses and the new electric lights of the little town glowed proudly across the fields, the railway-line and the bog. The face of the asylum was all lit up and the grass was wet in the light of the windows. Now and again a scream or a wild laugh rang out like a nightbird in sudden fright.

"Well, Frankie-boy," cried Motherway, "I hope you bear no grudge. All's fair in love and war you know."

"No," said Frankie quietly. "Not one bit, Jim. Not one bit."

Motherway's hand, for all that, stole to the belt under his waistcoat.

"But, I have a great regard for Sheila. As you know, Jim. So I said to myself, 'I'll talk to him about it.' "

"About what?"

"Where did you get all that money, Jim?" he asked very softly.

"What's that to you? Sh? That's my affair."

"Aye, sure. But leave me put it this way, so. Jim! Have you really got any money at all?"

Motherway threw back his head and laughed, at first silently. The moon came out and shone on the two wide bull's eyes that stared with unequal pupils up at it. A wild scream of laughter rang from one of the windows. Leydon shivered. He saw the gold teeth at the back of the mouth and the gold palate shone. Motherway was laughing aloud, now, and Leydon who had not been for fifteen years in a Madhouse without knowing the sound of it, clenched his fists.

"Frankie, boy," said Motherway at last, putting his big hand on the nurse's shoulder, "you're God's gift to mankind. Listen to me, boy! I could buy out this Madhouse, lock, stock, and barrell, and every mother's child in it."

He clicked his fingers. He flicked out from his breast-pocket a patent-leather wallet and rubbed from it the fat rubber-band.

He slipped out a sheaf of notes, all white, and large, and crinkling. On top was a ten-pound Bank of England note.

"See that man's name?" pointing to the signature. "That man owes me five thousand pounds."

"Aye, sure," said Leydon, watching him.

Motherway ruffled the notes like playing-cards and became excited.

"The Bank of Ballinrobe owes me ten thousand pounds."

When Leydon said nothing he grew angry.

"I hold an I.O.U.," he shouted, "from the Chase National Bank of New York for twenty thousand dollars."

Leydon's teeth were clenched. He stared under his cap at the other. In the moon he was pale as the slow clouds. After a while he said:

"Motherway," and he did not open his teeth to say it, "you're not going to marry Sheila. You're going to come inside with me and talk to Jollop-and-Wather."

He leaped and gripped the lunatic's two arms. The wallet fell. The notes floated.

"Let me go," screamed Motherway. "I'll kill you."

They fell in a heap on the grass. The madman strained for his knife. He drew it. The nurse kicked at the hand that held it and when the knife fell he flung himself on it. The other scrambled up and ran. He ran in and out through the waving cypresses. He ran out of sight.

For a while Frankie lay panting on the grass, and when he drew his hand across his mouth there was blood in his palm. Hours later he was still drawing his hand across his mouth, looking anxiously at it. Then he was sitting on his bed, with the open wallet in his hands, the coverlet littered with what he found there—the usual things, the usual signs of the G. P. I.—visiting cards for James Motherway, M.D., or James Motherway, LL.D., or copies of letters addressed to such people as the Governor, Bank of England, London. He tried to sleep a little but he was so exhausted that during the first hour he spat a little blood, and with difficulty he kept himself quiet until the dawn. As he saw the first cold light crushing its way between the hairy clouds and the black bogland he suddenly heard a singing below him in the grounds. It was like the morning-wind. It said:

O. Ero. My bright one.
O. Ero. Bright girl. . . .
    It is long since the dark night
    We first kissed with our mouths. . . .

For a while it wandered around the House like a cuckoo-call.
Then it stopped. Frankie rose and he stole along the corridors, now
deadly silent, when even the most foolish were at rest, and at her
door, on the women's side, he tapped lightly. When she did not
answer he opened the door and looked in. She was asleep. Her dark
hair was in two plaits over her slight bosom. Her soft mouth was
pursed like a child who is a sponge of sleep. Her arm was extended.
The ring was in place. He heard it below her window:

        Your mother was from home
        And your brothers were in bed.
            So we sat by the fire
            And the *daradaoil* crept by us
        While I Told You My Sad Tale

Her breasts rose and fell, evenly. He closed the door, and stole
away.

She is still in the Asylum, now the Head Matron—a good post.
Sometimes a new doctor flirts with her, for though she is no longer
young she has always had that bullrush height and she walks like
Pride. She should be content and she probably is, for she has a tidy
little fortune laid away—most of it what Frankie Leydon left when
he died; nearly three hundred pounds, all in ten-pound Bank of
England notes, white and crinkling, and a little cockled as if the
rain had got at them. Everyone in Ballindore likes her for her
laugh and her good spirits.

Not until I had known her for two years, and had been visiting
the asylum every week in the course of my work—I was grinding
a class of probationers for an examination—did I suspect anything.

Then one day I was looking for one of the girls, and heard she
was up in "Ballarat," and I asked the matron to show me the way.
She refused abruptly. When I got there I mentioned it idly to the
young nurse.

"Has Miss Considine something in her nose against me?" I asked.
"She seemed very distant today."

The girl looked at me. Then her look wandered to the long bench where the old women clicked their needles over the stockings or babbled to themselves.

I saw she was looking at a big hulk of a man in the coarse grey uniform of the place sitting among the old hags. He sat back, staring over the little lakes and rocky plain. He was crooning nasally, to the old mad woman beside him, in Irish, clearly without any sense of what he sang —

> O. Ero. My bright one . . .
> My heart is like a nut
> That has withered on the bough . . .

It is a lovely song and I knew it well and knew he had it all jumbled up in his brain.

I looked back at the nurse. She told me the story.

BUT FOR THIS . . .

By Lajos Zilahy

HE DIDN'T STOP TO WASH THE TURPENTINE FROM HIS HANDS, BUT merely dried them on the rag that was hanging on a nail behind the door.

Then he untied the green carpenter's apron from his waist and shook the shavings from his trousers.

He put on his hat and, before going out the door, turned to the old carpenter who was standing with his back to him, stirring the glue. His voice was weary as he said:

"Goodnight."

A strange mysterious feeling had shivered in him since morning.

There had been a bad taste in his mouth.

For a moment his hand would stop moving the plane, and his eyes would close, tired.

He went home and listlessly ate his supper.

He lived at an old woman's, the widow of Ferenz Borka, in a bare little room which had once been a wood shed.

That night—on the fourth day of October, 1874—at a quarter past one in the morning, the journeyman carpenter, John Kovacs, died.

He was a soft-spoken, sallow-faced man, with sagging shoulders and a rusty mustache.

He died at the age of thirty-five.

Two days later, they buried him.

He left no wife, nor child behind, no one but a cook living in Budapest in the service of a bank president, by the name of Torday.

She was John Kovacs' cousin.

Five years later, the old carpenter in whose shop he had worked, died, and nine years later death took the old woman in whose shed he had lived.

Fourteen years later, Torday's cook, John Kovacs' cousin, died.

Twenty-one months later—in the month of March of 1895—in a

pub at the end of Kerepesiut, cabbie, sat around a red clothed table drinking wine.

It was late in the night, it must have been three o'clock. They sprawled with their elbows on the table, shaking with raucous laughter.

Clouds of thick smoke from vile cigars curled around them. They recalled the days of their military service.

One of them, a big, ruddy-faced, double-chinned coachman whom they called Fritz, was saying:

"Once my friend, the corporal, made a recruit stick his head into the stove . . ."

And at this point he was seized by a violent fit of laughter as he banged the table with the palm of his hand.

"Jeez!" he roared.

The veins swelled on his neck and temples and for many minutes he choked, twitched and shook with convulsive laughter.

When he finally calmed down he continued, interrupting himself with repeated guffaws.

"He made him stick his head into the stove and in there he made him shout one hundred times 'Herr Zugsfierer, ich melde gehorsammst' . . . poor chump, there he was on all fours and we paddled his behind till the skin almost split on our fingers."

Again he stopped to get over another laughing spell.

Then he turned to one of the men. "Do you remember, Franzi?"

Franzi nodded.

The big fellow put his hand to his forehead.

"Now . . . what was the fellow's name . . ."

Franzi thought for a moment and then said: "Ah . . . a . . . Kovacs . . . John Kovacs."

That was the last time ever a human voice spoke the name of John Kovacs.

On November the tenth, in 1899, a woman suffering from heart disease was carried from an O Buda tobacco factory to St. John's Hospital. She must have been about forty-five years old.

They put her on the first floor in ward number 3.

She lay there on the bed, quiet and terrified; she knew she was going to die.

It was dark in the ward, the rest of the patients were already asleep: only a wick sputtered in a small blue oil lamp.

Her eyes staring wide into the dim light, the woman reflected upon her life.

She remembered a summer night in the country, and a gentle-eyed young man, with whom—their fingers linked—she was roaming over the heavy scented fields and through whom that night she became a woman.

That young man was John Kovacs and his face, his voice, the glance of his eyes had now returned for the last time.

But this time his name was not spoken, only in the mind of this dying woman did he silently appear for a few moments. The following year a fire destroyed the Calvinist rectory and its dusty records that contained the particulars of the birth and death of John Kovacs.

In January, 1901, the winter was hard.

Toward evening in the dark a man dressed in rags climbed furtively over the ditch that fenced in the village cemetery.

He stole two wooden crosses to build a fire.

One of the crosses had marked the grave of John Kovacs.

Again two decades passed.

In 1920, in Kecskemet, a young lawyer sat at his desk making an inventory of his father's estate.

He opened every drawer and looked carefully through every scrap of paper.

On one was written: "Received 4 Florins, 60 kraciers. The price of two chairs polished respectfully Kovacs John."

The lawyer glanced over the paper, crumpled it in his hand and threw it into the wastepaper basket.

The following day the maid took out the basket and emptied its contents in the far end of the courtyard.

Three days later it rained.

The crumpled paper soaked through and only this much remained on it:

". . . Kova . . . J. . . ."

The rain had washed away the rest; the letter "J" was barely legible.

These last letters were the last lines, the last speck of matter that remained of John Kovacs.

A few weeks later the sky rumbled and the rain poured down as though emptied from buckets.

On that afternoon the rain washed away the remaining letters.

The letter "v" resisted longest, because there where the line curves in the "v" John Kovacs had pressed on his pen.

Then the rain washed that away too.

And in that instant—forty-nine years after his death—the life of the journeyman carpenter ceased to exist and forever disappeared from this earth. . . . But for this . . .

A SHOT IN THE FOREST

By Felix Salten

THE TRAIN PULLED IN AT THE SMALL COUNTRY STATION. HERMINE followed her husband out through the car and watched him as he jumped down the steps and waited to help her down. He was tall, slim and straight, in spite of his snow-white hair; now he lifted his hands to Hermine with a solemn tenderness which always enchanted her.

Very lightly, she placed her hand on his arm and smiled at him. "I am terribly happy to be here again!"

Nicolaus asked gayly: "Hunt fever?"

"Yes, of course, that, too." Then, softly: "It will be marvellous, two weeks here in the forest, alone with you!"

He nodded a grateful acknowledgment.

A reception had been prepared for them: the station master was there, the headforester who handed Hermine a bunch of flowers, and the steward of Nicolaus' estate who stammered a short speech of greeting. Meanwhile, the baggage was stowed away by the servants who had arrived on the same train: Conrad, the valet, a tight-lipped, withered old man, and Nanni, Hermine's pretty young maid. An open four-in-hand, with a beautiful, yellow wickerwork body was waiting for the master, while the servants were to ride in the trap. The horses were restless, pawing the sand and champing at the bit.

As soon as the reception was over, Hermine hurried over to the carriage and gayly greeted the coachman: "How do you do, Mr. Brown!"

Mr. Brown was a stately figure on the box, holding the reins of his four horses in one hand, and his whip in the other. In response to Hermine's greeting, he lowered his whip in approved style. Once upon a time he had driven the wedding carriage of a king, but he had been forced out by the automobile to which he would never lower himself. It was a long time since he had last driven

317

through the streets of a big city. His was a greatness of the past; yet, he was still a master.

The carriage rolled away smoothly, driven at a beautifully even, fast clip.

Hermine had not even noticed the gamekeeper who had spread a warm rug over their knees and who was now sitting on the box beside the coachman. She reached for her husband's hand, pressed it affectionately and whispered: "Isn't all this magnificent!"

Nicolaus returned the pressure of her hand. His "Thank you, my dear!" was spoken so softly that it was hardly audible.

They passed through the small town and acknowledged graciously, like sovereigns, the greetings of the people who lined the main road, bowing and waving to the carriage. Soon they left the town behind them and drove out on a country road, between wooded hills whose rich foliage steeped the countryside in the warm light of autumn colors.

Hermine felt a feeling of deep gratitude surge up in her, intermingled with pangs of conscience. She had flirted a great deal all summer, at all the fashionable places where they had stayed. She could not break herself of it; she always had to play up to men, allowing them to make love to her, even inviting it, and she gloried in the tribute which her beauty evoked everywhere. When she caught herself at this game in the midst of an admiring crowd, intoxicated by the visible effects which her beauty produced in men, she tried to console herself with the assurance that she was not being really unfaithful. And she always attempted to justify herself with the thought that her husband was so much older than she was. But now, sitting beside Nicolaus on this beautiful drive, she again felt something akin to remorse. And remembering the tremendous height to which life had lifted her, a dizzying sense of happiness overcame her. Born the daughter of a poor school teacher, she had trained her voice, had achieved triumphs as an opera singer and had finally arrived at a comfortable and secure life. But it was only since she had been married to Nicolaus that she came to know the possibilities of life which only really immense wealth can afford. She had had her automobile, her villa, a box at the theater, jewelry and expensive clothes—all the extravagancies of city life which now seemed banal and cheap compared to the truly regal style of living, to the indescribable luxury which Nicolaus had brought into her life. Riding through endless forests which belonged to him, along farflung fields whose harvest would soon fill his vast barns, living in century old castles in which the best that past and present could offer, was combined for the owner's joy and delight—all this brought to Hermine the sense of living in a fairyland, but one that was permanent and secure. Gone were the battles with directors and conductors, the deadly jealousy of her rivals, the fickle favor of critics—her whole struggle for a few poor scraps from a rich man's table at which she was now permanently enthroned. Her triumphs on the stage which had to be wrung every time anew from an indifferent public, seemed like worthless tinsel. She shuddered to think of the constant terror in which she had been living for fear that a cold might ruin her voice, of the dreadful realization that some day surely time would tarnish the tinsel of her life.

Hermine turned her face to the forests. Dimly outlined in the distance, the undulating hills with their soft contours appeared like immense cushions, embroidered by the soft autumn colors like rare old tapestries. The bracing air carried a scent of moist earth and dried leaves, of damp wood and late-growing herbs.

In her ears, the rhythmic pattern of hoof beats sounded a sweet music against the background of creaking leather, the occasional snorts of a horse and the luxurious sound of soft cushioned wheels rolling over the dirt road.

And that would remain always, Hermine thought. The magnificent rides through forests, the castles and hunting lodges and town house, the happy, effortless travel through a beautiful world would always be hers, whether she could sing opera arias or not. It was permanent and dependable like Nicolaus and his love.

He had married her three years ago, disregarding every objection, and had become an affectionate, loving and trusting husband, full of kindness and admiration for her. She had accepted him in spite of the great difference in their age, in response to a vague instinct which had turned out to be correct. At the time she had believed she was making a sacrifice, but now she slowly realized how wise she had been to end her career at its peak, to leave her former life behind her and submerge in the carefree luxury of a free and tenderly-sheltered existence in which there was no place for the worries of her career and ambition.

Nicolaus interrupted her reverie by addressing a question to hir gamekeeper. Hermine was too preoccupied to listen and the sound of words only fell upon her ear as a muffled, unintelligible noise.

But suddenly she felt that a pair of eyes were resting on her. A pair of strange eyes. She looked up to the box and noticed to her surprise that the man sitting beside Mr. Brown had turned his face to her. It was an unusual face, cold and pale, with an ivory color that looked even paler under the green hunter's hat. Out of that face, two light grey eyes were reaching for her, stinging her, burying themselves in her own eyes. It lasted only for the fraction of a second, but from then on Hermine felt a vague sensation of danger, and of being carefully watched.

She was afraid and remained silent for a while, then she asked in an undertone: "Who is that man?"

"Don't you remember him?" Nicolaus wondered. "Why, this is Martin, my gamekeeper and general factotum here!"

She shook her head. "I have never seen him before."

Nicolaus smiled. "But Hermine, you met him last year!" He called up to the box in a jocular tone: "Martin . . . it seems my wife doesn't recognize you."

Again Hermine felt upon her the light grey eyes that reached for her with such an impudent, avid desire. She tried not to falter under his gaze, but did not succeed and had to look away.

Later, when his back was turned to her again, she watched him out of the corner of her eye, the nape of his neck, the part of his pale cheek which was all she could see.

He turned back to her once more just as the carriage entered the gate into the park.

By that time Hermine had regained her composure and she had almost expected his glance, so she smiled a hardly noticeable smile. Suddenly she blushed to her temples—his eyes had spoken to her in a loud voice! They had spoken an impudently intimate word, a caress, in a loud voice! His eyes had said it loud enough for anybody to see, to hear even!

She lowered her eyes and thus missed the first glimpse of the baroque castle which she loved so much. The carriage stopped at the vaulted ramp and the gamekeeper quickly jumped down from the box to help her alight. Hermine anxiously avoided his touch, however, and hurriedly greeted the servants who were assembled in the great hall. Nicolaus stopped to say something to Mr. Brown and then joined Hermine in the drawing room. He took her in his arms and suggested with tender concern: "You will rest a little before dinner, my dear, won't you?"

Hermine assented readily. She was nervous and embarrassed.

Through the windows of her room, she saw the four-in-hand drive slowly up and down under her windows, but thought nothing of it at the moment.

Nanni drew Hermine's bath, unpacked the baggage and busied herself in the closets. The maid also seemed nervous.

As Hermine stepped out of the tub, she again heard the carriage drive smartly past the windows and stop at the ramp. The impatient stamping of the horses was magnified many times in the vaulted arcades. A moment later, the coach rolled out into the drive way, with Nicolaus in the tonneau.

"Where is the Master going?" Hermine asked her maid.

"He is going to the station, I believe," Nanni answered.

Hermine again thought of the man who sat beside Mr. Brown, of the pale face with the brutal, black moustache, of the aggressive grey eyes. "Nanni," she said suddenly, "do you know the game-keeper Martin?"

Nanni shrugged her shoulders. "I don't bother with the men here in the castle."

"I hear he was here last year, too," Hermine persisted.

"Maybe." The tone of the maid was almost impudently curt.

Hermine dressed for dinner slowly and carefully. The carriage returned before she was ready but she paid no attention to it. When she was dressed, she sat down at the piano in her own small drawing room and sang: "L'amour est un oiseau rebelle. . . ." She was in magnificent voice.

II

There was a knock at her door and Hermine again found herself face to face with Martin. He bowed low and announced: "The gentlemen are ready."

Hermine was about to ask: "The gentlemen?" but she suppressed the question because she did not want to talk to that man, did not even want to look at him. Quickly, as if fleeing from something, she went past him and hurried to the library.

As she entered, she found Nicolaus talking to a young man. They rose to greet her and Nicolaus smiled happily "I have a surprise for you. . . ."

Now that the youth had stepped into the light of the chandelier, Hermine saw that he was a man of slight, graceful figure, no longer a youth, but with a face that made him seem younger than he was.

His delicate features were those of a medieval page, suffering from a beautiful romantic sorrow.

"Tonio Raspi!" Hermine rejoiced. "Where do you come from and how did you get here?"

"He just arrived on the Paris express," Nicolaus explained. "Wasn't it lucky I could persuade him to join us here!"

"Why, this is simply charming!" she agreed, while Tonio Raspi kissed both her hands.

The great violin virtuoso could permit himself certain liberties. He continued to kiss Hermine's hands with an ardour as if he had arrived at last at the satisfaction of his greatest longing.

"Are you going to hunt stag with us?" Hermine inquired.

"I should like to try it, under your guidance!"

She disengaged her hands, protesting smilingly. "Not under my guidance. I am only a beginner myself!"

They sat down and chatted. Martin served cocktails, offering the first glass to Hermine. His impudent grey eyes invited her: "Why don't you drink, my darling!"

With an impatient gesture, Hermine declined the glass proffered to her and quickly looked at the two men. Fortunately they had not noticed the little incident.

At dinner, Conrad, the valet, together with Martin, waited on table. The latter stood during most of the meal a few paces behind Nicolaus' chair, facing Hermine, and his eyes never left her alone for an instant. Now and then, when he turned to reach for something, she looked at him guardedly, with a shy, hurried glance. His face seemed shrouded in sinister energy, his black moustache covering a mouth that spoke of brutal forcefulness. During the whole meal she was tormented by his eyes which sometimes caught her during one of her short quick glances at him when she believed herself unobserved. In the electric light, his eyes seemed green and cruel, forcing her to take notice of them, forcing her to read their fanatically repeated question: "Will you have me?"

Hermine was confused because she found herself afraid of this lackey who walked so quietly around the room and who dared to let his eyes speak to her so loudly and unashamedly. She tried to conceal her nervousness behind a forced gayety and talked a little too much, exaggerating a haughty attitude toward the servants. She was amazed that Nicolaus and Raspi did not notice anything, although the old valet appeared to have become suspicious. It seemed to Hermine that he was casting now and then a worried and disapproving glance from her to the gamekeeper Martin.

After dinner they had coffee in the library. The head-forester came for a game of chess with Nicolaus, while Hermine sat before the fireplace with Toni Raspi. She permitted the great violinist to flirt with her, and she encouraged him, but it was only to calm her excited nerves and forget the impudent insult of this servant.

Martin seemed to have seen through her game, however, and he constantly interfered, bringing coffee, taking the cups away, offering liqueur, candy and cigarettes. Hermine felt that he behaved like a jealous lover.

Her nervousness rose to impatience and finally mounted to outright anger.

"Hermine, darling, what is wrong with you tonight?" Raspi asked her finally in his flattering, caressing voice.

Before she could answer, she felt that Martin was watching her closely, and so she pulled herself together and replied gayly: "Nothing, of course! Only I think we ought to get to bed early, since we have to get up practically at daybreak!" She rose, took a few casual steps toward Nicolaus and put her hand on his shoulder, saying, "How is the chess game getting on? Is it going to last much longer?"

Nicolaus immediately got up. "It is over now, if you like, my dear." He nodded to the head-forester. "Isn't it, Hansen?"

Hansen, who had also risen, bowed. "Of course."

"Are you tired? Don't you feel well?" There was tender concern in Nicolaus' voice.

"I feel perfectly well," Hermine protested. "I am just a little tired, that's all. And we will all have to get up very early tomorrow."

Nicolaus patted her hand. "Well, not so very early, not at this time of the year." He looked at the forester. "Half past six would do, wouldn't it?"

Hansen nodded assent.

Hermine insisted. "But I want to feel fresh tomorrow!" She was convinced that she could not stand Martin's shameless glance for another five minutes.

Nicolaus took her arm in his. "Why, darling, you really seem to have hunt fever!"

She said good-night to Raspi who pouted like a spoilt child.

At the door of her bedroom, Nicolaus gently put his arms around her. "Sleep well, dearest!"

While letting Nanni undress her, Hermine wondered whether her maid was especially clumsy tonight or whether it only seemed so as a reflection of her own nervousness and restlessness.

Once she imagined she could see Martin through the glass door, waiting in her dressing room. Impatiently, she ordered Nanni to lock the door and draw the curtains.

At last she stretched out under the warm blankets.

Nicolaus was in the room next to hers. That thought quieted her. And it was reassuring to know that the wooden shutters before her windows were securely locked and bolted.

Slowly, the sensation of happiness began to return to her. Then she thought of Tonio Raspi and again felt a little remorse. But sleep quickly wrapped her in his dark cloak.

III

They drove through the forest which was heavy with the mist of early morning. Tonio Raspi sat beside Hermine. He still had his dinner jacket on under his great-coat.

Hermine noticed it, but at the moment it did not strike her as particularly strange.

The barking of stags rent the air like short rolls of thunder, now near, now a long distance away.

Hermine shivered with cold. Nicolaus who sat facing her, breathed into her cupped hands to warm them.

Tonio Raspi remarked suddenly in a loud voice: "I am very curious!"

"Pst! Not so loud!" Nicolaus reminded him.

"Why not?" The violinist protested sulkily and without lowering his voice. "Because the stags are making love?"

The horses trotted over the narrow road through the forest which was beginning to clear a little in the first grey light of dawn.

Raspi explained: "I am in love, too! At the present moment I am in love with your wife."

He said that so naïvely that Hermine and Nicolaus had to laugh.

The carriage stopped at a deer path.

Nicolaus lifted Hermine out. "Do you mind going with Martin today. . . . I want to take our guest and see that he gets in a good shot."

Of course! Hermine understood fully. Nicolaus must try to help Tonio Raspi bag his first game.

She walked quickly along the deer path, treading carefully on the soft ground which deadened her footsteps.

The gamekeeper followed her closely, so closely in fact that she could feel his breath on her neck. It frightened her, and yet it was a pleasant, tingling sensation.

"We will be there in a minute," Martin whispered.

Hermine did not answer. A strange curiosity took possession of her.

As they proceeded toward the clearing in the forest, the tall trees began to get sparse and the thick underbrush prevailed. Finally they arrived at the clearing which extended all the way up a hill where timber had been cut. On the summit of the hill, the underbrush again closed off the clearing like a barricade.

Now they stood before the ladder leading up to the shooting stand.

Hermine reached for the rungs and climbed up to the platform which was fenced in with boards extending up to her shoulder.

She looked around. "Like a ball room . . ." she thought as the clearing extended below her, surrounded and closed off by underbrush and young trees.

The faint light of early morning still had the paleness of the hour before sunrise. Deers were walking over the clearing, gracefully lifting their slim legs. A magnificent buck stood at the brink of the forest, motionless like a statue.

Meanwhile Martin had joined her. Again she found herself in close proximity to him, again she was forced to look into his light grey eyes with the greenish tinge which at once terrified and humiliated her.

A sudden terror gripped her.

Martin had put down his rifle.

Hermine turned away from him, but at that moment he reached for her.

She pushed him back. Her anger was aroused and it proved stronger than her fear. She fought him with all her strength, but he seemed to have gone completely mad. He was so much stronger than she, and she realized that her resistance was hopeless. She also knew that even her screams would not save her. Nicolaus was too far away and he could not hear her, perhaps could not even hear a shot.

Martin pressed her close to his body. He did not say one word; they fought silently and breathlessly.

Suddenly Hermine felt his hand on her breast. In the mad excitement of her struggle she could not understand how he could have done it. But yet his hand was on her naked breast. In spite of her violent struggle, in spite of the force which he had to use against Hermine who fought him with all her strength, he caressed her breasts, first one and then the other, softly, gently, lovingly. A pleasant sensation which she tried to resist, began to stream through her body, mingling with her anger and tormenting her.

In some inexplicable way, he succeeded in keeping his eyes always before her, although she turned and twisted in his strong grip. And in spite of her violent struggle, he caressed her breast with his hand so gently and softly as if she were suffering his intimacies without a protest.

"What is going to happen?" she thought. "My strength is leaving me. What is going to happen?"

Now! Here! As she glanced over the edge of the board fence, frantically looking for help, she suddenly saw it.

A magnificent buck had stepped into the clearing and walked slowly across, his head close to the ground as if he were following a scent.

Hermine trembled violently. The hunter had also seen the stag and he released her at once.

She held her hand before her mouth to stifle her loud breathing.

Martin handed her the rifle.

She lifted it to her shoulder, supported it on the edge of the balustrade and aimed at the stag . . . now the hair-cross in her gun sight was aiming exactly at the shoulder blade, now she pulled the hair trigger . . . now the shot rang out through the quiet forest.

The tremendous force of the projectile lifted the stag off the ground. He jumped with all four legs at once, tried a few lame leaps toward the underbrush and collapsed. His proud antlered head rocked slowly back and forth, scraping the ground.

With a commanding gesture Hermine turned to her gamekeeper. "Climb down and get him, quick!"

Martin obediently climbed down the ladder and hurried across the clearing. The stag was still moving. The bullet might have only grazed him.

Now the gamekeeper arrived at the stag, now he bent over him. . . .

Hermine was too confused to think clearly . . . she only knew that she must use this opportunity and release herself from this man.

Again she lifted the rifle, supporting the barrel on the board fence, and took careful aim. This time the gun was aimed at Martin's back. He was occupied with the animal and did not suspect anything.

Quickly, a thought flashed through Hermine's brain: "The stag was innocent . . . but this man. . . ."

Once more a shot thundered through the forest.

Martin dropped to the ground without a sound. He remained there as if asleep, his face buried in the grass. He did not stir.

A cold terror gripped Hermine.

"Murder!" she screamed. "Murder!" The word died in her mouth before she could finish it. She was only able to scream, without forming intelligible syllables. She knew that she wanted to shout "Murder" but at the same time she felt extremely sorry for herself.

She was still fully conscious, and yet her brain seemed confused.

What had happened to her? Was she having hallucinations? Nicolaus came running out of the forest, wringing his hands.

Tonio Raspi was standing on an enormous piano, fiddling.

Suddenly the forest was filled with police, armed with rifles. Lowering their bayonets, they surrounded the shooting stand and approached in a constantly narrowing circle.

The gamekeeper Martin raised himself from the ground and

leaped up and down before her like a jumping jack, screaming: "She killed me!"

Then the trumpets of Judgement Day sounded their terrifying call into Hermine's ears.

She could still think: "I am going insane, I have become insane." She screamed. . . .

IV

Mysterious seconds. . . .

Somebody shook Hermine. She opened her eyes, not yet fully conscious.

Nicolaus stood before her smiling.

Outside, under her windows, hunting horns called for the hunters to meet.

Slowly the terror within her soul ebbed and finally disappeared. She breathed a deep sigh of relief.

"What terrible things you must have dreamed!" Nicolaus asked.

Hermine laughed, sat up in bed and reached for the bell.

"It's no use," Nicolaus suggested. "There is no Nanni this morning!"

He sat down on the bed and explained: "Imagine the stupidity! She disappeared in the middle of the night . . . yes, really, . . . she ran away with my game keeper Martin."

Translated by Fritz Sallagar

THE NIGHT BEFORE
CHANCELLORSVILLE

By F. Scott Fitzgerald

I TELL YOU I DIDN'T HAVE ANY NOTION WHAT I WAS GETTING INTO or I wouldn't of gone down there. They can have their army—it seems to me they were all acting like a bunch of yellow bellies. But my friend Nell said to me:

"Look here, Nora, Philly is as dead as Baltimore and we've got to eat this summer." She'd just got a letter from a girl that said they were living fine down there in "old Virginia." The soldiers were getting big pay offs and figuring maybe they'd stay there all summer, till the Johnny Rebs gave up. They got their pay regular too, and a good clean-looking girl could ask—well, I forget now, because after what happened to us I guess you can't expect me to remember anything.

I've always been used to decent treatment—somehow when I meet a man, no matter how fresh he is in the beginning, he comes to respect me in the end and I've never had things done to me like some girls, getting left in a strange town or had my purse stolen.

Well, I started to tell you how I went down to the army in "old Virginia." Never again! Wait till you hear.

I'm used to travelling nice—once when I was a little girl my daddy took me on the cars to Baltimore—we lived in York, Pa.— and we couldn't have been more comfortable; we had pillows and the men came through with baskets of oranges and apples, you know, singing out:

"Want to buy some oranges or apples—or beer."

You know what they sell—but I never took any beer because ——

Oh I know, I'll go on—You only want to talk about the war, like all you men. But if that's their idea what a war is ——

Well, they stuck us all in one car and a fresh guy took our tickets and winked and said:

"Oh, you're going down to Hooker's army."

The lights was terrible in the car, smoky and not cleaned so

329

everything looked sort of yellow. And say that car was so old it was falling to pieces.

There must have been forty girls in it, a lot of them from Baltimore and Philly. Only there were three or four that weren't gay —I mean they were more, oh you know, rich people that sat up front; every once in a while an officer would pop in his head from the next car and ask them if they wanted anything. I was in the seat behind with Nell and we heard him whisper:

"You're in pretty terrible company but we'll be there in a few hours and we'll go right to headquarters, and I'll promise you solid comfort."

I never will forget that night. None of us had any food except some girls behind us had some sausage and bread, and they gave us what they had left. There was a spigot you turned but no water came out. After about two hours, stopping every two minutes it seemed to me, a couple of lieutenants, loaded to the gills, came in from the next car and offered Nell and me some whisky out of a bottle. Nell took some and I pretended to and they sat on the side of our seats. One of them started to make up to her but just then the officer that had spoken to the women, pretty high up I guess, a major or a general, came back again and asked:

"You all right? Anything I can do?"

One of the ladies kind of whispered to him, and he turned to the drunk that was talking to Nell and made him go back in the other car. After that there was only one officer with us; he wasn't really so drunk, just feeling sick.

"This certainly is a jolly looking gang," he says. "It's good you can hardly see them in this light. They look as if their best friend just died."

"What if they do," Nell answered back. "How would you look yourself if you come all the way from Philly and then climbed in a car like this?"

"I come all the way from the Seven Days, Sister," he answered; pretty soon he left and said he'd try and get us some water or coffee, which was what we wanted.

The car kept rocking and it made us both feel funny. Some of the girls was sick and some was sound asleep on each other's shoulders.

"Hey, where is this army?" Nell demanded. "Down in Mexico?"

I was kind of half asleep myself by that time and didn't answer.

The next thing I knew I was woke up by a storm, the car was stopped again and I said, "It's raining."

"Raining!" said Nell. "That's cannon—they're having a battle."

"Oh. Well, after *this* ride I don't care who wins."

It seemed to be getting louder all the time, but out the windows you couldn't see anything on account of the mist.

In about half an hour another officer came in the car—he looked pretty messy as if he'd just crawled out of bed: his coat was still unbuttoned and he kept hitching up his trousers as if he didn't have any suspenders.

"All you ladies outside," he said, "we need this car for wounded."

"What?"

"Hey!"

"We paid for our tickets, didn't we?"

"I don't care. We need all the cars for the wounded and the other cars are about filled up."

"Hey! We didn't come down to fight in any battle!"

"It doesn't matter what you came down for—you're in a battle, a hell of a battle."

I was scared I can tell you. I thought maybe the Rebs would capture us and send us down to one of those prisons you hear about where they starve you to death unless you sing Dixie all the time and kiss niggers.

"Hurry up now!"

But another officer had come in who looked more nice.

"Stay where you are, ladies," he said, and then he said to the officer, "What do you want to do, leave them standing on the siding! If Sedgewick's Corps is broken like they say the Rebs may come up in this direction!" Some of the girls began crying out loud. "These are northern women after all."

"These are ——"

"Oh shut up—go back to your command. I'm detailed to this transportation job, and I'm taking these girls to Washington with us."

I thought they were going to hit each other but they both walked off together, and we sat wondering what we were going to do.

What happened next I don't quite remember. The cannon were sometimes very loud and then sometimes more far away, but there was firing of shots right near us and a girl down the car had her window smashed. I heard a whole bunch of horses gallop by our windows but I still couldn't see anything.

This went on for half an hour—gallopings and more shots. We couldn't tell how far away but they sounded like up by the engine.

Then it got quiet and two guys came into our car—we all knew right away they were rebels, not officers, just plain private ones with guns. One had on a brown blouse and one a blue blouse and I was surprised because I thought they always wore grey. They were disgusting looking and very dirty; one had a big pot of jam he'd smeared all over his face and the other had a box of crackers.

"Hi, Ladies."

"What you gals doin' down here?"

"Kaint you see, Steve, this is old Joe Hooker's staff."

"Reckin we ought to take em back to the General?"

They talked outlandish like that—I could hardly understand they talked so funny.

One of the girls got hysterical, she was so scared and that made them kind of shy. They were just kids I guess, under those beards, and one of them tipped his hat or whatever the old thing was:

"We're not fixin to hurt you."

At that moment there was a whole bunch more shooting down by the engine and the rebs turned and ran. We were glad I can tell you.

Then about fifteen minutes later in came one of our officers. This was another new one.

"You better duck down!" he shouted to us, "they may shell this train. We're starting you off as soon as we load two more ambulances on board."

Half of us was on the floor already. The rich women sitting ahead of Nell and me went up into the car ahead where the wounded were—I heard one of them say to see if they could do anything. Nell thought she'd look in too, but she came back holding her nose— she said it smelled awful in there.

It was lucky she didn't go in because two of the girls did try and see if they could help, but the nurses sent them right back, as if they was dirt under their feet.

After I don't know how long the train began to move. A soldier came in and poured the oil out of all our lights except one and took it into the wounded car, so now we could hardly see at all.

If the trip down was slow the trip back was terrible. The wounded began groaning and we could hear in our car, so nobody couldn't get a decent sleep. We stopped everywhere.

When we got in Washington at last there was a lot of people in the station and they were all anxious about what had happened to the army, but I said you can search me. All I wanted was my little old room and my little old bed. I never been treated like that in my life. One of the girls said she was going to write to President Lincoln about it.

And in the papers next day they never said anything about how our train got attacked or about us girls at all! Can you beat it?

A PLACE TO LAY ONE'S HEAD

By Waldo Frank

THE NIGHT WAS LIKE WARM WINE; HIS BAG WAS LIGHT. AS HE STEPPED from the tiny station, he spurned the boy and the motor-bus which plied to the one hotel, four miles away on the sea—I'll walk. He wanted the night; he wanted to put off, as long as might be, the dull impersonal hotel room from which this murmurous summer would be barred, in which there would be nothing but sleep.

Sleep on such an evening in June! He walked under trees awake with leafy song. Fire-flies were spangling star-bits. And in the heaven, the stars were fire-flies.

When at last he saw the face of the hotel within the pines, he rebelled that the hour's walk was over. The trees were a rebuke to his leaving them: warm, they enfolded him and tried to keep him. "Why not lie down with us?" He was tempted. He could make a pillow of the velvet lichen running on the roots of a hemlock. He could turn his face to the stars and the sea. With the pulse of the universe upon his eyes, he could close his eyes and let dream's little universe, rhythmic within the great one, woo him and take him.

But while he wondered why he did not stay and sleep with the night, he had stepped up the hotel porch and opened the door. The place seemed deserted. In the narrow lobby there was no guest.

Two hooded lamps shadowed the panels of raw pine, cast brooding bits of darkness on a table littered with magazines and papers, and on the cushioned nooks. Silence. Night was compressed in this room; its whisperings and songs crushed out. Night, here, was distilled into a heady liquor. He turned to escape. A thirst was in him for the cool cadence of outdoors. He did not like this hotel. He would go to the trees . . .

"Are you looking for some one, sir?"

His eyes turned, almost guiltily, toward the voice. Behind a desk, close to a lamp, in a corner of the room stood a girl. He hesitated—

from the open door came the breath of pines and the Pacific. Then he no longer heard. He shut the door and stepped nearer to the girl.

"Pardon me," he said. "Of course! I'm looking for a room."

"Oh, you missed the bus? What a pity! You walked?"

"It is not a pity. I liked the walk."

His gaze began to condense from the vague revery of his hour with the wind and the trees; still, he scarce saw the girl—he saw merely that she looked at him.

"I hope it is not too late," he went on quickly, "to disturb you —for a room?"

She was silent. Then quite simply she repeated:

"It is a pity that you missed the bus."

He put her down for the usual country clod with no taste for anything but cars and city styles.

"You *have* a room?" He wanted to get away—why don't I go?

"I'm sorry," she said. "It is a pity. There is no room."

Then he first saw her: a chestnut cloud of hair over her eyes. She wore a waist flimsy and cool about the warm firm breast. Her arms were bare.

"No room?"

"There were four guests with the bus. And we had just four rooms. It's a pity, sir. If you had taken the bus . . . if you had stepped in quicker than one of the others."

He was close now to the desk; he placed his right hand on it. "This is a problem!" He had forgotten the inviting trees. Beside his hand was hers upon the wood. Her hand was an active presence; it disturbed the quiet of his own, making him conscious of it. He strummed on the wood.

"Nothing?"

"Nothing, sir. It is a pity."

"No other hotel, hereabouts?"

"At the station—across from it—the postmistress might take you in." She looked up and added "—if she is not asleep."

"I might phone at once."

"She is very deaf. If she's asleep, you'll never wake her."

"Ah-ah." He thrummed with his fingers; grew aware of it. She took her hand away; he withdrew his.

"I might leave my bag and walk back. How many miles is it?"

"If you came," her voice was oddly clear as if she talked to convince some stupid child, "—if you came by the wood road, you walked four miles. There's a path by the sea that is six. A lovelier way."

Both had forgotten his suggestion of the phone; and he, the rebuking, inviting, sensuous trees.

There was silence, easy as if it were natural that he should pause ere he came to a decision on a weighty matter. His mind flew to chess—my move. Then he saw again . . . and alone . . . the girl who with a smile, polite but visibly indulgent, doubtless waited his going. He had forgotten utterly the woods; there was no outside. The room was alive and close about them.

"Not a nook for me, *anywhere?*" he said.

"Not anywhere," she answered slowly.

"And all your guests have gone to bed?"

"We are early sleepers, here, sir. The night train is the last event of the day. Mail is not distributed till morning."

He held his hat in his left hand; he placed it on the desk. And his left hand, falling beside it, began again to strum the wood. The beat of the fingers was periodic, subtle . . . somewhat like telegraphic jottings. He felt beside his hand a presence that displaced it. He looked; her hand lay demurely at her edge of the desk. He watched her hand, and there came from it, through his hand to him, a tension bittersweet; soon, an intolerable tension.

"If you were kind," he heard his words come dry, he was outside his words, and they amazed him, "if you were kind you would not, at this hour, send me walking six miles back—to a deaf woman's door."

There was no saliva in his mouth; yet what he said seemed to concern him only mildly, as if it were a formula with a foregone conclusion.

"You would take me in. You would find—you would give me a place to lay my head." The room was breathing with them. His voice, clear as dry twigs, amazed him:

"*You* have a room?"

There, an instant, were his words between his eyes and hers; then his words were gone, as if her eyes had absorbed them.

Her face turned to a little stair behind her.

"Go up there, and wait."

Her face had been but a post to show the way. There was no

feeling in it, no recognition. He took his hat, leaving his bag at the desk.

It was not the guest-stair. It was a dark backstair that turned, halfway, so that the upper hall was black. In the balustrade below, a mere crack of light. He stood motionless in the black, and he waited.

There was no thought in him. He did not wait, unmoving because he feared if he moved he might rouse some sleeper. He waited, motionless and thoughtless, feelingless, because he was in equilibrium: cradled perfectly in some imminent presence.

He waited a long time.

There was a step below. The little crack of gleam within the balustrade winked out: so silent its demise, that it was like a signal from a distance. He felt her coming toward him. Her shoulder faintly touched his. Then he followed her in the dark with a knowledge that was thoughtless, sightless. His following her was the mere wake of her walking—like some immutable effect of a cause in nature. A door shut behind them both; he heard it lock.

*   *   *

Sleep softly pushed him to a dawn whose light was the stirring of his mingled senses. He turned his head, and only then opened his eyes which fell, already focused, on her face. The girl slept. Her hair was a chaos all about her ordered slumber. The shut eyes tremored faintly; a hand lay open on the coverlet. Still without thought, he rose, dressed and went.

When he reached the sea, he again flung off his clothes and swam. The water on his flesh was, strangely, a salute: the sea seemed to accept him, infinitesimal and yet its equal.

At nine o'clock, the sun stood high on the pines which margined the earth from the Pacific. He thought it safe, now, to return to the hotel. He had designed his little strategy. Thought, he had forced himself at last to come. And with thought, as he came out of the perfection of his trance in which act and impulse had been so miraculously attuned, came a quaver of self-satisfaction—a self-salute at his prowess.

He strode, still glowing from the sea, into the hotel lobby. It was a dingy transformation from the night before: men and women were grouped in it like clumsy grotesques of a perverse creator gibing his own beauty.

Behind the old-fashioned desk squatted a round and ruddy woman, the proprietress.

"Good morning," he smiled at her.

She stared at this creature, as if his presence were impossible; indeed for her it was, coming in connection with no train or bus. Her bosom, high as a shelf beneath her dress, did not budge as she ducked her head.

He pointed to his bag which still stood where he had placed it.

"I arrived late last evening. There was no room for me. So I left my bag and went. It was a beautiful night. Can you accommodate me, today? I hope to stay some time."

The landlady's face took on a puzzled frown.

"You were here last night?"

He nodded.

"No room, you say?"

"I missed the bus . . . The young lady was most kind. But there was no room."

"She said there was no room! Why, that is strange. And you had to tramp all the way back to the village! What a pity! How careless of the girl. *Of course* there was a room!"

THE KID ACROSS THE RIVER

By WILLIAM McFEE

A STRANGE THING HAPPENED THIS SUMMER WHILE WE WERE IN THE country. We had taken a house on a river. It ran right below our porch, and rippled over big stones that made a sort of dam and gave me a chance to fish. On the other side was a dense tangle of bushes and trees. I think it was the river decided us to take that house. The youngsters had set their hearts on a beach bungalow such as we always had, but they couldn't resist the river. It was a change from the city, to sit on the porch and listen to the murmur of the waters.

Suddenly one evening in early summer we saw a little boy on the other bank. We hadn't seen him come. He was just there, standing and looking across at us, a finger on his lips. My wife waved, and one of the children said "hello!" but he didn't answer. He just stood at the edge of the waters, a bare-legged kid of ten or so, with khaki knickers and a torn blue shirt. His fair hair was bleached by sunlight. There was a big dog just behind him too. Suddenly he was gone again. None of us saw him go. He just vanished.

"I suppose he belongs to the big house we see through the trees," said my wife. "I heard their property runs down to the river here."

"I've heard more than that," I said. "Sounds of revelry by night. They have a swimming pool the real estate man said they wanted to rent this summer, but it was too dear for us. You can see a great glare at night. And you can hear saxophones too."

"Hear what?" said my wife severely, as one of the boys laughed. "They have plenty of visitors. You can hear the cars going away, late."

"I'd call it early," I said. "It was four o'clock one morning when I heard a crash. And their gate was busted when I went by to get the nine fifteen."

"Hm," said my wife. "But it may have been innocent merriment for all you know."

It was about a week later that we saw him again. There he was, in the same spot, where the river ran over the stones. He was certainly a nice kid. Our children were having a picnic on the beach, so our place was quiet. The big dog, Dalmatian I think, was standing beside him. It was getting dusk, and we were thinking of going in on account of the mosquitoes, but we waited. At last I said "Hello!" and a very faint, sweet, child's treble replied, "Oh, hello!"

I said "How are you?" and so on.

"Oh, I'm fine, thanks," he said. He looked down at the big dog and patted his neck. I said we'd be glad if he came over and visited us.

"Maybe I will," he said, in that sweet far-away voice. I turned to say something to my wife and she turned to me. Only for a moment, but in that moment he vanished again.

It was after some days of intense heat and drought, so that the river sank and the stones grew dry, that we saw the little boy again. We had gotten ourselves into an argument about him. My wife said, "I wish we could be *sure*." I knew well enough what she meant, but I didn't want to stimulate her desire for mysteries.

"You can't think we both imagine things," I told her. And she had said, "Well . . ." in a certain tone of voice that I understood.

But we saw him that time. I mean we actually saw him appear. He pushed the leaves away, and there he was, with his dog. "Hello!" I said. "Aren't you coming over?"

My wife gave an exclamation. "He's coming!" she said as though she hadn't believed in him at all before that.

He ran lightly and silently on his bare brown feet, from stone to stone, the big dog following without a sound. They came up the steps to the porch and stood there. He was an awfully nice kid, it seemed to me. My wife said something about him looking like a little angel.

"Haven't you any playmates beside that dog?" I asked him. He shook his head. "Not now, not any more," he said. At least, that was what it sounded like to me. My wife insists he said something else, but what it was she won't say. I asked him how his family were, just to give him a lead.

"Oh, they're all tight," he remarked. My wife insists that he said they were all right, and I admit that sounds more rational. But I happen to be quite positive. I was too flabbergasted to make any comment. He began to move away. I said he'd better stay a while. The kids were sure to bring back some ice cream.

"I have got to go now," he said. "They wouldn't like me to be here. Goo'bye." He gazed very earnestly at us for a moment.

I was going to protest, but he ran silently down the steps and flitted across the dry stones. I am not sure I saw the dog go. But we heard a kid crying and the deep bay of of the dog a moment later, in the woods.

Saturdays a young man used to come around on a bicycle with a basket of crullers. We generally took a dozen for the children. I happened to be fixing the kitchen screen door, and I said I supposed he left a few at the big house up the road. He shook his head. He said there were no children there any more. My wife and I looked at him.

"Used to be a kid there," he said. "He used to come to the gate and give me a quarter. Him and a big dog. But they was killed."

We stared at him, but we did not speak.

"They was comin' home late," he went on, "and they was liquored up, I guess. Car turned over and the ambulance took 'em all to the hospital. The kid and the dog was killed. That was jus' about a year back. Their houseman sez he reckons they drink just to forget it. Well, I guess I'll be gettin' along. But they's no kid there now . . ."

STRIKE-PAY

By D. H. LAWRENCE

STRIKE-MONEY IS PAID IN THE PRIMITIVE METHODIST CHAPEL. THE crier was round quite early on Wednesday morning to say that paying would begin at ten o'clock.

The Primitive Methodist Chapel is a big barn of a place, built, designed, and paid for by the colliers themselves. But it threatened to fall down from its first form, so that a professional architect had to be hired at last to pull the place together.

It stands in the Square. Forty years ago, when Bryan and Wentworth opened their pits, they put up the "squares" of miners' dwellings. They are two great quadrangles of houses, enclosing a barren stretch of ground, littered with broken pots and rubbish, which forms a square, a great, sloping, lumpy playground for the children, a drying-ground for many women's washing.

Wednesday is still wash-day with some women. As the men clustered round the Chapel, they heard the thud-thud-thud of many pouches, women pounding away at the wash-tub with a wooden pestle. In the Square the white clothes were waving in the wind from a maze of clothes-lines, and here and there women were pegging out, calling to the miners, or to the children who dodged under the flapping sheets.

Ben Townsend, the Union agent, has a bad way of paying. He takes the men in order of his round, and calls them by name. A big, oratorical man with a grey beard, he sat at the table in the Primitive schoolroom, calling name after name. The room was crowded with colliers, and a great group pushed up outside. There was much confusion. Ben dodged from the Scargill Street list, to the Queen Street. For this Queen Street men were not prepared. They were not to the fore.

"Joseph Grooby—Joseph Grooby! Now, Joe, where are you?"

"Hold on a bit, Sorry!" cried Joe from outside. "I'm shovin' up."

There was a great noise from the men.

"I'm takin' Queen Street. All you Queen Street men should be ready. Here you are, Joe," said the Union agent loudly.

"Five children!" said Joe, counting the money suspiciously.

"That's right, I think," came the mouthing voice. "Fifteen shillings, is it not?"

"A bob a kid," said the collier.

"Thomas Sedgwick—How are you, Tom? Missis better?"

"Ay, 'er's shapin' nicely. Tha'rt hard at work today, Ben." This was a sarcasm on the idleness of a man who had given up the pit to become a Union agent.

"Yes. I rose at four to fetch the money."

"Dunna hurt thysen," was the retort, and the men laughed.

"No—John Merfin!"

But the colliers, tired with waiting, excited by the strike spirit, began to rag. Merfin was young and dandiacal. He was choirmaster at the Wesleyan Chapel.

"Does your collar cut, John?" asked a sarcastic voice out of the crowd.

"Hymn Number Nine.
 'Diddle-diddle dumpling, my son John
 Went to bed with his best suit on.' "
came the solemn announcement.

Mr. Merfin, his white cuffs down to his knuckles, picked up his half-sovereign, and walked away loftily.

"Sam Coutts!" cried the paymaster.

"Now, lad, reckon it up," shouted the voice of the crowd, delighted.

Mr. Coutts was a straight-backed ne'er-do-well. He looked at his twelve shillings sheepishly.

"Another two bob—he had twins a-Monday night—get thy money, Sam, tha's earned it—tha's addled it, Sam; dunna go beout it. Let him ha' the two bob for 'is twins, mister," came the clamour from the men around.

Sam Coutts stood grinning awkwardly.

"You should ha' given us notice, Sam," said the paymaster suavely. "We can make it all right for you next week ——"

"Nay, nay, nay," shouted a voice. "Pay on delivery—the goods is there right enough."

Get thy money, Sam, tha's addled it," became the universal cry, and the Union agent had to hand over another florin, to prevent a disturbance. Sam Coutts grinned with satisfaction.

"Good shot, Sam," the men exclaimed.

"Ephraim Wharmby," shouted the payman.

A lad came forward.

"Gi' him sixpence for what's on t'road," said a sly voice.

"Nay, nay," replied Ben Townsend; "pay on delivery."

There was a roar of laughter. The miners were in high spirits.

In the town they stood about in gangs, talking and laughing. Many sat on their heels in the market-place. In and out of the public-houses they went, and on every bar the half-sovereigns clicked.

"Comin' ter Nottingham wi' us, Ephraim?" said Sam Coutts, to the slender, pale young fellow of about twenty-two.

"I'm non walkin' that far of a gleamy day like this."

"He has na got the strength," said somebody, and a laugh went up.

"How's that?" asked another pertinent voice.

"He's a married man, mind yer," said Chris Smitheringale, "an' it ta'es a bit o' keeping' up."

The youth was teased in this manner for some time.

"Come on ter Nottingham wi's; tha'll be safe for a bit," said Coutts.

A gang set off, although it was only eleven o'clock. It was a nine-mile walk. The road was crowded with colliers travelling on foot to see the match between Notts and Aston Villa. In Ephraim's gang were Sam Coutts, with his fine shoulders and his extra florin, Chris Smitheringale, fat and smiling, and John Wharmby, a remarkable man, tall, erect as a soldier, black-haired and proud; he could play any musical instrument, he declared.

"I can play owt from a comb up-ards. If there's music to be got outer a thing, I back I'll get it. No matter what shape or form of instrument you set before me, it doesn't signify if I niver clapped eyes on it before, I's warrant I'll have a tune out of it in five minutes."

He beguiled the first two miles so. It was true, he had caused a sensation by introducing the mandoline into the townlet, filling the hearts of his fellow-colliers with pride as he sat on the platform in evening dress, a fine soldierly man, bowing his black head, and scratching the mewing mandoline with hands that had only to grasp the "instrument" to crush it entirely.

Chris stood a can round at the White Bull at Gilt Brook. John Wharmby took his turn at Kimberly top.

"We wunna drink again," they decided, " 'till we're at Cinder Hill. We'll non stop i' Nuttall."

They swung along the high-road under the budding trees. In Nuttall churchyard the crocuses blazed with yellow at the brim of the balanced, black yews. White and purple crocuses clipt up over the graves, as if the churchyard were bursting out in tiny tongues of flame.

"Sithee," said Ephraim, who was an ostler down pit, "sithee, here comes the Colonel. Sithee at his 'osses how they pick their toes up, the beauties!"

The Colonel drove past the men, who took no notice of him.

"Hast heard, Sorry," said Sam, "as they'm com'n out i' Germany, by the thousand, an' begun riotin'?"

"An commin' out i' France simbitar," cried Chris.

The men all gave a chuckle.

"Sorry," shouted John Wharmby, much elated, "we oughtna ter go back under a twenty per zent rise."

"We should get it," said Chris.

"An' easy. They can do nowt biout us, we'n on'y ter stop out long enough."

"I'm willin'," said Sam, and there was a laugh. The colliers looked at one another. A thrill went through them as if an electric current passed.

"We'n on'y ter stick out, an' we s'll see who's gaffer."

"Us!" cried Sam. "Why, what can they do again' us, if we come out all over th' world?"

"Nowt!" said John Wharmby. "Th' mesters is bobbin' about like corks on a rassivoy a'ready." There was a large natural reservoir, like a lake, near Bestwood, and this supplied the simile.

Again there passed through the men that wave of elation, quickening their pulses. They chuckled in their throats. Beyond all consciousness was this sense of battle and triumph in the hearts of the working-men at this juncture.

It was suddenly suggested at Nuttall that they should go over the fields to Bulwell, and into Nottingham that way. They went single file across the fallow, past the wood, and over the railway, where now no trains were running. Two fields away was a troop of pit ponies. Of all colors, but chiefly of red or brown, they clustered thick in the field, scarcely moving, and the two lines of trodden earth patches showed where fodder was placed down the field.

"Theer's the pit 'osses," said Sam. "Let's run 'em."

"It's like a circus turned out. See them skewbawd uns—seven skewbawd," said Ephraim.

The ponies were inert, unused to freedom. Occasionally one walked round. But there they stood, two thick lines of ruddy brown and piebald and white, across the trampled field. It was a beautiful day, mild, pale blue, a "growing day," as the men said, when there was the silence of swelling sap everywhere.

"Let's ha'e a ride," said Ephraim.

The younger men went up to the horses.

"Come on—co-oop Taffy—co-opp Ginger."

The horses tossed away. But having got over the excitement of being above-ground, the animals were feeling dazed and rather dreary. They missed the warmth and the life of the pit. They looked as if life were a blank to them.

Ephraim and Sam caught a couple of steeds, on whose backs they went careering round, driving the rest of the sluggish herd from end to end of the field. The horses were good specimens, on the whole, and in fine condition. But they were out of their element.

Performing too clever a feat, Ephraim went rolling from his mount. He was soon up again, chasing his horse. Again he was thrown. Then the men proceeded on their way.

They were drawing near to miserable Bulwell, when Ephraim, remembering his turn was coming to stand drinks, felt in his pocket for his beloved half-sovereign, his strike-pay. It was not there. Through all his pockets he went, his heart sinking like lead.

"Sam," he said, "I believe I'n lost that ha'ef a sovereign."

"Tha's got it somewheer about thee," said Chris.

They made him take off his coat and waistcoat. Chris examined the coat, Sam the waistcoat, whilst Ephraim searched his trousers.

"Well," said Chris, "I'n foraged this coat, an' it's non theer."

"An' I'll back my life as th' on'y bit a metal on this wa'scoat is the buttons," said Sam.

"An't it's non in my breeches," said Ephraim. He took off his boots and his stockings. The half-sovereign was not there. He had not another coin in his possession.

"Well," said Chris, "we mun go back an' look fir it."

Back they went, four serious-hearted colliers, and searched the field, but in vain.

"Well," said Chris, "we s'll ha'e ter share wi' thee, that's a'."

"I'm willin'," said John Wharmby.

"An' me," said Sam.

"Two bob each," said Chris.

Ephraim, who was in the depths of despair, shamefully accepted their six shillings.

In Bulwell they called in a small publichouse, which had one long room with a brick floor, scrubbed benches and scrubbed tables. The central space was open. The place was full of colliers, who were drinking. There was a great deal of drinking during the strike, but not a vast amount drunk. Two men were playing skittles, and the rest were betting. The seconds sat on either side the skittleboard, holding caps of money, sixpences and coppers, the wagers of the "backers."

Sam, Chris and John Wharmby immediately put money on the man who had their favour. In the end Sam declared himself willing to play against the victor. He was the Bestwood champion. Chris and John Wharmby backed him heavily, and even Ephraim the Unhappy ventured sixpence.

In the end, Sam had won half-a-crown, with which he promptly stood drinks and bread-and-cheese for his comrades. At half-past one they set off again.

It was a good match between Notts and Villa—no goals at half-time, two-none for Notts at the finish. The colliers were hugely delighted, especially as Flint, the forward for Notts, who was an Underwood man well known to the four comrades, did some handsome work, pulling the two goals through.

Ephraim determined to go home as soon as the match was over. He knew John Wharmby would be playing the piano at the "Punch Bowl," and Sam, who had a good tenor voice, singing, while Chris cut in with witticisms, until evening. So he bade them farewell, as he must get home. They, finding him somewhat of a damper on their spirits, let him go.

He was the sadder for having witnessed an accident near the football ground. A navvy working at some drainage, carting an iron tip-tub of mud and emptying it, had got with his horse onto the deep deposit of ooze which was crusted over. The crust had broken, the man had gone under the horse, and it was some time before the people had realized he had vanished. When they found his feet sticking out, and hauled him forth, he was dead, stifled dead in the mud. The horse was at length hauled out, after having its neck nearly pulled from the socket.

Ephraim went home vaguely impressed with the sense of death, and loss, and strife. Death was loss greater than his own, the strike was a battle greater than that he would presently have to fight.

He arrived home at seven o'clock, just when it had fallen dark. He lived in Queen Street with his young wife, to whom he had been married two months, and with his mother-in-law, a widow of sixty-four. Maud was the last child remaining unmarried, the last of eleven.

Ephraim went up the entry. The light was burning in the kitchen. His mother-in-law was a big, erect woman, with wrinkled loose face, and cold blue eyes. His wife was also large, with very vigorous fair hair, frizzy like unravelled rope. She had a quiet way of stepping, a certain cat-like stealth, in spite of her large build. She was five months pregnant.

"Might we ask wheer you've been to?" inquired Mrs. Marriott, very erect, very dangerous. She was only polite when she was very angry.

"I'n bin ter th' match."

"Oh, indeed!" said the mother-in-law. "And why couldn't we be told as you thought of jaunting off?"

"I didna know mysen," he answered, sticking to his broad Derbyshire.

"I suppose it popped into your mind, an' so you darted off," said the mother-in-law dangerously.

"I didna. It wor Chris Smitheringale who exed me."

"An' did you take much invitin'?"

"I didna want ter go."

"But wasn't there enough man beside your jacket to say no?"

He did not answer. Down at the bottom he hated her. But he was, to use his own words, all messed up with having lost his strike-pay and with knowing the man was dead. So he was more helpless before his mother-in-law, whom he feared. His wife neither looked at him, nor spoke, but kept her head bowed. He knew she was with her mother.

"Our Maud's been waitin' for some money, to get a few things," said the mother-in-law.

In silence, he put five-and-sixpence on the table.

"Take that up, Maud," said the mother.

Maud did so.

"You'll want it for us board, shan't you?" she asked, furtively, of her mother.

"Might I.ask if there's nothing you want to buy yourself, first?"

"No, there's nothink I want," answered the daughter.

Mrs. Marriott took the silver and counted it.

"And to you," she said, towering upon the shrinking son, but speaking slowly and statelily, "think I'm going to keep you and your wife for five-and-sixpence a week?"

"It's a' I've got," he answered, sulkily.

"You've had a good jaunt, my sirs, if it's cost four-and-sixpence. You've started your game early, haven't you?"

He did not answer.

"It's a nice thing! Here's our Maud an' me been sitting since eleven o'clock this morning! Dinner waiting and cleared away, tea waiting and washed up; then in he comes crawling with five-and-sixpence. Five-and-sixpence for a man an' wife's board for a week, if you please!"

Still he did not say anything.

"You must think something of yourself, Ephraim Wharmby!" said his mother-in-law. "You must think something of yourself. You suppose, do you, *I'm* going to keep you an' your wife, while you make a holiday, off on the nines to Nottingham, drink an' women."

"I've neither had drink nor women, as you know right well," he said.

"I'm glad we know aummat about you. For you're that close, anybody'd think we was foreigners to you. You're a pretty little jockey, aren't you? Oh, it's a gala time for you, the strike is. That's all men strike for, indeed. They enjoy themselves, they do that. Ripping and racing and drinking, from morn till night, my sirs!"

"Is there ony tea for me?" he asked, in a temper.

"Hark at him! Hark-ye! Should I ask you whose house you think you're in? Kindly order me about, do. Oh, it makes him bug, the strike does. See him land home after being out on the spree for hours, and give his orders, my sirs! Oh, Strike sets the men up, it does. Nothing have they to do but guzzle and gallivant to Nottingham. Their wives'll keep them, oh yes. So long as they get something to eat at home, what more do they want! What more *should* they want, prithee? Nothing! Let the women and children starve and scrape, but fill the man's belly, and let him have his fling. My sir, indeed, I think so! Let tradesmen go—what do they matter! Let rent go. Let children get what they can catch. Only the man will see *he's* all right. But not here, though!"

"Are you goin' ter gi'e me ony bloody tea?"

His mother-in-law started up.

"If tha dares ter swear at me, I'll lay thee flat."

"Are yer—goin' ter—gi'e me—any blasted rotten, cossed, bloody tea?" he bawled, in a fury, accenting every other word deliberately.

"Maud!" said the mother-in-law, cold and stately, "if you gi'e him any tea after that, you're a trollops." Whereupon she sailed out to her other daughter's.

Maud quietly got the tea ready.

"Shall y'ave your dinner warmed up?" she asked.

"Ay."

She attended to him. Not that she was really meek. But—he was *her* man, not her mother's.

GERONIMO DE AGUILAR

By JACOB WASSERMANN

AT THE TIME THE DISCOVERY OF NEW WORLDS KEPT THE IMAGINATION of Europe at fever heat, there lived in Spain an impoverished nobleman by the name of Geronimo de Aguilar, a restless character in whom, as soon as the exploits of Christopher Columbus and other explorers began to be talked about, there awoke an overwhelming desire to emulate those heroic adventures.

"By the Heart of Mary!" he vowed, "what this lucky dog Columbus has done is nothing to what I shall do! If they'll only let me, please God, I'll prove it! I will find you the lost Atlantis. I will conquer lands boasting more gold than cobblestones. And I'll bring your ships back so weighted down with treasure that you could give children jewels to play with, jewels as big as those locked in the Royal Treasury. But delay no more, for the time is ripe!"

Such glowing speeches he made everywhere, his black eyes ablaze as if a raging fire consumed the man from within. Many, of course, took him for a braggart, others believed him to be possessed by the devil; but also there were those in whose opinion it might well be worth the gamble to outfit a vessel and send such a man across the sea—a man in whom surges the power to do great deeds, said they, needn't talk about them with the timidity of a schoolmaster.

One day Count Callinjos, a former Chancellor who had been banished from Court, a wealthy man and an eccentric, invited Geronimo to call. On the latter's arrival he pointed to a table aglitter with gold pieces, and said:

"Here are ten thousand pesetas, Senor de Aguilar. I have heard of your great promises and your boasts, and am willing to risk this sum. With this you can equip my brigantine 'Elena' which lies at anchor in the port of Cadiz. I give you three years. If at the end of that time nothing's been heard from you I shall consider ship, money and men as lost. If, on the other hand, you return unsuc-

351

cessful you will be. branded a talkative swashbuckler, and I shall have you punished as a rogue."

On any other occasion so arrogant a speech would have made the proud Geronimo's blood boil. Now, however, he felt only a wild joy race through his veins. Without a word he took the count's hand, bent over it and pressed it to his lips.

Thenceforth he became a completely changed man. The talkative, violent, impetuous Geronimo his friends had known now became reticent, cold, calculating. While assembling a crew and fitting out the ship he took full advantage of all the experience his predecessors in adventure had gained by success and failure, and proved so clever and efficient that he evoked no end of surprise and praise. By the fall his preparations were at an end, and on a clear October morn the brigantine weighed anchor and made for the open sea, with the acclaim and prayers of the populace assembled at the pier ringing in Geronimo's ears. He stood on the poop deck, like a flame, as his native country sent him a last greeting. He sailed away without regrets or heartache, for behind him he left no heart, no home, no friend, not even a dog. He was alone. Enmeshed in his intoxicating visions he had long since ceased to have time for sentimental attachments of any sort.

The brig made fine time before the wind, and with mounting expectation all on board turned their faces westward. Yet even the most hardened members of the crew felt superstitious shudders creep along their spines as the stars they had known since childhood dropped lower and finally disappeared beyond the horizon, while the sight of strange skies and phosphorescent clouds forcibly reminded them of the perils that lay ahead. Geronimo alone did not waver from florid thoughts of the glory awaiting him and, as a veritable Midas of his dreams, he turned into gold whatever entered the realm of his hopes and fancies, knowing full well that the wealth he sought was the lone path to glory, and its only guarantee.

Now then, during the sixth week a terrific storm broke which lasted many days and drove the ship far out of its course in a northerly direction. The masts had to be cut. The rudder snapped under the strain of the heavy seas, and thus the crippled vessel was left to the winds and the currents of the uncharted water.

When at last one of the sailors in the crow's-nest sang out the long hoped for "Land!" there was a general feeling aboard that they were saved. Nevertheless they gazed intently and with heavy hearts toward the distant, low-lying coastline, wondering where they were and what fate held in store for them. Drawing nearer the brig was suddenly engulfed by a raging surf, and before they could hold counsel and decide what to do, it struck a sunken reef. There was a terrific heave and a sickening drop. The vessel quivered, and in next to no time the hull filled up while the seething sea hurled tons of water across the decks, washing most of the men overboard in the first moments of confusion. Those who managed to keep their footing tried to launch a lifeboat, but it was futile. Within a few minutes the ship and every soul on it but one had gone to a watery grave.

Perhaps some superhuman will to live, against which even the elements are powerless, spares men like Geronimo de Aguilar when dangers annihilate the weaker ones. A gigantic wave heaved him through a narrow channel in the reef and washed him ashore. When he regained consciousness, opened his brine-filled eyes and collected his scattered senses he found himself surrounded by strangely clad people. One bent on one knee and helped him to drink from a copper vessel. Another one helped him to rise. Then they led him into a large village. Gesticulating, they conveyed to him the fact that they were curious to know whence he came; he pointed towards the east. With solemn strides a group of older men, obviously priests, approached him followed by others caparisoned in flowers and precious garments whom he took to be chieftains. They addressed him in melodious sounds. He answered in the tongue of his homeland. Then he pointed heavenward, to the sea, and again to his tattered clothes.

The following day he was escorted to a town full of magnificent squares, gardens, palaces, battlements and towers which excited his wonder. At last entering an ornate edifice he was led into a hall where, seated on a throne, was the young prince, or Kazike, who wore a blue and white cloak spangled with emeralds and whose feet were shod in gold-embroidered half-shoes. The prince, after a pleasant greeting, studied him with childlike but gracious curiosity.

Geronimo was impressed by all that he saw. Observing the style of living and the behavior of this unknown people, he was overwhelmed by their wealth and beauty. They gave him to under-

stand that he was not a prisoner but a guest, and after much ceremony led him to a house adjoining the palace of the prince where
he was to live.

Geronimo did not know, of course, that he was in the vast realm
of the Aztecs, each province of which constituted a kingdom, for
he was the first white man ever to set foot on the soil of Mexico.
He could not even have said in which clime he found himself; so
that sometimes he imagined he had been transported to another
star. Everything was new to him; the air he breathed, the colorful
robes they gave him to wear, each tree and animal, every eye that
rested on him, the everyday sounds; not to mention the deep solitude to which he surrendered himself—the solitude of the thinking
man among barbarians, or so it appeared to him—a tormenting
solitude like an unbridgeable chasm separating him from his homeland. While surveying this veritable fairyland with the lust of the
conqueror and eyeing its marvels with the proud mien and the sense
of superiority of the noblest of races across the sea, he knew it to
be but an empty dream and a mockery. For him all this meant
nothing, less than nothing. Although he had attained his goal his
venture would bear no fruit, the achievement was sterile of any
guerdon; the world he had discovered would remain a chimera so
long as he could not clarion the news to the world. Because he considered himself the rightful owner of all he surveyed, and the
people and prince his slaves, the mocking fate which bound him,
the owner of this fabulous wealth, to idleness while the precious
days went by, threw him into such despair that he tossed night after
night sleeplessly on his pallet and sent up prayers to heaven which
sounded more like blasphemy than incantation.

He noticed that gradually the aborigines split into two factions
in their attitude toward him. Despite their attestations of friendliness he knew he was all the time surrounded by spies and closely
guarded at every step. In time his naturally sharp wits, stimulated to
undue attentiveness, gained him some knowledge of the language;
and thus several youths who had been appointed his personal
servants made things easier for him, their gossip divulging the fact
that unusual doings were afoot and that disaster hung over his head.

As it happened, there existed an ancient prophecy among these
Mexicans which had been handed down for centuries, according
to which a son of the Sun, a demi-god, would some day come out

of the East and assume dominion over their country. Many believed Geronimo to be the long waited deity. This accounted for the fear and the shy adoration he had encountered on many faces and which, preoccupied as he was with his own misfortune, he had taken no trouble to explain. The high priest violently opposed this view concerning the shipwrecked stranger, arguing effectively that a son of the Sun would have made his appearance more impressively arrayed than this hapless mortal. Against this it was argued that it might easily be a ruse of the gods; but the priests stood by their leader's opinion that Geronimo belonged to an unknown people, well educated, to be sure, and of beautiful stature, but withal threatening betrayal and certain to bring danger in his wake. They demanded that he be sacrificed and that his heart be burned on the jade block in honor of the god of war.

The prince and his nobles were opposed to this. The holy law of hospitality must not be desecrated. So heated grew the controversy that the prince finally summoned a number of the most influential citizens of his realm, and addressed them as follows:

"We do not wish to treat the stranger unjustly. If he is of divine origin he must be capable of giving us a sign of his godhead. What, however, is the strongest proof of godliness? I think it is the power to resist that which conquers all humans: love for a woman, the temptation of the senses. Let us test him; if he succumbs to temptation, then the priests shall have their way; otherwise he may dwell on peacefully among us."

They all declared their accord with this decision of the wise and gracious young prince, certain that he would properly arrange everything. As for Geronimo, although unable to find out what they wanted to do with him, he sensed danger; and his shrewdness impelled him to make a demand of the Kazike which might supply a hint as to the nature of his fate. Throwing himself at the prince's feet he begged to be allowed to build a ship. Privately he realized it would be next to impossible, for the Aztecs knew nothing whatever of shipbuilding though they were otherwise able to accomplish marvels with their primitive tools of obsidian and firestone. Yet, his growing restlessness had fired Geronimo with the wild idea of attempting to reach one of the islands of New Spain.

"What would you with a ship, Malinke?" the prince asked him gently. Malinke was the pet name the Mexicans had invented for the swarthy stranger; the same which, much later, they used often and plaintively when addressing the Spanish Conquistadors.

"To go home," Geronimo answered.

"We cannot build a ship sturdy enough to carry you so far," replied the young ruler.

"You need but order your carpenters to do as I tell them to do, and the ship will be built," Geronimo ventured, pale with excitement.

"Perhaps, when the moon is full again," said the prince meaningly and with all his almost girlish charm. "Not now, but perhaps when the moon is full again."

The ruse had worked. Geronimo now knew approximately how near the danger was, for the moon was young. He prepared to be incessantly on the alert, but who can say what his end would have been had he not, while out walking in the company of his two servants, saved a boy from the claws of a puma. The animal had broken from his cage and attacked the boy who was already bleeding from several wounds. Geronimo rushed in and drove off the puma. On the morrow the lad's father, an old and richly garbed man, came to his house, thanked him profusely, stared at him, suddenly brought his lips down to his ear and whispered:

"If you touch a woman you are lost!"

The old man, on leaving, committed suicide, unable to endure the thought that he had betrayed his prince.

A few days later a representative of the Kazike called on Geronimo and asked him in the name of his ruler whether he did not desire to take one of the daughters of the land to wife. Geronimo bowed deeply but simply shook his head. Later the same day a second emissary appeared to apprise him that the wealthiest and most beautiful maiden, of noble birth and pure in heart, desired him as a husband. He intimated that the prince would be displeased if Geronimo declined the offer. But Geronimo, made doubly cautious by this obvious insistence, rejected this second offer in the same manner as before.

Waking from a deep slumber the following night, he was astonished to find himself not in his own room. He was in a spacious chamber dimly illumined from above and pervaded by bluish dusk. Floor and walls were covered with a carpet of fresh flowers whose scent had the weird effect of simultaneously dulling his senses and stirring up sensuous desires. The Aztecs were adept in the subtle art of mixing scents, an art related to black magic, and could produce effects otherwise obtainable only by potions or narcotics. They revered flowers and frequently held flower festivals where men, women and children, bedecked in blossoms of every description, danced in processions through the landscape.

Geronimo saw sixteen youths striding through the wide open portal and approaching him. They carried beautiful objects in their hands: tapestries spun of golden strands, jewel-incrusted shoes, carved weapons, a vessel full of multicolored precious stones, another filled to the brim with pearls, marvelous figurines of agate and silver, a cob of Indian corn fashioned out of pure gold and wrapped in broad silver leaves; and last, borne by two youths, a fountain throwing a golden stream into the air while miniature animals and small birds, also of gold, adorned the rim.

In breathless amazement Geronimo looked on at this spectacle, and when finally the leader of the treasure carriers told him that all this belonged to him he realized there was enough within the reach of his eyes to buy a whole Spanish province! Still he did not blink an eyelash but pressed his fists against his breast, aware of impending danger. After a while he raised his eyes again and saw, aligned against the far wall, twelve raven-haired virgins who squatted on the floor in groups of threes, their hands busy at some mysterious task but their smiles telling him that their actions were intended only to disarm. There were three basket weavers, three wreath winders, three brocade makers and three pearl stitchers. Occasionally one of them sprang to her feet and whirled around in a dance, baring her olive-hued breasts while the others looked on with false, tempting smiles. Then in chorus they sang a soft, dark melody interrupted every now and then by the shrill cry: "Tochrua!"

Abruptly they all fell silent, drew close together, and, like one single body, began crawling toward his couch, stretching out their arms entreatingly; twelve pairs of lips parted sensuously while twelve bodies seemed to writhe forth from their very garments. Flesh shone in deep carmine, a roseate scent wafted to his nostrils. The girls *gurred* like pigeons, pressed ever closer, ever nearer, laughing softly as if they were being kissed. Then their hands began caressing him all over like soft little animals. Geronimo only shut his eyes tighter, turned away, and buried his face in the cushions, resolved to remain so whatever might happen. And thus he fell into a sound sleep as the seductive sounds died away.

When morning came he was once again in his own room. He felt limp and tired, and tried to overcome his lassitude by winging his thoughts insistently across the sea to his own country.

During the next night he awoke in the hall of flowers once more, and this time it dawned upon him that his captors must have mixed a sleeping potion with his food or the water he drank. Whereas the flowered walls the night before had been covered mainly with blue and white blossoms, they now were decked out in dark red flowers, punctuated here and there by a yellow bud. He heard a sound like faraway drums, then the clear tones of a gong, then the prolonged note of a flute, then laughter and blood-quickening lust-drenched outcries—all happening in utter darkness, for the mysterious light from above had vanished. Frantically Geronimo looked about for the best way to protect himself, when unexpectedly light came and five tender young girls moved toward his bed. Each bore in her hand an emerald of great size and incomparable lustre. The first emerald was shaped like a snail, the second like a horn, the third in the form of a fish with golden eyes, the fourth had been artfully carved into a loop, while the fifth and most beautiful was a vessel with golden legs. These five jewels they proffered him, at the same time saying in dulcet tones:

"This is Tochrua's gift to you."

"And this."

"And this."

"And this."

"And this."

Their circle was pierced by the lithe figure of a young woman clad in a purple veil who floated up to him.

"Tochrua," sang the girls, and she greeted the kneeling maidens in a voice that rang like tempered metal and broke off in a sob. Wound around her neck and falling in great oval coils down her breast she wore strings of pearls which shimmered behind the gauze. As she came close she whispered to Geronimo:

"Malinke, take me."

Geronimo understood full well the import of her words but steeled himself not to answer, not even to stir. As she threw out

her arms like spread wings the girl with caressing fingers drew the
veil down from over her head, and Geronimo beheld a miracle of
beauty, a creature with skin as red as cedar wood, eyes melancholy
and entreating, and a mouth like a ripe, cut open peach.

"Malinke, take me," she repeated again and again, pouring the
ever new music of her voice into each more impassioned plea.

Geronimo paled and turned away, but now dark, haunting melo-
dies assailed his ears from all sides, above and below. He tried to
distract himself by conjuring up pictures with which he had of
late comforted himself in his solitude, pictures of his return home
and of his ultimate triumph; but in vain did he try to suppress the
rising fever of his blood. The light in the room grew dimmer, until
Tochrua was but a shadow; every one of her languorous gestures
awakened in him a torturing curiosity and he was perilously close
to losing his grasp of memory and conscience under the spell of
the mysterious, alluring sounds floating through the darkness.

Morning found him on his accustomed couch, disquieted and
sad. Lazily the day crept on; nobody came to see him; in silence
the servants slunk through the house; the noises of market and
street languished on his threshold. Wherever he turned he saw
Tochrua's eyes fixed on him. Wild desire and anguish weighed
heavily upon his chest. When evening came a white-haired, dark-
skinned, emaciated priest entered the room, stared at him during
a long silence, and finally said:

"Mark well, stranger! Tochrua must die if you spurn her."

With these words he went away and left Geronimo to his despair.

Nothing happened during the following night or the one after.
But this only made Geronimo more unhappy and distraught than
ever, for while he perceived their cunning his helplessness condemned him to patience. On the third night he awoke under a high
cupola and his first glance about rested upon a pair of lovers locked
in close embrace who gave the illusion of being suspended thus
in mid-air. The cupola, supported by pillars, stood in a garden
eerily illumined by tiny blue flames, surrounded by dark foliage
among whose leaves were hidden silent white birds while along
the paths copper-colored snakes crawled or lay coiled up. Geronimo caught no more than the flash of a woman's white shoulder,
a fleeting glimpse of a face newly escaped from passion and still
bright with its rapture, and again naked fleeing bodies gliding by

like torches. No more, yet it proved an unending, excruciating torture. His veins were afire. A strange torpor befell him. He craved the sight of Tochrua again. All around his bed invisible hands heaped treasure upon treasure. The air heaved with sighs, and from below countless white arms stretched up toward him. Girls danced by flitting like swallows, youths drifted to and fro, and the unreal, libidinous beauty of it all threw Geronimo into a state of complete terror. No matter that he clamped his eyelids tight shut, he sensed these phantoms through his skin, he breathed their alluring odor, their steps pattered by, their garments rustled all around, every other moment the fragile but suggestive voices of stringed instruments quivered amid the medley; lust and terror made him tremble and look again.

He now beheld a wreath of diaphanous human forms, head to head, loin to loin, made spectral by the dim light. All at once Tochrua, nude and like living marble, appeared. Geronimo half arose; it seemed as though nothing on earth could prevent him any longer from clutching this wondrous apparition to his breast. At the same time he noted that her face was serious and sad; in it shone genuine understanding and exalted pity, forewarning him of their entwined fates: death for him if he took her, death for her if he did not. Thus, at the very brink of the plunge into the abyss of passion he became once more conscious of the danger, and sank back and lay rigid.

When that night was over and he again dared to open his eyes and look around, a procession of boys and girls in white robes, white flowers stuck in their hair, flowed into the room. It was unmistakably a sorrowful procession; and, while singing a monotonous dirge, they intermittently cried out: "O, Malinke! O, Malinke!"

The unfortunate Geronimo understood that his vague fears had at last become definite and real; and the turmoil in his soul turned into an icy catalepsy when, during the ensuing night—and this time he was not spirited from his own room—they carried in the lifeless form of Tochrua. On a platter of blue stone a slave bore Tochrua's heart which seemed still to beat, its red blood glistening on the bright stone. Unrestrained tears rolled down Geronimo's cheeks and all his desires seemed, suddenly, dead. All trace of lust fled from his breast, even the lust of ambition, and he felt himself growing morbidly indifferent to everything that had seemed desirable and worthy to him in the past. He felt as if he were but a thing, inanimate, far from life and death. For once he was aware of the fact that he had charged through his years like a man without a soul and that he owned nothing in this world because he had loved nothing.

And so it came to pass that no matter what artifices they conceived thereafter, whether their graceful bodies swam through the opalescent shadows like a fish in lukewarm liquid or performed their ivory dances, whether silent or singing, nothing could revive his lust; for death had taken part in the game, and also because they were so beautiful to watch, these men and women, that the very pleasure of watching snuffed out the flame of desire.

One night the youths roused him and led him into the open. After a while he found himself at the foot of a tower of ascending steps the crest of which was lost in the blue-black ether. Geronimo began to climb upward. As he carried the night aloft with him and could let his eyes roam in a limitless vista, he had the sensation of having recuperated from a dangerous malady; the magnificent panorama unfolded before him wrought a complete change in his heart.

Mexican night! The heavens an overwhelming screen of stars, the horizon aflame with the livid breath of the volcanoes; near and yet far away the sea; palms rising from the night; the bluish green of the cacti; fireflies and luminous bugs humming through the branches of the mango-woods; from the forest the voices of birds, the hoarse barking of the *tukans*, the shriek of the tree-panther, and from the depth the cry of the *selvas* which even to the aborigine sounds weird.

Two priests, waiting for him on the platform of the tower, approached him with solemn tread and bowed low as a sign that he had passed the test; at that moment an irrevocable resolution took seed in Geronimo never, either by word or action, to reveal to his prosaic countrymen the existence of this fairyland. Who would call him to account?

Back home they would think the sea had swallowed him, and it would be centuries, he thought, centuries before the civilized world would stumble upon this land. How droll! A man discovers a new country and resolves to keep it a secret—as though it were a bauble one might lock away in a drawer. Geronimo felt like a man who has been forced into marrying a woman he does not want, only to discover in her such traits of body and spirit that he flees with her where he may enjoy his unexpected happiness hidden jealously from all men. He had come to love this indigo sky, this lavishly fertile soil, with an ardor completely new to his nature. He loved the mountain looming up toward the sun like yellow marble; loved the impenetrable forests; the banana trees, the locust trees, the towering jaguar-palm and the lianes thrusting their serpentine embrace from tree to tree.

The naiveté of the natives moved him profoundly when he viewed in retrospect the villainy and corruption of his own countrymen; their physical grace and good humor and half-angelic amorality made him ashamed of the moodiness and heaviness he had been accustomed to encounter in his own kind. He remembered the obstacles he had had to hurdle from his early youth in a world controlled by envy, futility and hatred. And that he should have wanted to go back to a clime and nature which, their genesis eons gone, created humanity out of fever and suffering and turmoil and damned them to a soulless pseudo-existence, now seemed utterly incomprehensible to him.

(*Translated by Eric Posselt and Michel Kraika*)

LET ME PROMISE YOU

By MORLEY CALLAGHAN

ALICE KEPT ON RETURNING TO THE WINDOW. STANDING WITH HER short straight nose pressed against the window pane, she watched the rain falling and the sidewalk shining under the street light. In her black crepe dress with the big white nunlike collar and with her black hair drawn back tight from her narrow nervous face she looked almost boldly handsome.

Earlier in the evening it had started to snow, then it had begun to drizzle and now the rain was like a sharp sleet. As Alice stood at the window, she began to wish that the ground had been covered with an unbroken layer of fine thin snow, a white sheet that would remain undisturbed till Georgie came with his single line of footprints marking a path up to her door. Though her eyes remained wide open, she began to dream of a bitterly cold dry evening, of Georgie with a red scarf and a tingling face bursting in on her, grinning, his arms wide open. But the wind drove the sleet steadily against the pane. Sighing, she thought, "He won't come in such weather. But he would if it weren't for the weather. I can't really expect him tonight." So she walked away from the window and sat down.

Then her heart began to thump so slowly and heavily inside her she could hardly move, for someone was knocking. Opening the door in a rush, she cried, "Georgie, you dear boy, I'm so glad you came," and she put out her hands to help him off with his dripping coat. In the light belted coat he looked very tall and he had a smooth round face that would never look old. The wind and the rain had left his face wet and glowing, but he was pouting because he was uncomfortable in his damp clothes. As he pushed his fair wavy hair back from his eyes, he said, "This isn't exactly a night for visiting." He sat down, still a bit embarrassed by her enthusiasm, and he looked around the room as if he thought now that he had made a mistake in coming and didn't expect to be very

363

comfortable. "It's rotten out on a night like this when it can't make up its mind to snow or rain. Maybe you didn't think I'd come."

"I wanted you to come, and because I wanted it, I thought you would, I guess," she said candidly. So many days seemed to have passed since she had been alone with Georgie that now she wanted to take his head in her hands and kiss him. But she felt too shy. A year ago, she knew, he would have been waiting anxiously for her to kiss him.

"Alice," he said suddenly.

"What's bothering you, Georgie, frowning like that?"

"What did you want me for? You said you wanted to speak about something in particular."

"Such curiosity. You'll just sit there unable to rest till you find out, I suppose," she said. She knew he was ill at ease, but she wanted to pretend to herself that he was just impatient and curious. So her pale handsome face was animated by a warm secret delight as she went across the room to a chest of drawers and took out a long cardboard box which she handed to him after making a low girlish curtsy. "I hope you like it . . . darling," she said shyly.

"What's this? What's the idea?" Georgie said as he undid the box and pulled out the tissue paper. When he saw that she was giving something to him, he became embarrassed and almost too upset to speak, and then, because he did not want to hurt her, he tried to be full of enthusiasm, "Lord, look at it," he said. "White, turtle necked sweater. If I wore that I'd look like a movie actor in his spare time. Should I put it on now, Al?" Grinning at her, he took off his coat and pulled the white sweater over his shirt. "Do I look good? How about a mirror, Al?"

Alice held the mirror in front of him, watching him with the same gentle expression of devotion all the time, and feeling within her a contentment she had hardly dared to hope for. The high necked sweater made his fair head look like a faun's head.

"It's pretty swell, Al," he said, but now that he couldn't go on pleasing her with enthusiasm, his embarrassment increased. "You shouldn't be giving me this, Al," he said. "I didn't figure on anything like this when you phoned me and said you wanted to see me."

"Today is your birthday, isn't it, Georgie?"

"Imagine you remembering that. You shouldn't be bothering with birthday presents for me now."

"I thought you'd like the sweater," she said. "I saw it this afternoon. I knew it would look good on you."

"But why give me anything, Al?" he said, feeling his awkwardness increasing.

"Supposing I want to?"

"You shouldn't waste your money on me."

"Supposing I have something else, too," she said teasing him.

"What's the idea, Al?"

"I saw something else, something you used to want an awful lot. Do you remember? Try and guess."

"I can't imagine," he said, but his face got red and he smiled awkwardly at being forced in this way to remember a time which only made him feel uncomfortable now when he recalled it.

Laughing huskily and showing her small even teeth because she was glad to be able to hold out something before him and tease him as she used to do, she moved lazily over to the chest of drawers, and this time took out a small leather watch case. "Here you are," she said.

"What is it, let me see," he said, for he couldn't help being curious. He got up. But when he held the watch in his hand, he had to shake his head to conceal his satisfaction. "It's funny the way you knew I always wanted something like that, Al," he said. All his life he had wanted an expensive wrist watch like this one, but had never expected to be able to buy it, and he was so pleased now that he smiled serenely.

But after a moment he put the watch irresolutely on the table, and was too embarrassed to speak. Walking the length of the room he began to whistle. As she watched him halt by the window, Alice knew he was uneasy. "You're a great girl, Al," he was saying. "I don't know anybody like you." After pausing, he added, "Is it never going to stop raining? I've got to be on my way."

"You're not going now, Georgie, are you?"

"Yes, I promised to see a fellow. He'll be waiting."

"Georgie, don't go. Please don't," she said, and she clenched the wet sleeve of the coat he had lifted from the chair. He was really ashamed to be going, especially if he picked up the watch from the table, but he felt if he stayed it would be like beginning everything all over again. He didn't know what to do about the watch, so he put out his hand hesitantly, knowing she was watching him and picked it up.

"So you're just coming here like this and then going?" she said.

"I've got to."

"Have you got another girl?"

"No. I don't want another girl."

"Yet you won't stay a little while with me?"

"That's over, Al. I don't know what's the matter with you. You phoned and wanted me to drop in for a moment."

"It wasn't hard to see that you liked looking at the watch more than at me," she said moodily.

"Here, if you don't want me to take the watch, all right," he said, and with relief, he put it back on the table, and smiled.

For a moment she stared at the case, almost blinded by her disappointment, and hating his smile of relief, and then she cried out, "You're just trying to humiliate me. Take it out of my sight." She swung the back of her hand across the table, knocked the case to the floor and the watch against the wall where the glass broke, and trying not to cry, she clenched her fists and glared at him.

But he didn't even look at her. With his mouth drooping open, he looked longingly at the watch, for he realized how much he wanted it now that he saw it smashed on the floor. He had always wanted such a watch. As he looked up at her, his blue eyes were innocent with the sincerity of his full disappointment. "Gee, Al," was all he said.

The anger began to go out of her, and she felt how great was his disappointment. She felt helpless. "I shouldn't have done that, Georgie," she said.

"It was a crazy thing to do. It was such a beauty," he said. "Why did you do it?"

"I don't know," she said. She knelt down and started to cry. "Maybe it's not broken much," she faltered, moving around on her knees and picking up the pieces of glass carefully. In her hand she held the pieces but her eyes were blinking so that she could not see them. "It was a crazy thing to do," she was thinking. "It helps nothing. It can't help bring him back to me. Why does he stand there like that? Why doesn't he move?" At last she looked up at him and saw his round smooth chin above the white neck of the sweater, and her dark eyes were shining with tears, for it seemed, as he watched her without speaking or moving, that everything ought to have turned out differently. They both looked at the broken pieces of glass she held in her hand in such abject despair, and for that moment while they looked, they began to share a common, bitter disappointment which made Georgie gravely silent and drew him close to her. "Never mind, Al," he said with awkward tenderness. "Please get up."

"No. Go away. Leave me alone."

"You've got to get up from there. I can't stand here like this with you there."

"Oh, why don't you go. I know I'm mean and jealous. I wish someone would shake me and hurt me. I'm a little cat."

"No, you're not, Al. Who'd want to shake you? Please get up," he said, coaxing. "Here, come on," he said, bending down and putting his hand on her shoulder.

"Say you'll stay, Georgie," she said, holding on to his hand. "It's so warm here: It's miserable outside. Just listen to the wind. Do you hear it? I'll get you something to eat. You don't want to go, do you?"

"It's no worse than when I came," he said, but his sudden tenderness for her was making him uneasy. He had known Al so well for a long time, she had been one of his girls, one he could feel sure of and leave at any time, but now he felt that he had never looked right at her and seen her before. He did not know her. Nor did he know himself now. He could not leave her. The warmth of her love began to awe him. Her dark head, her pale oval face seemed so close to him that he might have put out his hand timidly and touched her and felt her whole ardent being under the cloth of her dress, but the sharp tremor inside him made him catch his breath and destroyed all his old confidence. Faltering, he said, "Gee Al, I never got you right. Not in this way. I don't want to go. Look how I want to stay."

"Georgie, listen to me," she said eagerly. "I'll get that watch for you. Or I'll get a new one. I'll save up for it. Or I'll get you anything else you say."

"Don't think about it," he said, shamefaced. "I feel just like a bum."

"But I want so much to do it, and you can look forward to it. We both can look forward. Please let me promise it to you."

She was still crouched on the carpet. He glanced at her handsome dark face above the white nunlike collar and at her soft pleading eyes. "You look lovely right now, Al," he said. "You look like a wild thing. Honest to God you do."

Touched by happiness, she smiled. Then with all her heart she began to yearn for something more to give him. If there were only more things she had and could give, she thought; if she could only give everything in the world and leave herself nothing.

THE LONESOME VIGILANTE

By JOHN STEINBECK

THE GREAT SURGE OF EMOTION, THE MILLING AND SHOUTING OF THE people fell gradually to silence in the town park. A crowd of people still stood under the elm trees, vaguely lighted by a blue street light two blocks away. A tired quiet settled on the people; some members of the mob began to sneak away into the darkness. The park lawn was cut to pieces by the feet of the crowd.

Mike knew it was all over. He could feel the let-down in himself. He was as heavily weary as though he had gone without sleep for several nights, but it was a dream-like weariness, a grey comfortable weariness. He pulled his cap down over his eyes and moved away, but before leaving the park he turned for one last look.

In the center of the mob someone had lighted a twisted newspaper and was holding it up. Mike could see how the flame curled about the feet of the grey naked body hanging from the elm tree. It seemed curious to him that Negroes turn a bluish grey when they are dead. The burning newspaper lighted the heads of the up-looking men, silent men and fixed; they didn't move their eyes from the hanged man.

Mike felt a little irritation at whoever it was who was trying to burn the body. He turned to a man who stood beside him in the near-darkness. "That don't do no good," he said.

The man moved away without replying.

The newspaper torch went out, leaving the park almost black by contrast. But immediately another twisted paper was lighted and held up against the feet. Mike moved to another watching man. "That don't do no good," he repeated. "He's dead now. They can't hurt him none."

The second man grunted but did not look away from the flaming paper. "It's a good job," he said. "This'll save the county a lot of money and no sneaky lawyers getting in."

"That's what I say," Mike agreed. "No sneaky lawyers. But it don't do no good to try to burn him."

The man continued staring toward the flame. "Well, it can't do much harm, either."

Mike filled his eyes with the scene. He felt that he was dull. He wasn't seeing enough of it. Here was a thing he would want to remember later so he could tell about it, but the dull tiredness seemed to cut the sharpness off the picture. His brain told him this was a terrible and important affair, but his eyes and his feelings didn't agree. It was just ordinary. Half an hour before, when he had been howling with the mob and fighting for a chance to help pull on the rope, then his chest had been so full that he had found he was crying. But now everything was dead, everything unreal; the dark mob was made up of stiff lay-figures. In the flame-light the faces were as expressionless as wood. Mike felt the stiffness, the unreality in himself, too. He turned away at last and walked out of the park.

The moment he left the outskirts of the mob a cold loneliness fell upon him. He walked quickly along the street wishing that some other man might be walking beside him. The wide street was deserted, empty, as unreal as the park had been.

The two steel lines of the car tracks stretched glimmering away down the street under the electroliers, and the dark store windows reflected the midnight globes.

A gentle pain began to make itself felt in Mike's chest. He felt with his fingers; the muscles were sore. Then he remembered. He was in the front line of the mob when it rushed the closed jail door. A driving line forty men deep had crashed Mike against the door like the head of a ram. He had hardly felt it then, and even now the pain seemed to have the dull quality of loneliness.

Two blocks ahead the burning neon word BEER hung over the sidewalk. Mike hurried toward it. He hoped there would be people there, and talk to remove this silence; and he hoped the men wouldn't have been to the lynching.

The bartender was alone in his little bar, a small, middle-aged man with a melancholy moustache and an expression like an aged mouse, wise and unkempt and fearful.

He nodded quickly as Mike came in. "You look like you been walking in your sleep," he said.

Mike regarded him with wonder. "That's just how I feel, too, like I been walking in my sleep."

"Well, I can give you a shot if you want."

Mike hesitated. "No—I'm kind of thirsty. I'll take a beer. Was you there?"

The little man nodded his mouse-like head again. "Right at the last, after he was all up and it was all over. I figured a lot of the fellas would be thirsty, so I came back and opened up. Nobody but you so far. Maybe I was wrong."

"They might be along later," said Mike. "There's a lot of them still in the park. They cooled off, though. Some of them trying to burn him with newspapers. That don't do no good."

"Not a bit of good," said the little bartender. He twitched his thin moustache.

Mike knocked a few grains of celery salt into his beer and took a long drink. "That's good," he said. "I'm kind of dragged out."

The bartender leaned close to him over the bar, his eyes were bright. "Was you there all the time—to the jail and everything?"

Mike drank again and then looked through his beer and watched the beads of bubbles rising from the grains of salt in the bottom of the glass. "Everything," he said. "I was one of the first in the jail, and I helped pull on the rope. There's times when citizens got to take the law in their own hands. Sneaky lawyer comes along and gets some fiend out of it."

The mousy head jerked up and down. "You God-dam right," he said. "Lawyers can get them out of anything. I guess the nigger was guilty all right."

"Oh, sure! Somebody said he even confessed."

The head came close over the bar again. "How did it start, mister? I was only there after it was all over, and then I only stayed a minute and then came back to open up in case any of the fellas might want a glass of beer."

Mike drained his glass and pushed it out to be filled. "Well, of course everybody knew it was going to happen. I was in a bar across from the jail. Been there all afternoon. A guy came in and says, 'What are we waiting for?' So we went across the street, and a lot more guys was there and a lot more come. We all stood there and yelled. Then the sheriff come out and made a speech, but we yelled him down. A guy with a twenty-two rifle went along the street and shot out the street lights. Well, then we rushed the jail doors and bust them. The sheriff wasn't going to do nothing. It wouldn't do him no good to shoot a lot of honest men to save a nigger fiend."

"And election coming on, too," the bartender put in.

"Well the sheriff started yelling, 'Get the right man, boys, for Christ's sake get the right man. He's in the fourth cell down.'

"It was kind of pitiful," Mike said slowly. "The other prisoners was so scared. We could see them through the bars. I never seen such faces."

The bartender excitedly poured himself a small glass of whiskey and poured it down. "Can't blame 'em much. Suppose you was in for thirty days and a lynch mob came through. You'd be scared they'd get the wrong man."

"That's what I say. It was kind of pitiful. Well, we got to the nigger's cell. He just stood stiff with his eyes closed like he was dead drunk. One of the guys slugged him down and he got up, and then somebody else socked him and he went over and hit his head on the cement floor." Mike leaned over the bar and tapped the polished wood with his forefinger. " 'Course this is only my idea, but I think that killed him. Because I helped get his clothes off, and he never made a wiggle, and when we strung him up he didn't jerk around none. No, sir. I think he was dead all the time, after that second guy smacked him."

"Well, it's all the same in the end."

"No it ain't. You like to do the thing right. He had it coming to him, and he should have got it." Mike reached into his trousers pocket and brought out a piece of torn blue denim. "That's a piece of the pants he had on."

The bartender bent close and inspected the cloth. He jerked his head up at Mike. "I'll give you a buck for it."

"Oh no you won't!"

"All right. I'll give you two bucks for half of it."

Mike looked suspiciously at him. "What do you want it for?"

"Here! Give me your glass! Have a beer on me. I'll pin it up on the wall with a little card under it. The fellas that come in will like to look at it."

Mike haggled the piece of cloth in two with his pocket knife and accepted two silver dollars from the bartender.

"I know a show card writer," the little man said. "Comes in

every day. He'll print me up a nice little card to go under it." He looked wary. "Think the sheriff will arrest anybody?"

" 'Course not. What's he want to start any trouble for? There was a lot of votes in that crowd tonight. Soon as they all go away, the sheriff will come and cut the nigger down and clean up some."

The bartender looked toward the door. "I guess I was wrong about the fellas wanting a drink. It's getting late."

"I guess I'll get along home. I feel tired."

"If you go south, I'll close up and walk a ways with you. I live on south Eighth."

"Why, that's only two blocks from my house. I live on south Sixth. You must go right past my house. Funny I never saw you around."

The bartender washed Mike's glass and took off the long apron. He put on his hat and coat, walked to the door and switched off the red neon sign and the house lights. For a moment the two men stood on the sidewalk looking back toward the park. The city was silent. There was no sound from the park. A policeman walked along a block away, turning his flash into the store windows.

"You see?" said Mike. "Just like nothing happened."

"Well, if the fellas wanted a glass of beer they must have gone someplace else."

"That's what I told you," said Mike.

They swung along the empty street and turned south, out of the business district. "My name's Welch," the bartender said. "I only been in this town about two years."

The loneliness had fallen on Mike again. "It's funny—" he said, and then, "I was born right in this town, right in the house I live in now. I got a wife but no kids. Both of us born right in this town. Everybody knows us."

They walked on for a few blocks. The stores dropped behind and the nice houses with bushy gardens and cut lawns lined the street. The tall shade trees were shadowed on the sidewalk by the street lights. Two night dogs went slowly by, smelling at each other.

Welch said softly—"I wonder what kind of a fella he was—the nigger, I mean."

Mike answered out of his loneliness. "The papers all said he was a fiend. I read all the papers. That's what they all said."

"Yes, I read them, too. But it makes you wonder about him. I've known some pretty nice niggers."

Mike turned his head and spoke protestingly. "Well, I've knew some damn fine niggers myself. I've worked right long side some niggers and they was as nice as any white man you could want to meet.—But not no fiends."

His vehemence silenced little Welch for a moment. Then he said, "You couldn't tell, I guess, what kind of a fella he was?"

"No—he just stood there stiff, with his mouth shut and his eyes tight closed and his hands right down at his sides. And then one of the guys smacked him. It's my idea he was dead when we took him out."

Welch sidled close on the walk. "Nice gardens along here. Must take a lot of money to keep them up." He walked even closer, so that his shoulder touched Mike's arm. "I never been to a lynching. How's it make you feel—afterwards?"

Mike shied away from the contact. "It don't make you feel nothing." He put down his head and increased his pace. The little bartender had nearly to trot to keep up. The street lights were fewer. It was darker and safer. Mike burst out, "Makes you feel kind of cut off and tired, but kind of satisfied, too. Like you done a good job—but tired and kind of sleepy." He slowed his steps. "Look, there's a light in the kitchen. That's where I live. My old lady's waiting up for me." He stopped in front of his little house.

Welch stood nervously beside him. "Come into my place when you want a glass of beer—or a shot. Open 'til midnight. I treat my friends right." He scampered away like an aged mouse.

Mike called "Good night."

He walked around the side of his house and went in the back door. His thin petulant wife was sitting by the open gas oven warming herself. She turned complaining eyes on Mike where he stood in the door.

Then her eyes widened and hung on his face. "You been with a woman," she said hoarsely. "What woman you been with?"

Mike laughed. "You think you're pretty slick, don't you? You're a slick one, ain't you? What makes you think I been with a woman?"

She said fiercely, "You think I can't tell by the look on your face that you been with a woman?"

"All right," said Mike. "If you're so slick and know-it-all, I won't tell you nothing. You can just wait for the morning paper."

He saw doubt come into the dissatisfied eyes. "Was it the nigger?" she asked. "Did they get the nigger? Everybody said they was going to."

"Find out for yourself if you're so slick. I ain't going to tell you nothing."

He walked through the kitchen and went into the bathroom. A little mirror hung on the wall. Mike took off his cap and looked at his face. "By God she was right," he thought. "That's just exactly how I do feel."

YOU, THE PHANTOM

By THEODORE DREISER

WHAT TO ME IN LIFE ACHIEVES THE ULTIMATE OF THE FANTASTIC as well as the ridiculous, is the exaltation of the human as opposed to, or set over against, the natural or creative forces by which man finds himself surrounded. When he is not busy overestimating his own significance and powers as compared to these others, he becomes fearful and falls down before them—and more—in the past at least, proceeded to symbolize them as Gods—10,000 or more. When he was not doing that, he, where he possessed any of the mental significance he was so ready to ascribe to himself, was to be found, prying or peeping through chinks and mouse holes such as microscopes and telescopes, at the vast illimitable processes of nature or the universe without and about him. Yet these, in turn, he described, and still does, as "mechanistic" and so decidedly not *mental* like himself, either in their content or result! Imagine! Indeed the stone, or plaster, or wooden images that he set up, and at the feet of which he too often worshiped—and still does—were, as he sensed them, better symbols of the forces above him than all their illimitable and quite visible reality about him. The image he could grasp. The other not.

But how odd, considering that a man comes into the world via these processes and mechanisms at which he so blindly peeks! And how still more odd, that after centuries and centuries of peeping and prying and arguing with this earthly authority and that; reading what has been or is being written by this or that or the other so-called *mind* and examining and copying as many of the natural processes as he can, and testing their accuracy for himself, or a process, or a theory that no more than duplicates some already functioning process of nature, proceeds to celebrate forthwith not the wonder of the natural and creative forces about him, but the wonder and originality and power of his own mind.

For instance, an Anaxagoras (B. C. 400) decides that the atom alone must be the basic unit of the universe. And forthwith how astounding is the mind of Anaxagoras. Or a Leonardo, after puzzling over the flying of birds, succeeds in suspecting that some day man must fly. How astounding the mind of Leonardo! Again, a Newton seeing an apple fall to the ground discovers the law of gravitation! How supremely great Newton! But before Anaxagoras, were atoms. And before Leonardo, birds flew. And before Newton, there was the law of gravitation.

And what was it that arranged and maintained all these? A nonthinking, non-reasoning mechanism? If not, then what becomes of the so-called amazing mental distinction of these individuals who did no more than observe the seemingly changeless and hence, as they would say, highly *mechanistic* processes of nature which they copy? Yet today—and day after day—whenever any one individual here on earth finally senses (and that owing wholly to a sensitive equipment provided by this other so-called "mechanistic" process of force, operating not only outside but through him) we hear other men exclaiming in admiration and awe: Hearken! Behold! How great is the mind of man! He has discovered that apples fall to the ground, that birds, because of this or that mechanical form, and this or that metabolism or chemism fly. But can it be that he and not his universe is the mechanism? And that by it he has been definitely limited to a state this side of reason? It is not possible—even in many ways self evident.

At least for myself, finding myself an extension of these same "mechanical" mysteries which the great mind of man has for so long stared at and pondered over and spied upon, as might any cat at a mouse hole, or any rat peering out upon infinite mystery from the entrance to its petty shelter, I can find nothing that is not mind, neither myself, nor any lesser or greater thing. But some is free moving mental energy, or impulse, or both, and some, as in the case of men, animals, trees, etc., is but the implementation of the same. But with energy connections with the whole which permit of partial movement.

Take myself for instance. I am a minute assemblage of other more minute and yet amazingly coordinated beings—or energy containers (none so small but that if disarranged or disordered, may, and even will, end me—my so-called being). More, as a part of myself—a somewhat larger mechanism than themselves yet of which they may or may not be conscious—they function quite well in me as a part of my structure, as one of me and I, because of them and other forces above them and which same controls all of us, functions fairly well among other such mechanism as myself, so much so that at last I am convinced that I am not so much an individual force but a mechanism for the mind and the intention of some exterior and larger mental process which has constructed me and these minor entities which help to make me what I am, but not, probably, for any individual purpose of my own, but rather, and quite obviously to me, for some purpose of its own. In other words, I am not wholly and individually living—but being lived by something else that has constructed me and is using me, along with all other forms and creatures and elements and forces, for purposes of its own. So much so that I am but the minutest fraction of some process of living which, in turn, is a product of this other exterior as well as interior reality and power, and which same (thanks be) has, for some infinitely small fraction of its much larger and more mysterious life, included me as some minute part, or movement, of its immensely greater life. Yet its relation to me is what?—Its process of functioning through me and so using me as a minute expression of itself how? Well, let us see what that is like.

A man is painting a house, or a picture. The man either is or is not an extension of an idea of a man, emanating from somewhere and definitely characterized as an idea by the fact that endless billions of men, like the one under discussion, have come and gone, are coming and going, and will come and go. This makes the *man idea* the only reality or actual man, the physical man whom we see painting the house or picture being nothing more than an extension, nay, even a mimeograph copy of the man model above described. Yet both are, if you choose, the invention, or possibly accident of something desiring to express itself, for the time being at least, in the man form. That this something seems also to desire to express itself in bird, flower, fish, insect, rock, gas, planet, and other forms is obvious and goes without saying. In short, a universe (and of those there are many) seems to be one of its (in a very immense sense) forms or extensions.

None the less, this replica of the man form, who is painting the house or picture, is moved by emotions or impulses which he

does not create. They are created in him by other things, both internal and external—usually external. More, the materials with which
he works, the wood of the house, the cloth of the canvas, the
metals and elements of the paint he is using, are all alive and are
also extensions of this universal creature. And now we know that
all things are composed of identically the same vital atoms or their
component parts—electrons, protons, neutrons, etc., etc. But how
many? We are unable to calculate. The main thing is that all are
alive, active, busy forming (for what reason—by what command?)
new matter, or gases, or nebulae, or suns, and yet all are an extension of creative. energy, the very energy-body of the universe
itself, they having no life or being apart from it. Not only that,
but they are, accurately or indifferently, as you will, disposed of
by the larger creative force or energy wheresoever and, seemingly,
howsoever it wills.

In the present instance they are of course only partially subject
to the mood or impulse of the man extension—the replica man—
who in turn is obviously an extension and a part of the mood of
the universal creative will or force. Yet also they are partially
independent and are therefore only partially, not totally, at the
disposal of the mood or intention of the man.

To be sure, he will put the paint on the house, or the canvas,
and arrange it according to his mood of the moment, thus seemingly fixing certain atoms or protons or neutrons, for the time
being, in a given place. Actually, however, if one can accept the
latest developments in connection with electro-physics and thermo-
dynamics or chemics, or what have you, not any single atom is
definitely and permanently fixed anywhere—all are moving and
changing—one electron of an atom packing its bag and departing
for where we do not know, the while another electron is entering
and taking its place. None the less, there is this present arrangement of them on the part of the man replica—his mood or desire,
which, in turn, is imposed upon him by something outside him.
Indeed, insofar as these atoms are concerned, there remains a
probably total unconsciousness on their part of the use that the
replica man is making of them, just as in our personal lives and
instances where we are arranged as employees of, let us say, the
Standard Oil Company, the General Electric Company, or the

Bell Telephone Company, we have no least notion of the plans, of say, the Electric Company and the real use it is making of us, any more than it has of the details of our private lives or minds. It can only guess what we are thinking or doing, just as we can only guess what it, via its executives and their business arrangements, is doing. Yet there both are, being moved and fixed by the replica man, just as he is being moved and fixed by the creative process of which he is an expression. In other words, the creative process, or something behind it again, is thinking, planning, doing something important in connection with all of its manifestations, or it is idling and dreaming. And we replica men, like the rest of the creatures of the world we know, and of the other worlds we see but do not know, and the universe, are, or may be, important or not important—mere shadow or foam, sound and fury—signifying nothing.

Yet one thing more. A secondary phase of this universal thinking is the man painting. A tertiary phase—if we men mimeographs want to be vain—are these same atoms which constitute his paint, and colors, and which, in the arrangement he is moved to give them, serve to illustrate his ideas or moods on the canvas or house, as may be. Also the atoms in us. A fourth phase is the electrons in them. Yet no doubt all of those things, men, atoms, electrons, gases and what not, are, as I have said, acting according to mathematical laws which are plainly the concealed and directed orders or thoughts or intentions of a universal creative energy at the very same time that they appear to be responding to lesser laws of their being and their environment. In short, while they are seeming entities and "on their own" as we say, still they are subject to the moods and the movements not only of the man mind, but, beyond him, of the universal creative mind. All either are an integral part of the universal mind, or they are differentiated portions of it—either itself—or superiorly differentiated by the whole of which they are still an integral part.

To my thinking, the great creative energy seems to wish to bloom forth or breathe itself outward into all of the endless forms that we see. Their actions and counteractions and reactions are no more than conditions of its nature—not theirs—yet all together being in some larger way conditions (perhaps) of universal thinking or being. Who is to say? Yet all to one purpose, namely, the fell and important or idle and unimportant desire or mood on the part of something, which is *the all*, to express itself either meaningly or meaninglessly. (A fine thing to be thinking as one goes home on the five-fifteen.)

SNOWFALL IN CHILDHOOD

By Ben Hecht

I GOT OUT OF BED TO SEE WHAT HAD HAPPENED IN THE NIGHT. I WAS thirteen years old. I had fallen asleep watching the snow falling through the half-frosted window.

But though the snow had promised to keep falling for a long time, perhaps three or four days, on opening my eyes I was full of doubts. Snowstorms usually ended too soon.

While getting out of bed I remembered how, as I was nearly asleep, the night outside the frosted window had seemed to burst into a white jungle. I had dreamed of streets and houses buried in snow.

I hurried barefooted to the window. It was scribbled with a thick frost and I couldn't see through it. The room was cold and through the opened window came the fresh smell of snow like the moist nose of an animal resting on the ledge and breathing into the room.

I knew from the smell and the darkness of the window that snow was still falling. I melted a peephole on the glass with my palms. I saw that this time the snow had not fooled me. There it was, still coming down white and silent and too thick for the wind to move, and the streets and houses were almost as I had dreamed. I watched, shivering and happy. Then I dressed, pulling on my clothes as if the house were on fire. I was finished with breakfast and out in the storm two hours before school time.

The world had changed. All the houses, fences, and barren trees had new shapes. Everything was round and white and unfamiliar.

I set out through these new streets on a voyage of discovery. The unknown surrounded me. Through the thick falling snow, the trees, houses and fences looked like ghost shapes that had floated down out of the sky during the night. The morning was without light, but the snowfall hung and swayed like a marvelous lantern over the streets. The snowbanks, already over my head in places, glowed mysteriously.

I was pleased with this new world. It seemed to belong to me more than that other world which lay hidden.

I headed for the school, jumping like a clumsy rabbit in and out of snowbanks. It seemed wrong to spoil the smooth outlines of these snowdrifts and I hoped that nobody else would pass this way after me. In that case the thick falling snow would soon restore the damage. Reassured by this hope I continued on my devastations like some wanton explorer. I began to feel that no one would dare the dangers of my wake. Then, as I became more aware of the noble proportions of this snowstorm I stopped worrying altogether about the marring of this new and glowing world. Other snows had melted and been shoveled away, but this snow would never disappear. The sun would never shine again and the little Wisconsin town through which I plunged and tumbled to school on this dark storm-filled morning was from now on an arctic land full of danger and adventure.

When eventually, encased in snow, I arrived at the school, I found scores of white-covered figures already there. The girls had taken shelter inside, but the boys stayed in the storm. They jumped in and out of the snowdrifts and tumbled through the deep unbroken white fields in front of the school.

Muffled cries filled the street. Someone had discovered how far-away our voices sounded in the snowfall and this started the screaming. We screamed for ten minutes, delighted with the fact that our voices no longer carried and that the snowstorm had made us nearly dumb.

Tired with two hours of such plunging and rolling, I joined a number of boys who like myself had been busy since dawn and who now stood for the last few minutes before the school bell with half-frozen faces staring at the heavily falling snow as if it were some game they couldn't bear to leave.

When we were finally seated in our grade room we continued to watch the snowstorm through the windows. The morning had grown darker as we had all hoped it would, and it was necessary to turn on the electric lights in the room. This was almost as thrilling as the pale storm still floating outside the windows.

In this yellow light the school seemed to disappear and in its place a picnic spread around us. The teachers themselves seemed to change. Their eyes kept turning toward the windows and they kept looking at us behind our desks as if we were strangers. We grew excited and even the sound of our lessons—the sentences out of geography and arithmetic books—made us tremble.

Passing through the halls during recess we whispered to one another about the snowstorm, guessing at how deep the snowdrifts must be by this time. We looked nervously at our teachers who stood in the class-room doorways stiff and far removed from our secret whispers about the snow.

I felt sorry for these teachers, particularly for the one who had taught me several years ago when I was in the Fifth Grade. I saw her as I walked by the opened door of her room. She was younger than the other teachers, with two dark braids coiled around her head, a white starched shirtwaist and soft dark eyes that had always looked kindly at me when I was younger. I saw her now sitting behind her large desk looking over the heads of her class out of the window and paying no attention to the whispers and giggles of her pupils.

As for my own teacher, a tall, thin woman with a man's face, by afternoon I had become so happy I could no longer hear what she was saying. I sat looking at the large clock over her head. My feeling on the way to school that it would never be light again and that the snowstorm would keep on forever had increased so that it was something I now knew rather than hoped. My eagerness to get out into the world of wind, gloom, and perpetual snow, kept lifting me out of my seat.

At three o'clock we rushed into the storm. Our screams died as we reached the school entrance. What we saw silenced us. Under the dark sky the street lay piled in an unbroken bank of snow. And above it the snowfall still hung in a thick and moving cloud. Nothing was visible but snow. Everything else had disappeared. Even the sky was gone.

I saw the teachers come out and look around them, frowning. The children of the lower grades stood chattering and frightened near the teachers. I waited until the teacher with the two black braids saw me and then, paying no attention to her warning, spoken in a gentle voice, I plunged into the storm. I felt brave but slightly regretful that Miss Wheeler could no longer see me as I pushed into the head-high piles of snow and vanished fearlessly into the storm. But I was certain that she was still thinking of me and worrying about my safety. This thought added excitement to the snowstorm.

After an hour I found myself alone. My legs were tired with jumping and my face burned. It had grown darker and the friendliness seemed to have gone out of the storm. The wind bit with a sharper edge and I turned toward my home.

I arrived at the house that now looked like a snow drift and ploughed my way up to its front door. My heart was beating violently. I stopped to take a last look at the storm. It was hard to leave it. But for the first time in my life an adult logic instructed me. There would be even more snow tomorrow. And in this wind and snow-filled gloom and even in the marvelously buried street, there was something now unplayful.

I entered the house calling for something to eat, but as soon as I had taken my coat off and shaken myself clean, I was at the window again. The way this storm was keeping on was hard to believe.

At the table I was too excited to eat. I trembled and was unable to hear what was being said around me. In this room I could feel the night outside and the storm still blowing on my face. It seemed as if I were still in the street. My eyes kept seeing snow and my nose breathing it. The room and the people in it became far away. I left the table, taking a slice of bread and butter with me, and ran upstairs to my own room.

There were a lot of things to do, such as making my leather boots more waterproof by rubbing hard on them, putting my stamp collection in order, sharpening a deer's-foot knife I had recently acquired, winding tape on my new hockey stick, or reading one of the half dozen new books I had bought with my last birthday money. But none of these activities or even redrawing the plans for the ice-boat on which I was working was possible. I sat in a chair near the window unable to think. The pale storm in the night seemed to spin like a top and, keeping the window frost melted with my palms, I sat and watched it snowing for an hour. Then, becoming sleepy, I went to bed. I thought drowsily of how happy Miss Wheeler would be to see me alive on Monday after the way I had rushed into the storm.

There was no seeing through my window when I awoke. The furnace never got going until after seven and before that hour on a winter's morning the house creaked with cold and the windows were sheeted thick with ice. But I knew as I dressed that the snowfall was over. There was too much wind blowing outside and the breath that came in from the snow-banked window ledge was no longer as fresh as it had been.

It was still dark. The bleak and gusty dawn lay over the snow like a guttering candle. The sky had finished with its snowing but now the wind sent the snowbanks ballooning into the air and the roof tops burst into little snowstorms.

I went outside and explored for ten minutes. When I came back into the house I needed no warning against going out to play. My skin was almost frozen and the wind was too strong to stand up in. I settled down as a prisoner in front of the fireplace after breakfast, lying on my stomach and turning the pages of a familiar oversized edition of Dante's "Inferno." It was full of Doré's nightmarish pictures.

The house bustled with cooking and cleaning. But these were the dim activities of grown-ups. I felt alone and took care of the fire to keep it from going out and leaving me to freeze to death. I carried logs all morning from the cellar and lay perspiring and half-scorched on the hearthstone. Every half-hour I went to the window to have a look at the enemy. The sight of the whirling snowbanks and the sound of the brutal wind as it hit against the houses sent me back to the fireplace to scorch myself anew.

In this way I spent the day until late afternoon. It grew dark early. The snow turned leaden. The wind stopped. The dead storm lay in the street and as far as I could see from the window there were no inhabitants in the world. The dark snow was empty. I shivered and went back to the fireplace.

A half-hour later our door bell rang. Company had arrived for supper. They were the Joneses, who lived in the town of Corliss some eight miles away. They had brought their daughter Anna.

The lights went on in the house. Baked and dizzy with the fire's heat, I joined the two families in the larger parlor. They were talking excitedly about the damage done by the storm. Accounts of store windows blown in, roofs blown off, signs blown down, and wagons abandoned in the drifts, were exchanged and I listened happily. Later when the talk turned to duller topics I became aware of Anna.

She was sitting in a corner watching me. She was a blondish girl two years older than I was and she went to high school. I had known her for a long time but had never liked her because she was too calm, never laughing or running, but always looking at people with a sad smile or just a stare as if she had something important on her mind. But now that she was watching me that way I felt suddenly interested in her. I wondered what she could be thinking of me and what made her smile in that half-sad way at me.

I sat next to her at the table and after looking at her several times out of the side of my eyes and catching her eyes doing the same thing, my heart started beating faster. I lost interest in eating. I wanted to be alone with her so we could sit and look at each other without the others noticing.

After supper the two families let us go to the hall upstairs, where I kept most of my possessions, without asking us any questions. I found a deck of cards and a cribbage board for a table. Underneath the lapboard our knees touched.

She played cribbage better than I and smiled at me as I kept losing. But I was only half aware of the game. I kept looking at her, unable to talk, and the light pressure of her knees began to make me feel weak. Her face seemed to become brighter and more beautiful as we played. A mist appeared around her eyes and her smile became so close, as if it were moving swiftly toward me, that I began to tremble. I felt ashamed of being so tongue-tied and red-faced, but with a half-frightened blissful indifference to everything—even Anna—I kept on playing.

We hardly spoke. I grew too nervous to follow the game and I wanted to stop. But I thought if we stopped we could no longer sit this way with our knees touching. At moments when Anna withdrew her touch I trembled and waited as if I were hanging from somewhere. When finally her knees returned to their place against mine, I caught my breath and frowned at the cards as if I were completely taken up with them.

As the hour passed, my face began to feel swollen and lopsided and it seemed to me my features had grown ugly beyond words. I tried to distract Anna's attention from this phenomenon by twisting my mouth, screwing up my eyes and making popping noises with my cheeks as we played. But a new fear arrived to uncenter my attention. I became afraid now that Anna would notice her knees were touching mine and move them away. I began at once pretending a deeper excitement in the game, complaining against my bad luck and denouncing her for cheating. I was determined to keep her interested in the game at any cost, believing that her interest in what we were doing made her unaware of her knees touching mine.

Finally Anna said she was tired of the game. She pushed the cribbage board away. I waited, holding my breath, for her to realize where her knees were and to move them away. I tried not to look at her but I was so frightened of this happening that I found myself staring at her. She seemed to be paying no attention to me. She was leaning back in her chair and her eyes were half closed. Her face was unsmiling and I felt she was thinking of something. This startled me. My throat filled with questions but I was so afraid of breaking this hidden embrace of our knees under the lapboard that I said nothing.

The mist seemed to have spread from her eyes to her hair and over the rest of her face. Wherever I looked this same glow rested around her. I noticed then that her hand was lying on the lapboard. I thought desperately of touching it but there was something disillusioning in this thought. I watched her fingers begin to tap gently on the board as if she were playing the piano. There was something strange about her hand as if it did not belong to the way her knees were touching mine or to the mist that rose from her eyes.

The minutes passed in silence and then Anna's mother called her from downstairs.

"I guess they're going home," I said and Anna nodded. She pressed closer against me but in my confusion I couldn't figure out whether this was the accidental result of her starting to get out of her chair or on purpose.

"Why don't you ride out with us?" she said. She leaned over the lapboard toward me. "We've got the wagon sleigh and there's plenty of room."

Before I could answer she had stood up. My knees felt suddenly cold. I slid the lapboard to the floor, ashamed and sad. Anna, without looking back at me, had gone down the stairs. I kept myself from running after her. I was sure she was laughing at me and that she was saying to herself, "He's a big fool. He's a big fool."

The Joneses were ready to leave when I came into the parlor. Anna's mother smiled at me.

"Why don't you come and visit us over Sunday?" she said. "There's even more snow in Corliss than here."

"More snow than you can shake a stick at," said another member of the Jones family. They all laughed and while they were laughing my mother hustled me off for my wraps. I was to drive away with the Jones family in the sleigh drawn by the two strong horses that stood in front of our house.

I pulled on my leather boots, sweater, and overcoat while the goodbyes were being made. I kept trying to catch Anna's attention, but she was apparently unaware that I was in the room. This made me sad, and slowly my eagerness to go to Corliss left me. I wanted instead to go up to my room and slam the door forever on all the Joneses. Anna's gayety, the way she said goodbye over and over again and laughed and kissed all the members of my family as if nothing had happened to her, as if she hadn't sat with her eyes closed pressing against my knees in the hallway upstairs, made me almost ill. I felt abandoned and forgotten.

Finally I stood muffled and capped and scowling as my family offered some final instructions for my behavior. I heard nothing of what was said but turned over and over in my mind what I was going to do on the ride and after we got to Corliss. Chiefly I was going to ignore Anna, neither speak to her nor show her by a single look that I knew she was alive.

At this point Anna, having said goodbye to everybody several times, seized my arm unexpectedly and whispered against my ear.

"Come, hurry," she said. "We want to get a good place."

Without a word I rushed out of the house, slipping down the snow-caked steps and tumbling headlong into a snowdrift. I scrambled after Anna into the wagon sleigh. It was a low-sided farm wagon placed on wide, heavy wooden runners and piled with warm hay and horse blankets. There was room for only one on the seat. The rest of the Joneses, seven including me, would have to lie in the hay covered by the robes.

Anna was already in the wagon half-buried in the hay, a blanket over her. She gave me excited orders to brush the snow from my clothes, to cover myself well and not to get out and run alongside the horses when we were going up hill.

"It doesn't help any," she said. "They can pull just the same if you stay in here. And besides I don't want you to."

The rest of the Joneses came out and crowded into the wagon around us. Anna's father took his place on the driver's seat, assuring my mother, who had come out with a shawl over her head, that there was no danger because the State plow had cleared the road even to way beyond Corliss. I heard my mother ask where I was. Mrs. Jones answered that I was buried somewhere in the hay and Anna whispered close to me not to answer or say anything. I obeyed her.

The sleigh started off. I heard the horses thumping in the snow and the harness bells falling into a steady jingling. Lying on my back I looked into the night. Stars filled the sky and a white glare hung over the house tops. The street was silent. I could no longer see the snow-covered houses with their lighted windows. My nose filled with the fresh smell of snow and the barn smells of hay and horse blankets, I lay listening to the different sounds—the harness bells and the snow crunching under the runners.

The stillness of this winter's night was as intense as the storm that had raged for three days. I felt that all the wind and snow there was had blown themselves out forever and that the night as far as the highest star had been emptied by the storm. This emptiness as I lay looking into it was like being hypnotized. It was something to run out into, to fly up into, as the snowfall had been. I began to want to see further and the star-filled sky that had seemed so vast a few minutes ago now didn't seem vast enough.

I had almost forgotten about Anna when I felt a now familiar warmth press against me. She had moved closer as if joggled by the sleigh. I held my breath waiting for her to order me to move away and give her room, but she was silent.

My hand at my side touched her fingers. Now I forgot the sky and the great sprinkle of stars that seemed like a thin, far-away snowfall that had stopped moving. The night, the glare of snow, the jingling harness bells died away; only my fingers were alive.

When I had looked at her hand tapping gently on the lapboard, it had seemed strange and the thought of touching it somehow disillusioning. But now under the horse blankets, hidden in the hay, this hand seemed more breathing and mysterious and familiar than anything about her. I lay unable to move closer to it, our fingertips barely touching. I grew dizzy wishing to reach her hand but I felt as powerless to move toward it as to fly.

The minutes passed. Two of the Joneses started singing. The thump of the horses, the jingling of the sleighbells, and the crunching of the snow under the runners seemed part of this soft singing. I too wished to sing, to stand up suddenly in this sweeping-along sleigh and bellow at the silent night.

Then the fingers for which I had been wishing until I was dizzy, seemed to start walking under the horse blankets, seemed to be running toward me in the warm hay. They came as far as my hand, closed around it, and I felt the throb of their tips against my palm. The night turned into a dream. I opened my eyes to the wide sprinkle of stars and a mist seemed to have come over them. The snow-covered hills over which we were gliding sparkled behind a mist and suddenly the night into which I was looking lost its hours. It stretched away without time as if it were not something that was passing like our sleigh over the snow, but a starfilled winter's night that would never change and never move.

Lying beside Anna, her hand in mine, with the sleigh now flying in a whirl of snow down the white hill, I thought this night would never end.

THE SEVEN MEN OF ROUEN

By George Slocombe

SHIPS WERE UNLOADING ON THE QUAYS AS CLARE MURPHY AND HIS wife drove into Rouen. The transporter bridge made an arch over the river like a rainbow bent in two places and the clouds hung low over the hills as they always hang low over Rouen. Clare followed the wide cobbled quays, turned right at the rue Jeanne d'Arc and drove through streets which became narrow and narrower until they came at last to the old marketplace. He parked his car as usual in front of the little wineshop which faces the statue of Joan. The wooden-legged park attendant came forward, and stood with his worn cap in his great gnarled hand until they had closed and locked the doors of the car, shaken the wrinkles out of their clothes, set their hats at the jaunty angle of adventure, looked once critically and appreciatively at the familiar landmarks of the place, and stepped out carefully over the worn, uneven flagstones to the dark, arched door of the Couronne.

They had left Paris late in the morning, and they were hungry. Louella sank into a chair from which she could look through green-paned windows into the market bustle of the square and sighed with happiness. "I want," she said, "nothing but that fish they cook here with mussels and mushrooms and truffles and cream. I couldn't eat a thing more."

Murphy looked at her reminiscently. "Sole Normande!" he said. "You shall have it. You will also eat a chicken roasted before a fire of apple boughs, several pounds of pommes soufflées, a half a Camembert cheese, and maybe a crêpe Suzette or so. There are also some very good-looking Doyenne de Comice pears if you still feel hungry."

Louella screamed in indignation and delight. "Do you want me to lose my figure?"

"You've lost it," said Murphy ungallantly. "But you are very beautiful all the same."

392

The patron himself took the order. Louella protested, in a tone of outraged but helpless virtue, at the enormity of the repast, then suddenly smiled at the patron. The patron, who had seen many women surrender in his time, and not merely to gastronomic temptations, smiled back in perfect comprehension.

"Madame will have no regrets."

Louella had none.

They drank a Meursault with their fish and a red wine of Bordeaux with the poulet à la broche. The wine was good but not too good. If instead of chicken Murphy had chosen, as he had once been tempted, a canard Rouennais, the wine would have been a better one. But he knew enough to content himself on modest occasions with something less than perfection. This was not yet the day for perfection. But it would come.

With their coffee, nevertheless, Murphy commanded a Calvados irreproachable in age, maturity and subtlety. They drank each a glass, and then Louella subsided into rapt contemplation of the smoke rings from her cigarette. Clare ordered a second glass and then proceeded to ruminate blissfully.

Afterwards, as was their wont on such visits, they walked through the market, priced the meat, fish and fruits on the stalls, gazed at the carved stone panels of the meeting of Henry the Eighth and François Premier on the Field of the Cloth of Gold, went into the dim coolness of the cathedral, threw coins into the cap of the unshaven beggar at the door, and as they emerged into the sunlight blinked up at the incomparable stone façade which Claude Monet had painted tirelessly from the window over the clothing store across the street.

Then, weary with the fatigue and complacent with the satisfaction of tourists they went back to the marketplace and found their car. The square was empty now and silent. The wooden-legged man shuffled forward from the doorway of the little wineshop, took off his worn cap and held it meekly in his brown gnarled hand as they got in. Clare dropped a coin into the hat and smiled his thanks. The man had soft brown eyes like a retriever dog. "Merci, Monsieur," he said, and stood cap in hand until they drove away.

The road to Paris followed the river and every few miles along its course the river was gay with a procession of brightly painted barges, red and blue and black, on which the washing of the bargees and their women fluttered like pennants. The barges moved swiftly with the current, sometimes under their own power, sometimes towed by a steam tug or by another barge. Children ran up and down on the decks of some of the barges and shouted and waved their hands to the passing cars, Louella waved back.

"No other river," she said, "has such pretty barges."

Clare grunted for sole reply.

"Do you know," confided Louella, "I believe I've had too much good food."

But she made this admission unreproachfully, and continued to watch the river and the barges and the poplars and willows on the long green islands which lie in the Seine between Paris and Rouen like a rope of emeralds.

Suddenly she said:

"What are you thinking of, Clare?"

He did not seem to hear her, and she repeated the question a trifle impatiently.

He answered defensively. "Nothing."

"Don't be silly. I always know when you are thinking hard. What is it, darling?"

He allowed two cars to overtake them, and frowned at the long straight road over the hills which dip into Gaillon, where the sister of Henry of Navarre was born. Then he said reluctantly:

"I was only thinking about that man in Rouen."

"What man in Rouen? Do try to be more explicit, darling."

"The man with the wooden leg at the parking place."

"Well, what about him?"

"I was just thinking that the second wooden-legged man was not the same as the first wooden-legged man."

Louella made an elegant sound expressive of mild derision. "Darling," she purred, "you must have drunk too much Calvados."

"Perhaps I drank too much Calvados, but I'm neither drunk nor crazy, and I say that the first wooden-legged man was not the same man as the second wooden-legged man."

"Then there must have been two of them," said Louella concisely, and for the remainder of the journey into Paris she closed her eyes with the air of one who has found the world too complicated.

*   *   *

The Murphys had spent the winter and spring in North Africa. They had been married five years and neither of them had been married previously. They were still interested if no longer excited by each other. They found their own company on most occasions agreeable enough to dispense with that of others. They liked travel, life in small hotels and in small crowded countries, the pitfalls of foreign languages, foreign food and drink and foreign customs. In some of these distractions, Clare had more than a mere traveler's interest, being occupied in writing an anthropological study for a research foundation.

During the past year they had wandered together through the villages of the High Atlas, shared the fleas, the rancid butter, the goaty mutton and the mint tea of Arab and Berber, washed the astonishing blue eyes of light-skinned Berber children in vain struggle with flies and dirt, and generally indulged the pure, if irritating instincts of the explorer, the social worker, the missionary and the philanthropist at all times and everywhere. And now they were in Paris living in two rooms at the top of an old hotel on the Ile Saint Louis, and Clare, in the long intervals between his attempts to concentrate on his report on the customs and feuds of the blue-eyed populations of the Upper Atlas, could resume his pre-graduate habit of drinking wine with the blue and brown and grey-eyed folk of Gaul.

After his return from the trip to Rouen Murphy found it harder and harder to stick to his typewriter. The small neat pile of type-written sheets which he had begun in Morocco and hoped to finish in Paris remained distressingly small. Between him and the virgin page intruded with irritating frequency the memory of a man with the worn cap of a sailor held in a brown hand, a man with soft brown eyes in a tanned and lined face, who walked with a stick and whose steps made separate sounds upon the stone flags of the marketplace in Rouen, a soft sound for the leg which was whole and a harsh ringing sound for the leg which had been lost.

One day, therefore, when Louella was busy bargain hunting in the Marché aux Puces, Clare Murphy got into his car and drove back to Rouen alone. Once he was on the road through the Seine valley he forgot the object of his journey entirely. He found himself thinking of the Berber children. In Mantes, where he stopped to look again at the cathedral outside which William the Conqueror had lost his life, thrown from a horse, scorched by embers from the burning town, he began to remember Louella, decided that he was still in love with her, and that he missed her badly.

He thought of Louella all the way across the hills into Rouen, then promptly forgot her for a while. It was a fine clear day and for once the clouds which eternally threaten the city were absent. The sun sparkled on the river, on the bridges, on the ships loading and unloading, on the bright red filling stations, on the rectangular steel rainbow at the end of the town. Over the brown tile roofs rose the copper green spire of the cathedral and the square rosy greyness of its stone towers. With a sudden sensation of freedom and happiness Clare drove into the old marketplace and backed into the space before the little wineshop, which faces the site of the stake and the faggots upon which Joan was burned.

The park attendant came out of the wineshop, making that queer one-legged sound upon the stone steps and the worn cobbles. Clare looked at him in silence. He was a lean man with a brown lined face and a scar on one cheek. He came to a halt and leaned his weight on his sound leg, then took off his black sailor's peaked cap, and bowed.

"Bonjour, Monsieur!" he said.

Clare saw that his eyes were grey. It was the first wooden-legged man, not the second.

"Louella," said Clare, "was right. There are two of them."

Unaccountably relieved in his mind, he went into the Couronne and ordered his lunch: a modest repast beginning with a pâté de liévre and continuing with a grilled lamb cutlet, to wind up somewhat unsatisfactorily with a salad. He hated salads since he had lived in Arab countries. Herbs, he reflected, were meant to be eaten dry and not in the green state. He drank a whole bottle of wine. If Louella had been with him his share would have been twothirds. He tried to counter this excess by drinking only one glass of eau de vie. He now began to miss Louella badly.

When he left the restaurant the sun was hidden. He wandered unhappily about the town. The marketplace was empty and the marketstalls covered with boards. The narrow streets were grey, and the sky above them low and threatening. The old Bourgthérolde house with the marvelous bas reliefs of the Pageant of the Field of Cloth of Gold was closed. He walked under the great gilt clock in the rue de l'Horloge and found his way to the cathedral. The streets, usually so full of people in gay and noisy progress, were dull and empty. The cathedral was dark, the rosy grey tower of stone now merely grey, the blue windows at the far end without life, the unshaven beggar irritating. He decided suddenly that he would go back to Paris and take Louella to the theatre.

His was the only car parked outside the wineshop when he returned to the old marketplace. He unlocked the door, started the motor and was about to drive away when he heard a voice say softly, "Bonjour, Monsieur!" and the wooden-legged park attendant appeared at the door.

Clare felt in his pocket for a coin, found it and dropped it into the outstretched cap, worn and soiled, the peaked cap of a sailor. Then he looked into the man's face. It was a brown face, lean and lined, but the eyes were neither grey nor brown. They were blue. It was a wooden-legged man he had never seen before.

"My God," said Clare, "there are not two but three of them!"

The third wooden-legged man stood waiting for him to drive away, still holding his cap in his hand, and standing so that his weight was borne by his sound leg. He had uttered a polite "Merci, Monsieur!" when Clare had given him the coin. He now said nothing, but waited for him to depart.

Clare threw in the clutch and drove out of the marketplace. There were no other cars in it. As he turned into the road leading to the river he saw, out of the tail of his eye, the figure of the wooden-legged man shuffling down the stone steps into the wineshop. The marketplace was now empty.

*　　*　　*

He had driven past two of the Rouen bridges and was in sight of the green hills outside the town before he remembered that Louella would not be at the hotel when he returned. She was dining with her mother that night. Clare cursed the situation eloquently but impotently.

To add to his wrath, it was beginning to rain. The night had fallen early. He hated driving alone in the rain. He was thinly clad, and the air was cold with a keen autumnal chill. He began to regret the scruple which had forbidden him the second glass of apple brandy. Suddenly he thought of the wineshop. It would be warm and bright inside. There would be a zinc bar and a low roof with dark rafters and old oak tables worn smooth by many elbows. He turned the car round and drove back, feeling foolish but defiant.

There were lights in the windows of the wineshop, although the marketplace was cold and silent in the dark and falling rain. He switched off his motor and slid almost noiselessly to a halt before the two stone steps. Then he got out of the car and went into the *bistrot*.

As he had anticipated, the place was light and warm, with an encouraging smell of roasting coffee, alcohol, scaferlati and spilt wine. There was a low roof with dark beams, and the plaster between the beams was the color of old ivory. There were small oak tables in front of a long bench covered with worn black oilcloth, and there was a bright zinc bar covered with bottles. At the zinc bar were standing three men. They all had lean brown faces and brown gnarled hands. They all wore black sailor's caps with a shiny black peak. And they all had wooden legs.

Clare sat down at one of the oak tables against the oilcloth-covered bench and ordered a glass of Calvados. Then he looked carefully at the three men.

They also were drinking Calvados in small glasses. He recognized the first man with the grey eyes. He recognized the second man with the brown eyes. But the third was a wooden-legged man he had not seen before.

The apple brandy burned Clare's throat, but he felt a chill run down his spine as he looked at the three men. Each of them stood with his weight on the sound leg, and sometimes they swung their wooden legs idly in the air. They kept their sailor's caps on their heads. And once, when one of them, who was addressed by his companions as Gaston, pushed back the peak of the cap to scratch his head, Clare saw that the scar which covered his cheekbone ran up over the temples.

Behind the zinc bar stood the owner of the *bistrot*. He was a little man with a round red face and a bald head. He wore a blue apron and his shirt sleeves were rolled up above his elbows. At a summons from Clare, he poured out another glass of Calvados and brought it to the little oak table.

Gaston was speaking now. Clare listened carefully but did not understand all that was said. He spoke in a Norman dialect. The names of the other two wooden-legged men, Clare found, were Marcel and Pierre. The men seemed to be quarreling, but over what Clare could not at first comprehend. Then he caught references to "la guerre" and "la Marne," and he guessed that the men were fighting their battles over again.

Suddenly there was a noise of footsteps on the stone steps outside the café, the door was pushed open, and other men entered. The wineshop was all at once full of dark figures of men with black cloth caps with shiny peaks, whose feet made alternately a muffled and a ringing sound upon the stone floor.

"Bonjour Désiré!" said Gaston and Marcel and Pierre to the first of the newcomers, and Clare looking at Désiré, saw the man with the blue eyes who had stood hat in hand before his car on his departure from the old marketplace earlier that day.

"Bonjour Paul!" said Gaston and Marcel and Pierre to the second of the newcomers, and Clare looked at this man but did not recognize him, for he was a fifth wooden-legged man and he also wore a cloth cap and had a brown lean face and he also had grey eyes like Gaston.

"Bonjour Octave!" said Gaston and Marcel and Pierre to the third newcomer, and Clare saw that Octave was the sixth wooden-legged man in the wineshop, brown and lean and tired looking like the others, and with brown eyes like Marcel.

But to the last of the newcomers, who was the seventh of the wooden-legged men, Gaston and Marcel and Pierre said nothing, and Clare saw that the seventh man was younger than the rest and shy looking, and that he did not join in the conversation at the zinc bar but stood looking down abstractedly at his little glass of Calvados and turning it round and round in hands that were less knotted and worn than the hands of the other men.

With the arrival of the other wooden-legged men the quarrel between the three at the zinc bar had been forgotten but soon it seemed to Clare that it was being revived and now the other men joined in it. They spoke quickly in their Norman dialect and used many oaths that were familiar even to Clare and they emptied their glasses hastily and ordered them to be refilled. But the seventh man took no part in the quarrel and stood moodily over his glass and said nothing.

And Clare also stared moodily into an empty glass and thought of Louella and wished she were there with him instead of dining with her mother in a Paris hotel. The wineshop was warm and noisy and filled with tobacco smoke and his head had begun to ache and he remembered that he was hungry and that Paris was nearly two hours away and that he wouldn't see Louella until nearly midnight.

Suddenly there was a lull in the rough argument at the bar and he looked up from the table and saw that a girl had come in and was drinking with the wooden-legged men. She was a thin young girl with red hair and she wore a green frock. In the light from the yellow electric globe over the bar her eyes seemed green too, but perhaps it was only the reflection from the bottles of green and yellow and red liqueurs on the shelves against the fly-spotted mirror.

"What a lot of *bêtises* you talk, you men!" said the girl calmly between sips of the apple brandy.

"What do you know about our *bêtises*?" demanded the man who was called Gaston.

"More than you think," said the girl derisively.

"Bah," said Marcel, "she has never been in a war."

"She has never had to fight for her life," said Paul.

"Except with an agent de police!" jeered Désiré.

"She has never lost a leg," complained Octave bitterly.

"Or been buried alive," added Pierre.

"Or lain out all night in a shell hole full of stinking water," completed Gaston.

"Drink this my girl!" adjured Marcel loftily, and pushed his glass towards her. "Leave serious argument to people with more experience of the world."

The girl took the glass and emptied it. Then she tossed her red head and her green eyes flashed.

"Listen, you men," she said contemptuously. "I don't need to learn about fighting from you. I have fought whole armies, and I was a woman and alone, whereas you were men and there were many of you. And if you have left limbs in far places I have left my body also. The dust of it is scattered even now, for they threw it on the waters of the river and it was carried out to sea and the seven seas beyond."

And at this the seventh wooden-legged man looked up suddenly from his empty glass and would have spoken for the first time, but the other six men laughed so loudly that the wineshop shook to its rafters.

"She is crazy!" said Gaston and turned to the landlord to have his glass refilled.

"She is laughing at us, the green-eyed witch!" said Marcel.

"Aye, she is pulling our legs," said Désiré with a throaty chuckle.

The girl only smiled and shrugged her shoulders. Then she turned to the youngest of the woden-legged men and in a voice which fell like a trumpet of silver upon the sudden lull in the place she said to him:

"Come, Céleste!"

And without waiting for the seventh of the wooden-legged men to answer she ran out of the wineshop and up the stone steps into the square. Through the open door Céleste ran after her and it seemed to Clare Murphy that for the first time his steps, neither that of the sound foot nor that of the wooden one, made a sound upon the stone cobbles.

The other wooden-legged men stood gaping, then one of them cried, "After them, boys!" and each dropped his glass and ran out into the square, and Clare after them.

The rain had ceased and the moon had come out behind the clouds and shone like a great yellow mound of Normandy butter behind the tower of the cathedral which is called the Tour de Beurre. In the middle of the marketplace was the girl and the moonlight gleamed on her red hair and in her green eyes and round her were the wooden-legged men. Their hands were joined and they were dancing in a round dance, and the legs which they had lost made a sound like iron upon the cobbles of the square.

In the midst of them stood the girl and the girl seemed to Clare to be singing and the sound of her voice was like silver but the only word that Clare Murphy could distinguish was the word "*Jésus*" repeated over and over again and then the word "*France*." And the wooden-legged men danced around her in a circle and now it was the turn of Clare to stand and gape.

When the song ended the dancers halted, and suddenly the great ringing sound of their iron-ferruled legs ceased and there was a silence in the square and in the middle of the silence the girl broke through their ranks and ran on light feet out of the marketplace towards the road which runs down to the river, and the young man, Céleste, ran after her. And when the other wooden-legged men would have followed her, and Clare with them, she had vanished, and they saw nothing but the reflection of the moon on the river and the green spire of the cathedral and the grey tower of the Tour de Beurre rising above the roofs of Rouen.

* * *

In the silence Clare went back to the wineshop to pay his reckoning and he heard the sound of iron-ferruled steps behind him. When he had settled with the owner of the *bistrot* he looked at the zinc bar and saw but two wooden-legged men standing there. One of them was the grey-eyed Gaston and the other was the brown-eyed Marcel. They had begun to argue again, and when one of them pushed back the peaked sailor's cap to scratch his head Clare saw the long scar running up over the temples.

"Where are the others?" Clare asked.

"What others does Monsieur refer to?" inquired Marcel politely.

"The men who were with you. There were seven of you."

"Monsieur is mistaken. We are but two," said Gaston.

"But Octave—where is Octave?"

"There is no Octave," said Marcel, "but my father's name was Octave. And he is long dead. He was killed at Sedan."

"And Pierre and Désiré and Paul?" demanded Clare. "What has become of them?"

"Pierre and Désiré were with me in the regiment," said Gaston. "They lie in the Argonne."

"And Paul," added Marcel, "was killed on the Marne."

"And the young man, Céleste," said Clare. "Is he dead too?"

"Nay, I know of no Céleste," said Marcel.

"Perchance," said Gaston eagerly, and in his voice was great love and pride, "Perchance he speaks of the little Céleste, my son. My son who is not yet old enough to fight."

BLACK TOBIAS AND THE EMPIRE

By HEINZ WERNER

FROM THE TIME I FIRST BEGAN TO FREQUENT CAFES IN VIENNA, I knew "Black Tobias." It would have been difficult not to know him, for his lustrous, flowing black beard which gave him his name was a familiar sight to the Viennese public, the larger portion of whose life was spent in these cafés. He was a tall man of swarthy complexion whose age might have been anywhere from thirty to fifty.

He was married. Few of us had ever seen Hannah, but she was familiar to all, for he constantly spoke of her. It was apparent that she was a bit of a nag; it was also apparent that he was devoted to her and that he firmly believed her mild scolding a somewhat original, and to him, delightful manifestation of her love. Tobias bragged of his wife's fault-finding as other men brag of their wives' cooking. They seemed to enjoy a harmony in marriage that was carried into their business.

Hannah ran a small store in which she sold soap, oils, and candles. Tobias spent his mornings there carrying cases, cleaning the store, fixing the windows and putting everything in good order for the day's business.

But this was not his life's work. Ah no! It was in the afternoons and evenings that Tobias really lived. It was then that his business brought him into contact with society, nobility and military men of high rank.

He was a peddler. He carried with him a box of neatly arranged small merchandise, such as matches, shoe laces, pencils and key rings. From five in the afternoon to eleven in the evening he covered a number of cafés, and from midnight on he worked night clubs and cabarets until early morning. He lived a well regulated life and his earnings were considerable. This was largely because, as he explained, "my patrons hardly ever bother to take a box of matches or a pair of shoe laces but always deposit on my tray fifty Heller, or if they are noblemen, a whole Krone."

There were many peddlers in Vienna but none like Black Tobias. He was more than a vendor for he was the peg on which all the wits of Vienna hung their favorite stories, true and untrue. Tobias was variously credited with the sagacity of a patriarch, the stupidity of a clod, the cupidity of a peasant, and the generosity of an Oriental potentate.

He knew his business, but more than that, he knew people. The wiseacres were not all wrong; Tobias was indeed all things to all men. He sensed and acted the role in which one chose to cast him.

But there was one role which required no acting, that of a devoted subject of the Hapsburgs.

Hannah's store was on the Leopoldsgasse, a street through which Archduke Carl passed every day on the way to see his mother in the Augarten. Black Tobias knew that the carriage went by every day at ten-thirty in the morning, and every day for years he would bow deeply when the carriage passed and greet the Archduke heartily "Good Morning, Majesty."

When I once objected that though Crown Prince Ferdinand was dead, Carl was not yet the Emperor, and that the Empire cannot have two majesties, he only smiled and said, "Well, with the Emperor being eighty-six, Carl is practically His Majesty. Besides, he likes to be called so, and furthermore, I am his friend. He said so publicly to about a dozen generals and colonels. Yes, I am his friend and he is my friend."

He probably read some doubt in my face because he continued, "Yes, one evening, some six months ago, he called me his friend. Do you want to hear it?" And not waiting for my answer, he continued:

"It happened like this. My night route brought me to the Trocadero. Do you know the Trocadero, were you ever there? You know, it is a frightfully expensive place. It's really only for princes and noblemen and war profiteers and high officers and such.

"Well, my peddler's box and I come in, and there I notice His Majesty, I mean the Crown Prince, amid a group of generals or colonels. They sat at a table and two waiters were serving from three champagne coolers. Judging from the loud laughter, these champagne coolers must have been refilled many times before I came.

"I was a little embarrassed. After all, who am I to see His Maj-

esty, I mean the Crown Prince, in an—hem—ahem—hem—undignified condition? And then, also—well, you see, I love my peddler's
profession and wouldn't change it for any other—but I wanted His
Majesty always to think of me as the shopkeeper on Leopoldsgasse,
the owner of a soap and candle store. Well, when I saw His Majesty
at the center table, I quickly turned away and began to peddle at
the tables toward the entrance. I wanted to get out as quickly as
I could without attracting attention. But it was too late. His Majesty noticed me, or perhaps my black beard, because I heard him
shout 'There is my friend from the Leopoldsgasse. Waiter, don't
let him go out, bring him to me!' And before I knew, two strong
waiters grabbed my arms and there I stood before His Majesty.

"And His Majesty got up, just a little unsteady on his legs, and
turning to his circle of friends, said: 'Gentlemen, this is my good
friend, my good Jewish friend from the Leopoldsgasse. He greets
me every morning when I am on my way to the Augarten. And
when I hear his "Good Morning, Majesty," I know that all is well
in the Empire. And on some mornings, when I do not feel like
driving out to the Augarten, I still do it, because I could not disappoint my friend. It has practically become a superstition with me.
I sometimes fear that if one day he would not be there to greet
me, or I would not appear to be greeted, why, the Empire would
fall apart, the end would come for the Hapsburgs! Gentlemen,
here is a toast to my friend from the Leopoldsgasse!' It was a great
moment. Just think, all the uniforms getting up from their seats and
drinking to me, toasting me, me, Black Tobias. I stood there, surrounded by all the generals, and they gave me a glass of champagne,
and another, and urged me to drink. And I drank champagne with
His Majesty. Do you understand, I, Black Tobias, drank with a
Hapsburg!

"And then His Majesty said: 'Now my friend, I see you are
a merchant. A merchant in a small way, but a merchant just the
same. Very laudable, very laudable. Tell me, what else do you do
besides selling your wares? I mean—do you play an instrument,
do you know any tricks, do you dance—what I mean, do you do
anything for recreation?'

"I never dreamt that His Majesty would be interested in his
subjects, in so humble a subject as 'Black Tobias.' I was bewildered,
I was speechless—my knees almost gave in—and then, I gathered

all my courage, bowed deeply and said: 'Your Majesty, what hobbies can a poor peddler have? Instruments? Tricks? Dance? No,
Your Majesty, I regret. I only peddle all week long, and on Saturdays, I go to the Temple. We never fail to include a prayer for
Your Majesty's health and for victory for our armies. It is a happy
prayer and the Temple is filled with joy because a week of hard
work is behind and our Sabbath is given to prayer and rest. We
rejoice and we chant our psalms. It is a day to which I look forward
all week long, Your Majesty. But tricks, hobbies, no Your Majesty,
I am sorry!'

"And then His Majesty asked me whether I can sing the psalms
we sing in the Temple. 'Yes, Your Majesty,' I answered, 'I know
many of them by heart, I think, I know all of them by heart.'
'Well,' he said, 'let's hear them.'

"And because it was His Majesty's command and because I knew
God will forgive me the blasphemy, I swallowed and said, almost
in a whisper, 'If it pleases Your Majesty.'

"His Majesty and the generals made a circle around me and
made me stand up on a chair. The Master of Ceremonies was motioned to disappear, the orchestra stopped in the middle of a fox
trot, and suddenly it was quiet in the night club. The Trocadero
was transformed into a Temple, into a House of God, and I, Black
Tobias, was chosen to sing for the glory of our God, with His
Majesty as my audience. And I began. My voice shook and I did
not remember the Hebrew words. And then all went black before
my eyes, I forgot the Trocadero, I forgot His Majesty and his
generals. I was again in my Temple, it was Sabbath, I was chanting
our holy songs to our God.

"I cannot tell how long I sang. One psalm followed another,
my voice seemed stronger, clearer, my body swayed back and
forth, my voice grew higher and higher and when it reached the
highest pitch, I shouted 'Shemah Yisroel'—and stopped.

"And suddenly I was back in the Trocadero. Although I stopped,
all was quiet around me and for a moment I thought that His
Majesty was displeased. But then, as if awakened, all applauded,
His Majesty too, and the Trocadero was again as noisy as when
I entered. I was exhausted and barely whispering 'Thank you,
Majesty,' I walked out of the night club but not before I heard
His Majesty softly say, 'Thank you, mein lieber Freund.' The night

was early and I continued on my route, first to the Simplicissimus, then to the Ronacher, and finally to the Apollo.

"The next morning at ten-thirty His Majesty passed again and I was there with my usual 'Good Morning, Majesty.' He smiled as usual and I was sure that he did not remember that I sang for him the night before, just a few hours ago.

"But soon I had occasion to find out that he was my friend. During the war, soap and oil became very scarce and the Police were systematically raiding stores and confiscating supplies which were found in excess of a certain ration. One evening the Police raided my wife's store and took away all we had. Two truck loads were removed to Police Headquarters—we were ruined.

"I was desperate. I was determined to appeal to the highest authority, to my friend, the Emperor. And the next morning at ten-thirty, when I saw the imperial carriage approaching, I ran out into the street and fell on my knees in front of the horses. The carriage stopped and His Majesty leaned out of the carriage. 'What is it, my friend?' he asked in a perfectly natural, not irritated voice. 'Mercy, Your Majesty, and forgiveness for my impertinence. Your poor servant begs your mercy. The Police have confiscated all my merchandise, emptied my store. I am ruined, Majesty, mercy.' His Majesty smiled, 'Your merchandise shall be returned to you, my dear fellow. What is your name?'

"And you wouldn't believe it. The very afternoon, two truck loads parked in front of the store and unloaded cases upon cases of soap and barrels of oil, and candles—in fact, all that was confiscated the day before. All that was done without any explanation, for there could be no explanation. The policemen did not know that the Emperor and I were old friends and they would not have believed it if I told them so."

Time passed. The old Emperor Franz Joseph died and Carl became Emperor. The war entered now the fourth year, the mass murder for false ideals continued and seemed to gain momentum as if drawing renewed strength from secret, superhuman sources. I no longer frequented the cafés along Black Tobias's route, they were too expensive. Thus it was purely by accident that I met him shortly after the war. He had changed greatly. There was no doubt now about his age. I asked him how he had been getting along and he threw up his hands in an inimitable gesture of despair: "Oh, these years, these last black years . . ." He sounded really tragic and I wondered what could have brought such a change in Tobias's sanguine outlook on life. It was not difficult to persuade him to have coffee with me and once in the café, he repeated, "Yes, yes, black years these have been . . ."

"Tell me, Tobias," I prompted, "what happened after the Emperor had your merchandise returned?"

"What happened! What hasn't happened?" Tobias seemed excited and utterly unhappy. He continued:

"The old Emperor Franz Joseph died and my Majesty became Emperor. But still he followed his old habits and I saw him every morning. It now became a duty with me. Hadn't the Majesty said in the Trocadero that night that the House of Hapsburg would fall if we two did not meet every morning?

"The war seemed to last forever. The second, the third year came to an end, the fourth year was almost over—and the armies were still fighting with ever increasing fury. Millions died, other millions were crippled, the people all over Europe were starving, but the armies fought battle after battle.

"I was peddling my peddler's box night after night. Business was not good. The people no longer put coins in my box but actually bought my matches and shoe strings and even bargained for lower prices. Imagine my patrons asking the price of a pair of shoe laces?

"My Hannah was not well for a long time, she didn't even nag any more. Many big doctors were my customers and all offered their help. She had good care, my Hannah, but little by little she seemed to fade away and late one night she died. The Temple and the Congregation were notified and funeral services were held on the third day, as the ritual prescribes.

"It was November eleventh, nineteen eighteen, a cold, dreary morning when the funeral procession began. They dressed me in my Sabbath clothes, put me in a carriage and we proceeded toward the Zentral-Friedhof, the Central Cemetery. My wife was dead—my Hannah was dead . . . The rain drops were repeating it—my wife was dead—my heart hammered it—my Hannah was dead . . . Forgotten was my Emperor, forgotten the war, its victories and defeats—my Hannah was dead . . . That night and the previous three, four nights, I did not visit the night clubs. I did not notice anything around me, I didn't read the newspapers,

I was dead to the world and the world was dead to me, my Hannah was gone. . . .

"Three days later—I happened to look at the clock, it was ten-fifteen. My thoughts automatically wandered to the Emperor and I wondered whether he noticed that I was not at the customary place to bid him the customary good morning. My curiosity was aroused and I decided to step out into the street and wait for the Emperor. Ten-thirty, ten-forty-five, and still no carriage and no Emperor. I looked at my watch and asked a passerby for the right time. It was ten to eleven. That was strange, what could have happened to His Majesty? Perhaps he left for the front, perhaps his army needed moral support? Was he ill?

"Herr Kratochwil, the Socialist, just then came out of his apartment and I stopped him: 'Did you see the Emperor pass by today, or yesterday?'

"He stared at me—and then laughed out loud and began calling the neighbors together: 'That's a good one! Listen, folks, that's a good joke! Black Tobias asks for his Majesty, for his Emperor! Ha—ha—ha—ha—Black Tobias wants to bow deeply. 'Good Morning, Majesty! Ja, ja, your Majesty, ha—ha—ha.'

"I walked away from that disrespectful crowd which joined Kratochwil in wild laughter. I was bewildered. I did not understand the meaning of all this. I escaped into the store of Herr Spira and asked him.

"'Where were you the last few days, Tobias?' he asked. 'Did you not hear what happened? Don't you know about the revolution, about the abdication of Emperor Carl? Don't you know that there is no more an Austrian-Hungarian Empire? Don't you know that the war is lost? That Emperor Carl was chased out of Vienna? That new republics were established? That you live now in the Republic of Austria? Yes, Tobias, the Empire is gone, the Hapsburgs are gone, ach, what a world . . .'

"'Yes,' I said, 'Yes, I know now. Yes, it is all my fault, all my fault . . .' But Herr Spira, of course, did not understand, he could not understand. And as I walked toward my room, I whispered to myself the words the Emperor said in the Trocadero that night, long, long ago—'I fear that if one day he would not be there to greet me, the Empire would fall apart, the end would come for the Hapsburgs' . . ."

THE FIVE-*PENGÖ* GIRL

By Sandor Hunyady

ONE WINTRY DAY, ABOUT TWO O'CLOCK IN THE AFTERNOON, A GIRL came up to see me in my hotel room. She wanted me to give her some kind of help because she was destitute. She was a very common-looking brunette, dressed in plain clothes. But penury was written on her face. I could tell that she was scared to death by the step she was taking. She sat terrified on the edge of her chair, clutching desperately the worn-out purse in her lap.

She wasn't an ugly girl; a nineteen-year-old girl can never be ugly. She had open, dark eyes. But poverty had left its stamp on her hands and on her complexion. The daughters of village store-keepers, who work from daybreak until midnight in the cold store, have such frozen, swollen-red hands.

She stammered out that she was a Transylvanian girl. She had been advised by someone who knew someone who knew me to come to me, since I, too, was from Transylvania. Perhaps I might be able to help her. She would stop after every third word, stand up, apologize, start leaving, like one who had exhausted her courage.

"Are you sick?" she asked me worriedly.

I assured her that I was not sick, only an inveterate night-owl. The reason that I was still in bed at two o'clock in the afternoon was that I went to bed late in the morning, having spent the previous night playing cards.

This confession made the girl blush, just as if I had told her something risqué about myself. Generally speaking, everything embarrassed and disturbed her. Especially the furniture of the hotel room, which apparently seemed elegant to her. Covertly, with deep respect, she stroked the plush covering of her chair. Her eyes were full of amazement. This in spite of the fact that I live in a very simple room. Then, in addition, I had just had lunch: a few slices of bologna and an apple. In the plate on the night table she could still see the bologna-rinds and the apple core. This refuse certainly did not lend my milieu a ducal appearance.

But to the frozen-handed girl even this was too much. She seemed to fear and respect me. Seeing this, I resorted to an old trick to make her feel more at ease. I asked her to do me a favor:

"Look here, my girl, I don't want to get up from this bed: there's a glass on the bowl. Would you mind giving me some water?"

The girl was imbued with celestial happiness. It was heartbreaking to see how readily she ran to the faucet, how she rinsed the glass, how she brought the water to my bed.

"Would you like another glass?" she asked in raptures.

I wasn't thirsty any more, but, just to please her, I drank down another glass of water. To let her feel the importance of her assistance.

This way we got to be quite friendly. She became bolder and more loquacious. Within a few minutes her whole life was opened up before me. The remembrance of the tenements. Her father's death. The utter financial ruin of her relatives. Now she was all alone. No relatives; hardly any friends. She had tried everything to earn a living. She had made paper bags. She had waited on tables in cheap restaurants. She had worked in a wholesale cheese store. She had sewn, washed, run errands.

But now she had nothing. It was terrible! She had no idea what was going to happen next week if there wasn't a turn in her affairs. Already she owed a week's bed-money in the flophouse, and they were pressing her for it.

I was wracking my brains to find some means of helping her. In my final desperation it even occurred to me that the poor wench could perhaps get a job in a theatre as an extra.

But when I looked at her, I gave up. This starved little proletarian was a long way off from that world, with her thin silver ring imbedded in her swollen index finger.

I lighted a cigarette and began coughing. I usually cough like bloody hell after awakening, just as if I were going insane. The girl watched in the blackest despair how I writhed and bored my head in the pillow. She ran for water. Then, when a little relieved, I began breathing, she valiantly offered to go down to the pharmacy to get me some cough drops. "They are very good for the chest!" she informed me.

I explained to her that no cough drops could help me any more, that I was way beyond the limits of their feeble efficacy.

This developed into a longer discussion on the subject of coughing. Our parts were being more and more exchanged. It was I who was doing the complaining, and she who was trying to cheer me up.

By half past two we were such good friends that, after we had discussed a variety of different jobs, she blurted out the confession: she was still a virgin, but she had come to the point where she wouldn't mind if she could find a steady friend who would be willing to keep her . . .

I looked at her in amazement. There was silence.

The girl's face turned crab-red. She pulled out from her purse her painfully crumpled handkerchief. She turned aside and blew her nose in embarrassment.

The strange part of it was that I found nothing frivolous in what she had said. The girl had referred to the possibility of having a "friend" who "would be willing to keep her" as if it had been just another job that might be considered. Worse than being a seamstress, but still a job. A final refuge.

Even I got a little embarrassed.

"You don't mean me, by any chance?" I asked her, sour and teasing.

The girl became even redder. She tortured the handkerchief in her hands, and looked at her shoes:

"Oh, no! . . . I really didn't mean that . . . I just thought that you might know somebody . . . That you would mention it to some of your friends . . .

This offer, to put it plainly and briefly, contained the following proposition: I should act for her as a pimp, or at least as a go-between. I should sell her, just as a favor one countryman would do another. And I couldn't even feel insulted.

Apparently this unsophisticated girl didn't have a clear idea of what she had said, what kind of offer she had made. Her muddled speech was a result of her hopeless situation. She was at the point where one makes one's last attempt before picking a convenient bridge above the Danube.

It would have been supercilious inhumanity on my part to preach this poor, ignorant girl a sermon on chastity and virginity. Rather, since that had been her own approach, I began discussing the financial aspects of the affair:

"Don't do that, my girl, it really doesn't pay. Men are all poor nowadays; they haven't got the money to keep mistresses."

The girl's answer to this was that she was very modest. Without taking her eyes off her shoes, she said softly:

"Five *pengös* a week would be enough for me to live on . . ."

I held my hand to my ear as if I hadn't heard her correctly:

"How much?"

Now she fixed the persecuted glance of her dark eyes on me:

"Five *pengös!*" she said more loudly, but still very scared. "Do you think it's too much? . . ."

"Hell, no!" I was getting mad. "Don't feed me that stuff! How could any grown-up person possibly exist on five *pengös* a week?"

Then she explained to me that it would be quite sufficient for her. She gave me accurate figures. For her bed she had to pay two *pengös* a week in the boarding house run by a pensioned railwayman and his wife.

She cooked where she lived, on the people's small stove. Sixteen *fillérs* for two kilos of potatoes; twenty-six *fillérs* for ten decas of butter; fifteen *fillérs* for a kilo of frozen apples; and the street vendors give one a whole capful of peanuts for ten *fillérs*. Even the amortization of cosmetics was included in the five *pengös*. So much to be set aside for soap per week; so much for tooth paste . . .

I couldn't be convinced.

"And what about clothes?" I asked inimically. "You have to have some kind of clothes, don't you?"

She shuddered as if she had been caught in a lie, and raised her budget penitently:

"With clothes it's six . . . Six-fifty . . . I would save the one-fifty every week . . . It really wouldn't take long to save up a very nice sum that way . . ."

Some kind of bad conscience began pricking me in the nose. It occurred to me that the night before I had lost just enough on cards to pay for this girl's board for six months . . . That her weekly budget would amount to just about one dollar in American money . . .

I crawled out of bed and scraped out of my trouser pocket the change left in it. I had fifteen *pengös*. I offered my guest six of them. At first she didn't want to accept.

Then I put the money in her purse by force, and looked around to see what else I could give her. I had a bottle of Cologne water I couldn't use because it was too smelly; so I gave that to her. She got, in addition, three handkerchiefs, and a pictorial stage magazine. For this last item I felt genuinely sorry because I had done half of the cross word puzzle in it.

She started to cry. This was too much for me; so I sent her away.

Then, when she had left, I called up the doorman, and even gave instructions to the bell boy; in fact, I told everybody to take a better look next time whom they let in, because I didn't like to be disturbed. But somehow I didn't feel good; I had a hunch that the dark-eyed girl didn't belong to the brotherhood of professional visiting beggars whom I loathe so much.

* * *

It was the end of January when the girl came to see me. Now the affair had an aftermath. Yesterday a small, nicely-wrapped parcel was sent up to my room with the morning mail.

It was an oblong little box wrapped in tissue paper, tied around with a golden thread, with a little bunch of lilies-of-the-valley pinned on its top. It contained twenty decas of assorted cough drops and six shiny silver *pengös* separately wrapped in tinfoil. There was also a note in the box.

The parcel had been left with the doorman by the five-*pengö* girl. She told me in the note that I had brought her luck. Already the day after she had been up to see me she had got a job in an automatic buffet.

It was a wonderful place. She was still holding the job. She had been able to save up the six *pengös* from her salary to pay her debt to me. She had had the money for a week, she said. She wanted to give it to me personally; she had come back to the hotel three times, but they wouldn't let her in. As for the cough drops, I should really try them and I would see that they would help my coughing.

I turned the note over. There was neither name nor address on it. This honest little woman didn't want an answer to her cough drops. The candy had been just interest accrued, a little nicety she had thought of. How much did she have to go without to buy it? . . .

I tried to apologize to myself. Some people guard their money. I had no money; so I tried to guard my privacy. But still I felt lousy when I imagined how the girl had been sent away, perhaps even from my very threshold; how she must have gone down the staircase from the third story, on the thick, ornate carpet held in place by shining brass strips. Poor little wench, she probably didn't even dare open her mouth. . . . Her heart must have been very heavy under her phony velvet coat as she swung outside through the revolving glass door . . . Like mine, now.

NEVER COME MONDAY

By Eric Knight

THE FIRST ONE TO NOTICE IT WAS OLD CAPPER WAMBLEY. AND CAPPER was a very important man. He was the knocker-up in the village of Allerby Brig—that is to say, he got up early every morning and went round with his pole, tapping on the bedroom windows and waking up the people in time for them to get to work. And this particular morning old Capper knew there was something wrong.

He felt it first as he stepped outside his cottage and coughed in the dark to clear his lungs, and looked up at the sky to see what kind of weather it was. He felt that there was something wrong with the day, and then he decided what it was. It was still Sunday.

For a moment or two he felt fair flabbergasted at this, for he remembered that the day before had been Sunday, too.

"Ba gum," Capper said to himself. "This is a champion do, it is an' all. No doubt summat should be done."

Now old Capper Wambley was very old, so he sat down on the edge of the curb, and after a while he came to the conclusion that what ought to be done was to think about it. So he began thinking about the very strange event.

"Now," he said to himself, "it don't seem reasonable and proper that we should hev two Sundays in a row. Let us see if we can get it sorted out. Now the thing for a chap to do to prove it, is to decide what is the difference between a Sunday morning and a weekday morning."

Old Capper thought and thought, and he saw that the only difference between the two was that on a weekday morning he wakened the people up, and on a Sunday morning he didn't.

"So, if Ah doan't wakken the village up this morning, it *is* a Sunday morning," he said to himself.

Of course, it took old Capper a long time to figure this out, because you can see it was no light matter. Here was one man, as you might say, who was holding the calendar in his hands. It was

416

a very important decision. But once Capper had decided, he knew he must be right, for he was a Yorkshireman.

"Because Ah'm net wakkening onybody, it maun be a Sunday morning. And because it's a Sunday morning, Ah maun't wakken onybody up. So no matter which way a lad looks at is, the answer cooms out that it's Sunday."

But now he had decided it was Sunday, Capper saw that not wakening people up might not be sufficient. "Some of them may wake up of their own accord," he thought, "and not knowing this is the second Sunday in a row, will go walking down to the mill. And God knows they have to get up early often enough, and it would be a tarrible shame not to let them have this extra piece of rest that is so miraculously sent."

So old Capper got up slowly from the curb, and went stomping down the street, and stopped at his first call, which was the home of John Willie Braithwaite, who was the fireman at the mill. Old Capper got his long pole with the trident of wire at the end and lifting it so that the wire rested against the upstairs window pane, began twirling and twisting the pole in the palms of his hands so that the wire clacked and chattered fit to wake the soundest sleeper.

Soon the window went up, and John Willie Braithwaite's head popped out of the window.

"Ah'm wakkened," John Willie said. "Whet time is't?"

Now old Capper could see that John Willie wasn't awake, but was just moving in his sleep the way men did from their tiredness and weariness of getting up before dawn. But he knew it didn't matter this morning.

"Ah just wakkened ye to tell ye it's another Sunday morning," old Capper said. "Soa tha c'n goa on back to bed an' sleep i' peace."

At this John Willie Braithwaite closed the window and went back to bed and got in beside his wife without ever having really wakened up. Meanwhile old Capper was on his rounds, busily going up and down the village in the not-yet-dawn, rapping and tapping on all his customers' windows, and telling them they needn't get up because it was still Sunday.

Naturally, the news caused quite a little bit of a fuss. Some people gladly went back to sleep, but others woke up and got dressed, remembering that the day before had been Sunday. They packed their breakfasts and put on their clogs and their smocks and their shawls and went clacking up the streets until they got by the Green, and there they saw old Capper Wambley.

"Now lad," they said, "whet's t'idea o' telling us this is another Sunday?"

"Well, it is," Capper said.

"How does'ta know it is?" Golliker Dilkes asked him.

"Ah can't explain it, but Ah'm full sure summat varry wonderful has happened, and it is," old Capper told them.

Some people were inclined to believe Capper, and some were not.

"Now lewk here, Capper," Golliker said, "Ah doan't but admit that it does seem Sundayish, like, but how are we off to be sure?"

Old Capper thought a while. Then he saw the answer.

"Well, here's the way us can tell," he said. "Now if this be a weekday, the mill whistle'll blaw the fifteen minutes, wean't it?"

"Aye," they agreed.

"But if it be a Sunday, like Ah say, the mill whistle wean't blaw the fifteen minutes, will it?"

They all agreed that was true. So they stood round old Capper, who had one of the few watches in the village, and they waited. They all looked at his watch and saw it said twenty to six, then nineteen to six, then eighteen and seventeen and sixteen. And the second hand went round and finally it said quarter to six. But no whistle blew—largely because John Willie Braithwaite who was supposed to be there at 5:30 and get up steam and pull the whistle cord, was still home and sleeping warmly beside his wife.

"Well," old Capper says. "That shows it maun be a Sunday again, and now ye can all away hoam and get another hour's sleep."

So they all went home, glad to get another hour's sleep, and full of praises for old Capper because he had had the sense to perceive that it was another Sunday instead of a Monday morning.

Old Capper went off home himself, and was just making himself a little bit of breakfast, when Rowlie Helliwell came in.

"Capper," Rowlie said, "Ah hear that tha discovered this is another Sunday."

"Aye, that's soa," Capper replied.

"Well," Rowlie went on, "isn't heving two Sundays in a row just a varry little bit irregular, as tha maught say?"

"It is that, lad," Capper told him. "But tha maun remember us is living in varry unusual times."

"We are that," Rowlie agreed. "And Ah'm glad tha discovered it in time. For if tha hedn't, Ah would ha' gone and rung the school bell like a gert lummox, thinking it were a Monday. But now Ah know it's a Sunday, Ah maun goa and ring the church bell."

"Ah should say that all sounds right and proper to me," old Capper agreed.

"Me too," Rowlie said. "And Ah thank thee for saving me from a gert mistake.

"Eigh, it's nowt, lad," old Capper said modestly.

So away went Rowlie, and Capper settled down to his breakfast, but he was soon interrupted again. Some of the villagers, all dressed in their Sunday clothes, came up and told him that people from other villages who worked at the Allerby Brig mill were at the mill-gates insisting it was Monday. So Capper picked up a bit of bloater to eat on the way and went down there and told the people it was Sunday.

"But if it's Sunday in Allerby Brig, what day is it i' Wuxley Green?" someone asked.

"Aye, and i' Rombeck an' Tannerley?" someone else added.

"Well, happen it's Sunday theer, too," Capper told them. "Only you didn't notice it. When two Sundays come in a row ye could hardly blame a chap for mistaking the second one for Monday. Soa Ah advise ye to goa back and enjoy Sunday."

"Well," said Tich Mothersole, "Ah'm reight glad to hev another day o' rest; but Ah wish Ah'd known it afore Ah started, because ma Mary Alice allus brings me ma breakfast to bed o' Sunday morning."

"Nay, if tha hurries tha's still time enow to gate hoam and pop back into bed," the Capper pointed out. "Then the minute thy wife sees thee theer she'll knaw it's a Sunday and she'll up and hev a bit o' bacon o't' fire i' noa time."

They were just ready to move away when Mr. Bloggs arrived. Mr. Bloggs was late, but then that didn't matter, because he lived in another town, and Mr. Bloggs owned the mill.

" 'Ere, 'ere, 'ere, my good men," he said. "What's all this, 'ey? What's the idea you aren't all in the mill?"

So they explained to him that a second Sunday had arrived.

"Why, what nonsense," he said. "When I left 'ome it was a Monday. 'Ow can it be Sunday 'ere when it was a Monday in Puttersleigh?"

"Ah doan't knaw," old Capper said. "Unless," he added slowly, "it happens to be Sunday in Puttersleigh, too, and tha didn't realize it."

"It's Monday, I tell you. Come on in to work," Mr. Bloggs shouted. "How can it be two Sundays in a row?"

"It's Sunday," they said.

"It's not. It's Monday. And any man 'oo ain't in this mill in five minutes, is discharged."

"It's Sunday," they said.

"How can it be Sunday?" he shouted, "it's impossible."

He stared at them, and just then they heard the boom—boom—boom, of the church bell ringing for Matins.

"That proves," they said, "it's a Sunday, and it'd be a sin to work on Sunday."

So they all turned round and went back to their homes, leaving Mr. Bloggs alone by his mill gates. He stood there, shaking his head, and finally he clumped upstairs and opened the office himself and sat down all alone at his desk to think the whole matter out.

Meanwhile in the homes of the village the people knew that since it was a Sunday, they would have to do all the things that one does on a Sunday. The men rested at home in comfortable chairs, and the women started mixing Yorkshire puddings for the big noontime dinner. The children were dressed in their nicest clothes and instead of going to school, they went up to the church for Sunday School. Ethel Newligate, who taught the Sunday School, went with them. Mr. Sims, the schoolteacher, hearing the church bell, knew it must be Sunday and off he went to play the organ. Rowlie Helliwell was already there to pump the bellows. The church folk went up and stood in the pews. So the old Reverend Mr. Stoninghorn put on his cassock and surplice. He was a little puzzled as to whether it should be now the Fifth Sunday before Epiphany or the Fourth, but he compromised by giving the same service as he had done the day before, and preaching the same sermon. And many of the church folk said the sermon sounded a right lot nicer the second time than the first, because you could see just where it was going, in a manner of speaking.

All this time, of course, the mill was closed, but Mr. Bloggs wasn't idle. He picked up his telephone, which was the only one in the village, and asked the operator to get him the Greenwich Observatory. Mr. Bloggs always liked to be exact. When he got them he asked them what day it was, and they told him that it was Monday.

Armed with this fact, Mr. Bloggs went out and met the people just as they were coming out of church.

"Now see here," he said. "It's no use pretending. This is a Monday."

But they pointed out that they were just coming out of church, so how could it be Monday?

At this Mr. Bloggs got so angry that he shouted at them, and the noise brought the Rev. Mr. Stoninghorn to the church steps.

"You must not profane the Sabbath," he said, looking very handsome in his white surplice, and with his long white hair like a dandelion gone to seed.

Mr. Bloggs began to see he could get nowhere against Yorkshiremen by blustering, so he took another tack. He pointed out to the minister that while this may be Sunday, one would have to admit that it was a little bit unusual to have two Sundays in a row. Mr. Stoninghorn admitted this, and he agreed that a meeting ought to be called to look into the matter.

So it was announced through the village that a meeting was to be called at the school for four o'clock that afternoon. The Rev. Mr. Stoninghorn was asked to preside, but inasmuch as he was unsure whether or not it was the Sabbath, he declined. So Mr. Polkiby, the school master, agreed to take over the gavel and run a meeting in which everyone should have a chance to state his views on whether it was or wasn't Sunday.

At meeting time there wasn't a seat to be had, and after Mr. Polkiby rapped with the gavel, Mr. Bloggs got up and stated that it was Monday, and he could prove it because he had called up the Greenwich Observatory.

Then Taylor Huckle, the publican, got up and said it was Monday, because yesterday had been Sunday and the day after Sunday had always been Monday, for years and years, man and boy, as far back as he could remember.

After this there was a wait, because nobody liked to get up in

front of so many people and put in their hap'orth; though a lot of
people were dying to, because they knew Huckle was in favor of
Monday for if it were Sunday he'd have to go on early closing
hours.

So there was a long wait until somebody said: "Where's Sam
Small?"

"Here Ah am," said a voice at the back of the hall, and they all
spoke up and said: "Come on, Sam, let's hev thy opinion."

Now this Sam Small was a man whose word was worth listening
to at any time, and on any subject. He was the inventor of the
Sam Small Self-Doffing Spindle and had made a pile of brass from
it, and was much traveled, not only having been to London and
other parts, but to foreign lands as well on a cruise. So they waited
politely as Sam walked down the aisle and clambered up on the
stage.

"Well lads," he said, "it's this way. A day's a day, but then again,
it ain't, in a manner of speaking. The time Ah went round t'world,
one day it were Tuesday, and the next morning the captain said it
were Thursday—and so it were, because Ah've nivver yet found
that lost day. And on t'other hand, a lad on the ship told me if we'd
gone round the world t'other way, we should of hed two Tuesdays. Now if we can have two Tuesdays when we're going round
the world, Ah maintain we maught just as easy hev two Sundays
when the world is going round us, which ivvery scientist knaws it
is doing."

"Piffle," said Mr. Bloggs.

"Oh, aye?" asked Sam, his dander getting up. "Can tha tell me
what day it is now i' Japan?"

"It's Monday," Mr. Bloggs said.

"Oh, pardon me, Mr. Bloggs," the schoolmaster said. "Just as
a matter of academic accuracy . . ." and here he studied his watch
carefully . . . "but in Japan now it is Tuesday."

"Tuesday?" roared Mr. Bloggs.

"There, tha sees," Sam said. "There don't seem to me to be noa
sense to this day stuff. If it's Monday, as tha says, down i' Greenwich; and if it's Tuesday, as t'schoolmeaster says, i' Japan; then
Ah says it's just as liable to be Sunday up here."

"Nonsense," yelled Mr. Bloggs. "I know what the matter is.

You're all lazy and you wanted another day off. So you call it Sunday."

"Nay lad," Sam replied. "There's six weekdays to one Sunday, so it seems to me like it were six to one i' thy favor that we'd hev an extra workday i'stead of an extra restday. Simply because tha lost, tha maun't be a bad sport about it."

At this the people applauded Sam, and seeing he was at a good place to stop, he got down off the platform.

"Fiddlesticks," Mr. Bloggs said, now thoroughly angry. "If this is Sunday, then what's tomorrow? Is it Monday or Tuesday? Or do we lose a day?"

"Happen Ah'm the man to clear that up," the Capper said, rising to his feet. "Us doesn't skip noa day at all. T'thing is that t'days o'to'week have gate tired o'turning, soa now they've stood still and wean't goa no further, they wean't."

"How ridiculous," Mr. Bloggs snorted. "If that were so we'd get no further and tomorrow would be Sunday, too, wouldn't it?"

The Capper scratched his head and thought a moment. Then he looked up quickly.

"Ba gum, lad," he said. "Tha's hit t'nail o't'yead. Tomorrow is off to be Sunday."

At this the meeting broke up, and everyone started for home. They crowded around old Capper and asked him about the next day.

"Ah'm reight sure it'll be Sunday, lads," old Capper said. "But when Ah coom round to wakken ye up, Ah'll tell ye."

"Nay, Ah gate a better idea," John Willie Braithwaite said. "If it's a Sunday, it'd be a fair shame to disturb a little bit o' good extra sleep. That'd mak' it as bad as a weekday 'most. So supposing, if it's another Sunday, just thee doan't bother to coom round—and when tha doesn't coom we'll knaw for sure that way it's Sunday."

"Aye, that's fine," old Capper said, "but Ah'll lose all me collections that way."

They all saw that was so, but they agreed that even if it kept on being Sunday, they would pay old Capper just the same as if it had become the rotation of weekdays and he'd made his rounds.

"Nay, Ah couldn't tak' it," Capper protested.

"Nay, we'd like thee to," they protested.

"Well, if ye say," Capper agreed. "But how about lads i't'other villages. It's hard on them thinking it's a weekday and walking all the way here to find it's a Sunday."

"Well," John Willie said, "we'll form a committee, like, right now, and the members will each tak' a village and goa reight ovver theer and tell ivveryone that it's staying Sunday these days—that the days o't'week is stuck, like."

Everyone thought it a good and orderly idea, and so it was done.

The next morning people in the village woke up, and they lay abed and listened. But they heard no trident of wire chattering in the greyness of the morning, nor old Capper's voice wheezing: "'Awf pest fower, ist'a oop?" They waited but they heard no clogs clattering on the cobbles, and no whistle at the mill saying that if they didn't get there in fifteen minutes they'd be locked out.

So they knew it must be Sunday again, and they went back to sleep, and the next thing they knew was the church bell ringing once more. So that made it Sunday and they were sure of it.

And in the other towns roundabout, the people didn't go to work, and so they knew it was Sunday, too. They put on their best clothes, and did a bit of gardening and the men mended things about the house and the children didn't go to school, and everyone had a fine rest so that their work-tired bodies began to grow glad and proud again.

The next day the news that the days of the week were stuck at Sunday had spread all over Yorkshire, and was percolating up to the Tyneside where the shipworkers were, and over into Lancashire where the youngsters worked before cotton mills and looms, and down into the black country where the men hauled at steel and went down into the mines, and down into Staffordshire where they toiled at the potteries and the car factories.

The newspapers sent men around to find out what had happened to the lost weekdays, and one of them came to the village and looked up old Capper. At first he laughed, until Ian Cawper came along. Ian Cawper was the biggest man in Yorkshire for sure, and happen the biggest and strongest man in all England without doubt. So he just asked the newspaper lad for a penny, and then he bent the penny in two, and the newspaper lad stopped laughing.

"Nah, lad," Ian said. "Happen tha'd better tellyphone thy paper that this is Sunday."

"Indeed I will," the young man said, very appreciatively.

Now although the wonderful thing that it was still Sunday found great gratification in the hearts of all the men who worked long hours handling steel and wood and cotton and iron and glass and fabric and paper and silk, at furnaces and forges and foundries and looms and jennies and sides and presses and drills and lathes and assembly belts, there were some men who were quite upset by the miraculous happening. And in spite of the fact that everyone else in the country now saw that a beautiful series of Sundays had happened, these men kept on trying to persuade everyone that they were just ordinary days of the week that people merely *thought* were Sundays.

These men soon saw that if it kept on being Sunday they'd never be able to make any more battleships and gasbombs and motor cars and airplanes and radios and badminton rackets and all the rest of the things that are civilizing influences upon the world. And, to go further, if they didn't make those things, they wouldn't be able to go on making more money than they had already.

This was quite an abhorrent state of affairs. So they went to the Prime Minister about it.

"I yield my reverence for religion, especially the Church of England, to no one," one of them said. "In fact, I am thoroughly in accord with religion—one day a week."

"Hear, hear," the others said.

"But, Mr. Prime Minister, think of my stockholders! Many are orphans. Many are widows. If my factory doesn't make money, these poor people will be destitute—because always having drawn dividends, they've never had to learn how to work. We cannot let them suffer."

"Gentlemen," said the Prime Minister, "you may rest assured that His Majesty's Government will do all within its power to safeguard that industry and commerce which is the backbone of our nation—indeed, of our Empire."

Then the Prime Minister went away and thought. Being a Prime Minister he didn't think as you or I would. You or I, in the same case, might have said to ourselves: "Come, come now. What we've got to decide is whether this is Sunday or isn't." Which is probably why you and I will never be Prime Ministers.

This Prime Minister thought of a lot of things all at once. Suddenly, he called his secretary and said:

"Carrington-Smaithe. It is a Sunday today, I hear, and it will be a Sunday again tomorrow. Pack my things. We're going away for the week end."

"But sir," said the secretary, "what about the International Crisis? We have two ultimatums which must be answered immediately."

"Dear me," said the Prime Minister. "That is a nuisance; but all the world knows the British week end is inviolate, and if this is Sunday, as it seems to me it must be, then I won't be able to answer till the week end is over."

"But when will it stop being Sunday, sir?"

"Well, Carrington-Smaithe, how long will it take our fastest cruiser squadron to get round to that troublesome part of the world?"

"Oh, about thirty-six more hours, sir."

"Hmmmph! Then I think it will stop being Sunday in about thirty-six more hours."

And with this the Prime Minister caught the five-fifteen train and went off to the country. And when the newspapers heard of it they printed it, and all the people in England—in fact, in all the world—knew that it was officially Sunday.

And back in Allerby Brig all the people were that proud of old Capper Wambley. For hadn't he been the first man in all the land to notice that the days of the week were stuck and every day kept turning up a Sunday.

And all over the land toil-weary people sighed with happiness at their escape from industrial chains. They rested their tired bodies. Some went to church every day. The men went walking with their dogs, or did odd jobs round the house, tinkering and gardening and cobbling and putting up shelves. In the cities people took busses out into the country and had picnics. The grownups lay in the sun and the children played in the fields, and the young men and women walked in the lanes and made love. There was only one flaw. Being Sundays, the pubs had to go on Sunday closing hours, which allows no man to buy a pint of beer unless he is a legal traveler who has come so many miles. But this did good in a way, because many men walked the legal number of miles, and that way they saw parts of their own country they never would have seen otherwise, and they saw what other towns and villages looked like.

And all the time that went on, the Prime Minister sat in his garden and read detective novels, or snoozed in the sun with a couple of his favorite spaniels at his feet, until there came a wireless message.

"Sign here," said the boy.

So the Prime Minister signed, and then he got a code book and decoded the message. Immediately he had done so, he called his secretary and said:

"Carrington-Smaithe! What day is today?"

"Sunday, sir," the secretary said.

"Nonsense," said the Prime Minister. "I am tired of this blundering-through policy with its shilly-shallying. If this goes on, we shall have a Constitution Crisis!"

"A Constitutional Crisis, sir?"

"Yes, Carrington-Smaithe. So you'd better pack and we'll get back to the City. We must act immediately. I shall issue a statement that His Majesty's Government hereby declares officially that today is Friday, and tomorrow shall be officially Saturday, and the days of the week must now go on officially in their regular and accustomed order."

"But isn't this really Sunday, sir? Hasn't a miraculous thing happened that has stopped the days of the week from arriving?"

"I don't know, my boy. But I do know this. Even if it is Sunday, and we all, everywhere, decide to call it Monday or Tuesday, then it becomes Monday or Tuesday because we all believe it is Monday or Tuesday."

"Yes, I see, sir."

And so the secretary packed, and the Prime Minister went back to London where he now could answer his ultimatums quite forcefully, and all the newspapers of the land carried the news that today was Friday and tomorrow would be Saturday—officially.

It wasn't until the next morning that this news reached Allerby Brig where it had all started. Mr. Bloggs got the news first, of course, and so he ordered the siren blown at the mill. So everybody hurried off to the mill because if you weren't there fifteen minutes after the siren went you were locked out and lost half a day's pay.

But as they trooped into the yard, old Capper stopped them.

"Hold on, a minute, mates," he said. "Just what day is it?"

"Now come on in to work," Mr. Bloggs called. "It's Saturday."

"Nay," Capper said. "Yesterday were Sunday, so today maun be Monday, onless us's started slipping and now we're off to hev t'days backwards."

This remark of Capper's got everyone mixed up again and some said it was Saturday and some Monday while some still stuck to Sunday.

The upshot was that they decided to call Sam Small again to get his opinion. Sam arrived in about a half hour, and heard all sides. Then he looked around, and spoke in the voice of one who is used to handling such matters.

"There's nobbut one thing to dew, lads," he said. "And Ah'm the chap that's off to dew it."

With that he walked into the office, and picking up the telephone, he said:

"Connect me with His Majesty, the King."

Before you could wink the connection was made.

"Is this His Majesty, the King?" Sam asked.

"Why Sammywell Small, lad!" said the King, recognizing the voice. "If it doan't dew ma heart and sowl good to hear thy voice again. How's'ta been, Sam lad?"

"Reight nicely, Your Majesty," Sam said.

"And how's that reight bonnie wife o' thine, Dally?" asked the King, who, as you will have noticed, spoke the dialects fluently. It is things like that, that make a good king. Little things like passing laws can be left to lads who have nothing but brains.

"Dally's reight well," Sam said. "And how's thy missus and bairns, if tha doan't mind the question."

"Nay, Sam lad, Ah'm that glad tha axed ma," the king said. "My littlest 'un was a bit poorly last week. It's teethin' tha knaws. But she's feeling champion now."

"Well, Ah'm glad to hear that," Sam answered.

"Thanks," the king said. "Well, Sam, Ah doan't suppose tha called me oop just for idle barneying. Whet c'n Ah dew for thee, lad?"

"Well, it's this way, Your Majesty," Sam said. "Ah hoap tha'll net think ma gormless for axing, but could'ta tell me just whet day o' t'week it is for thee."

"Eigh Sam," the King said, "Ah doan't monkey wi' things like that. Ah leave all that to ma ministers and such. But Ah've just gate official information from 'em that today's Sat'day."

"Your Majesty," said Sam, "if Sat'day's good enow for thee, then there's noa moar argyment. Thank you varry much."

"Net at all, Sam," the king said. "And by the way, Sam Small, it is our royal wish that tha doesn't wait soa long afore tha calls ma oop again. There's been sivveral things lately Ah would ha liked thy opinion on. When's'ta off to coom to Lunnon?"

"Nay, Your Majesty, Ah give oop traveling," Sam replied.

"Too bad, Sam. Too bad. Well, give me a ring soom time soon, will'ta?"

"That Ah will, lad."

"Well, so long," said the King.

"So long, Your Majesty," said Sam.

All during this conversation, of course, the people of the village had been crowding breathlessly round the door of the office, listening to Sam. And right in the forefront was Mr. Bloggs.

"Well, what did he say?" Mr. Bloggs breathed as Sam hung up.

"He said," said Sam, "that today was Sat'day."

"There, didn't I tell you," Mr. Bloggs shouted. "Now, doesn't that make it Saturday?"

Everyone thought it did, but they weren't quite sure. They thought the matter over quite a while, and then John Willie Braithwaite said:

"T'only trouble is, it doan't *feel* like Sat'day to me."

"But I tell you it is officially Saturday," Mr. Bloggs cried.

"Wait a minute, lads," Sam Small put in. "Now Ah doan't wark here, soa Ah play no favorites. But Ah c'n tell ye for sure how ye'll all knaw it's a Sat'day?"

"How can we tell?" they asked.

"Why, it's that simple," Sam replied. "Ye'all knaw that ivvery Sat'day morning at a quarter to twelve, ye get paid a week's wages. Now if soa be this is Sat'day, Mr. Bloggs will begin paying each man a week's money exactly ten minutes from now. And, on t'other hand, then if he doan't start paying a week's brass i' ten minutes—it can't be Sat'day—and the chances are it's off to keep on being Sunday for a long time."

"Outrageous," Mr. Bloggs cried.

He argued and shouted, but they just stood and shook their heads and said that if it were a Saturday they'd draw a week's pay at exactly a quarter to twelve, as they always did on Saturday. And finally Mr. Bloggs, seeing no other way of getting the days of the week started properly again, gave in and paid off each man and woman and girl and boy.

By the time they were paid it was Saturday noon, and so they all trooped as usual down the stairs of the mill and into the yard to go home. And there old Capper stopped them.

"But if it's a Saturday today, lads and lasses, what day is it tomorrow?"

"It'll be Sunday," they all roared.

"Now ain't that champion," old Capper beamed. "If it's Sunday we'll all be able to lie abed late and get a bit o' extra sleep for a change."

THE GIRL FROM THE RIVER BARGE

By WALTER SCHOENSTEDT

WE LIE AMONG THE TALL REEDS UNDERNEATH THE WILLOW. OUR bare feet are hanging over the mossy river bank into the quiet green water of the Deime. From the dark outline of the barge in the middle of the river come the sharp fumes of coal tar. I become aware of the sweat of the horses which has sunk into my clothing. The cuffs of my shirtsleeves are brown at the edge from the moisture of the manger. Maria, the girl from the barge, has pressed her knee tightly against mine. Her eyes are half-closed to avoid the slanting rays of the sun. But she is happy, not pensive. I can feel the warmth of her breath, warmer than the sultry air. Her dark hair has fallen over her face, but there is no evening breeze yet to blow it softly back and forth. Soon it will come, and then her hair will sway gently, like a clump of dry hay. The corner of her oval mouth looks sun-dried; a little piece of skin clings to her lower lip.

"What are you thinking about?" she asks suddenly, without moving.

"Nothing. I was just looking at you. Come, let's go in."

"I'm too tired now. And you can't get really cool in the water. Tell me something about the city, about what the women do there and what you do . . ."

"I've told you so much already. It's dull. The city's always dull, anyway, much more dull than it is here. The city's no place for you. You'd begin to look pale and your mouth would be greasy red."

Maria laughs. Her hands brush against my chin. They are small hands, but hard, and they smell of fresh perch and of the black barge.

As I climb down into the water, I see that Maria is completely naked under the blue linen dress. I dive and when I open my eyes under the water I can see a broad streak of sunlight across shifting, watery circles. The pressure on my eardrums keeps getting stronger.

The water pushes me upward, but I still have the strength to bring my feet to the surface first. My head stays under. Now I can no longer stand the pressure in my ears. Then my head is in the sunlight. Maria's laughter seems to come to me from a distance, because my ears are still ringing.

I draw myself slowly over the mossy ridge onto the meadow. . . .

I know that Maria is lonely and that she has many desires, desires such as only young people have. She does not yet know the pain of living, but she will soon learn it, although she is very pretty. I know this and I am sad because of it. Right now, I feel the way I felt when Paul died of consumption. His father had had no money to send him into the mountains, into the sunlight. His mother sobbed for a long time over the little body. . . .

The drops of water from my body fall upon her face. They look like tears, but not tears of sorrow, for she is smiling. I want to control myself. If I can't, if the way she is sitting in front of me now makes me want her too much, then I'll chase her away roughly. Go back to your barge, I'll say. She won't understand that. Her head will sink down, a little wrinkle will run across her forehead from the top of her nose, and her lips will become tightly compressed. Then she will go, without looking around, and then I'll want terribly to see her cry, so that I may have a memory to cling to.

"I must get the horses," I say to her, when I have finished dressing. "After supper I'll come up to the boat for a while and smoke a pipe with your father."

"No, I'm coming along," she says, and she stands up. Then we walk through the tall grass toward the wood, near which the corral stands in a little hollow. The horses are already standing at the rickety gate. The black gelding has laid his head across the neck of the brown mare; out of his mouth thick green threads of spittle are dribbling into her golden-brown mane. The horses look at us with warm, friendly eyes. Their nostrils tremble eagerly. Only the yellow stallion seems to be in bad temper; he picks at a wild caraway shrub that gives him no pleasure. A songless lark soars into the approaching dusk. At the corral it is darker because of the nearness of the wood; already the mist hovers in the straight forest lanes.

I untie the rope on the gate. The horses press close. I ask Maria:
"Which one do you want to ride?"

"The yellow stallion," she answers swiftly.

"Count him out! If he throws you, it's your own fault."

As Maria approaches, the yellow stallion stands still and raises
his head. The peasant I work for has told me that stallions can
tell the difference between a man and a woman. I hate the yellow
stallion. Maria puts her hands on his back; I take hold of her hardy,
strong hips. She is light; I am glad when the horse begins to prance.
Her hands seize his mane. For myself, I get the long-limbed black
gelding that always drives the stallion away. Then we begin to
ride slowly.

Under our mouths lie the manes of the horses, and the mossy
soil of the meadow slaps against their bellies. The path is straight
and covered with logs, so that the wagons will not bog down.
The Deime gleams, almost silver, to the left of us. In front, poplars
rise into the purpling horizon. On the path, too, there is no wind,
but it is fragrant with fresh-cut hay. The backs of the horses pitch.
Maria sways with every movement of the stallion, as if she were
rocking herself. She hums a melody. Her thighs rub against the
rough hide. Then the horses try to step out. We hold them back
and keep to a trot. On this path it is easy to fall. "Come on, come
on! my little yellow stallion, giddap, giddap!" Maria croons. We
climb past the gravel pit up to the well behind the rambling old barn.
Slowly we slip from the warm backs of the horses. I draw the
pail high up on the pole. It is somewhat cooler at the well. The
horses need a good deal of water today. The wooden sides of the
well are foul and wet. Far down, at the surface of the water, there
is a greenish gleam, although it is very dark. The pail rattles on the
pole again and the weighted handle draws it swiftly upward. As
I raise my head for a minute I see Maria standing on the other side
of the trough. She blinks at me, very tiredly, I think. Then she
lowers her head and her hair falls down in thick bunches. Behind
Maria, almost at the horizon, I see the outline of the black barge,
which is leaving tomorrow. Angrily I raise the last pail of water.
Hunchbacked Daniel is running around the farm, shrieking like mad
at the hens. Whenever he does that he makes a racket and goes:
cluck-cluck-kim-cmere. The old chicken-maid comes out with the
kitchen pail. First she looks at me, then at Maria. Then she leers

nastily. Sunday, in church, she'll again slobber all over herself. On the way home, she'll sneak the bottle of schnaps out from under her wide coat and gulp it down. In three days she'll bake the usual four enormous breads and with her filthy fingers write on the kneaded loaves: W-C-A-G (With Charity And Grace), one letter on each bread. The bread with the C is my bread. She stands in the twilight for a time. Her face is yellow. I can see the ugly stumps of teeth in her mouth. She says nothing, merely leers, nods her head a bit and then walks quickly back to the yard. Now the horses have drunk enough; they raise their heads. The stallion trots into the stable first, followed by the brown mare and then by the other horses.

I toss hay down from the loft, for their peaceful evening meal. As she shoves the hay into the rack with a little pitchfork, Maria talks to the stallion. Tomorrow I'll harness the beast as lead-horse to the triple-shared plow! Maria's voice sinks into the warmth of the stable. I descend the ladder slowly and stand close to her.

"Why don't you go and eat supper?" I ask roughly. "You have to get up early in the morning and travel on in your barge." I nearly said "stinking barge" but if I said that she'd be sure to think I meant everything connected with her.

"I'm going," she says very mildly. "You can eat with us, you know. You'll get the same thing anyway."

We go slowly down to the Deime, walking far apart. A star has risen over the water. The river moves softly, and we are silent. But now there comes a gentle wind. The tall grass is wet against our legs. Maria keeps looking straight ahead. I am afraid to take her hand. It will be moist again, and the tiny seeds of the meadow cress will be sticking between her fingers. Around us is the heavy East-Prussian night, calm and peaceful. The wind bends the grass, uncovers the silver shimmering stalks. Now the wind rustles through Maria's hair which is still dark. We are silent. Maria is warm and vital, like the stallion. Tomorrow Maria will go away; she will sit near the big steering-pole and she will not turn around to look back. Then we shall never see each other again. . . .

Go, Maria. You will not come back. On the Gilde or on the Pregel you'll find a coarse lover, a peasant from the peat-bog districts or a sailor from the Baltic Sea. The first thing your children will learn will be the odor of the water and of smelt. But then your skin will become dry and your mouth will lose its curve and its color. Then I should like to see you and read in your eyes how you have learned the pain of living that has now become for you the whole landscape, that always, now, pours down into your life from above. Then I should like to ask you about it—about love and what it meant to you. Perhaps then your eyes will hold more than beauty, perhaps they will be stern and wise and you will answer: poverty has played so great a part in my life that it has choked love. Now I neither cry nor laugh. I have never been able to struggle for love because the struggle for bread has consumed all my strength. . . .

But now we are young, the meadow is covered with silver, about us is the night, and tomorrow you depart. On the barge it is darker; the star has disappeared. Maria goes in front of me over the narrow gangplank. Suddenly, the voice of the old man speaks from the darkness:

"Well, it's about time you came, Maria!"

I can hear the old fellow spitting into the water. All about him is the reek of tobacco. Wordlessly, he shakes hands with me. We climb down the steps into the cabin. Maria's mother sits numbly at the table and stares at us vacantly. The battered kerosene lamp smokes thickly. Potatoes lie on the table, covered by a linen cloth to keep them warm. On the wall there is a picture of a white angel with fat cheeks. It is in a black frame decorated with myrtle leaves. Diagonally beneath it, a long cherry-wood pipe bobs back and forth. Maria sits down, takes a potato, and begins to peel it. Her eyes are warm and brown. The old woman puts a clay pot, with linseed oil, on the table. She digs her fingernail into a potato, peels it, and dips it into the oil. The old man does not peel his potatoes. He stuffs the whole potato into his mouth and chews. The oil leaves little drops of fat on the lips. Maria's mouth becomes fuller. Her breasts press against her dress, large as apples.

Outside, the water gurgles. A clock ticks. The air in the cabin is sultry. Set into the wall is Maria's bed. Her father has painted it with roses, bright-red roses. The bedcovers are blue-checked, like those the peasants use. . . . Empty eyes, warm potatoes and beads of grease on the lips. . . . The fingers of the two old people are crooked. Maria's fingers are smooth. Potato peels stick to them and become curled up. In the clay pot, in the oil, a piece of potato floats.

The old man fills his pipe and hands me the tobacco-pouch which is made of a dried pig's bladder. And then we smoke. The women begin to clear the table, I go on deck with the old man. A little formally, we sit down. I feel the wind again. The meadow and the water merge into each other.

"Well, we're leaving tomorrow," the old man begins. "Thank you for the milk. We don't often get it. Or the peasants want too much money. It's pretty tough on the barge. . . ."

His words drip softly into the darkness. His voice is like our surroundings. I should like to ask him why he doesn't sail up this way all the time, but then Maria comes and sits beside us. Sparks fall and hiss past us as they die. Maria see-saws back and forth. It makes her seem nervous, but her eyes are closed and peaceful. The old man does not go. . . .

"Well then, thank you very much," he repeats. "We probably won't see each other again, I guess. . . ."

Suddenly I feel Maria's brown eyes, which have become large and moist and which keep looking at me as she has never yet looked at me.

She raises her head and gets up. The wind presses the thin dress against her body. Very quietly, I say to the old man:

"No, I don't think so either. We won't see each other again."

But now he still does not leave and I know that he will not go. Maria says sluggishly: "Pat the yellow stallion for me, and don't work him to death. And mother says to thank you for the milk, too. She has already gone to bed. By the time you are out in the fields with the horses, tomorrow, we'll already be in Labiau."

Her father gets up and shakes hands with me heartily. But he remains standing and looks out past me. Maria lowers her head again. I stroke her arm. Dew falls, or a tear. The old man slowly turns around and draws Maria along behind him. Maria is fragrant with hay. She turns around once more. The wind becomes stronger.

I go over the gangplank. I can hear the old woman grumbling because she has been awakened. But Maria seems to undress without saying anything.

The meadow is damp. The wind is among the blades of grass. New stars have risen. At the well, I look back, but the barge has faded into the darkness. Then I go into the stable.

THE WHOLE WORLD IS OUTSIDE

By Manuel Komroff

"COME CHILDREN, I THINK THE TIME HAS ARRIVED. REACH ME THE woolen shawl and I will try to sit up. Come here beside me. Your mother wants to hold you close and she has a lot of things to tell you. . . . And you must listen carefully to what she says."

The children brought the woolen shawl to the edge of the bed and the dying woman wrapped it about her shoulders. Peter who was ten years old was the first to get up on the bed and nestle beside his mother. He was two years older than his sister Ellen but in many ways he was still an infant. His mother stroked his head and he rested it upon her shoulder and close to her face. Ellen hesitated a moment and then came to the other side of her mother and curled up among the blankets.

"Now you know what we spoke about yesterday?"

The children nodded.

"And Peter will take the dollar and you will go and visit your Auntie Pauline and play with Jerry. Won't that be nice?"

The children nodded for they knew that Jerry, the high-strung wire terrier, was always ready to play and he could catch a rubber ball in his mouth. For some reason or other they had seen much less of Jerry than they would have liked. It was a rare occasion when their mother visited her sister.

"Yes, you will be able to play with Jerry as long as you like and you will sleep there and Jerry will sleep with you so you will not be afraid, will you?"

"No," they said together.

"Your mother will not be with you and so you will have to be big children. And at night if you want a glass of water or something you will not disturb your auntie when she is sleeping. Just light the light and then you will see how to get it for yourself just like grownups do. You know. And your Auntie Pauline will love you and you must remember to be sure to love her also. And she will be very good to you I know, and you must also be good and do what she tells you. She will send you to school. You want to go to school and play with other children, don't you?"

"Yes, Mummie," said Peter, while Ellen nodded her flaxen braided head.

"You remember, children, where your Auntie Pauline lives?"

"Fairwoods," they replied.

"And you know how to go there?"

They nodded.

"Go, Peter and take the dollar and bring me the box from the top bureau drawer."

Peter left his mother's side and got the dollar bill from its hiding place and brought the box she asked for.

"You will be sure not to lose the dollar. Let me see where you put it? That's good. And Ellen you see where he put it so he knows what pocket it is in."

She opened the small box that he brought to the bed.

"Here, now this is very important. See what it says on this card. I will read it for you. Mrs. Pauline Monroe, 227 Hillside Avenue, Fairwoods, New York. Now don't lose it. That is where you are going and you show this to a man in Grand Central Station and give him the dollar and he will put you on the train. And when you get off at Fairwoods you show it to the man at the station and he will bring you to the house. Now Peter put the card in your pocket. And Ellen dear, here is a letter for you to give your Auntie when you get there. You see the same name and address is on it. You can keep it in your coat pocket. . . . You must be careful when you go to the station and not cross the street until the light changes. And Peter, you will hold Ellen's hand."

"Yes, Mummie."

"Now I have something very nice for both of you. Here, Peter, is your daddy's watch and chain. You will take care of it. I will wind it up and set it for you and tomorrow you can wind it yourself. It is now two o'clock."

She wound the silver watch and placing it in his pocket attached the end of the chain to a buttonhole in his vest.

"There now. And do you remember what your father's name was?"

"George," they both said at once.

"Yes. You will always remember his name was George. And here, Ellen, is your grandma's locket but before I put it on I want to place this ring on the chain. Some day the ring may fit you."

She drew the ring from her finger and placing it on the chain, clasped it about Ellen's neck.

"There, it looks very pretty. Now that is all your Mummie has to give you. She would like to give you a lot more but the best thing she can give you now is to let you go back to school. She has kept you home too long and you have taken good care of her. If only attention and devotion were a medicine it would have cured her. And now you will go back to school and your Auntie Pauline and Uncle Fred will look after you much better than anyone. And your Mummie will go away on a long long journey."

"Far?" asked Ellen.

"Yes, very far."

"And will you visit us?"

"I will try. Somehow or other I will try. But you will be good children anyway and when you grow up you will understand everything. And Peter, you must promise me that you will look after your sister and always take good care of her and she will love you as I have loved you and that love will make you a strong and big man. If you stay together there is no strength in the world that could defeat you. And so you must promise me that you will never quarrel no matter what the cause may be. You promise, don't you?"

"Yes, Mummie."

"And you, Ellen dear. Soon you will be a little lady and you will try and see that your brother does not catch cold or do foolish things."

She nodded her head.

"Now there is nothing more to say because it would be too much for you to remember. Only one thing. Try and be brave. Don't be afraid. And if you are not afraid then you will be brave. It is sometimes very hard to be brave. . . . Now give your Mummie a good hug and a nice kiss and go put on your hats and coats."

She embraced her children and kissed them passionately. Her strength was gone and she dropped her head back into the pillow.

She watched them put on their coats and hats and when they were ready to go she said in a feeble voice: "Try and be brave. Your Mummie tries very hard to be brave and she wants you to try also."

"Yes, Mummie," they said together.

"Now go and leave the door a tiny bit open; just a crack. And Peter, take your sister's hand when you are outside. The whole world is outside and may God love you and watch over you."

The fingers of one hand were close to her mouth but the other hand she reached out from under the quilt and waved very slowly.

The children stood at the door and also waved to their mother. They saw her smile and they smiled back, not a full broad smile, only a little stifled smile. Slowly they backed out and Peter closed the door leaving just a crack.

As they walked down the stairs Ellen suddenly stopped, waved her arm and called: "Good-bye, Mummie."

"She can't see you from here," said Peter. "Come."

As soon as the door had closed the woman in bed could restrain herself no longer. Cast iron would have melted long before this. She put her fingers in her mouth and sobbed, and a tiny rivulet in zig-zag path streamed down her face and into the pillow. And now the last hold was torn away and it seemed easy to stretch her limbs and close her eyes.

It was a dozen blocks to Grand Central Station and these the children walked hand in hand. They were now walking in the great world that is outside. Now and then they paused to look into the shop windows where toys or novelties were displayed and when they had paused long enough Peter said: "Come."

Once they stopped before a movie house and looked at the big colored poster showing a man embracing a woman. This was a kind of love; but they hated this love and thought it quite unnecessary. It was not like the love their mother had for them. They did not tarry long.

At the station Peter paused beside a newsstand and bought a strawberry lollypop with five pennies that he happened to have in his pocket. He gave it to Ellen as though she were a child and he the parent.

They walked to the information desk and displayed the card.

"So you want to go to Fairwoods?"

"Yes," he showed the dollar.

"Who is this person in Fairwoods?"

"Our Auntie Pauline."

The clerk called a colored porter who brought them to a ticket window and bought them two one-half tickets to Fairwoods. There was a little change from the dollar which Peter put in his pocket.

"This way," said the porter.

As they crossed the big hall Peter drew out the silver watch and compared it with the station clock. Ellen looked at him to see if he was doing this worldly business properly. And while she looked at him she sucked on the strawberry lollypop.

While walking down the platform the porter spoke to the children.

"Where your mother is?"

"She has gone away."

"On a trip?"

"Yes."

"Where did she go?"

"She went where people go when they go to die."

"Lordie, Lordie. Is that so!"

"Yes, sir. She did not want to tell us but we know."

And Ellen nodded her head to say that this was true.

Jerry nearly jumped out of his skin when he discovered the children walking up the drive hand-in-hand. He knew now that he would have someone to play with. He ran out on the lawn and found his rubber ball and brought it close to the house.

"Why, it's the children, you darlings!" cried Mrs. Monroe and she gave them each a hug and a kiss.

"Your mother sent you, I suppose, for she knows how fond we are of you."

The children were silent.

"She is well?"

Peter nodded as though everything were all right.

She rang the bell and asked the maid to bring some slices of cake and fruit, for while she had no children of her own she knew that children were often hungry at odd hours.

The children were anxious to play with Jerry and therefore they hurried through with the cake and fruit. Then followed a full hour of joyous running up and down on the lawn and tossing the ball in the air for Jerry to catch, and throwing it far off to have Jerry chase it madly and bring it back.

Suddenly Peter remembered the letter and reminded Ellen. She went to the hall closet and drew it from her coat pocket and gave it to her Auntie Pauline.

"What is this?"

"A letter from Mummie," she said simply.

She opened the envelope and read: "Pauline, here are the children. I cannot take them with me and they are too old to leave on a doorstep. I returned your last few letters unopened because there really was no use. You cannot approve of anything and I am sick and tired of listening to your smug remarks.

"Yes, Pauline, I married a drunkard. But while he lived we were happy, very happy. This is something you have never known and I doubt if you are capable of knowing it. Your husband has given you diamonds and furs and mine has left me but poverty and a widow's veil. But I had the children and we have managed as best we could. For God's sake Pauline, the kids are innocent. Do not hold against them what you would hold against me. Try not to criticize death. If you love them they will bring you much happiness. More I could not leave anyone. Your sister, Laura."

Ellen was standing beside her aunt and watched as she read the letter.

"Do you know what is in this letter?"

She nodded her braided flaxen head. Yes, she knew.

It was then as she nodded her head that her aunt noticed that the child was wearing the old chain and locket that once her own mother wore. She kissed the child and went quickly to the telephone to call her husband.

"Fred, Fred. I'm glad I got you before you left the city. The children are here. Yes. . . . About an hour ago."

"I am glad you made it up with your sister at last. I've missed those kids," he called from the other end.

"No, I haven't made it up. Listen to me. The children are here. They are here for good. Just a minute and you will understand. Please take a taxi right away and go over. No, there is no telephone. And call me back. Do anything necessary. Good-bye."

Fred Monroe arrived at the apartment, but the visitor Death had crept in before him. The door was still open just a tiny crack.

There were a lot of things to be done and it was fairly late that evening when Uncle Fred got back to Fairwoods.

"Yes," he said, "I did everything necessary. Are the children asleep?"

"I put them to bed an hour ago."

"Uncle Fred," came a small voice from an upstairs bedroom.

"Yes, darling. Coming."

The children were not asleep at all. And their uncle was very happy to see them. They climbed all over him and hugged him and laughed and told him about a new trick that they taught Jerry.

After a time Ellen still quite cheerful asked: "Did you see Mummie?"

Their uncle did not want to reply.

"She told us to be brave," Peter said. "And so we know all about it."

"What do you know?"

"We know she went away, far away. She was going to visit God. Did she go?"

"Yes. She went."

That seemed all that needed to be said. The children soon went back to bed, closed their eyes and slept. They slept soundly and dreamed of very nice things, the kind of things that hang on Christmas trees and things that come out at Easter time, like rabbits and chocolate eggs and that sugar crystal egg that has a whole village scene inside with a shepherd and a little "bitzie" lamb.

The sun rose up to call out the morning of a new day. Jerry, that four-legged piece of nervous energy covered with a coat of wire hair, was already standing in the kitchen waiting for his biscuit soaked in fresh milk. He shook himself to get the sleep out of the marrow of his bones and lapped up the food with great noise. The drops of milk were still dripping from his blunt muzzle as he stood waiting for the children to get up and play.

Soon they were all in the yard with the rubber ball. They never seemed to tire of this game. Ellen paused for a moment and asked her brother: "Mummie isn't coming back?"

He shook his head.

"Not at all?" she asked.

"No. She won't come back."

"What does it mean when they say the whole world is outside?"

"I don't know."

He handed her the ball and they went on playing.

AUGUST AFTERNOON

By Erskine Caldwell

VIC GLOVER AWOKE WITH THE NOON-DAY HEAT RINGING IN HIS ears. He had been asleep for only half an hour, and he was getting ready to turn over and go back to sleep when he opened his eyes for a moment and saw Hubert's black head over the top of his bare toes. He stretched his eyelids and held them open as long as he could.

Hubert was standing in the yard, at the edge of the porch, with a pine cone in his hand.

Vic cursed him.

The colored man raked the cone over the tops of Vic's toes and stepped back out of reach.

"What do you mean by standing there tickling me with that dad-burned cone?" Vic shouted at Hubert. "Is that all you can find to do? Why don't you get out in that field and do something to those boll-weevils? They're going to eat up every pound of cotton on the place if you don't stop them."

"I surely hated to wake you up, Mr. Vic," Hubert said, "but there's a white man out here looking for something. He won't say what he wants, but he's hanging around for something."

Vic was wide awake by that time. He sat up on the quilt and pulled on his shoes without looking into the yard. The white sand in the yard beat the glare of the sun directly into his eyes and he could see nothing beyond the edge of the porch. Hubert threw the pine cone under the porch and stepped aside.

"He must be looking for trouble," Vic said. "When they come around and don't say anything, and just sit, it's trouble they're looking for."

"There he is, Mr. Vic," Hubert said, nodding his head across the yard. "There he sits up against that water oak."

Vic looked around for Willie. Willie was sitting on the top step at the other end of the porch, directly in front of the stranger. She did not look at Vic.

445

"You ought to have better sense than to wake me up while I'm taking a nap. This is no time of day to be up. I've got to get a little sleep every now and then."

"Boss," Hubert said, "I wouldn't wake you up at all, not at any time, but Miss Willie just sits there high up on the steps and that white man has been out there whittling on a little stick a pretty long time without saying anything. I've got scared about something happening when he whittles that little stick clear through, and it's just about whittled down to nothing now."

Vic glanced again at Willie, and from her he turned to stare at the stranger sitting under the water oak tree in his front yard.

The piece of wood had been shaved down to paper thinness.

"Boss," Hubert said, "we ain't aiming to have no trouble today, are we?"

"Which way did he come from?" Vic asked.

"I never did see him come, Mr. Vic. I just looked up, and there he was, sitting against that water oak whittling on a little stick. I reckon I must have been sleeping when he came, because when I looked up, there he was."

Vic slid down over the quilt until his legs were hanging over the edge of the porch. Perspiration began to trickle down his neck as soon as he sat up.

"Ask him what he's after, Hubert."

"We ain't aiming to have no trouble today, are we, Mr. Vic?"

"Ask him what he wants, I said."

Hubert went almost half way to the water oak tree and stopped.

"Mr. Vic says what can he do for you, white-folks."

The man said nothing. He did not even glance up.

Hubert came back to the porch, the whites of his eyes becoming larger with each step.

"What did he say?" Vic asked him.

"He ain't said nothing yet, Mr. Vic. He acts like he don't hear me at all. You'd better go talk to him, Mr. Vic. He won't give me no attention. Appears to me like he's just sitting there looking at Miss Willie on the high step. Maybe if you was to tell her to go in the house and shut the door, he might be persuaded to give some notice to what we say to him."

"Can't see any sense in sending her in the house," Vic said. "I can make him talk. Hand me that stilyerd."

"Mr. Vic, I'm trying to tell you about Miss Willie. Miss Willie's been sitting there on that high step and he's been looking up at her a right long time, Mr. Vic. If you won't object to me saying so, Mr. Vic, I reckon I'd tell Miss Willie to go sit somewhere else, if I was you. Miss Willie ain't got much on today, Mr. Vic. That's what I've been trying to tell you."

"Hand me that stilyerd, I said."

Hubert went to the end of the porch and brought the cotton steelyard to Vic. He stepped back out of the way.

"Boss," Hubert said, "we ain't aiming to have no trouble today, are we?"

Vic was getting ready to jump down into the yard when the man under the water oak reached into his pocket and pulled out another knife. It was about nine inches long, and both sides of the handle were covered with hairy cowhide. There was a spring-button on one end. The man pushed the button with his thumb, and the blade sprang open. He began playing with both knives, throwing them up in the air and catching them on the back of his hands.

Hubert moved to the other side of Vic.

"Mr. Vic," he said, "I ain't intending to mix in your business none, but it looks to me like you got yourself in for a mess of trouble when you went off and brought Miss Willie back here. It looks to me like she's got up for a city girl, more so than a country girl."

Vic cursed him.

"I'm telling you, Mr. Vic, a country girl wouldn't sit on a high step in front of a man, not when she wasn't wearing nothing but that blue wrapper, anyhow."

"Shut up," Vic said, laying the steelyard down on the quilt beside him.

The man under the water oak closed the blade of the small knife and put it into his pocket. The big cowhide-covered knife he flipped into the air and caught easily on the back of his hand.

"What's your name?" he asked Willie.

"Willie."

He flipped the knife again.

"What's yours?" she asked him.

"Floyd."

"Where are you from?"

"Carolina."

He flipped it higher, catching it underhanded.

"What are you doing in Georgia?"

"Don't know," he said. "Just looking around."

Willie giggled, smiling at him.

Floyd got up and walked across the yard to the steps and sat down on the bottom one. He put his arm around his knees and looked up at Willie.

"You're not so bad-looking," he said. "I've seen lots worse looking."

"You're not so bad yourself," Willie giggled, resting her arms on her knees and looking down at him.

"How about a kiss?"

"What would it be to you?"

"Not bad. I reckon I've had lots worse."

"Well, you can't get it sitting down there."

Floyd climbed the steps on his hands and feet and sat down on the next to the top step. He leaned against Willie, putting one arm around her waist and the other over her knees. Willie slid down to the step beside him.

"Boss," Hubert said, his lips twitching, "we ain't going to have no trouble today, are we?"

Vic cursed him.

Willie and Floyd moved down a step without loosening their embrace.

"Who is that yellow-headed sap-sucker, anyhow?" Vic said. "I'll be dad-burned if he ain't got a lot of nerve—coming here and fooling with Willie."

"You wouldn't do nothing to cause trouble, would you, Mr. Vic? I surely don't want to have no trouble today, Mr. Vic."

Vic glanced at the nine-inch knife Floyd had, stuck into the step at his feet. It stood on its tip eighteen inches high, while the sun was reflected against the bright blade and made a streak of light on Floyd's pant leg.

"Go over there and take that knife away from him and bring it here," Vic said. "Don't be scared of him."

"Mr. Vic, I surely hate to disappoint you, but if you want that white-folk's knife, you'll just have to get it your own self.

I don't aim to have myself all carved up with that thing. Mr. Vic, I surely can't accommodate you this time. If you want that white-folk's knife, you'll just be bound to get it yourself, Mr. Vic."

Vic cursed him.

Hubert backed away until he was at the end of the porch. He kept on looking behind him all the time, looking to be certain of the exact location of the sycamore stump that was between him and the pine grove on the other side of the cotton field.

Vic called to Hubert and told him to come back. Hubert came slowly around the corner of the porch and stood a few feet from the quilt where Vic was sitting. His lips quivered and the whites of his eyes grew larger. Vic motioned for him to come closer, but he would not come an inch farther.

"How old are you?" Floyd asked Willie.

"Fifteen."

Floyd jerked the knife out of the wood and thrust it deeper in the same place.

"How old are you?" she asked him.

"About twenty-seven."

"Are you married?"

"Not now," he said. "How long have you been?"

"About three months," Willie said.

"How do you like it?"

"Pretty good so far."

"How about another kiss?"

"You've just had one."

"I'd like another one now."

"I ought not to let you kiss me again."

"Why not?" Floyd said.

"Men don't like girls who kiss too much."

"I'm not that kind."

"What kind are you?" Willie asked him.

"I'd like to kiss you a lot."

"But after I let you do that, you'd go away."

"No, I won't. I'll stay for something else."

"What?"

"Let's go inside for a drink and I'll tell you."

"We'll have to go to the spring for fresh water."

"Where's the spring?"

"Just across the field in the grove."

"All right," Floyd said, standing up. "Let's go."

He bent down and pulled the knife out of the wood. Willie ran down the steps and across the yard. When Floyd saw that she was not going to wait for him, he ran after her, holding the knives in his pocket with one hand. She led him across the cotton field to the spring in the pine grove. Just before they got there, Floyd caught her by the arm and ran beside her the rest of the way.

"Boss," Hubert said, "we ain't aiming to have no trouble today, are we?"

Vic cursed him.

"I don't want to get messed up with a heap of trouble and maybe get my belly slit open with that big hairy knife. If you ain't got objections, I reckon I'll mosey on home now and cut a little firewood for the cook-stove."

"Come back here!" Vic said. "You stay where you are and stop making moves to go off."

"What are we aiming to do, Mr. Vic?"

Vic eased himself off the porch and walked across the yard to the water oak. He looked down at the ground where Floyd had been sitting and then he looked at the porch steps where Willie had been. The noonday heat beat down through the thin leaves overhead and he could feel his mouth and throat burn with the hot air he breathed.

"Have you got a gun, Hubert?"

"No, sir, boss," Hubert said.

"Why haven't you?" he said. "Right when I need a gun, you haven't got it. Why don't you keep a gun?"

"Mr. Vic, I aint got no use for a gun. I used to keep one to shoot rabbits and squirrels with, but I got to thinking one day, and I traded it off the first chance I had. I reckon it was a good thing I traded, too. If I had kept it, you'd be asking for it like you did just now."

Vic went back to the porch and picked up the steelyard and hammered the porch with it. After he had hit the porch four or five times, he dropped it and started out in the direction of the spring. He walked as far as the edge of the shade and stopped. He stood listening for a while.

Willie and Floyd could be heard down near the spring. Floyd

said something to Willie, and Willie laughed loudly. There was silence for several minutes, and then Willie laughed again. Vic was getting ready to turn back to the porch when he heard her cry out. It sounded like a scream, but it was not exactly that; it sounded like a shriek, but it was not that either; it sounded more like someone laughing and crying simultaneously in a high-pitched voice.

"Where did Miss Willie come from, Mr. Vic?" Hubert asked. "Where did you bring her from?"

"Down below here a little way," he said.

Hubert listened to the sounds that were coming from the pine grove.

"Boss," he said after a while, "it appears to me like you didn't go far enough away."

"I went far enough," Vic said. "If I had gone any farther, I'd have been in Florida."

The colored man hunched his shoulders forward several times while he smoothed the white sand with his broad-soled shoes.

"Mr. Vic, if I was you, the next time I'd surely go that far."

"What do you mean, the next time?"

"I was figuring that maybe you wouldn't be keeping her much longer than now, Mr. Vic."

Vic cursed him.

Hubert raised his head several times and attempted to see down into the pine grove over the top of the growing cotton.

"Shut up and mind your own business," Vic said. "I'm going to keep her till the cows come home. Where else do you reckon I'd find a better-looking girl than Willie?"

"Boss, I wasn't thinking of how she looks—I was thinking how she acts."

"She acts that way now because she's not old enough to do different. She won't act that way much longer. She'll get over the way she's doing pretty soon."

Hubert followed Vic across the yard. While Vic went towards the porch, Hubert stopped and leaned against the water oak where he could almost see over the cotton field into the pine grove. Vic went up on the porch and stretched out on the quilt. He took off his shoes and flung them aside.

"I surely God knowed something was going to happen when

he whittled that stick down to nothing," Hubert was saying to himself. "White-folks take a long time to whittle a little piece of wood, but after they whittle it down to nothing, they're going to be up and doing."

Presently Vic sat upright on the quilt.

"Listen here, Hubert ——"

"Yes, sir, boss."

"You keep your eye on that stilyerd so it will stay right where it is now, and when they come back up the path from the spring, you wake me up in a hurry. Do you hear?"

"Yes, sir, boss," Hubert said. "Are you aiming to take a little nap now?"

"Yes, I am. And if you don't wake me up when they come back, I'll break your head for you when I do wake up."

Vic lay down again on the quilt and turned over on his side to shut out the blinding glare of the early afternoon sun that was reflected upon the porch from the hard white sand in the yard.

Hubert scratched his head and sat down against the water oak facing the path from the spring. He could hear Vic snoring on the porch above the sounds that came at intervals from the pine grove across the field. He sat staring down the path, singing under his breath. It was a long time until sundown.

THE EARS OF JOHNNY BEAR

By JOHN STEINBECK

THE VILLAGE OF LOMA IS BUILT, AS ITS NAME IMPLIES, ON A LOW, round hill that rises like an island out of the flat mouth of the Salinas Valley in central California. To the north and east of the town a black tule swamp stretches for miles, but to the south the marsh has been drained. Rich vegetable land has been the result of the draining, land so black with wealth that the lettuce and cauliflowers grow to giants.

The owners of the swamp to the north of the village grew covetous of the black land. They banded together and formed a reclamation district. I work for the company which took the contract to put a ditch through. The floating clam-shell digger arrived, was put together and started eating a ditch of open water through the swamp.

I tried living in the floating bunkhouse with the crew for a while, but the mosquitoes that hung in banks over the dredger and the heavy pestilential mist that sneaked out of the swamp every night and slid near to the ground drove me into the village of Loma, where I took a furnished room, the most dismal I have ever seen, in the house of Mrs. Ratz. I might have looked farther, but the idea of having my mail come in care of Mrs. Ratz decided me. After all I only slept in the bare, cold room. I ate my meals in the galley of the floating bunkhouse.

There aren't more than two hundred people in Loma. The Methodist church has the highest place on the hill; its spire is visible for miles. Two groceries, a hardware store, an ancient Masonic Hall and the Buffalo Bar comprise the public buildings. On the side of the hills are the small wooden houses of the population, and on the rich southern flats are the houses of the landowners, small yards usually enclosed by high walls of clipped cypress to keep out the driving afternoon winds.

There was nothing to do in Loma in the evening except to go

453

to the saloon, an old board building with swinging doors and a wooden sidewalk awning. Neither prohibition nor repeal had changed its business, its clientele nor the quality of its whiskey. In the course of an evening every male inhabitant of Loma over fifteen years old came at least once to the Buffalo Bar, had a drink, talked a while and went home.

Fat Carl, the owner and bartender, greeted every newcomer with a phlegmatic sullenness which nevertheless inspired familiarity and affection. His face was sour, his tone downright unfriendly, and yet—I don't know how he did it. I know I felt gratified and warm when Fat Carl knew me well enough to turn his sour pig face to me and say with some impatience, "Well, what's it going to be?" He always asked that although he served only whiskey, and only one kind of whiskey. I have seen him flatly refuse to squeeze some lemon juice into it for a stranger. Fat Carl didn't like fumadiddles. He wore a big towel tied about his middle and he polished the glasses on it as he moved about. The floor was bare wood sprinkled with sawdust, the bar an old store counter, the chairs were hard and straight; the only decorations were the posters and cards and pictures stuck to the wall by candidates for county elections, salesmen and auctioneers. Some of these were many years old. The card of Sheriff Rittal still begged for re-election although Rittal had been dead for seven years.

The Buffalo Bar sounds, even to me, like a terrible place, but when you walked down the night street, over the wooden sidewalks, when the long streamers of swamp fog, like waving, dirty bunting, flapped in your face, when finally you pushed open the swinging doors of Fat Carl's and saw men sitting around talking and drinking, and Fat Carl coming along toward you, it seemed pretty nice. You couldn't get away from it.

There would be a game of the mildest kind of poker going on. Timothy Ratz, the husband of my landlady, would be playing solitaire, cheating pretty badly because he only took a drink when he got it out. I've seen him get it out five times in a row. When he won he piled the cards neatly, stood up and walked with great dignity to the bar. Fat Carl, with a glass half filled before he arrived, asked, "What'll it be?"

"Whiskey," said Timothy gravely.

In the long room men from the farms and the town sat in the

straight hard chairs or stood against the old counter. A soft, monotonous rattle of conversation went on except at times of elections or big prizefights, when there might be orations or loud opinions.

I hated to go out into the damp night, and to hear far off in the swamp the chuttering of the Diesel engine on the dredger and the clang of the bucket, and then to go to my own dismal room at Mrs. Ratz'.

Soon after my arrival in Loma I scraped an acquaintance with Mae Romero, a pretty half-Mexican girl. Sometimes in the evenings I walked with her down the south side of the hill, until the nasty fog drove us back into town. After I escorted her home I dropped in at the bar for a while.

I was sitting in the bar one night talking to Alex Hartnell who owned a nice little farm. We were talking about black bass fishing, when the front doors opened and swung closed. A hush fell on the men in the room. Alex nudged me and said, "It's Johnny Bear." I looked around.

His name described him better than I can. He looked like a great, stupid, smiling bear. His black matted head bobbed forward and his long arms hung out as though he should have been on all fours and was only standing upright as a trick. His legs were short and bowed, ending with strange, square feet. He was dressed in dark blue denim, but his feet were bare; they didn't seem to be crippled or deformed in any way, but they were square, just as wide as they were long. He stood in the doorway, swinging his arms jerkily the way halfwits do. On his face there was a foolish happy smile. He moved forward and for all his bulk and clumsiness, he seemed to creep. He didn't move like a man, but like some prowling night animal. At the bar he stopped, his little bright eyes went about from face to face expectantly, and he asked, "Whiskey?"

Loma was not a treating town. A man might buy a drink for another if he were pretty sure the other would immediately buy one for him. I was surprised when one of the quiet men laid a coin on the counter. Fat Carl filled the glass. The monster took it and gulped the whiskey.

"What the devil—" I began. But Alex nudged me and said "Sh."

There began a curious pantomime. Johnny Bear moved to the

door and then he came creeping back. The foolish smile never left his face. In the middle of the room he crouched down on his stomach. A voice came from his throat, a voice that seemed familiar to me.

"But you are too beautiful to live in a dirty little town like this."

The voice rose to a soft throaty tone, with just a trace of accent in the words. "You just tell me that."

I'm sure I nearly fainted. The blood pounded in my ears. I flushed. It was my voice coming out of the throat of Johnny Bear, my words, my intonation. And then it was the voice of Mae Romero—exact. If I had not seen the crouching man on the floor I would have called to her. The dialogue went on. Such things sound silly when someone else says them. Johnny Bear went right on, or rather I should say I went right on. He said things and made sounds. Gradually the faces of the men turned from Johnny Bear, turned toward me, and they grinned at me. I could do nothing. I knew that if I tried to stop him I would have a fight on my hands. And so the scene went on, to a finish. When it was over I was cravenly glad Mae Romero had no brothers. What obvious, forced, ridiculous words had come from Johnny Bear. Finally he stood up, still smiling the foolish smile, and he asked again, "Whiskey?"

I think the men in the bar were sorry for me. They looked away from me and talked elaborately to one another. Johnny Bear went to the back of the room, crawled under a round card table, curled up like a dog and went to sleep.

Alex Hartnell was regarding me with compassion. "First time you ever heard him?"

"Yes, what in hell is he?"

Alex ignored my question for a moment. "If you're worrying about Mae's reputation, don't. Johnny Bear has followed Mae before."

"But how did he hear us? I didn't see or hear him."

"No one sees or hears Johnny Bear when he's on business. He can move like no movement at all. Know what our young men do when they go out with girls? They take a dog along. Dogs are afraid of Johnny and they can smell him coming."

"But good God! Those voices ——"

Alex nodded. "I know. Some of us wrote up to the university

about Johnny, and a young man came down. He took a look and then he told us about Blind Tom."

"You mean the Negro piano player? Yes, I've heard of him."

"Well, Blind Tom was a half-wit. He could hardly talk, but he could imitate anything he heard on the piano, long pieces. They tried him with fine musicians and he reproduced not only the music but every little personal emphasis. To catch him they made little mistakes, and he played the mistakes. He photographed the playing in the tiniest detail. The man says Johnny Bear is the same, only he can photograph words and voices. He tested Johnny with a long passage in Greek and Johnny did it exactly. He doesn't know the words he's saying, he just says them. He hasn't brains enough to make anything up, so you know that what he says is what he heard."

"But why does he do it? Why is he interested in listening if he doesn't understand?"

Alex rolled a cigarette and lighted it. "He isn't, but he loves whiskey. He knows if he listens in windows and comes here and repeats what he hears, someone will give him whiskey. He tries to palm off Mrs. Ratz' conversation in the store, or Jerry Noland arguing with his mother, but he can't get whiskey for such things."

I said, "It's funny somebody hasn't shot him while he was peeking in windows."

Alex picked at his cigarette. "Lots of people have tried, but you just don't see Johnny Bear, and you don't catch him. You keep your windows closed, and even then you talk in a whisper if you don't want to be repeated. You were lucky it was dark to-night. If he had seen you, he might have gone through the action too. You should see Johnny Bear screw up his face to look like a girl. It's pretty awful."

I looked toward the sprawled figure under the table. Johnny Bear's back was turned to the room. The light fell on his black matted hair. I saw a big fly land on his head, and then I swear I saw the whole scalp shiver the way the skin of a horse shivers under flies. The fly landed again and the moving scalp shook it off. I shuddered too, all over.

Conversation in the room had settled to the bored monotone again. Fat Carl had been polishing a glass on his apron towel for the last ten minutes. A little group of men near me was discussing fighting dogs and fighting cocks, and they switched gradually to bull fighting.

Alex, beside me, said, "Come have a drink."

We walked to the counter. Fat Carl put out two glasses. "What'll it be?"

Neither of us answered. Carl poured out the brown whiskey. He looked sullenly at me and one of his thick, meaty eyelids winked at me solemnly. I don't know why, but I felt flattered. Carl's head twitched back toward the card table. "Got you, didn't he?"

I winked back at him. "Take a dog next time." I imitated his clipped sentences. We drank our whiskey and went back to our chairs. Timothy Ratz won a game of solitaire and moved to the bar.

I looked back at the table under which Johnny Bear lay. He had rolled over on his stomach. His foolish smiling face looked out at the room. His head moved and he peered all about, like an animal about to leave its den. And then he came sliding out and stood up. There was a paradox about his movement. He looked twisted and shapeless, and yet he moved with complete lack of effort.

Johnny Bear crept up the room toward the bar, smiling about at the men he passed. In front of the bar this insistent question arose. "Whiskey? Whiskey?" It was like a bird call. I don't know what kind of bird, but I've heard it—two notes on a rising scale, asking a question over and over, "Whiskey? Whiskey?"

The conversation in the room stopped, but no one came forward to lay money on the counter. Johnny smiled plaintively. "Whiskey?"

Then he tried to cozen them. Out of this throat an angry woman's voice issued. "I tell you it was all bone. Twenty cents a pound, and half bone." And then a man, "Yes, ma'am. I didn't know it. I'll give you some sausage to make it up."

Johnny Bear looked around expectantly. "Whiskey?" Still none of the men offered to come forward. Johnny crept to the front of the room and crouched. I whispered, "What's he doing?"

Alex said "Sh. Looking through a window. Listen!"

A woman's voice came, a cold sure voice, the words clipped. "I can't quite understand it. Are you some kind of monster? I wouldn't have believed it if I hadn't seen you."

Another woman's voice answered her. a voice low and hoarse

with misery. "Maybe I am a monster. I can't help it. I can't help it."

"You *must* help it," the cold voice broke in. "Why you'd be better dead."

I heard a soft sobbing coming from the thick smiling lips of Johnny Bear. The sobbing of a woman in hopelessness. I looked around at Alex. He was sitting stiffly, his eyes wide open and unblinking. I opened my mouth to whisper a question, but he waved me silent. I glanced about the room. All the men were stiff and listening. The sobbing stopped. "Haven't you ever felt that way, Emalin?"

Alex caught his breath sharply at the name. The cold voice announced, "Certainly not."

"Never in the night? Not ever—ever in your life?"

"If I had," the cold voice said, "if ever I had, I would cut that part of me away. Now stop your whining, Amy. I won't stand for it. If you don't get control of your nerves I'll see about having some medical treatment for you. Now go to your prayers."

Johnny Bear smiled on. "Whiskey?"

Two men advanced without a word and put down coins. Fat Carl filled two glasses and when Johnny Bear tossed off one after the other, Carl filled one again. Everyone knew by that how moved he was. There were no drinks on the house at the Buffalo Bar. Johnny Bear smiled about the room and then he went out with that creeping gait of his. The doors folded together after him, slowly and without a sound.

Conversation did not spring up again. Everyone in the room seemed to have a problem to settle in his own mind. One by one they drifted out and the back swing of the doors brought in little puffs of tule fog. Alex got up and walked out and I followed him.

The night was nasty with the evil smelling fog. It seemed to cling to the buildings and to reach out with free arms into the air. I doubled my pace and caught up with Alex. "What was it?" I demanded. "What was it all about?"

For a moment I thought he wouldn't answer. But then he stopped and turned to me. "Oh, damn it. Listen! Every town has its aristocrats, its family above reproach. Emalin and Amy Hawkins are our aristocrats, maiden ladies, kind people. Their father was a congressman. I don't like this. Johnny Bear shouldn't do it. Why! they feed him. Those men shouldn't give him whiskey. He'll haunt that house now—now he knows he can get whiskey for it."

I asked, "Are they relatives of yours?"

"No, but they're—why, they aren't like other people. They have the farm next to mine. Some Chinese farm it on shares. You see, it's hard to explain. The Hawkins women, they're symbols. They're what we tell our kids when we want to—well to describe good people."

"Well," I protested, "nothing Johnny Bear said would hurt them would it?"

"I don't know. I don't know what it means. I mean, I kind of know. Oh! Go on to bed. I didn't bring the Ford. I'm going to walk out home." He turned and hurried into that slow squirming mist.

I walked along to Mrs. Ratz' boarding house. I could hear the chuttering of the Diesel engine off in the swamp and the clang of the big steel mouth that ate its way through the ground. It was Saturday night. The dredger would stop at seven Sunday morning and rest until midnight Sunday. I could tell by the sound that everything was all right. I climbed the narrow stairs to my room. Once in bed I left the light burning for a while and stared at the pale insipid flowers on the wallpaper. I thought of those two voices speaking out of Johnny Bear's mouth. They were authentic voices, not reproductions. Remembering the tones I could see the women who had spoken, the chill-voiced Emalin, and the loose, misery-broken face of Amy. I wondered what caused the misery. Was it just the lonely suffering of a middle-aged woman? It hardly seemed so to me, for there was too much fear in the voice. I went to sleep with the light on and had to get up later and turn it off.

About eight the next morning I walked down across the swamp to the dredger. The crew was busy bending some new wire to the drums and coiling the worn cable for removal. I looked over the job and at about eleven o'clock walked back to Loma. In front of Mrs. Ratz' boarding house Alex Hartnell sat in a Model-T Ford touring car. He called to me, "I was just going to the dredger to get you. I knocked off a couple of chickens this morning. Thought you might like to help with them."

I accepted joyfully. Our cook was a good cook, a big pasty man;

but lately I had found a dislike for him arising in me. He smoked Cuban cigarettes in a bamboo holder. I didn't like the way his fingers twitched in the morning. His hands were clean—floury like a miller's hands. I never knew before why they called them moth millers, those little flying bugs. Anyway I climbed into the Ford beside Alex and we drove down the hill to the rich land of the southwest. The sun shone brilliantly on the black earth. When I was little, a Catholic boy told me that the sun always shone on Sunday, if only for a moment, because it was God's day. I always meant to see if it were true. We rattled down to the level plain.

Alex shouted, "Remember about the Hawkins'?"

"Of course I remember."

He pointed. "That's the house."

Little of the house could be seen, for a high thick hedge of cypress surrounded it. There must be a small garden inside the square too. Only the roof and the tops of the windows showed over the hedge. I could see that the house was painted tan, trimmed with dark brown, a combination favored for railroad stations and schools in California. There were two wicket gates in the front and side of the hedge. The barn was outside the green barrier to the rear of the house. The hedge was clipped square. It looked incredibly thick and strong.

"The hedge keeps the wind out," Alex shouted.

"It doesn't keep Johnny Bear out," I said.

A shadow crossed his face. He waved at a whitewashed square building standing out in the field. "That's where the Chink sharecroppers live. Good workers. I wish I had some like them."

At that moment from behind the corner of the hedge a horse and buggy appeared and turned into the road. The grey horse was old but well groomed, the buggy shiny and the harness polished. There was a big silver H on the outside of each blinder. It seemed to me that the check rein was too short for such an old horse.

Alex cried, "There they are now, on their way to church."

We took off our hats and bowed to the women as they went by, and they nodded formally to us. I had a good look at them. It was a shock to me. They looked almost exactly as I thought they would. Johnny Bear was more monstrous even than I had known, if by the tone of voice he could describe the features of his people. I didn't have to ask which was Emalin and which was Amy. The clear straight eyes, the sharp sure chin, the mouth cut with the precision of a diamond, the stiff, curveless figure, that was Emalin. Amy was very like her, but so unlike. Her edges were soft. Her eyes were warm, her mouth full. There was a swell to her breast, and yet she did look like Emalin. But whereas Emalin's mouth was straight by nature, Amy *held* her mouth straight. Emalin must have been fifty or fifty-five and Amy about ten years younger. I had only a moment to look at them, and I never saw them again. It seems strange that I don't know anyone in the world better than those two women.

Alex was shouting, "You see what I meant about aristocrats?"

I nodded. It was easy to see. A community would feel kind of —safe, having women like that about. A place like Loma with its fogs, with its great swamp like a hideous sin needed, really needed the Hawkins women. A few years there might do things to a man's mind if those women weren't there to balance matters.

It was a good dinner. Alex' sister fried the chicken in butter and did everything else right. I grew more suspicious and uncharitable toward our cook. We sat around in the dining room and drank really good brandy.

I said, "I can't see why you ever go into the Buffalo. That whiskey is ——"

"I know," said Alex. "But the Buffalo is the mind of Loma. It's our newspaper, our theatre and our club."

This was so true that when Alex started the Ford and prepared to take me back I knew, and he knew, we would go for an hour or two to the Buffalo Bar.

We were nearly into town. The feeble lights of the car splashed about on the road. Another car rattled toward us. Alex swung across the road and stopped. "It's the doctor, Doctor Holmes," he explained. The oncoming car pulled up because it couldn't get around us. Alex called, "Say, Doc, I was going to ask you to take a look at my sister. She's got a swelling on her throat."

Doctor Holmes called back, "All right, Alex, I'll take a look. Pull out, will you? I'm in a hurry."

Alex was deliberate. "Who's sick, Doc?"

"Why Miss Amy had a little spell. Miss Emalin phoned in and asked me to hurry. Get out of the way, will you?"

Alex squawked his car back and let the doctor by. We drove on.

I was about to remark that the night was clear when, looking ahead, I saw the rags of fog creeping around the hill from the swamp side and climbing like slow snakes on the top of Loma. The Ford shuddered to a stop in front of the Buffalo. We went in.

Fat Carl moved toward us. He reached under the bar for the nearby bottle. "What'll it be?"

"Whiskey."

For a moment a faint smile seemed to flit over the fat sullen face. The room was full. My dredger crew was there, all except the cook. He was probably on the scow smoking his Cuban cigarettes in a bamboo holder. He didn't drink. That was enough to make me suspicious of him. Two deck hands and an engineer and three levermen were there. The levermen were arguing about a cutting. The old lumber adage certainly held for them: "Women in the woods and logging in the honky-tonk."

That was the quietest bar I ever saw. There weren't any fights, not much singing and no tricks. Somehow the sullen baleful eyes of Fat Carl made drinking a quiet, efficient business rather than a noisy game. Timothy Ratz was playing solitaire at one of the round tables. Alex and I drank our whiskey. No chairs were available, so we just stayed leaning against the bar talking about sports and markets and adventures we had had or pretended we had— just a casual barroom conversation. Now and then we bought another drink. I guess we hung around for a couple of hours, Alex had already said he was going home, and I felt like it. The dredger crew trooped out, for they had to start to work at midnight.

The doors unfolded silently, and Johnny Bear crept into the room, swinging his long arms, nodding his big hairy head and smiling foolishly about. His square feet were like cats' feet.

"Whiskey?" he chirruped. No one encouraged him. He got out his wares. He was down on his stomach the way he had been when he got me. Sing-song nasal words came out, Chinese I thought. And then it seemed to me that the same words were repeated in another voice, slower and not nasally. Johnny Bear raised his shaggy head and asked, "Whiskey?" He got to his feet with effortless ease. I was interested. I wanted to see him perform. I slid a quarter along the bar. Johnny gulped his drink. A moment later I wished I hadn't. I was afraid to look at Alex; for

Johnny Bear crept to the middle of the room and took that window pose of his.

The chill voice of Emalin said, "She's in here, doctor." I closed my eyes against the looks of Johnny Bear, and the moment I did he went out. It was Emalin Hawkins who had spoken.

I had heard the doctor's voice in the road, and it was his veritable voice that replied, "Ah—you said a fainting fit?"

"Yes, doctor."

There was a little pause, and then the doctor's voice again, very softly, "Why did she do it, Emalin?"

"Why did she do what?" There was almost a threat in the question.

"I'm your doctor, Emalin. I was your father's doctor. You've got to tell me things. Don't you think I've seen that kind of a mark on the neck before? How long was she hanging before you got her down?"

There was a longer pause then. The chill left the woman's voice. It was soft, almost a whisper. "Two or three minutes. Will she be all right, doctor?"

"Oh, yes, she'll come around. She's not badly hurt. Why did she do it?"

The answering voice was even colder than it had been at first. It was frozen. "I don't know, sir."

"You mean you won't tell me?"

"I mean what I say."

Then the doctor's voice went on giving directions for treatment, rest, milk and a little whiskey. "Above all, be gentle," he said. "Above everything, be gentle with her."

Emalin's voice trembled a little. "You would never—tell, doctor?"

"I'm your doctor," he said softly. "Of course I won't tell. I'll send down some sedatives tonight."

"Whiskey?" My eyes jerked open. The horrible Johnny Bear smiling around the room.

The men were silent, ashamed. Fat Carl looked at the floor. I turned apologetically to Alex, for I was really responsible. "I didn't know he'd do that," I said. "I'm sorry."

I walked out the door and went to the dismal room at Mrs. Ratz'. I opened the window and looked out into that coiling, pulsing fog. Far off in the marsh I heard the Diesel engine start slowly and warm up. And after a while I heard the clang of the big bucket as it went to work on the ditch.

The next morning one of those series of accidents so common in construction landed on us. One of the new wires parted on the inswing and dropped the bucket on one of the pontoons, sinking it and the works in eight feet of ditch water. When we sunk a dead man and got a line out to it to pull us from the water, the line parted and clipped the legs neatly off one of the deck hands. We bound the stumps and rushed him to Salinas. And then little accidents happened. A leverman developed blood poisoning from a wire scratch. The cook finally justified my opinion by trying to sell a little can of Marijuana to the engineer. Altogether there wasn't much peace in the outfit. It was two weeks before we were going again with a new pontoon, a new deck hand and a new cook.

The new cook was a sly, dark, little long-nosed man, with a gift for subtle flattery.

My contact with the social life of Loma had gone to pot, but when the bucket was clanging into the mud again and the big old Diesel was chuttering away in the swamp I walked out to Alex Hartnell's farm one night. Passing the Hawkins place, I peered in through one of the little wicket gates in the cypress hedge. The house was dark, more than dark because a low light glowed in one window. There was a gentle wind that night, blowing balls of fog like tumbleweeds along the ground. I walked in the clear a moment, and then was swallowed in a thick mist, and then was in the clear again. In the starlight I could see those big silver fog balls moving like elementals across the fields. I thought I heard a soft moaning in the Hawkins yard behind the hedge, and once when I came suddenly out of the fog I saw a dark figure hurrying along in the field, and I knew from the dragging footsteps that it was one of the Chinese field hands walking in sandals. The Chinese eat a great many things that have to be caught at night.

Alex came to the door when I knocked. He seemed glad to see me. His sister was away. I sat down by his stove and he brought out a bottle of that nice brandy. "I heard you were having some trouble," he said.

I explained the difficulty. "It seems to come in series. The men have it figured out that accidents come in groups of three, five, seven and nine."

Alex nodded. "I kind of feel that way myself."

"How are the Hawkins sisters?" I asked. "I thought I heard some-one crying as I went by."

Alex seemed reluctant to talk about them, and at the same time eager to talk about them. "I stopped over about a week ago. Miss Amy isn't feeling very well. I didn't see her. I only saw Miss Emalin." Then Alex broke out, "There's something hanging over those people, something ——"

"You almost seem to be related to them," I said.

"Well, their father and my father were friends. We called the girls Aunt Amy and Aunt Emalin. They can't do anything bad. It wouldn't be good for any of us if the Hawkins sisters weren't the Hawkins sisters."

"The community conscience?"

"The safe thing," he cried. "The place where a kid can get gingerbread. The place where a girl can get reassurance. They're proud, but they believe in things we hope are true. And they live as though, well, as though honesty really is the best policy and charity really is its own reward. We need them."

"I see."

"But Miss Emalin is fighting something terrible and—I don't think she's going to win."

"What do you mean?"

"I don't know what I mean. But I've thought I should shoot Johnny Bear and throw him in the swamp. I've really thought about doing it."

"It's not his fault," I argued. "He's just a kind of recording and reproducing device, only you use a glass of whiskey instead of a nickel."

We talked of some other things then, and after a while I walked back to Loma. It seemed to me that that fog was clinging to the cypress hedge of the Hawkins house, and it seemed to me that a lot of the fog balls were clustered about it and others were slowly moving in. I smiled as I walked along at the way a man's thought can rearrange nature to fit his thoughts. There was no light in the house as I went by.

A nice, steady routine settled on my work. The big bucket cut out the ditch ahead of it. The crew felt the trouble was over too, and that helped, and the new cook flattered the men so successfully that they would have eaten fried cement. The personality of a cook has a lot more to do with the happiness of a dredger crew than his cooking has.

In the evening of the second day after my visit to Alex I walked down the wooden sidewalk trailing a streamer of fog behind me and went into the Buffalo Bar. Fat Carl moved toward me polishing the whiskey glass. I cried "Whiskey," before he had a chance to ask what it would be. I took my glass and went to one of the straight chairs. Alex was not there. Timothy Ratz was playing solitaire and having a phenomenal run of luck. He got it out four times in a row and had a drink each time. More and more men arrived.

At about ten o'clock the news came. Thinking about such things afterwards you never can remember quite what transpired. Someone comes in; a whisper starts; suddenly everyone knows what has happened, knows details. Miss Amy had committed suicide. Who brought in the story? I don't know. She had hanged herself. There wasn't much talk in the barroom about it. I could see the men were trying to get straight on it. It was a thing that didn't fit into their schemes. They stood in groups, talking softly.

The swinging doors opened slowly and Johnny Bear crept in, his great hairy head rolling, and that idiot smile on his face. His square feet slid quietly over the floor. He looked about and chirruped, "Whiskey? Whiskey for Johnny?"

Now those men really wanted to know. They were ashamed of wanting to know, but their whole mental system required the knowledge. Fat Carl poured out a drink. Timothy Ratz put down his cards and stood up. Johnny Bear gulped the whiskey. I closed my eyes.

The doctor's tone was harsh. "Where is she, Emalin?"

I've never heard a voice like the one that answered, cold control, layer and layer of control, but cold penetrated by the most awful heartbreak. It was a monotonous tone, emotionless, and yet the heartbreak got into the vibrations. "She's in here, doctor."

"H-m-m." A long pause. "She was hanging a long time."

"I don't know how long, doctor."

"Why did she do it, Emalin?"

The monotone again. "I don't—know, doctor."

A longer pause, and then, "H-m-m. Emalin, did you know she was going to have a baby?"

The chill voice cracked and a sigh came through. "Yes, doctor," very softly.

"Is that why you didn't find her for so long—No, Emalin, I didn't mean that, poor dear."

The control was back in Emalin's voice. "Can you make out the certificate without mentioning ——"

"Of course I can, sure I can. And I'll speak to the undertaker, too. You needn't worry."

"Thank you, doctor."

"I'll go and telephone now. I won't leave you here alone. Come into the other room, Emalin. I'm going to fix you a sedative ——"

"Whiskey? Whiskey for Johnny?" I saw the smile and the rolling hairy head. Fat Carl poured out another glass. Johnny Bear drank it and then crept to the back of the room and crawled under a table and went to sleep.

No one spoke. The men moved up to the bar and laid down their coins silently. They looked bewildered, for a system had fallen. A few minutes later Alex came into the silent room. He walked quickly over to me. "You've heard?" he asked softly.

"Yes."

"I've been afraid," he cried. "I told you a couple of nights ago. I've been afraid."

I said, "Did you know she was pregnant?"

Alex stiffened. He looked around the room and then back at me. "Johnny Bear?" he asked.

I nodded.

Alex ran his palm over his eyes. "I don't believe it." I was about to answer when I heard a little scuffle and looked to the back of the room. Johnny Bear crawled like a badger out of his hole and stood up and crept toward the bar.

"Whiskey?" He smiled expectantly at Fat Carl.

Then Alex stepped out and addressed the room. "Now you guys listen! This has gone far enough. I don't want any more of it." If he had expected opposition he was disappointed. I saw the men nodding to one another.

"Whiskey for Johnny?"

Alex turned on the idiot. "You ought to be ashamed. Miss Amy gave you food, and she gave you all the clothes you ever had."

Johnny smiled at him. "Whiskey?"

He got out his tricks. I heard the sing-song nasal language that sounded like Chinese. Alex looked relieved.

And then the other voice, slow, hesitant, repeating the words without the nasal.

Alex sprang so quickly that I didn't see him move. His fist splatted into Johnny Bear's smiling mouth. "I told you there was enough of it," he shouted.

Johnny Bear recovered his balance. His lips were split and bleeding, but the smile was still there. He moved slowly and without effort. His arms enfolded Alex as the tentacles of an anemone enfold a crab. Alex bent backward. Then I jumped and grabbed one of the arms and wrenched at it, and could not tear it loose. Fat Carl came rolling over the counter with a bung starter in his hand. And he beat the matted head until the arms relaxed and Johnny Bear crumped. I caught Alex and helped him to a chair. "Are you hurt?"

He tried to get his breath. "My back's wrenched, I guess," he said. "I'll be all right."

"Got your Ford outside? I'll drive you home."

Neither of us looked at the Hawkins place as we went by. I didn't lift my eyes off the road. I got Alex to his own dark house and helped him to bed and poured a hot brandy into him. He hadn't spoken all the way home. But after he was propped in the bed he demanded, "You don't think anyone noticed, do you? I caught him in time, didn't I?"

"What are you talking about. I don't know yet why you hit him."

"Well, listen," he said. "I'll have to stay close for a little while with this back. If you hear anyone say anything, you stop it, won't you? Don't let them say it."

"I don't know what you're talking about."

He looked into my eyes for a moment. "I guess I can trust you," he said. "That second voice—that was Miss Amy."

PART IV

ON THE BLUE WATER

By ERNEST HEMINGWAY

CERTAINLY THERE IS NO HUNTING LIKE THE HUNTING OF MAN AND those who have hunted armed men long enough and liked it, never really care for anything else thereafter. You will meet them doing various things with resolve, but their interest rarely holds because after the other thing ordinary life is as flat as the taste of wine when the taste buds have been burned off your tongue. Wine, when your tongue has been burned clean with lye and water, feels like puddle water in your mouth, while mustard feels like axle-grease, and you can smell crisp, fried bacon, but when you taste it, there is only a feeling of crinkly lard.

You can learn about this matter of the tongue by coming into the kitchen of a villa on the Riviera late at night and taking a drink from what should be a bottle of Evian water and which turns out to be *Eau de Javel*, a concentrated lye product used for cleaning sinks. The taste buds on your tongue, if burned off by *Eau de Javel*, will begin to function again after about a week. At what rate other things regenerate one does not know, since you lose track of friends and the things one could learn in a week were mostly learned a long time ago.

The other night I was talking with a good friend to whom all hunting is dull except elephant hunting. To him there is no sport in anything unless there is great danger and, if the danger is not enough, he will increase it for his own satisfaction. A hunting companion of his had told me how this friend was not satisfied with the risks of ordinary elephant hunting but would, if possible, have the elephants driven, or turned, so he could take them head-on, so it was a choice of killing them with the difficult frontal shot as they came, trumpeting, with their ears spread, or having them run over him. This is to elephant hunting what the German cult of suicide climbing is to ordinary mountaineering, and I suppose it is, in a way, an attempt to approximate the old hunting of the armed man who is hunting you.

473

This friend was speaking of elephant hunting and urging me to hunt elephant, as he said that once you took it up no other hunting would mean anything to you. I was arguing that I enjoyed all hunting and shooting, any sort I could get, and had no desire to wipe this capacity for enjoyment out with the *Eau de Javel* of the old elephant coming straight at you with his trunk up and his ears spread.

"Of course you like that big fishing too," he said rather sadly. "Frankly, I can't see where the excitement is in that."

"You'd think it was marvelous if the fish shot at you with Tommy guns or jumped back and forth through the cockpit with swords on the ends of their noses."

"Don't be silly," he said. "But frankly I don't see where the thrill is."

"Look at so and so," I said. "He's an elephant hunter and this last year he's gone fishing for big fish and he's goofy about it. He must get a kick out of it or he wouldn't do it."

"Yes," my friend said. "There must be something about it but I can't see it. Tell me where you get a thrill out of it."

"I'll try to write it in a piece sometime," I told him.

"I wish you would," he said. "Because you people are sensible on other subjects. Moderately sensible I mean."

"I'll write it."

In the first place, the Gulf Stream and the other great ocean currents are the last wild country there is left. Once you are out of sight of land and of the other boats you are more alone than you can ever be hunting and the sea is the same as it has been since before men ever went on it in boats. In a season fishing you will see it oily flat as the becalmed galleons saw it while they drifted to the westward; white-capped with a fresh breeze as they saw it running with the trades; and in high, rolling blue hills the tops blowing off them like snow as they were punished by it, so that sometimes you will see three great hills of water with your fish jumping from the top of the farthest one and if you tried to make a turn to go with him without picking your chance, one of those breaking crests would roar down in on you with a thousand tons of water and you would hunt no more elephants, Richard, my lad.

There is no danger from the fish, but anyone who goes on the sea the year around in a small power boat does not seek danger.

You may be absolutely sure that in a year you will have it without seeking, so you try always to avoid it all you can.

Because the Gulf Stream is an unexploited country, only the very fringe of it ever being fished, and then only at a dozen places in thousands of miles of current, no one knows what fish live in it, or how great size they reach or what age, or even what kinds of fish and animals live in it at different depths. When you are drifting, out of sight of land, fishing four lines, sixty, eighty, one hundred and one hundred fifty fathoms down, in water that is seven hundred fathoms deep you never know what may take the small tuna that you use for bait, and every time the line starts to run off the reel, slowly first, then with a scream of the click as the rod bends and you feel it double and the huge weight of the friction of the line rushing through that depth of water while you pump and reel, pump and reel, pump and reel, trying to get the belly out of the line before the fish jumps, there is always a thrill that needs no danger to make it real. It may be a marlin that will jump high and clear off to your right and then go off in a series of leaps, throwing a splash like a speedboat in a sea as you shout for the boat to turn with him watching the line melting off the reel before the boat can get around. Or it may be a broadbill that will show wagging his great broadsword. Or it may be some fish that you will never see at all that will head straight out to the northwest like a submerged submarine and never show and at the end of five hours the angler has a straightened-out hook. There is always a feeling of excitement when a fish takes hold when you are drifting deep.

In hunting you know what you are after and the top you can get is an elephant. But who can say what you will hook sometime when drifting in a hundred and fifty fathoms in the Gulf Stream? There are probably marlin and swordfish to which the fish we have seen caught are pygmies; and every time a fish takes the bait drifting you have a feeling perhaps you are hooked to one of these.

Carlos, our Cuban mate, who is fifty-three years old and has been fishing for marlin since he went in the bow of a skiff with his father when he was seven, was fishing drifting deep one time when he hooked a white marlin. The fish jumped twice and then sounded and when he sounded suddenly Carlos felt a great weight and he could not hold the line which went out and down and down irresistibly until the fish had taken out over a hundred and fifty fathoms. Carlos says it felt as heavy and solid as though he were hooked to the bottom of the sea. Then suddenly the strain was loosened but he could feel the weight of his original fish and pulled it up stone dead. Some toothless fish like a swordfish or marlin had closed his jaws across the middle of the eighty pound white marlin and squeezed it and held it so that every bit of the insides of the fish had been crushed out while the huge fish moved off with the eighty-pound fish in its mouth. Finally it let go. What size of a fish would that be? I thought it might be a giant squid but Carlos said there were no sucker marks on the fish and that it showed plainly the shape of the marlin's mouth where he had crushed it.

Another time an old man fishing alone in a skiff out of Cabañas hooked a great marlin that, on the heavy sashcord handline, pulled the skiff far out to sea. Two days later the old man was picked up by fishermen sixty miles to the eastward, the head and forward part of the marlin lashed alongside. What was left of the fish, less than half, weighed eight hundred pounds. The old man had stayed with him a day, a night, a day and another night while the fish swam deep and pulled the boat. When he had come up the old man had pulled the boat up on him and harpooned him. Lashed alongside the sharks had hit him and the old man had fought them out alone in the Gulf Stream in a skiff, clubbing them, stabbing at them, lunging at them with an oar until he was exhausted and the sharks had eaten all that they could hold. He was crying in the boat when the fishermen picked him up, half crazy from his loss, and the sharks were still circling the boat.

But what is the excitement in catching them from a launch? It comes from the fact that they are strange and wild things of unbelievable speed and power and a beauty, in the water and leaping, that is indescribable, which you would never see if you did not fish for them, and to which you are suddenly harnessed so that you feel their speed, their force and their savage power as intimately as if you were riding a bucking horse. For half an hour, an hour, or five hours, you are fastened to the fish as much as he is fastened to you and you tame him and break him the way a wild horse is broken and finally lead him to the boat. For pride and because the fish is worth plenty of money in the Havana market, you gaff him at the boat and bring him on board, but the having him in the boat isn't the excitement; it is while you are fighting him that is the fun.

If the fish is hooked in the bony part of the mouth I am sure the hook hurts him no more than the harness hurts the angler. A large fish when he is hooked often does not feel the hook at all and will swim toward the boat, unconcerned, to take another bait. At other times he will swim away deep, completely unconscious of the hook, and it is when he feels himself held and pressure exerted to turn him, that he knows something is wrong and starts to make his fight. Unless he is hooked where it hurts he makes his fight not against the pain of the hook, but against being captured and if, when he is out of sight, you figure what he is doing, in what direction he is pulling when deep down, and why, you can convince him and bring him to the boat by the same system you break a wild horse. It is not necessary to kill him, or even completely exhaust him to bring him to the boat.

To kill a fish that fights deep you pull against the direction he wants to go until he is worn out and dies. It takes hours and when the fish dies the sharks are liable to get him before the angler can raise him to the top. To catch such a fish quickly you figure by trying to hold him absolutely, which direction he is working (a sounding fish is going in the direction the line slants in the water when you have put enough pressure on the drag so the line would break if you held it any tighter); then get ahead of him on that direction and he can be brought to the boat without killing him. You do not tow him or pull him with the motor boat; you use the engine to shift your position just as you would walk up or down stream with a salmon. A fish is caught most surely from a small boat such as a dory since the angler can shut down on his drag and simply let the fish pull the boat. Towing the boat will kill him in time. But the most satisfaction is to dominate and convince the fish and bring him intact in everything but spirit to the boat as rapidly as possible.

"Very instructive," says the friend. "But where does the thrill come in?"

The thrill comes when you are standing at the wheel drinking a cold bottle of beer and watching the outriggers jump the baits so they look like small live tuna leaping along and then behind one you see a long dark shadow wing up and then a big spear thrust out followed by an eye and head and dorsal fin and the tuna jumps with the wave and he's missed it.

"Marlin," Carlos yells from the top of the house and stamps his feet up and down, the signal that a fish is raised. He swarms down to the wheel and you go back to where the rod rests in its socket and there comes the shadow again, fast as the shadow of a plane moving over the water, and the spear, head, fin and shoulders smash out of water and you hear the click the closepin makes as the line pulls out and the long bight of line whishes through the water as the fish turns and as you hold the rod, you feel it double and the butt kicks you in the belly as you come back hard and feel his weight, as you strike him again and again, and again.

Then the heavy rod arc-ing out toward the fish, and the reel in a band-saw zinging scream, the marlin leaps clear and long, silver in the sun long, round as a hogshead and banded with lavender stripes and, when he goes into the water, it throws a column of spray like a shell lighting.

Then he comes out again, and the spray roars, and again, then the line feels slack and out he bursts headed across and in, then jumps wildly twice more seeming to hang high and stiff in the air before falling to throw the column of water and you can see the hook in the corner of his jaw.

Then in a series of jumps like a greyhound he heads to the northwest and standing up, you follow him in the boat, the line taut as a banjo string and little drops coming from it until you finally get the belly of it clear of that friction against the water and have a straight pull out toward the fish.

And all the time Carlos is shouting, "Oh, God the bread of my children! Oh look at the bread of my children! Joseph and Mary look at the bread of my children jump! There it goes the bread of my children! He'll never stop the bread the bread the bread of my children!"

This striped marlin jumped, in a straight line to the northwest, fifty-three times, and every time he went out it was a sight to make your heart stand still. Then he sounded and I said to Carlos, "Get me the harness. Now I've got to pull him up the bread of your children."

"I couldn't stand to see it," he says. "Like a filled pocketbook jumping. He can't go down deep now. He's caught too much air jumping."

"Like a race horse over obstacles," Julio says. "Is the harness all right? Do you want water?"

"No." Then kidding Carlos, "What's this about the bread of your children?"

"He always says that," says Julio. "You should hear him curse me when we would lose one in the skiff."

"What will the bread of your children weigh?" I ask with mouth dry, the harness taut across shoulders, the rod a flexible prolongation of the sinew pulling ache of arms, the sweat salty in my eyes.

"Four hundred and fifty," says Carlos.

"Never," says Julio.

"Thou and thy never," says Carlos. "The fish of another always weighs nothing to thee."

"Three seventy-five," Julio raises his estimate. "Not a pound more."

Carlos says something unprintable and Julio comes up to four hundred.

The fish is nearly whipped now and the dead ache is out of raising him, and then, while lifting, I feel something slip. It holds for an instant and then the line is slack.

"He's gone," I say and unbuckle the harness.

"The bread of your children," Julio says to Carlos.

"Yes," Carlos says. "Yes. Joke and no joke yes. *El pan de mis hijos*. Three hundred and fifty pounds at ten cents a pound. How many days does a man work for that in the winter? How cold is it at three o'clock in the morning on all those days? And the fog and the rain in a norther. Every time he jumps the hook cutting the hole a little bigger in his jaw. Ay how he could jump. How he could jump!"

"The bread of your children," says Julio.

"Don't talk about that any more," said Carlos.

No it is not elephant hunting. But we get a kick out of it. When you have a family and children, your family, or my family, or the family of Carlos, you do not have to look for danger. There is always plenty of danger when you have a family.

And after a while the danger of others is the only danger and there is no end to it nor any pleasure in it nor does it help to think about it.

But there is great pleasure in being on the sea, in the unknown wild suddenness of a great fish; in his life and death which he lives for you in an hour while your strength is harnessed to his; and there is satisfaction in conquering this thing which rules the sea it lives in.

Then in the morning of the day after you have caught a good fish, when the man who carried him to the market in a handcart brings the long roll of heavy silver dollars wrapped in a newspaper on board it is very satisfactory money. It really feels like money.

"There's the bread of your children," you say to Carlos.

"In the time of the dance of the millions," he says, "a fish like that was worth two hundred dollars. Now it is thirty. On the other hand a fisherman never starves. The sea is very rich."

"And the fisherman always poor."

"No. Look at you. You are rich."

"Like hell," you say. "And the longer I fish the poorer I'll be. I'll end up fishing with you for the market in a dinghy."

"That I never believe," says Carlos devoutly. "But look. That fishing in a dinghy is very interesting. You would like it."

"I'll look forward to it," you say.

"What we need for prosperity is a war," Carlos says. "In the time of the war with Spain and in the last war the fishermen were actually rich."

"All right," you say. "If we have a war you get the dinghy ready."

THE EUTHANASIAN GARDEN

By HAVELOCK ELLIS

"I BELIEVE IN INDIVIDUALISM, THAT EACH INDIVIDUAL HAS A RIGHT to the Sacraments of Sun, Air, and Water, of Love and of Beauty, the Right of Life, the Right of Death. I would say that the present Laws—both moral and legal—in regard to Suicide and Euthanasia are obsolete and need revision, that the Individual has as much Right to Die—proviso it harms no other individual—as to be Born, Married, go on a Journey. In some enlightened future World there will be public Lethal Chambers—both compulsory and voluntary—as there are now Public Baths and Libraries. Individuals will be free to die, may even be taught that it is sometimes their Duty to die. Death will be restored to its long lost Divinity."

I quote from a long letter I have just received from a young woman of twenty-five. She lives in a large English city, where she has done office work for important firms, efficiently I gather. But of late various physical defects and disorders have compelled her to give up office work, while attempts at other work have failed, and she now subsists on the small dole. She has an original mind (note her fondness for capital letters) and has cultivated it by much serious reading and music. She is, as she admits, neurotic, and she feels unable to outlive and forget an old love-disappointment. She sees nothing ahead but death. Her long letter to me, she says, may be one of the last she ever writes.

I do not yet know whether I can persuade my correspondent to consider the matter a little longer before deciding that life holds no further possibilities. But it is the social, not the personal, problem in which I am mainly interested, and as a social problem it is really less concerned with self-destruction than with bringing the lives of others to an end. Today, indeed, the subject is becoming actual. Not long since, a distinguished English physician, Lord Horder, called attention to it, as one of the pressing questions of the immediate future, though, as he pointed out, it is not one in which the medical profession can play a pioneering part, since it is the business of medicine to prolong life, not to end it. But here and there among the general public practical action has been taken in advance of the law.

Thus, last year, a woman in Yorkshire, a Mrs. Brownhill, was charged with the wilful murder of her son, aged 30. It appeared that the son was a helpless imbecile, and unable to do anything for himself; his mother, who was constantly devoted to him, had her bed in the same room so as to attend to all his wants. But she was herself in bad health and the time came when it was imperative for her to go to a hospital for a serious operation. She would not see her helpless son abandoned. She decided to give him a large dose of aspirin to produce sleepiness and then place the gas tube in his mouth. "I have put Denis to sleep," she said. "The time may come," the judge told the jury, "when it may be the law that an idiot may be sent to a merciful death. That is not the law at the present time, and neither you nor I have the right to make laws. We have to take the law as it is." The jury immediately returned a verdict of "Guilty, with the strongest recommendation to mercy." Mrs. Brownhill was formally sentenced to death, but at once put into the prison hospital and not long afterwards quietly released.

More recently in Manchester two sisters were charged with murdering their imbecile brother, who happened to be of the same age as Denis Brownhill, in a similar manner. There was insanity in several members of the family, and the mental condition of this brother was such that he could never be let outside the house; one or other of the sisters had constantly to watch over him. "The thing we have done," said one of the sisters, "has not only been a duty, but a promise to a dying mother. It was loving devotion to a hapless and helpless being." (She meant that her mother enjoined on them always to care for their brother.) "Not to rid myself of a burden," said the other sister, "but because I could go on no further. I had lived for him and loved him." The jury found a verdict of "Guilty but insane," and the judge, in ordering their detention in an asylum added that he would say nothing to add to the trials they had gone through.

The reasonable attitude of the judges at both these trials may be taken to indicate that they might welcome a change in the law. Such a change, at all events, so far as the voluntary aspects of the problem are concerned, has in England been proposed, and notably by Dr. Killick Millard in his Presidential Address to the Society of Medical Officers of Health, which has been republished as a pamphlet (with a Foreword by Sir Arbuthnot Lane) under the title of *Euthanasia: A Plea for the Legalization of Voluntary Euthanasia under Certain Conditions.*

Dr. Millard, who is distinguished by his valuable and wide-ranging activities in causes of public welfare, is not content with a mere plea. He has brought together the confirmatory opinions of eminent public men in Church and State, and he is setting up a Voluntary Euthanasia Legalization Society to promote the cause. The cause takes shape in a Bill, The Voluntary Euthanasia (Legislation) Bill, for submission to Parliament. It has now been re-drafted by a legal authority accustomed to the drafting of bills, and will in due course be introduced. It would provide for the application by persons over twenty-one years of age suffering from incurable disease to a Euthanasian referee appointed by the Minister of Health, the application to be heard in camera and to be supported by two medical certificates, and the applicant to have first consulted his nearest relative and set his affairs in order. The proceeding would thus be as cautiously guarded as possible, and furnishes no support for the recent foolish statement of a coroner at an inquest over a suicide that "if everyone adopted this method there would soon be no one left in the world." Nor does it definitely deal with that "humanitarian extermination of imbeciles" advocated by some today as being even in the interests of low-grade defectives themselves, though they might not be of the mental capacity to take action under the proposed Bill. It would, however, be simple to modify the Bill in this direction. Even as it stands, it indicates a wholesome and more discerning attitude towards the problem of death. Suicide was reasonably viewed in the classic world, though in later times it has commonly been regarded at first as a crime, and then as a disease. Undoubtedly suicide is sometimes a psychopathic question.

But, as Lord Horder rightly points out, we are not here in the main concerned with a medical problem, however valuable medical experience may prove. "The larger decision should be left to the developing good sense and judgment of the community." Now that the question is taking shape it is time for that good sense and judgment to speak out and make itself felt.

In a forthcoming book, *Paradise Discovered*, Mr. Wicksteed Armstrong describes the community of the future. He places this Land of Eugenia in Brazil, and claims that he has found suggestions of it in an existing European colony in South America.

I will not anticipate his narrative of a supposed visit to this future State. But there is one chapter which deals with the question here before us. It is entitled "The Euthanasian Garden."

The inhabitants of this future city of Paradise, it is needless to say, cultivate life and strive for health and happiness. But they also realize the necessity of facing death. So they are prepared, when necessary, to cultivate death as well as life. They have revolted against the rule, still prevailing in our present society during a prolonged death of slowly drawn out agony for the dying person and his friends, meekly and helplessly to await its final stage. The control of life, they believe, in a wholesomely constituted society must be accompanied by the control of death.

The rule prevailing in this State is: Thou shalt not cause suffering. If a man feels that life is becoming intolerable and desires to bring it to an end the question for the community to decide is whether his death would cause more suffering to friends and relations than he himself would suffer by living, and if so, euthanasia would not be allowed. At the same time it would not be permitted for relations to be too selfish and to deny euthanasia when there were sound reasons for it. Moreover, in the case of persons whose heredity clearly rendered them unfit for procreation, the choice is given between sterilization and euthanasia, some, it is said, preferring the latter.

On entering the Garden of Euthanasia, a palace of crystal and marble is seen. There is music, there are flowers. There are lovely girls dancing. The candidate for euthanasia may associate with a beautiful girl and accept from her a poisonous bouquet. If he prefers he may, like Socrates, die in converse with his friends. There is a waterfall which is immediately fatal. And for exceptional persons of sadistic tastes, who may prefer to die cruelly, there is a cage of jaguars and leopards.

This fantasia is not embodied in the Voluntary Euthanasia (Legislation) Bill. But it shows, once more, the direction in which thought today is flowing.

ATTORNEY FOR THE DEFENSE

By Clarence Darrow

THE AUDIENCE THAT STORMS THE BOX-OFFICE OF THE THEATER TO gain entrance to a sensational show is small and sleepy compared with the throng that crashes the court house door when something concerning real life and death is to be laid bare to the public.

Everyone knows that the best portrayals of life are tame and sickly when matched with the realities. For this reason, the sophisticated Romans were wont to gather at the Colosseum to feast their eyes and other senses on fountains of real blood and await breathlessly the final thrust. The court room is a modern arena in which the greatest thrills follow closely on each other. If the combat concerns human life it presents an atmosphere and setting not unlike those cruel and bloody scenes of ancient Rome. The judge wears the same flowing robe with all of the dignity and superiority he can command. This sets him apart from his fellowmen and is designed to awe and intimidate and to impress the audience with seeming wisdom oftener than with kindliness and compassion.

One cannot help wondering what happens to the pomp and pretense of the wearer while the cloak is in the wash, or while changing into a maturer, more monarchical mantle, as his bench becomes a throne, or when he strolls along the street in file with the "plain clothes" people.

When court opens, the bailiff intones some voodoo singsong words in ominous voice that carries fear and respect at the opening of the rite. The court room is full of staring men and women shut within closed doors, guarded by officials wearing uniforms to confound the simple inside the sacred precinct. This dispels all hope of mercy to the unlettered, the poor and helpless, who scarcely dare express themselves above a whisper in any such forbidding place.

The stage, the arena, the court, are alike in that each has its audience thirsting to drink deeply of the passing show. Those playing the parts vie for success and use whatever skill and talent they possess. An actor may fumble his lines, but a lawyer needs to be letter-perfect, at least, he has to use his wits, and he may forget himself, and often does, but never for a moment can he lose sight of his client.

Small wonder that ambitious, imaginative youths crowd the profession of law. Here, they feel, they, themselves, will find the opportunity to play a real part in the comedies as well as the tragedies of life. Everyone, no matter how small his chance may be, tries to hold the center of some stage where the multitude will scan his every move. To most lads it seems as though the courts were organized to furnish them a chance to bask in the public eye. In this field the adventure of life will never pall, but prove interesting, exciting and changeful to the end. Not only will he have the destinies of men to protect and preserve, but his own standing and success to create.

Chancery cases are not especially interesting nor exciting, however. These are supposed to be heard by a judge. He listens long enough to feel satisfied that the case promises to consume considerable time and work and interfere with many hours of leisure, so he refers it to a "Master in Chancery," a lawyer-friend of his own appointment, who is paid by fees that come directly from the litigants; the Master in Chancery employs a court reporter who takes the evidence in shorthand while the Master may take a nap in an adjoining office. After the clients' resources are exhausted by the court reporters and Masters in Chancery, the documents are locked up in a safe to await the blowing of Gabriel's horn.

If it is a real case, criminal or civil, it usually is tried by a jury with the assistance and direction of the judge. In that event, every moment counts, and neither the lawyers nor the audience, or even the court, goes to sleep. If it is a criminal case, or even a civil one, it is not the law alone or the facts that determine the result. Always the element of luck and chance looms large. A jury of twelve men is watching not only the evidence but the attitude of each lawyer, and the parties involved, in all their moves. Every step is fraught with doubt, if not mystery.

Selecting a jury is of the utmost importance. So far as possible, the lawyer should know both sides of the case. If the client is a landlord, a banker, or a manufacturer, or one of that type, then jurors sympathetic to that class will be wanted in the box; a man who looks neat, and trim and smug. He will be sure to guard your interests as he would his own. His entire environment has taught him that all real values are measured in cash, and he knows no other worth. Every knowing lawyer seeks for a jury of the same sort of men as his client; men who will be able to imagine themselves in the same situation and realize what verdict the client wants.

Lawyers are just as carefully concerned about the likes and dislikes, the opinions and fads of judges as of jurors. All property rights are much safer in the hands of courts than of jurors. Every lawyer who represents the poor avoids a trial by the court.

Choosing jurors is always a delicate task. The more a lawyer knows of life, human nature, psychology, and the reactions of the human emotions, the better he is equipped for the subtle selection of his so-called "twelve men, good and true." In this undertaking, everything pertaining to the prospective juror needs be questioned and weighed; his nationality, his business, religion, politics, social standing, family ties, friends, habits of life and thought; the books and newspapers he likes and reads, and many more matters that combine to make a man; all of these qualities and experiences have left their effect on ideas, beliefs and fancies that inhabit his mind. Understanding of all this cannot be obtained too bluntly. It usually requires finesse, subtlety and guesswork. Involved in it all is the juror's method of speech, the kind of clothes he wears, the style of haircut, and, above all, his business associates, residence and origin.

To the ordinary observer, a man is just a man. To the student of life and human beings, every pose and movement is a part of the personality and the man. There is no sure rule by which one can gauge any person. A man may seem to be of a certain mold, but, a wife, a friend, or an enemy, entering into his life, may change his most vital views, desires and attitudes, so that he will hardly recognize himself as the man he once seemed to be.

It is obvious that if a litigant discovered one of his dearest friends in the jury panel he could make a close guess as to how certain facts, surrounding circumstances, and suppositions, would affect his mind and action; but as he has no such acquaintance with the stranger before him, he must weigh the prospective juror's words, manner of speech and, in fact, hastily and cautiously "size him up" as best he can. The litigants and their lawyers are supposed to want justice, but, in reality, there is no such thing as justice, either in or out of court. In fact, the word cannot be defined. So, for lack of proof, let us assume that the word "justice" has a meaning, and that the common idea of the definition is correct, without even seeking to find out what is the common meaning. Then, how do we reach justice through the courts? The lawyer's idea of justice is a verdict for his client, and really this is the sole end for which he aims.

In spite of the power that the courts exercise over the verdict of a jury, still the finding of the twelve men is very important, sometimes conclusive. It goes without saying that lawyers always do their utmost to get men on the jury who are apt to decide in favor of their clients. It is not the experience of jurors, neither is it their brain power, that is the potent influence in their decisions. A skillful lawyer does not tire himself hunting for learning or intelligence in the box; if he knows much about man and his making, he knows that all beings act from emotions and instincts, and that reason is not a motive factor. If deliberation counts for anything, it is to retard decision. The nature of the man himself is the element that determines the juror's bias for or against his fellowman. Assuming that a juror is not a half-wit, his intellect can always furnish fairly good reasons for following his instincts and emotions. Many irrelevant issues in choosing jurors are not so silly as they seem. Matters that apparently have nothing to do with the discussion of a case often are of the greatest significance.

In the last analysis, most jury trials are contests between the rich and poor. If the case concerns money, it is apt to be a case of damages for injuries of some sort claimed to have been inflicted by some one. These cases are usually defended by insurance companies, railroads, or factories. If a criminal case, it is practically always the poor who are on trial.

The most important point to learn is whether the prospective juror is humane. This must be discovered in more or less devious ways. As soon as "the court" sees what you want, he almost always blocks the game. Next to this, in having more or less bearing on the question, is the nationality, politics, and religion, of the person examined for the jury. If you do not discover this, all your plans may go awry. Whether you are handling a damage suit, or your client is charged with the violation of law, his attorney will try to get the same sort of juror.

Let us assume that we represent one of "the underdogs" because of injuries received, or, because of an indictment brought by what the prosecutors name themselves, "the state." Then what sort of men will we seek? An Irishman is called into the box for examination. There is no reason for asking about his religion; he is Irish; that is enough. We may not agree with his religion, but it matters not; his feelings go deeper than any religion. You should be aware that he is emotional, kindly and sympathetic. If he is chosen as a juror, his imagination will place him in the dock; really, he is trying himself. You would be guilty of malpractice if you got rid of him, except for the strongest reasons.

An Englishman is not so good as an Irishman, but still, he has come through a long tradition of individual rights, and is not afraid to stand alone; in fact, he is never sure that he is right unless the great majority is against him. The German is not so keen about individual rights except where they concern his own way of life; liberty is not a theory, it is a way of living. Still, he wants to do what is right, and he is not afraid. He has not been among us long, his ways are fixed by his race, his habits are still in the making. We need inquire no further. If he is a Catholic, then he loves music and art; he must be emotional, and will want to help you; give him a chance.

If a Presbyterian enters the jury box and carefully rolls up his umbrella, and calmly and critically sits down, let him go. He is cold as the grave; he knows right from wrong, although he seldom finds anything right. He believes in John Calvin and eternal punishment. Get rid of him with the fewest possible words before he contaminates the others; unless you and your clients are Presbyterians you probably are a bad lot, and even though you may be a Presbyterian, your client most likely is guilty.

If possible, the Baptists are more hopeless than the Presbyterians. They, too, are apt to think that the real home of all outsiders is Sheol, and you do not want them on the jury, and the sooner they leave the better.

The Methodists are worth considering; they are nearer the soil. Their religious emotions can be transmuted into love and charity. They are not half bad, even though they will not take a drink, they really do not need it so much as some of their competitors for the seat next to the throne. If chance sets you down between a Methodist and a Baptist, you will move toward the Methodist to keep warm.

Beware of the Lutherans, especially the Scandinavians; they are almost always sure to convict. Either a Lutheran or Scandinavian is unsafe, but if both-in-one, plead your client guilty and go down the docket. He learns about sinning and punishing from the preacher, and dares not doubt. A person who disobeys must be sent to Hell; he has God's word for that.

As to Unitarians, Universalists, Congregationalists, Jews and other agnostics, don't ask them too many questions; keep them anyhow; especially Jews and agnostics. It is best to inspect a Unitarian, or a Universalist, or a Congregationalist, with some care, for they may be prohibitionists; but never the Jews and the real agnostics! And, do not, please, accept a prohibitionist: he is too solemn and holy and dyspeptic. He knows your client would not have been indicted unless he were a drinking man, and any one who drinks is guilty of something, probably much worse than he is charged with, although it is not set out in the indictment. Neither would he have employed *you* as his lawyer had he not been guilty.

I have never experimented much with Christian Scientists; they are too serious for me. Somehow, solemn people seem to think that pleasure is wicked. Only the gloomy and dyspeptic can be trusted to convict. Shakespeare knew: "Yond' Cassius has a lean and hungry look; he thinks too much; such men are dangerous." You may defy all the rest of the rules if you can get a man who laughs. Few things in this world are of enough importance to warrant considering them seriously. So, by all means, choose a man who laughs. A juror who laughs hates to find anyone guilty.

Never take a wealthy man on a jury. He will convict, unless the defendant is accused of violating the anti-trust law, selling worthless stocks or bonds, or something of that kind. Next to the Board of Trade, for him, the Penitentiary is the most important of all public buildings. These imposing structures stand for Capitalism. Civilization could not possibly exist without them. Don't take a man because he is a "good" man; this means nothing. You should find out what he is good *for*. Neither should a man be accepted because he is a bad sort. There are too many ways of being good or bad. If you are defending, you want imaginative individuals. You are not interested in the morals of the juror. If a man is instinctively kind and sympathetic, take him.

Then, too, there are the women. These are now in the jury box. A new broom sweeps clean. It leaves no speck on the floor or under the bed, or in the darkest corners of life. To these new jurors, the welfare of the state depends on the verdict. It will be so for many years to come. The chances are that it would not have made the slightest difference to the state if all cases had been decided the other way. It might, however, make a vast difference to the unfortunates facing cruel, narrow-minded jurors who pass judgment on their fellowmen. To the defendants it might have meant the fate of life rather than death.

But, what is one life more or less in the general spawning? It may float away on the tide, or drop to the depths of oblivion, broken, crushed and dead. The great sea is full of embryo lives ready to take the places of those who have gone before. One more unfortunate lives and dies as the endless stream flows on, and little it matters to the wise judges who coldly pronounce long strings of words in droning cadence; the victims are removed, they come and go and the judges keep on chanting senseless phrases laden with doom upon the bowed heads of those before them. The judge is as unconcerned about the actual meaning of it all as the soughing wind rustling the leaves of a tree just outside the court house door.

Women still take their new privilege seriously. They are all puffed up with the importance of the part they feel they play, and are sure they represent a great step forward in the world. They believe that the sex is co-operating in a great cause. Like the rest of us, they do not know which way is forward and which is backward, or whether either one is any way at all. Luckily, as I feel my services were almost over when women invaded the jury box.

A few years ago I became interested in a man charged with selling some brand of intoxicant in a denatured land that needed cheering. I do not know whether he sold it or not. I forgot to ask him. I viewed the case with mixed feelings of pity and contempt, for as Omar philosophized, "I wonder often what the vintners buy one-half so precious as the stuff they sell?" When I arrived on the scene, the court room looked ominous with women jurors. I managed to get rid of all but two, while the dismissed women lingered around in the big room waiting for the victory, wearing solemn faces and white ribbons. The jury disagreed. In the second trial there were four women who would not budge from their seats, or their verdict. Once more I went back to the case with distrust and apprehension. The number of women in the jury box had grown to six. All of them were unprejudiced. They said so. But everyone connected with the case was growing tired and skeptical, so we concluded to call it a draw. This was my last experience with women jurors. I formed a fixed opinion that they were absolutely dependable, but I did not want them.

Whether a jury is a good one or a bad one depends on the point of view. I have always been an attorney for the defense. I can think of nothing, not even war, that has brought so much misery to the human race as prisons. And all of it is so futile!

I once spent a winter on the shores of the Mediterranean Sea. In front of my windows, four fishermen were often wearily trudging back and forth, and slowly dragging a long net across the sand. When it was safely landed, a few small, flopping fish disclosed the results of their labors. These were scattered dying on the beach, while the really worth while fishes were left in the sea, which somehow reminded me of our courts and juries, and other aims and efforts of optimistic men and their idle undertakings, and disheartening results.

Judges and jurors are like the rest of humans. Now and then some outstanding figures will roll up their sleeves, as it were, and vigorously set to work to reform the courts and get an efficient administration of justice. This will be ably seconded by the newspapers, lashing courts and jurors, past, present and prospective, into a spasm of virtue that brings down the innocent and guilty together, assuming always that there are innocent and guilty. Then, for a time, every defendant is convicted; and soon the campaign reaches the courts; after ruining a few lives and reputations, the frenzy is over, and life goes on smoothly and tranquilly as before.

When I was a boy in the country, one of the standard occupations was whittling. It became as mechanical as breathing. Since then I have decided that this is as good a way to live as any other. Life depends on the automatic taking in and letting out of breath, but in no way is it lengthened or made happier by deep thinking or wise acting. The one big word that stands over courts and other human activities is FUTILITY.

The courts may be unavailing, lawyers stupid, and both as dry as dust, but the combination makes for something interesting and exciting, and it opens avenues that seem to lead somewhere. Liberty, lives, fortunes, often are at stake, and appeal for assistance and mercy rend the air for those who care to hear. In an effort to help, often a casual remark may determine a seemingly vital situation, when perhaps the remark, of all the palaver, was the least important one breathed forth. In all questions men are frequently influenced by some statement which, spoken at the eventful time, determines fate. The most unforeseen, accidental meetings sometimes result in seemingly new and strangely fateful family lines. In fact, all that occurs in life is an endless sequence of events resulting from the wildest chance.

Amongst the twelve in a jury box, are all degrees of alertness, all sorts of ideas, and a variety of emotions; and the lawyers, too, are important factors in the outcome. They are closely observed by the jurors. They are liked, or disliked. Mayhap because of what they say, or how they speak, or pronounce their words, or part their hair. It may be that a lawyer is disliked because he talks too little, or too much; more often the latter. But a lawyer of subtlety should know when to stop, and when to go on, and how far to go. As a rule, he must not seem to be above the juror, nor below him. He must not too obviously strive for effect. He often meets baffling situations not easily explained. Sometimes it is better for him to talk of something else. Explanations must not be too fantastic, or ridiculous. It does no harm to admit the difficulty of the situation, to acknowledge that this circumstance or that seems against him. Many facts point to guilt, but in another light these facts may appear harmless.

Lawyers are apt to interpret deeds and motives as they wish them to appear. As a matter of fact, most actions are subject to various inferences, sometimes quite improbable, but nonetheless true. Identifications show common examples of mistakes. Many men are in prison and some are sent to death through mistaken identifications. One needs but recall the countless errors he, himself, has made. How many have met some person whom they believed to be an old-time friend, and have found themselves greeting a total stranger?

This is a common mistake made in restaurants and other public places. Many identifications in court are made from having seen a person but once, and under conditions not critical. Many are made from descriptions and photographs, and urged on by detectives, lawyers, and others vitally interested in the results. From all of this it is easy to see that many are convicted who are guiltless of crime. In situations of strong agitation, acquittals are rare, and sentences made long and barbarous and inhuman.

The judge is, of course, an important part of the machinery and administration of the court. Like carpenters, and lawyers, bricklayers, and saloon-keepers, they are not all alike. No two of them have the same fitness for their positions. No two have the same education; no two have the same natural understanding of themselves and their fellowman, or are gifted with the same discernment and balance. Not that judges are lacking in knowledge of law. The ordinary rules for the administration of law are rather simple and not difficult to follow. But judges should be students of life, even more than of law. Biology and psychology, which form the basis of understanding human conduct, should be taken into account. Without a fair knowledge of the mechanism of man, and the motives and urges that govern his life, it is idle to venture to fathom a situation; but, with some knowledge, officers and the public can be most useful in preserving and protecting those who most need such help. The life of almost any unfortunate, if rightly understood, can be readjusted to some plan of order and system, instead of left to drift on to ruin, the victim of ignorance, hatred and chance.

If the physician so completely ignored natural causes as the lawyers and judges, the treatment of disease would be relegated to witchcraft and magic, and the dungeon and rack would once more hold high carnival in driving devils out of the sick and afflicted. Many of the incurable victims of crime are like those who once were incurable victims of disease; they are the product of vicious and incompetent sooth-sayers who control their destinies. Every human being, whether parent, teacher, physician, or prosecutor, should make the comfort and happiness of their dependents their first concern. Now and then some learned courts take a big view of life, but scarcely do they make an impression until some public brainstorm drives them back in their treatment of crime to the methods of sorcery and conjury.

No scientific attitude toward crime can be adopted until lawyers, like physicians and scientists, recognize that cause and effects determine the conduct of men.

When lawyers and courts, and laymen, accept the scientific theory which the physicians forced upon the world long years ago, then men will examine each so-called delinquency until they discover its cause, and then learn how to remove the cause. This requires sympathy, humanity, love of one's fellowman, and a strong faith in the power of knowledge and experience to conquer the maladies of men. The Forum of the lawyers may then grow smaller, the court house may lose its spell, but the world will profit a thousandfold by a kindlier and more understanding relation toward all humankind.

THE ART OF UNDERSTANDING WOMEN

By W. BÉRAN WOLFE, M.D.

THE WORLD IS FULL OF MEN WHO ARE GOOD TO THEIR MOTHERS, FAIR to their employees, kind to children and puppies, honest and upright in their business dealings, honorable and responsible toward their fellowmen, devoted to their ideals—for whom no woman will ever put an extra dab of powder on her nose. Some of these men are acutely unhappy because they cannot find the way to a woman's heart. Others delude themselves with various struthious mechanisms: they insist that women are false and unworthy of their love; they bury themselves in business so deeply that it appears they have no time for women; they occupy their leisure in the passionate pursuit of prowess in bridge, golf, politics, or polo. Some of these men even hide their quandaries behind bookish walls, or take refuge behind the ramparts of scientific research.

Try as they may to conceal their inner anxiety both from their own recognition and from the eyes of the rest of the world, the woman question obtrudes itself into their lives with something akin to malicious persistence. Some men sigh and marry their housekeepers in order to solve the problem and assuage their consciences quickly and effectively. Others hesitate and procrastinate so long that nature solves the problem for them by protecting them behind the sclerotic walls of senility. Most of the men who remain eternally mystified by the challenge of womankind make tentative attempts to solve the mystery, are frightened by their ineptitude, and retire to sigh and suffer for the rest of their lives.

It is a curious thing that in a world in which so much technical virtuosity is acquired in overcoming sales resistance, building better automobile engines, and manufacturing better cheese, no one has thought of founding a school for love. We have developed experts in the proper use of the mashie, in the technique of tooth extraction, even in the art of making the population banana-conscious, but no one has had the temerity to set himself up as an expert in the technique of the masculine approach to a woman's love. Many a magnificent lover has gone to waste for lack of the requisite technique of getting to first base (perhaps we should better say, to first bed!) in the game of love. Yet it requires no sage to point out that a man's millions are worthless if he cannot share them with the woman he really loves. No man would strive and sweat for honor and prestige if he did not feel that at the end of the long pull there was a woman who would approve and reward him for his efforts with the precious coin of tenderness, understanding and love. The paradox of our civilization is that we school ourselves assiduously for the attainment of unessential objectives at the same time that we blithely leave the preparations for the most essential and meaningful happiness that we can ever hope to attain largely to chance—and the timid aggressions of our women!

The average man who is unsuccessful in his relations to women blames his stars, the perfidy of women, or the confusion of the times for his failures. The fault is far more likely to be his own than that of the women who will not fall for him, the failure more likely to be caused by the ineptness of his approach, the inadequacy of his technique, the absence of a proper "follow-through," than by the difficulties and resistance of women. I shall devote this article to the clarification of the problem and the elaboration of some practical hints for timid men, be they bachelors or benedicts. It is obvious that merely being married is no certificate of proficiency in love. There are as many husbands whose lives are made unhappy by their ignorance of the soul of woman and the fine art of being a lover, as there are timid bachelors who fear to chance marriage because of an inner sense of insecurity born of their incompetence and maladroitness.

Let us approach the problem from its very fundamentals. For the last six or seven thousand years, as far as history can tell us, we, in the Western world, have been living in a patriarchal civilization. At some time near the dawn of history men discovered iron, fashioned tools, domesticated animals captured in the hunt, and built up a civilization based on the possession of flocks and grazing grounds. The older agricultural communal civilization was overturned, and with the transformation women, who had formerly been the dominant sex, became subordinated to their men folk. Evidently the men who first acquired power and prestige in those far off days were much afraid that their women folk would turn the tables on them at some future time, and, therefore, secured their newfound power by instituting laws and conventions which have kept women more or less enslaved ever since.

For centuries women were content to be classed as second-rate men. Those who attempted to rise out of their dependency and inferiority were usually burned as witches. Women had no chance to earn their living independently, and perforce, were constrained to remain at home and do the world's dirty work. All this changed with the birth of the machine age. The true emancipation of woman began with the death of feudalism and the rise of the middle class. With the development of machinery and international markets, women, for the first time in six thousand years of history, were able to maintain themselves by their own labor, and so to take their place as equals in the civilization of today.

I am interested not so much in explaining the sociology of woman's present rise to power as I am in demonstrating that this sociological, economic and political process has given rise to a very interesting psychological and human problem. Ever since women began demanding "rights" as human beings and getting privileges by earning them in economic competition with men, three main types of women have appeared on the scene. And no man who wants to be a successful lover can afford to be ignorant of this evolution of the modern woman.

The first of these three types is the "old-fashioned" girl. She still believes implicitly in the inferiority of women and the superiority of men. She wants to lean on a strong man, demands that she be treated chivalrously and protected as if she were a delicate and frail flower incapable of existence in a hard and matter-of-fact world.

The second type is the woman who has been caught in the revolutionary stream of emancipation. She rejects the old theory, and not only believes that she is as good as any man, but often insists that she is far better. She is aggressive, independent, "mannish," go-getting, and resents the imputation of weakness. She will have none of your old-fashioned chivalry. She wants to pay as she goes, wants to be treated "like a man."

The third type, and perhaps the rarest of the three, is the psychologically mature woman who recognizes that being a woman is neither a sign of inferiority nor of superiority. She wants to be a comrade, a complement, not an ornament. She is a helpmate in the best sense of the word. She wants to share both the privileges and the responsibilities of freedom and demands that her own spirit and independence be acknowledged for their true worth. She neither wants to cling to a man and play the weak sister, nor does she want to parody masculinity by expressing her "mannishness." She is the woman of the future, and I wish every man the good fortune of finding such a woman for his wife or lover. She is the most satisfactory, the most thrilling, the most completely human woman to have, the hardest to get, the most difficult to hold.

Of course all women do not fall into sharp categories, but most of them fall predominantly into one or the other of these three types. There is a fourth type which also requires description because women of this fourth type make up a great proportion of the women who populate urban America. These are the women who vacillate between the harems of the type I women, and the business offices of the type II women. They want the privileges of emancipation without its responsibilities, the solicitude, chivalry, and romanticism of feudalism without the concomitant inconveniences of chastity belts and chaperons. Women in this fourth type are hopelessly involved in the age-old problem of having their cake and eating it too. No woman has ever succeeded in solving this problem satisfactorily, and, therefore, most of the type IV women are serving long-term enlistment in the vast army of Neurosis. My advice to young men is to flee from type IV women as they would from the plague, for the man who has not the patience of the saints, the insight of a psychiatrist, and the sense of humor of a man able to crack jokes about ropes while being led to the gallows, will ever succeed in being happy with such a woman.

Now suppose that you are a thoroughly conservative and traditionally minded man who has a normal feeling of incompleteness without a woman, but who wants that woman to be an ornament and supplement to his own ego. You want to express your masculinity, you want to be a thorough he-man, you want to feel that no matter how hard the world treats you on the outside, you want to be the master in your own home, you want to dominate your own bed and board. You belong to the Old Guard of masculinity and you will want something of a clinging vine for your mate to properly set off your own independence and dominance (God help you!).

Psychologically you are going to be attracted by the active and aggressive woman of type II, who will challenge your masculinity by the impudence of her mannishness. If you want to succeed, you must avoid such a woman, for she will sell you out. To court a type II woman is to court eternal conflict, and unless you desire to spend the rest of your days in a cat-and-dog conflict for prestige, leave the hard-working, hard-hitting type II girl strictly alone, and concentrate on finding a type I woman. You can tell her by her coy gestures, her thoroughly feminine manners, her tendency to lean and to wait. A woman of this type will look up at you with big collie-like eyes of wonder and amazement, and your masculine heart will beat a tattoo to tell you that you have met her. Of course you must seek a formal introduction to such a woman.

When you have found her you must treat her with the utmost chivalry. Give her flowers and perfume for presents, and never take her to hockey games or prize fights. Always help her with her coat, lift her across curbstones, compliment her on her exquisite taste in dress and look soulfully into her eyes now and then. The usual movie technique will be just the right thing here, and do not fail to be nice to her mother and bring little presents for her younger sisters and brothers. You can brag about your athletic exploits, and let her feel your muscle. Play the he-man, take her to church, imitate her father, never tell her bawdy stories, and keep your copy of ESQUIRE safely hidden at your office.

But suppose you are fed up with the he-man stuff, and believe that a woman should do her part. Keep away from the type I woman who will always annoy you with her helplessness, and find a tailored girl among the type II candidates. You can open the conversation with a risqué story. She will appreciate it because she will sense the fact that you are approaching her "as if" she were a man, and your perspicacity in this will not go unrewarded. Let your first present be a new niblick, or a new cravat from your own haberdasher, or a cigarette lighter. Ask her whether she would not feel more comfortable if she shared in the week-end expenses. Let her drive your car and take her to a prize fight and do not hold her chair when she sits down at a table, and above all never help her across a street. Talk to her about her business or professional accomplishments, compliment her on her activities rather than on her looks, ask her advice on your business problems. Let her win an occasional golf game from you, and do not use the movie technique with her. Avoid sentimentalizing and patronage, and look for opportunities to let her take the initiative in your mutual activities. And unless I miss my guess, she will want to go home alone in a taxi rather than let you play the cavalier to her door.

With type III women—may Heaven make more of them!—you can be yourself. You need not display your masculinity, nor must you fear that you will insult her by offering to be courteous or normally solicitous. She will expect you to pay for cocktails, but will expect to share on the week-end. She will demand that you respect her—as a human being—not because she is a woman. She will be interested in children *and* sports, in a home *and* a career because she is a normal woman. Naturally, the man who can find such a woman should do everything in his power to honor her, and the beautiful part about type III is that she is the easiest one to get along with. And as I have said, when you see a type IV woman, a woman who wants freedom without responsibility, put on your running pants and streak!

Most of the men who cannot approach women and most of the men who cannot make women care for them are not suffering from a specific sexual maladroitness. It is their egoism and lack of community and social feeling that is basically at fault. Women are not essentially different from men. Women are human beings, and the same laws that apply to ordinary social intercourse apply equally cogently to the approach to women. Perhaps women are more sensitive to uncouthness than men—it may be a defensive gesture in their unconscious. The man who would be a success with women should pay especial attention to the finesse of dress and personal appearance. Dirty fingernails, unpolished shoes, bizarre color schemes in dress, unkempt hair and unshaven faces may not determine the true value of a man, but they are strong indications of the degree to which his social feeling has developed. Success with women is basically dependent upon the robustness of this social feeling, and most women who are worth their salt have a profound intuitive appreciation of these apparently unimportant indices.

In the foregoing paragraphs I have indicated certain types of women produced by the sociological, economic and historical determinants of our civilization. The type that appeals to you will be largely a matter of your own psychological maturity. Success in love, however, is based on something far deeper and more essential than the ability to distinguish these external categories of women and to make the appropriate approach to each. The man who would know and understand women, and thus be really successful with them, must have a basic understanding of the fundamental psychology of all women, a psychology which defies time and geographical locus, religions, race, and economic status. Show me a man whom women love, and I will show you a man who consciously or unconsciously has developed an appreciation of the deep unconscious needs of women.

The fundamentals of psychogynecology, as the science of understanding women might be called, are not difficult to learn. The first axiom of this science is that between man and woman there exists a certain "distance," a psychological and biological "distance," and that concomitant with this "distance" there is a perfectly normal tension, a difference of potential comparable to the difference of electrical potential between the negative and positive electrodes of a battery. The solution of the problems of distance and tension requires a certain degree of self-assurance on the part of the male. This self-assurance, together with complete psychological maturity is the premise without which that soul-shaking experience of the complete fusion of "I" and "You" into a novel, different, transmuted "We" cannot be consummated.

The distance between the sexes must be bridged by the symbolic acts of social cooperation and mutual esteem. The tension must be solved by the alternation of pursuit and surrender. It is a mistake to believe that man is always the hunter and woman always the prey. In her own fashion woman also is the aggressor, and man in many ways, the victim. The methods and techniques of the two sexes, however, are different. Most males fail in their approach because they want to play one rôle to the exclusion of the other. They want to appear, either as the aggressive pursuer or as the hopeless victim of the woman's charms. You may succeed in capturing your woman with one of these techniques, but you cannot hold her without the other. You must make a symbolic show of pursuit and a further symbolic show of surrender to her beauty and charm. This double process keeps love alive and interesting. Be masterful, but not domineering—the two are mutually exclusive. Pursue, but do not hunt down your prey! Surrender to the powerful magic of woman, but do not check your brains with your rubbers and umbrella at the gate!

The second axiom of psychogynecology is this: if you would have women love you, you must understand what every woman wants in a man. The love instinct in woman is not a simple thing. It is a complex structure composed of many elements rooted deep in a woman's unconscious. Every woman wants her man to be a combination of father, brother, lover, and child, and the man who would be beloved by women must know how to play all four of these strings that are stretched across her heart. By observation and identification a man can learn to sense which of these four strings plays the dominant melody in a woman's unconscious symphony of life, and he must learn to play predominantly on that string without becoming monotonous. The trouble with most men is that they are so wrapped up in their own unconscious strivings that they have neither the interest nor the time to investigate the emotional and psychological needs of the women they meet. Men are usually so busy broadcasting their own importance that they cannot tune in on the wave lengths that emanate from the unconscious depths of the woman they desire for a mate. Failure to alternate broadcasting with reception is a certain premise of failure in attaining the love of women.

Every man must symbolically play the four rôles of father, brother, lover and child to every woman. Any relationship, in which all four of these rôles are not occasionally touched, is incomplete, and sooner or later it becomes responsible for the break-up of the love relationship. The man who is certain of his own worth will not hesitate to play the rôle of baby or brother—it will not basically damage his self-esteem. Only a coward will be afraid of playing the baby rôle from time to time, thereby giving his woman the opportunity to express a deep and profound psychological craving which later should find its complete expression in motherhood.

I cannot too strongly urge upon you the necessity of understanding and acting out the symbolism of love. This begins usually with the man's demonstration of his superiority and strength, the admission of the woman's weakness and timidity. Then the chase begins between hunter and quarry, the "distance" is lessened by the man's mastery, the tension "solved" by the woman's apparent surrender. The hunter must indicate that he has accepted the challenge of the quarry's swiftness and elusiveness. All women want the semblance of being chased, because this gives them a sense of value and self-esteem. Moreover the hunt must not be too quickly terminated. The hunter must seem to hesitate and must appear confused by the quarry's elusiveness. Then with fresh determination and dominance, he must press forward his pursuit. Then only should come the "kill" in which the sweet moments of mystic fusion are symbolically enacted. This acme of love should be followed by expressions of tenderness and solicitude on the part of the pursuing male. The result of the well-enacted and oft-repeated drama of love is the true comradeship and sharing of a mature human relation. The pursuer must now relinquish all manifestations of superiority, and symbolically reiterate the magical attractiveness of the quarry. This symbolical ritual is all too frequently forgotten entirely, enacted only in part, or glossed over as unessential. Then it is that husbands and lovers are subsequently surprised and hurt to learn that their wives have gone elsewhere for love. No woman can live and be happy unless she can perennially renew her sense of self-esteem in this magical ritual. This ritual must be elaborated not only in each approach to a new lover, but also in every single contact with the woman with whom a man has decided to share a greater or lesser period of his life.

Thus, if you want to be loved by women you must understand them. You must recognize the existence of certain typical patterns of femininity and choose the woman you would have love you from the type which most closely complements your own needs. Having made this choice you must approach her first as a fellow human being, and only then as a woman. Finally, you must be aware of the hidden psychological craving present in all women, and be willing to vary your approach by playing shifting rôles of father, brother, lover, and child. The symbolic repetition of attraction, chase, domination, relinquishment of superiority and establishment of comradeship with the quarry must be "followed through" in each fresh contact. If you are too great an egotist to be capable of cooperation, too rigid to be willing to adjust and make compromises with a woman's psychological needs, too earth-bound to have imagination, too ambitious to be patient, too insecure in your own self-esteem to listen and to learn from women, or too matter-of-fact to understand the importance of the symbolic rituals of love, you might just as well relinquish all hopes of being a successful lover.

QUEEN IN THE PARLOUR CAR

By JOSEPH E. McDOUGALL

I FIRST SAW HER GOING THROUGH THE ROTUNDA OF THE HOTEL AND immediately I lost all interest in the antics of the convention. It was obvious at a glance that she was not one of the girls the local men had brought down to entertain us. I watched her cross the rotunda like a queen, a very young beautiful queen all holiday, happy and golden, and I do not believe I have ever before been smitten quite the way I was then.

I am not a sophomore and I've been around, but this girl glowed, and I glowed too as I watched her pass.

She swept down to the end of the rotunda all shining, and a young man, very dark and latin and handsome, met her there. He looked serious, I thought, and he hardly spoke to her as he led her into the dining room.

The orchestra inside was playing *Song of Songs*, I remember that clearly. I remember the words of Solomon's song running through my head as I went up to the convention floor in the elevator:

"Behold thou art fair, my love, behold thou art fair . . ."

I did not drink very much at the dinner, or afterwards. Somehow I didn't feel like it.

When I got on the evening train I went into the parlour car right away. I had a bottle of rye in my overcoat and I hung it up carefully so that the top of the bottle would not show. As I did so I observed that the car was almost empty. The seat next to me was occupied, and she was in it. When the train pulled out she was still alone.

She was looking out of the window, though it was too dark to see anything, and as I looked at her cautiously it seemed to me that her face had become a mask, a Benda mask perhaps, beautiful but set. I was glad I had remained sober and I wondered if I dared to speak with her. If I said nothing I could look at her all the way

506

to Buffalo; if I spoke to her and she refused to talk with me I would have to go into the smoker or sit there the whole three hours feeling uncomfortable, an intruder.

In a little while I called the porter for a pillow. As he was placing it behind my head he asked her if she would like one too and I offered her mine. She accepted it gracefully and we resumed our former silence. At length I could stand it no longer. I decided to be as direct as possible.

"Would you care for a drink?" I asked.

She looked at me steadily and searchingly for a minute and then, quite seriously she replied, "Yes, thank you, I would."

I had the porter set up a table and ordered soda.

We had that one and shortly afterward another. There was nothing flirtatious about her manner. She talked easily in a deep resonant voice that was a delight, about impersonal, commonplace things. She acknowledged my attempts at witticism without laughter and yet she succeeded in letting me know that she appreciated my efforts to be agreeable. All the time I seemed to feel her studying me, so that I was afraid to look too closely at her. I observed, however, that she was wearing a finely tailored suit of light blue. The soft ruching of her blouse at her throat imparted to her a flower-like quality. Her white, slender hand held her glass lightly. She wore no rings.

"I hope we're not late," she said, "I have to go across town to make connections when we get to Buffalo."

"So have I," I lied. I was spending the next day in Buffalo. "We can get a taxi together."

"That will be fine," she agreed.

She looked at me searchingly again and smiled. She drained her glass and said quietly,

"May I have another?"

I poured her one, a good one, and was about to ring for the porter, when she stopped me.

"I'll take this one neat, I think," she said.

I took one neat too.

We sat there for a moment without speaking so I began to tell her about the convention.

"You get fed up with them," I told her, "one convention is just like another. You never accomplish anything. They're just an

excuse for getting tight. I like to play, I suppose, as much as anyone but sometimes I begin to wonder what it's all about. I wasn't
always a salesman and maybe that's why I get tired of them. I used
to be on a newspaper and occasionally I sold a story or two to a
magazine. I didn't make as much money then but I know I was
happier."

So I told her about myself, about the novel I would finish some
day, about the girl who started me writing it long ago and how
much she reminded me of her. That last, I suppose, was not literally
true, but as I talked and looked at her it seemed to become more
and more so. She listened sympathetically.

"When I saw you tonight in the hotel, it seemed to bring all
that back to me," I said.

She suddenly looked very tired.

"You saw me tonight in the hotel?" she asked.

"Yes," I said. "You walked through the rotunda and met a man
at the entrance to the dining room. A tall, dark, good-looking
chap."

"Yes, I know," she said quickly. Then, "Do you think we could
have another drink?"

I pretended not to be surprised. As a matter of fact I was delighted. She apparently had confidence in me, and, for my part,
the whiskey I had poured myself had served to enhance her de-
sirability. Nevertheless, I was a little puzzled. She did not look like
a girl who drank much and yet the rye she had taken seemed to
be having no effect upon her at all.

As soon as I had attended to our glasses she raised hers.

"To a pleasant journey," she proposed.

We clicked glasses and I am sure it was accidentally that our
fingers touched. I was nettled that the electric effect of that contact seemed to leave her unmoved.

"I have known quite a few writers," she said, "one of them was
a poet; he was a very dear friend of mine."

"I have written a little poetry too," I said. "There was a thing I
wrote last year; I can't remember it, but there were three lines in it
you might like."

I quoted them. She did not enthuse, though in her steady gaze
I felt a disturbing understanding. This was not what I wanted.

I realized that I was tricking myself into allowing a gay little adventure to turn into a romance. I pulled myself up short.

"When we get in there's a little place I'd like to show you," I suggested. "We might have time to drop in for a quick one if you like. I always make a point of it."

"Fine," she agreed. "You be my guide. I think I'd like it."

This time she smiled at me, a little mechanically, but there was a revelation in her face when she smiled as though she had disclosed a glimpse of a warm and lovely soul.

What the hell! I thought, can't you take a drink any more? You know perfectly well why you're here and why you suggested going to Tony's. You hope she'll miss her train. You hope . . .

"I seem to have finished mine," she said. "Do you think there's one left for each of us?"

I looked hard at her. My last drink had been scarcely touched, yet I felt a gathered sensation around my eyes and she seemed as fresh and calm as when I had seen her in the hotel.

"I think, if you don't mind, I'll miss this one," I said as I poured hers.

"Not in the least," she assured me, "I just feel like a drink or two tonight I guess."

She drank that one neat too.

When we arrived at Buffalo there was plenty of time so we put our bags in a taxi and went straight to Tony's. In the warm, soft-lit bar we sat on stools and sipped old-fashioneds. The lights and the music and the people suddenly stimulated us, gave us both, I felt, the illusion of being in love. She became almost vivacious and laughed pleasantly, a little-girl laugh, but with a deep note in it. We leaned happily towards each other.

"Do you really have to catch that train?" I asked.

"I was waiting for you to ask me that."

She put down her glass and laid her hand lightly on mine. She looked straight into my eyes. For a second a look came over her face as though she expected me to strike her, but she smiled.

"They have lots of trains," she said. And a short hysterical laugh caught in her throat.

In the hotel room she seemed sad again. She had insisted that I buy a flask at Tony's and as soon as I had shut the door she asked me for it.

"I really think I ought to have a nightcap," she said.

"Why not save it for an eye-opener?"

She had taken off her coat and hat and stood quite close to me with her hair a glorious halo around her head. At my protest she stiffened and her voice was a command.

"I know what is best for me!" she said.

I gave her the flask and took two glasses into the bathroom to rinse them. In the mirror on the half open bathroom door I saw her put the flask to her lips and hold it there. I hastily rinsed the glasses and came out.

She was lying on the bed, completely out of the picture.

I held a towel under the cold water tap and bathed her forehead for several minutes but she did not come to. Her heart was beating naturally and her breathing was all that could be expected, so I gave up trying to revive her and sat on the other bed wrestling with a demon.

She was one of the most beautiful women I had ever seen. She was a theatrical photographer's vision of the ideal model. She was young and fresh and, even lying there passed out, she seemed to somehow dominate me. Her low voice was still singing in my ears and the memory of that second when our fingers touched made me tingle.

I stood up and looked at her closely. She undoubtedly expects me to make love to her, I told myself. She would laugh at me if I didn't. That dark man didn't look like the Angel Gabriel. She is a woman of the world and she is the most beautiful woman with whom I have ever been alone. Then the memory of her serious gaze studying me in the train came to me, and the smothered hysterical laugh . . .

Suddenly I bent and kissed her forehead. Then I took off her shoes and stockings and dress as if she were some lovely child. I pulled the covers over her and, slipping into my pyjamas, got into my own bed. I looked at her once before I turned out the light.

"Good night, my dear," I heard myself say.

When I awoke it was to find her sitting up on the edge of her bed. She must have had recourse to her make up; at any rate she looked as fresh as April.

She smiled at me companionably.

"What happened?" she laughed.

"I think we must have had something to drink," I suggested.

"Do you feel all right?" she asked.

"Not too bad, but what about you?"

"Why, I feel fine." She smiled. "Of course, why not?"

"No regrets?"

"Don't be silly. Besides, how can one regret what one does not remember?"

"I remember."

"Regrets?"

"None!"

"Did I make you happy?"

"Very," I said. I was determined never to let her know what a milksop I had been. Besides, I spoke the truth.

She stood up.

"That, I suppose, is just as it should be," she said. She took some things out of her suitcase and, picking up her dress from the end of the bed, she went into the bathroom. I heard her turn on the bath. While she was there I put on my clothes. I was nearly dressed when she came out. It was hard to believe that I had won this woman—well, technically won her, at least.

She smiled, acknowledging the admiration in my eyes.

"Will you do me a favour?" she asked.

"Anything."

"Would you buy me a pair of stockings? These have a run in them and I brought no others."

She gave me the size.

"Of course," I said. I hurried with my preparations and put on my coat and hat.

"I'll be back in a jiffy," I said.

As I reached the door, she stopped me. She came and put her hand on my shoulder, looking at me again with that serious expression of hers.

"I was going to say something," she said after a minute, "but I guess I won't."

We stood there. Then, suddenly, she kissed me, full on the mouth. It was the first time, though she could hardly have known that.

"You're a dear boy," she said. "Now, hurry, won't you?"

I found a woman's shop and bought the finest pair of stockings I could find. I took particular care in selecting them. Seeing them on the counter, I thought, how uninteresting and impersonal they seem now, before she has touched them, how infinitely less valuable than the cheapest torn pair she has ever discarded! I put the package in my pocket and raced back to the hotel. I watched the elevator indicator coming down, stopping as if deliberately to provoke me at almost every numeral.

As soon as I had entered the car it was filled with fools who lived on intervening floors. At last it reached my floor, our floor. I rushed down the corridor and knocked upon the door.

There was no response. I made certain it was the right room, knocked again, my heart beating wildly. I called, suddenly remembering that I did not know her name. I was answered by silence.

Suddenly afraid that she was ill, I called a maid and persuaded her to open the door. Inside were my grips and night clothes just as I had left them. Even the flask of rye was standing foolishly on the dresser exactly where she had placed it the night before. But she, and every trace of her, was gone.

I tore out into the hall, down the elevator, through the lobby. I looked up and down the street. Hailing a cab I drove to the station. I was alone.

She has committed suicide by leaping from the window, I thought. There was no commotion on the street because her body is lying on a ledge. Driving back to the hotel, I thought: she is playing a joke on me. She'll be there when I return. Nevertheless, I called at the desk for my key. It was there. The clerk handed me a note at the same time.

"Forgive me," it said, "if my leaving you like this seems a strange way of expressing my gratitude, for I *am* grateful, or I should be. You have helped me, helped me by breaking a spell by which I was bound. And if that sounds cryptic or melodramatic, it is nonetheless true. Our little comedy of last night released me from a faithfulness which, though it was not returned, has held me a captive for a great many years. And so I *am* grateful to you for setting me free."

Then, here, the handwriting seemed to change slightly.

"That is what I should say, I know," it went on, "but I am afraid I cannot bring myself to really mean it. I thought if I made myself completely sodden it would not be so difficult. Weakly, I know now that I want what you cannot give me—my faithfulness back again. God help me in my lonely freedom!"

There was no signature.

I walked slowly to the elevator, closed my bags and phoned for the porter. In the room there was the faintest trace of a delicate perfume.

ARE WRESTLERS PEOPLE?

By WESTBROOK PEGLER

OFTEN, AS I HAVE SAT AT THE RINGSIDE, WATCHING GREAT, HAIRY lumps of living meat spank, throttle and wring one another, it has occurred to me to wonder whether wrestlers love and are loved and whether they really suffer. Or are they, like the fishworm, incapable of emotion and insensible to pain?

Perhaps I am wrong in assuming that the fishworm has neither sentiments nor senses but I do assume as much because it spares my conscience on those rare occasions—the last one was in 1926— when I string him on the hook. I did have a twinge of misgiving some time ago when I read in a sporting-goods catalog of a device for luring the fishworm from his hole in the ground. This was an electrical apparatus, something like a tuning-fork, which, being jabbed in the ground near the worm-hole, uttered a faint mooing note and brought the male, or bull, worm charging out of the soil with his neck arched and his pulses pounding in his veins.

It suggested that the fishworm might have depths after all and that we might all be mistaken in our easy belief that because he does not quack, bark or snarl, he doesn't know he is being ill-treated. Maybe he is just reticent. There are New Englanders like that but we call them canny.

It would be very unchivalrous, I think, to impose upon the most beautiful sentiment of all in any of God's creatures with the siren call of love to seduce him to his doom. This, moreover, is quite aside from the moral aspect of the matter. Sex is something which Nature has implanted in all of us and in its proper relation to life is a very beautiful thing. But I would call it most immoral to inflame the fishworm's passions by artificial means even though we did not string him on a hook but merely left him there, bothered, bewildered and breathing hard.

The wrestler is a strange organism. It has certain characteristics which must test the conviction of the most confirmed Fundamentalist, suggesting that 'way, 'way back in some rocky cave all of us were wrestlers. It walks on its hind legs, it can be trained to speak and understand and Mr. Jack Curley, the promoter of wrestling shows, once had one in his herd which could cook a good dinner. However it cooked only one dinner for Mr. Curley.

He was entertaining a party of friends at his home in Great Neck, Long Island, that night and his wrestler had cooked pheasant for them. During the meal, Mr. Curley remarked to the lady sitting next him that his cook was a wrestler.

"Oh, I would like to see it," the lady said and Mr. Curley, clapping his hands, cried, "Wrestler! Come heren sie!"

That was Mr. Curley's way of addressing this wrestler. It was a German. When he wanted the wrestler to go down-stairs he said, "Wrestler! Down-stairsen sie" and when he wanted it to go upstairs he said, "Wrestler! Up-stairsen sie." The ablative, you know.

So when the lady said she would like to see the wrestler which had cooked the dinner, Mr. Curley clapped his hands and called, "Wrestler! Come heren sie!"

The kitchen door opened and the wrestler entered. It was wearing a pair of wool wrestling trunks and sneakers. Its hide and the fur on its chest were moist.

"Wrestler," said Mr. Curley, "dinner is very good tonight."

"Jah?" said the wrestler, puckering its face in an appreciative grin and blinking its knobby ears. "Fine. But boy it is hot in that kitchen. Look how the sweat runs off of me."

Many a night at the ringside I have heard laymen sitting in the forward rows explain to their ladies that the punishment which wrestlers inflict on one another really does not hurt them as they are used to it and cannot feel, anyway. This is of a piece with the assumption that the fishworm cannot feel. I am not sure that it is true.

The fishworm wiggles and squirms when it is put upon the hook and the wrestler trumpets terribly and wooshes and writhes when it is being twisted in the ring. This may only mean that some vague intuition, such as turtles possess, is telling the wrestler not to go over on its back. Yet the wrestler is so amenable to training that it is comparatively easy to teach it to recognize a signal and, in violation of a strong natural instinct, to roll over on its back momentarily after thirty or forty minutes of wrestling, while the referee gives its adversary a slap on the shoulder signifying that it has won the contest.

The word contest, of course, is merely a trade term. Most of the minor politicians who constitute the various prizefight commissions and supervise wrestling do not authorize its use in connection with wrestling bouts. They insist upon calling them exhibitions and the newspaper boys who cover them call them mockeries or make-believes and refer to that thirty of forty minutes of action which precedes the fall as the squirm.

Wrestling is the one hazardous occupation in the sport department of journalism because wrestlers are vindictive in a dumb way and one never can tell when one of them will pick up another and throw it at a correspondent sitting at the ringside. Moreover, after one has seen a few squirms one has seen them all and consequently one is likely to doze off during that time when the wrestlers are putting on the squirm. One learns to gauge these cat-naps and come out of it just in time for the signal.

But the wrestler may resent this as an affront to its art and retaliate by heaving 250 pounds of moist and rather smelly weight, usually foreign matter, into the journalist's lap. I have seen as many as six journalists mown down by one wrestler thrown in this manner and had a very exciting evening myself once when I made a mistake at the ringside.

One wrestler was sitting on top of another and, with the dumb concentration of a trick baboon untying a shoe-lace, was twisting a large, bare foot.

"Hey, wrestler!" I cried, in honest error, for they were badly tangled up, "you are twisting your own foot."

At that the wrestler let out a loud howl of "Ow-oo," thinking that if it was twisting its own foot it must be hurting itself, and let go. But it happened to be the other wrestler's foot after all and when the first one let go the other one jumped up.

This enraged the wrestler which had been twisting the foot and six times that evening it threw the other one at me with intent to inflict great bodily harm. But, fortunately, though it had plenty of swift, its control was bad. So nothing happened to me, although the New York World-Telegram was hit twice and the New York Times's typewriter was smashed.

The fact that wrestlers utter sounds of apparent anguish does not necessarily prove that they really feel pain. They are trained to that, too. In former times they wrestled without sound effects and these were introduced in recent years by Mr. Curley who hired an expert in bird-calls and animal cries to instruct the members of his herd. At first the wrestlers made some ludicrous mistakes and one sometimes heard a wrestler twittering gayly when it was supposed to bleat piteously.

As to whether they love and are loved I just have no way of knowing. Maybe so, though. Hippopotamuses do.

HIDE YOUR EYES

By EDWARD ACHESON

DR. KRESSMAN MADE A NOTE ON THE PAD BEFORE HIM AND LEANED back in the chair. What was she talking about now? Her misunderstood childhood again? She was an exhausting patient, this Mrs. Benson. Spoiled. Too much money. But a hard integrated personality. Suffering from a Compulsion Neurosis. Unable to stop counting. Common symptom . . . Counts steps, up and down, counts trees, rows of books, shuts her eyes and imagines series of things to count . . . Counts in her sleep . . . So simple if it could only be explained to the patient . . . Counts so she won't have to think of something, something she doesn't want to think about, something she's subconsciously determined she won't think about . . . But eventually she'll have to. If she keeps up the analysis, eventually it will come out, this despised thing she's trying to hide from herself . . . Then she'll stop counting . . . Then there'll be nothing to cover up . . . Talking about her father now? . . . No, her husband. She should have no difficulty in that relationship, the two men are so much alike . . . Nature's method of keeping the strain pure. Women always turning instinctively to men like their fathers. Well, *she* had . . . this Mrs. Benson. Her trouble wasn't as simple as that . . . Something deeper . . . Let her talk. The hour was almost up anyway.

Dr. Kressman stifled a yawn. He was very tired. He hadn't slept. He hadn't slept for a number of nights. Something kept gnawing at him. It wasn't true. He knew it wasn't true. But he couldn't get free of it. It waited beside his bed like a sentinel. And when he glanced over at his wife before switching off the light, he knew he wasn't going to sleep. And he didn't. He lay there, staring into the darkness, explaining away his fears. His wife's sudden interest in sculpture, modeling. Most likely a sublimation. They had no children. The maternal instinct rechanneled into

creative art. A natural outlet. Nothing whatsoever to do with this
fellow Newman. New-man. Interesting word psychologically,
New-man. Her animation. Had she been more animated lately?
More completely alive? . . . Physical, entirely. She'd been ill.
Now she was better. She just felt more poignantly the value of
what she'd regained. And her renewed interest in clothes wasn't
significant. Of course not! . . . She was young. Fifteen years
younger than he was. And youth did things by fits and starts. Trial
and error, part of the adjustment process.

And then the doctor would get up very quietly and go down
stairs to the sideboard. He'd pour out a drink and hold it up to
the light, mustering a smile. "Physician, heal thyself!" For he
knew the human mind and he knew rationalization when he met
it. He was trying to explain this Newman chap out of existence.
He knew what he was doing, but he couldn't stop doing it. Rationalizing him *into* existence, really. Then he'd take a second drink
and go back to bed and lie there and stare into the stillness. He was
very tired.

He yawned again and looked quickly to see whether Mrs. Benson had noticed. She hadn't. She was flat on her back with her
eyes closed, talking, talking, forever. The doctor listened absently.
She was back on the theme of Lady Chatterley's Lover. That book
seemed to be an obsession with Mrs. Benson. That was the fifth
time she'd brought it up in as many days. The doctor selected a
pencil and waited. Mrs. Benson's voice droned on. "What if she
was unfaithful to him. . . . Unfaithful! . . . If that isn't a male
word for you . . . Unfaithful. And Lawrence makes such an
unholy fuss over it, talks about it, loves it, rolls in it. I'd like to see
his mind psychoanalyzed. Probably look like a particularly nasty
garbage dump on a hot day . . . Filthy, low, unspeakable ——"

The doctor made a note of the three words, "Filthy, low, unspeakable." She had used them over and over again.

"And what if she was unfaithful to him? She didn't love him.
He didn't love her. Or else he did. I forget. But she didn't love
him . . ."

Dr. Kressman glanced at his clock. Almost five. He'd be through
at five. This was his last patient. And he was nearly through with
her for good. He drew a circle on his pad, and then a square inside

the circle. From the middle of three sides of the square he drew lines into the center. That was the way one found the center, where those lines crossed. He was almost at the center of Mrs. Benson's difficulty. So many lines pointed to it. She loved her husband, and she'd had an affair, either actual or imaginary, with someone else. Whether it was actual, or whether she'd just thought about it didn't matter. The affair itself didn't matter. It was the fact that Mrs. Benson was ashamed of it, that she fought against admitting it to herself. That was the thing she refused to think about, the thing that kept demanding to be thought about. So she counted. This last thing, this defense of Lady Chatterley which kept cropping out, was a perfect example of Projection. She transferred herself to the person of Lady Chatterley and then argued her cause, because her conscience wouldn't allow her to argue her own directly.

"Five o'clock, Mrs. Benson," the doctor said, trying not to sound relieved.

"Oh," Mrs. Benson said, and was silent. Finally she sat up. "There's no use going on, Doctor. We're not getting anywhere. And it tears me all to pieces. Worse now, really."

"Perhaps it will be," the doctor smiled. "We'll try it once more. Tomorrow at the same time."

"Well, once more," Mrs. Benson agreed wearily.

The doctor smiled to himself. They were all that way. The nearer they came to a solution of their problem, the harder they fought against the cure. How passionately we really love our maladies!

"Tomorrow, then," he said.

He rang for the nurse, who showed Mrs. Benson out. Then the nurse returned. "Your wife is here, Doctor. She's been waiting some time."

"Please bring her in right away."

The doctor leaned back and put his hand over his eyes. Psychoanalysis, what an infant industry! In its present development, like hand-weaving. So hard on the operator. Putting all those varicolored strands into a warp and woof, finding the pattern, tracing it . . .

The door opened and Mrs. Kressman came in. "Eugen, my darling, how tired you look!"

He opened his eyes. She was glorious. She was youth and beauty and enthusiasm. The doctor felt suddenly old. Old and very tired.

"I've had a hard day," he said. "And I'm looking forward to an evening at home. Wild horses couldn't drag me out tonight."

"Oh, Eugen! I *am* so sorry. I didn't know."

"Know what?"

"That you'd be tired this way. I accepted an invitation for you."

"Oh, Sweetheart, . . . !"

"I know. I shouldn't have. But, really, darling, couldn't you make the effort this once? Mr. Newman's giving a studio party, and I did so want to show you off."

He smiled. Those night-thoughts were so obviously pathologic. She actually wanted him to meet this Newman chap. He felt a little ashamed of himself. "Not I, dear. But you run on and show yourself off. If the man's half an artist, that ought to be more than he can bear."

She made a little grimace. "I won't go. Not without you."

"Certainly you will, my dear. They'll be counting on you, I know. Everybody does. You've got so much to offer."

"But I don't see why you can't come," she said.

"I've had a wretched day. Really, I have, dear. The patients may think it is hard on them, but I'll take their places any time they'll take mine."

"That same one?" Barbara asked. No names were ever exchanged in the Kressman household. Professional ethics. But the cases were known by familiar tags. "That same one" stood for Mrs. Benson.

"That very one!" the doctor smiled. "But we're coming to the end of the string there. She'll be a well woman in two weeks—or less, if she'll come every day."

"Oedipus Complex?" his wife asked. She like to think she "shared" things with her husband, and she had, as a matter of fact, gathered quite a good deal of the nomenclature without fixing the basic facts beneath.

"More complicated. That's involved, but the difficulty's deeper seated. She's a woman of very great moral stamina. She's done something that, in a weaker woman, wouldn't have made any difference. In her, the two sides of her nature are at war. She tries to forget. She tries to pretend she hasn't done it or thought it. But subconsciously she knows she has. And she can't bear to admit it even to herself, let alone to me. But it's coming nearer and nearer the surface."

"Unfaithful?" Barbara asked.

"I'm afraid so," the doctor answered, glancing at his notes.

"Did she tell you so?"

"Well, no. Not directly. But we have ways of finding those things for ourselves."

"And most of the time you're wrong," his wife smiled.

"Sometimes, I'll admit. But not very often. Almost never in a case like this. Projection is one of the most common psycho-phenomena. She identifies herself with some woman who hasn't been exactly virtuous, some woman in history, or fiction, or some acquaintance of hers, perhaps. And then she sets about defending *her*. Not herself, you understand. But the other woman. If she could defend herself, she'd be mentally healthy. But she can't."

"Perhaps she thinks she doesn't need any defense," Barbara pointed out.

"But she does. Her defense of those other women shows she does, or rather, that she thinks she does."

"On the other hand, there's just a chance you're wrong. And you make this poor woman come in here day after day and exhaust herself, while you test some inadequate theory of yours."

"Hardly inadequate, my dear, and it isn't a theory any longer. . . . Besides, the treatment's for her own good, I don't *make* her come, you know."

"It's the same thing. You're talking to her, wearing her down, day after day, just the way the Inquisitors did."

"But they were scarcely trying to cure. Some cures are unpleasant, you know, my dear. But very necessary."

"But the object's the same. You're trying to drag information out of her, make her confess to something she most likely didn't do."

"There's almost no doubt that she did."

"And what if she did! What if she was unfaithful. Perhaps her husband didn't love her. Or she him. You can't make blanket condemnations like that, you know."

"I'm not condemning anything. I'm merely trying to find out."

"But why? Why find out? Why not let her keep her secret? Most likely she had a thousand reasons for doing what she did.

Things aren't always either good or bad, you know. You can't just label things black or white. There are grays as well, and lots of them. A woman in a situation like that is always condemned. But her motives aren't necessarily as mean and low and unspeakable as people pretend they are."

The doctor didn't want to argue. He was very tired. He picked up his pencil and sat looking at the notes in front of him. His weary mind ran on in the channels of his profession: he was too tired to stop it. "Mean, low and unspeakable." Strange the way those words recurred. Almost a perfect pattern. And vicarious defense, a type of transference through projection. This last thing, this firm resistance to questioning, the feeling that the doctor was "prying." How familiar that was. He wished he had had stenographic notes of that argument for Mrs. Benson. An almost complete transference, offering vindication for yourself through the medium of another.

He picked up his pencil and drew the last line into the center of the circle before him. The "case history" on Mrs. Benson was complete. It was just a matter of getting her to admit it. He glanced up. Suddenly he realized he wasn't talking to Mrs. Benson.

A SHIPMENT OF MUTE FATE

By Martin Storm

THOUGH THE CHANCAY STEAMED PLACIDLY FROM LA GUAYRA through oily waters, that drowsy afternoon, three of those aboard her were distinctly not themselves. For their several reasons they had lost the tranquillity proper to the captain, the chief steward, and to Mother Willis.

An engineer, humming on his way to wash up, raised a black champion's fist—"Why Mother, I'm surprised! What's wrong today with my darlin'?" He peered reproachfully into the red eyes of his veteran shipmate. Mother was everybody's pet; a stewardess extraordinary, relic and treasure, she had not missed a voyage of the old Chancay for fifteen years.

"Oh, it's the same thing again, Charlie— It's Clara. Mr. Bowman won't stand for an extra cat aboard, but you would think that at a time like this, when she needs the kindest care . . . How could I help it if she came to me and just asked me to take her in, last winter? I tried to find her a good private home in New York—you know that."

"She was a dirty gray skunk, poor little feller." Feeley grinned at a memory. "Mangy, too. She sat there on the anchor chain, all covered with grease and oil. I says to Bowman, 'I'm afraid we'll have that object with us henceforward,' I says, 'moths and all,' and how he swore! Then she saw you."

"Well, it's only one of the exasperating things that's happened on this sailing day. There's no reason for Mr. Bowman to roar out at her. None of the other chief stewards ever used to say a word. He's too new, that's all! And it seems so cruel just at this time. If I only had her back I'd hide her."

"Where's Clara now?"

"He dumped her right off on the mole, before we pulled out. I better go now and fix supper for that lady's baby in 109. Good night, then, Charlie, dear boy."

Feeley patted her shoulder, staring sadly after the fading lights ashore. "Officers all seems to be cranky right at the start of the run —thassa bad sign. I heard that the old man himself was bawling out Bowman, so probably that's what killed the cat. Well, don't you worry, Mother. Night."

Mrs. Willis did worry as she carefully prepared trays for three baby passengers. She thought of the piteous way Clara had just sat there, abandoned, and glared up at the ship as if too miserable to meow or even move. How could she take care of herself now, on the eve of motherhood again? Something too terrible to imagine would happen to her—and why need all this be? Exactly as Charlie had said, everyone was plain cranky, even the captain, whose business it was to be calm, no matter if a particularly special relative of the company were aboard, pestering him with requests out of order.

What Mrs. Willis did not understand was that this young Warner in his way and despite his father's still ponderous fortune, was desperately in earnest about some things—the more wishful because of physical delicacy to distinguish himself for his own nerve and brains. That was why he had spent an insect-tormented and perilous vacation in hostile jungle above the Orinoco when he could have been at Sands Point. It was why he had made a silent, thrilling vow when the assistant in zoölogy, returning to New Haven from a spring reptile hunt, remarked to the group he was tutoring that while other poisonous snakes were a drug on the market, with everybody catching them and presenting them to collections, nowhere could you see a live bushmaster. When at Easter he casually asked his father to fix him up a passage on the Chancay, that gentleman had no idea that his listless son was already capturing bushmasters in his dreams, though as yet he did not even know what the creatures looked like.

To catch one alive proved a grimly different matter. Once, after weeks on the land and water trail, just once, he had an appalling sight of that mute death coiled upon the forest floor, waiting for them to take the next step, then shifting toward them. No one would help him try to bag it, and presently with insolent leisure it glided back into the depths of jungle. They did not come upon another, to the relief of everybody except Chris Warner, but on the way out the Indians of one unusually ambitious village agreed to see if they could get him any old bushmaster—for an irresistible price. Days after, they returned, bearing the horror in a rubber sack. With shuddering elation he transferred it to his ready canvas.

When the Customs officers learned of the nature of this portion of his baggage, however, they would only exclaim, "Impossible!" —"It is not to be arranged, unfortunately, senor." Since nothing got him any further, Chris wired New York and then went in anxious and indignant haste to his father's employe, Captain Wood of the Chancay. "Skipper, I seem to be in a little jam. Last thing I ever expected, any difficulty at this stage. I've spent a whole summer and a lot of money getting a prize I can't even take home! It looks like the whole expedition's wasted, as far as my part of it's concerned— and I can't tell you how much it means to me!"

"Mighty sorry, Christopher. I just cabled your father that I'd have done it for you if I possibly could. He asked me to."

The boy looked startled at this failure of his last recourse. "But I can't see your logic. You took a jaguar up last trip."

The captain glanced over toward the Customs pier where in a box with small, wire-covered openings, protected by an outer crate, his terrible passenger waited to embark. "The worst thing I know, to carry, is right there—the thing you want to take aboard a ship with women passengers. My judgment won't let me do it, even for you, son. Because something could happen, though I don't know what and there's only a chance in a thousand that it would. But those are just the things that do happen—know what I mean? I haven't a choice in the matter. Safety of passengers comes first."

"But with proper precautions? They carry snakes all the time."

"Not this snake they don't—I'd have obliged the scientists long ago—and they always want a bushmaster—if it was some other kind. Why are they so scarce, why are you so anxious now, if any-body'll transport one north? And I'm not superstitious, either, but I know what to be afraid of."

Young Warner left the cabin, seething. To be deprived at the last minute, by an old man's pig-headedness and exaggerated caution, of the one glory of his summer's labor! The unexpected ob-stacle chafed him intolerably. He made a hasty visit to the bank, then carefully composed a longer cable to New York. Within an hour of sailing time the captain sent ashore for him and with a face averted in displeasure laid down certain conditions. The company had cracklingly "desired" him to do this favor for Mr. Warner's son "if possible," which virtually meant, do it anyway.

"You'll have to put the thing into a box. That flimsy crate's no good."

"Tell you how I'll fix it, skipper." Chris was joyful and placatory. "The snake's got to have some air on this long hot voyage, of course, but I'll put the box with the wire-covered hole into another good stout box, quite a bit larger, with a chain and padlock. Then we can prop the lid up, just half an inch or so, with the box still locked."

"And in dirty weather the lid'll have to be fastened down tight. I'll take no chances."

"Right."

"And the whole thing will be kept during the entire run in my inner cabin, where I sleep. I won't have it in the baggage room." He thought, too late, that it would fortunately have suffocated in the hold.

"Just as you say, skipper, but I was planning to stick the box under my own berth."

As the three blasts of departure sounded from the ship's whistle Captain Wood remembered what was there in his room and his skin prickled, raising up the black hair on his wrists. Then he almost forgot about it, for the steward put a chintz table cover over the mysterious object and they had fine weather through the Caribbean. Not even Chico, the captain's boy, knew that a bushmaster was aboard.

Never for one peaceful instant could Chris Warner forget it. A vague distress brooded over his pleasure in the social life of the voyage. Yet, he kept telling himself, poisonous snakes were shipped often enough—rattlers, copperheads, coral snakes, even cobras could be negotiated if someone responsible were in charge. Why was it different with a bushmaster? Why did every skipper kick, as the captain said they did—and as the scarcity of the serpents proved, even to him—about taking aboard a bushmaster? What could be worse than a cobra? "Cobras will quiet down when they know they're caught," Dr. Sutton had told him last spring. "Some get quite dopey and docile if they're left alone. But a bushmaster's always alert and hostile, even after a feeding. I like most snakes, but not them. Still, I would to God I could get hold of one!"

That sudden glimpse of the creature in the forest returned to him: he saw it lying like a richly colored, horrible mat, with an undulant, S-shaped loop, ready to strike true and instantly at anything. Often it pursued animals not its natural prey with seeming sheer malignance. It boldly followed its own occasions along trails, fearing nothing—never fled. This was the most terrible of all snakes, pantomimed the Indian guide, because it would run right after a man! The natives never attempted a cure for the copious poison that flowed from those great fangs. It bore in earnest its chilling name—Lachesis muta.

On apparently social visits to the captain's quarters he would furtively peer in at his treasure, holding a flashlight to the wire-covered hole. Always he saw it coiled. This one was almost eleven feet long—Reddish brown, adorned above with dark lozenges that showed lighter spots on either side, its rough skin glistened like a strange, beauteous fabric, the pale yellow scales on the under part revealing a porcelain glaze. He was sumptuously clad, this ominous minister of the Parcae. But the spade-shaped head was that of very Antichrist.

"You're as white as my apron, Mr. Warner. What's the matter, dear boy?" caressed Mother Willis, meeting him with a pile of towels on the way to lunch.

"Well, I didn't have such a soft time on that jungle hike, Mother. Anyway, weather like this makes you feel low." He went on into the dining-room and strove to take an interest in Roseanne Crane, who sat next at the captain's table. "You know, this is positively a peculiar ship!" she complained. "I don't know exactly what it is, but it's something solemn—even in the smokingroom. Coming down we were all so jolly—foolishness and fun every minute. These elderly new passengers must be to blame!"

"It'll be all right when we run into nice cool weather," he promised her. "They were getting ready for a hurricane last night, I guess, they way the glass dropped, but apparently it was just a false alarm. It's probably off in the Gulf of Mexico by now."

Fine days met them. The sunlit languors of the Indies vanished, and out on the open Atlantic—"Five miles deep here," an officer at taffrail murmured—played brisk winds and hurrying, foam-laced water. It was on a blowy day when the waves looked huge, yet not phenomenal, though mounted on long swells, that a monster

green comber arose alone, slapped the ship terrifically to port and
boarded her, racing hungrily over empty decks, carrying away a
length of the rail, bashing in windows on the A-deck and falling
with fury upon the exposed wheelhouse of the old-fashioned liner.
Water drove through closed doors and tumbled downstairs in little
cataracts. Seamen were bruised and the third officer had his leg
broken, being hurled across the bridge. But as the captain had
ordered all passengers inside half an hour before, they were only
shaken up and scared. The carpenter and the doctor went to work,
the decks dried off, the sun smiled, and no brother of the awful
wave crossed the subsiding sea. Ladies calmed themselves by dressing for dinner, once wardrobe trunks were righted and puddles
mopped up.

At the captain's room Chico gave one look and then went to get
mops and another steward to help him. It had almost been carried
away, along with the wheelhouse, and water sloshed back and
forth on the floor. The pillow on the bed was soaked and the
mattress lay disarranged and sodden. The heavy desk had charged
right across the room; a chest of drawers had fallen over, mixing
bay rum with brine. "We'll be working half the night!" Grumpily
they righted furniture. "Whole blooming ship's a mess, but we
had to get the worst trick, as usual!"

"Poor old swivel-chair's busted for good. That desk must of
carried some tonnage."

"It's what the old man's hoarded inside of it. A lifetime's plunder,
if you only knew."

"God, look, what ——?"

"What where?"

"Something went out over the sill then when the water sloshed.
Like a hoseline or sumpin'."

"Search me. This box that the old man was so choice of, that's
stove in too."

"Just put it outside. Tell him about it before it goes over."

They had been mopping for half an hour and the room was
once more orderly if still very moist, when Captain Wood came
in from the bridge, looking drawn and weary, and motioned them
to get along.

"We got to bring you another chair, sir. That comber passed

right through your bunk on its way out. There's been a good deal of damage done, sir."

"Let it all go till morning—jump below. I'll lie down for twenty minutes before we run into something else." Chico thought "He's getting old" as he took the wet uniform and closed the door behind him, feeling rather sorry. He was recalled by a bellow that brought the officer on watch as well. "What in Holy Jesse have you done with the box that was under this bed?"

"It must have gone slidin' and floatin' around, captain. Anyway, something's fell on it—the bureau maybe—or the old desk charged up against it. Anyway ——"

"Where is it?"

"We was just going to pitch it over. It's broke so it's no good now, captain."

"There were two boxes, one inside of the other."

"Only look for yourself, sir. Split like kindling."

The captain closed the door and alone faced a room which he believed held death. For a moment he could not stir from that one little space in the middle of the floor—where he could see. He switched on every light and took out his flashlight, but a cold and slowly mounting horror, goading his weariness into tense vigilance, half paralyzed him.

He bent over at last, drew back, waited through another interval, and then forced himself to pass the light along under the bed. With a ruler he pushed open the closet door, standing well away, but no lidless eyes reflected the searching beam. He knocked the cushions from the wall-bench, lifted up the chintz curtain, holding his revolver ready. Nothing was there. If only it had been there! If only he himself, the man responsible, could have been the first and the last to meet it!

He pulled on his heavy coat and gave an order. "Send the chief steward and the purser right up. The chief, too, if he can come. Call the first officer."

As he stood before the small, grave conference, telling them hastily what had happened, he hoped that somehow the thing might not seem so horrible to them as now it was to him. One of these resourceful and experienced men could perhaps think of something to do—together. With a plan of action made the horror would lessen. Over their heads he saw young Warner's white face appear in the open door. He told him to step in.

"It would be easier if we didn't have to let all the crew and passengers know," said the mate. "It's panic I'm scared of. That's the most dangerous thing there is at sea, in my experience. Then lots of people—the lady passengers, the ignorant black gang—they'll be sort of fanatical. Just one ordinary snake loose on board would be enough to drive the whole bunch . . ."

"Why do we have to tell?" suggested the purser.

"Think what you're saying, Mr. Kane. Who knows where it is, where it's gone? In fairness they've got to be put on guard, every one of 'em, passengers and crew."

"It might have crawled overboard."

"That's the one hope, sir."

"And then again there's not a place on the ship where it might not be, except the boilers and galley stove. I had the Number Two hatch open, just now, to make sure no water had got through to that dry goods. It might have slid down there by this time."

"It might be in a fire-bucket, or one of the lifeboats—or a baby's bed."

Chris Warner had not spoken. He was arguing with himself, "But such a snake as that—it was so long, so awful to look at, how can it hide?" He turned hurriedly, but the captain detained him. "No one is to leave until we all decide exactly what to do."

"Captain," said Bowman, "all we can do is go now and look everywheres. I'll start now and take along a few boys I can trust for sense. Then if we haven't found anything by dark . . ."

"It's getting dark early tonight."

"Excuse me, captain—I don't think that's just." The purser was resolute. "Everyone aboard is in equal, constant danger. Everyone's got to look out for himself. Every living soul ought to be told right away. Or we might make one quick, thorough search."

"You don't know what the effect may be, to tell them—my God! I've seen passengers panicky at sea before."

"But it's right that everyone should be warned. At this minute that damned snake may be coiled under some woman's berth. We have to tell! There's nothing else to do."

"Anyway we can't make a search of the whole ship without giving reasons. Sooner or later someone will find out. We don't want it to be too late."

Captain Wood was surprised that he felt no real anger at Chris, sitting there so miserably without stirring or speaking, enduring a remorse that he alone could understand, along with the weight of the unuttered blame of the others: a feeling worse than fear. "We'll search now," he decided. "Afterward, if he have no luck, each steward will tell the passengers in his rooms, trying not to alarm them, and the officers will tell the crew. Don't worry so, Chris-topher—we'll give you one of the hardest places. Go take a look around the baggage room. It's been open—since?"

"Probably, sir. Some ladies usually want to get at a trunk for something, just before dinner." The chief steward was actually making some notes. His wrist shook. The peculiar dread that now informed the atmosphere seemed to render all their movements stiff. It was difficult to step freely . . . to breathe . . .

Captain Wood apportioned the ship among them, and with a strained nonchalance that puzzled passengers who chanced to be watching they moved about decks, corridors and general rooms, interested, apparently, in everything.

But no long reddish body marked with dark lozenges glided at them over the carpet nor lay coiled in a corner nor outstretched above a curtain pole. No deadly viper's head lifted from the gathering shadows. Alone in the dusky baggage room with its numberless lurking places, Chris turned sick and stood still in the middle of the floor, just as the captain had done in his cabin. Then he too forced himself to step about, to poke, to look. "This with the blame besides!" How did they know before?—How did they know that something always happens if you take a bushmaster aboard a ship? What is there about this one snake . . . Trembling and sweating, he kept up the search. He did not leave one dark corner without thrusting in his long stick, always thinking that this time surely death must rush out after it.

They all met again in the captain's room. No one had found any sign. The passengers would have to be warned.

The slow nightmare that followed and grew more frightful hour by hour was rarely relieved by natural sleep. Soon they could hardly eat or rest. Fear was a heavy fog in the lungs of the whole ship's company: they dreaded to move. Only the babies played happily, not reading the terror in their parents' wakeful eyes.

But as yet it remained a quiet, freezing fear. It had not broken into panic. Then, in full sight of many passengers, two colored stokers raced along the deck and leaped yelling into the sea. They went right down in the smother. Everyone thought that they must have seen the snake, but it was not found, and Bowman decided that they had merely gone crazy thinking about it. A few hours afterward an elderly woman turned to the group beside her and remarked seriously, "If we could only get off this ship we could fumigate it." Then she, too, suddenly made for the sea, but a steward caught her. Down in her little dark inside room, which she could hardly bear to enter now, even with a bright light, Mother Willis tried to sip some good hot tea and keep going. The women passengers needed her more than ever before, and the poor babies.

Starboard on the bridge the captain stood in a whooping rain-squall and prayed into its rush. "Three days and we'll be in—Lord, let nothing happen for three more days!" A wireless to the office had brought back prompt instructions to "Keep quiet and keep coming." Such a situation lost horror, no doubt, in the safe office. Well, there was no use asking other ships for help, anyway. Short of taking off all the passengers what could they do? And then the crew wouldn't stay. To keep his head, he always tried to believe that the bushmaster had gone overboard. That, too, was what Mother Willis told hysterical women who could not spend a third night awake with all the lights on, and who yet could not sleep; who screamed at the dark. "But you don't know," jabbered Mrs. Crane at her, all at once an old woman. "Nobody knows! And if anyone goes to sleep it may come through a ventilator. It may drop from somewhere. It may be in the bathroom. I can't turn my back—to anything—I keep whirling around!" The inescapable pursuit ceaselessly wore at them, and by some it could no longer be borne. A Venezuelan woman gave quieting medicine to herself and her baby until both were safe forever. "I wish I could get out of this that easy," thought Chris, ready to crack as he kept at his awful job of listening, peering, leaping back from nothing.

There were no longer nights and days. Only the light became the intolerable darkness. Some felt that they were always being watched by lidless eyes; some knew that they had heard the long body flop to the floor. For everyone it lay coiled beneath his bunk. With men calm to the sea's dangers but almost driven to run amok under the strain of this unknown, invisible horror the officers fought to keep up ship's discipline, their own minds invaded and shaken by the fanged uncertainty.

Carrying his flashlight for any treacherous corner the chief steward went at seven bells to the galley to see if all had been left neat for the night. Yes—only the watchman's coffee-pot stood on the shining stove. He turned to leave, and from the pan closet that ran along the floor to his left he saw two unwinking eyes give back the light. The bushmaster waited there among the tins, and as Bowman hesitated for an instant it began slowly to undulate over the sill, between him and the door. He could hear the faint scratching of its long scales. No heavy object that a man could move was within reach to throw at it. He carried only the flashlight. The call button was over by the door. He longed to yell but did not dare, lest any sound or movement hasten the thing after him or cause it to vanish.

The snake paused with half its length out of the cupboard, then taking its own time emerged entirely and lay coiled like a patterned kitchen mat by the stove. With wonder Bowman perceived that it was staring not at him but past him. And something else was moving, back under the sink. Despite himself he had to turn his head and look.

Slowly stepping toward the snake until she was just out of striking range came a gray, mangy skeleton of a cat. She confronted the coiled enemy, each gazing at the other with unwinking eyes.

Suddenly, and almost too quickly for sight, the bushmaster struck, and as quickly the cat evaded the lance-thrust of that spade-shaped head. Again and again it just missed her body and then as the snake began to tire a little she countered with one precise spat of a sharp-clawed paw. Now every time that the head shot out she caught it on her claws, just at the end of the lunge, bracing her absurdly meagre frame. Before Bowman grasped her strategy she had blinded the bushmaster in both lidless eyes.

It struck wildly and more rapidly, but always the countering paw was exactly there at the point and instant when its small strength could avail. The monster coiled no more, but slid after her in fury, eyes ripped, as she danced out of its way. With the agility of desperation Bowman made one leap above the melee and got his legs over the edge of the sink. Now the cat darted in among the twisting folds and fixed her teeth just in back of the great jaws; there with tooth and claw she clung. Lashing and flailing, striving to keep its crushing coils around her, the bushmaster thrashed about the galley, but both power and venom were used up; its wounds were mortal. The rough folds slackened at last.

In them Clara lay dead. Bowman saw, then, why she had challenged such an adversary and why she could not lose the fight, for out from under the sink, their tails straight as pokers, their eyes bright with curiosity, crept three new kittens. He gathered them up hastily and went with them toward Mother Willis's room.

AN IDEA FOR A STORY

By André Maurois

THE OTHER DAY I WAS THINKING OF THE GENERAL LAWS GOVERNING
a type of writing which I have always liked, while trying to make a
story out of a subject which had amused me. This is the subject:
Sexual pleasure has been the basis of an entire civilization, which
began about the twelfth century and now seems on the decline. It
is possible to argue indefinitely about these two dates, but not, I
think, about the phenomenon itself, the birth of romantic love
and its astounding influence on the art and morals of Europe. It is
rather extraordinary, I said to myself, that a simple physical need
should have given rise to such complex emotions and should be the
subject of almost every artistic masterpiece, whereas other needs,
equally urgent, like hunger and thirst, have remained rather primitive with most people.

A moment's reflection showed me that the difference is easily
explained by the completely egotistic satisfaction of hunger and
thirst. The civilizing and aesthetic value of love lies in the fact that
it presupposes the harmony of two human beings, and that, from
the time when both were free, owing to the relative emancipation
of women, every kind of harmony and discord entered into their
agreement. If human beings had been so constructed, I thought,
that the satisfaction of thirst was only possible or agreeable between
two people, then thirst would have been the cause of devastating
passion and the subject of sublime masterpieces.

Why, I thought, should it not be possible to imagine a race so
formed and governed by such desires, and to endow another form
of desire with all the passion of love? Then I saw an island on which
people like ourselves were living, but they had on their right arm
a growth like a breast, only smaller, culminating in a nipple. I
could see that this growth enabled them to satisfy each other's thirst,
and the picture was somewhat revolting.

I was immediately confronted by a physiological difficulty. Was

536

it not an unlikely supposition that food which was assimilable could come from a creature of the same species?

If these people could live only on the food which they gave each other, where did the liquid they secreted originally come from? Suppose that they secreted this liquid as plants produce sap. But plants draw their sustenance from the earth and from the heat of the sun. Should I endow the inhabitants of my island with green hair and vegetal functions? The more I thought of it the more I could see that the difficulty was not so great as I had imagined. These creatures could feed through the mouth and the digestive tract as we do, but they would require as some sort of supplementary nourishment this juice produced by the human body, just as children need animal milk, and ants need the liquid secreted by plant-lice.

The idea of the island suggested two characters which I had already invented for "The Voyage to the Island of the Articoles," a young French sailor, whom I called Pierre Chambrelan, and his wife, whose name, I believe, was Anne. It was easy to imagine, as Swift did for Gulliver, that these two people, having left the island of the Articoles, had visited other unknown countries, and that one of these was the island on which my monsters lived with breasts on their arms. It was necessary to give these people a name, so I thought it would be natural and euphonic to call them the Erophagi. Erotophagi was a more correct derivation, but pleased me less. I decided that Pierre Chambrelan and his wife, on leaving the Articoles, should arrive at the island of the Erophagi.

At the beginning of the story it would have been clumsy to reveal to the hero and to the reader the key of the narrative and the symbols on which the fiction was based. In the earlier chapters the secret of the intimate life of the Erophagi must not be apparent to the travellers. They must be impressed by the astounding immodesty of this race. The Erophagi would be nudists, a fact explicable by the warmth of the climate, but they would wear on their shoulders an armlet embroidered with lovely ornaments. They would attach no importance to the gestures of physical love, which took place in public amidst general indifference. It would be the custom of the island for people to ask their friends to come and make love, just as we invite people to come to dinner. The Erophagi would be surprised and shocked by the repugnance of Pierre and Anne towards these collective amusements. They would accuse the travellers of not understanding the most innocent joys of humanity.

Gradually the travellers would discover that young Erophagi couples met several times a day and hid themselves in their rooms, and that it was forbidden, in fact inconceivable, to disturb them. "With such freedom, what on earth can they find to do in secret?" Anne and Pierre Chambrelan asked in astonishment. Another phenomenon which seemed curious to them was that these immodest people have a curiously localized form of modesty, which is in their right shoulder. Everybody, both men and women, always keep the top of their right arm covered up. This is all the more extraordinary because these people spend most of their time in the sea. But then both sexes wear bathing armlets, which are swollen out by a curious protuberance. On the beach strict notices declare that bathing with bare shoulders is prohibited.

It is easy to imagine the episodes which would lead the travellers to discover the truth. Suddenly the secret life of the Erophagi would be revealed. They would discover that every Erophagus, man or woman, secretes in the arm a liquid which another person can absorb by suction. This liquid, whose taste is delicious, and which is not otherwise obtainable in nature, is essential to the life of the Erophagi. If they are deprived of it, they do not die, but become prematurely old and are afflicted by slow and deadly diseases.

Obviously the problem is more complicated than would appear from this first outline. If each of these creatures could derive the necessary liquid from any other, then no deep feelings would be aroused by this simple physiological need, but the drama of their lives consists in the fact that, although the chemical composition of the individual liquids is very similar, and an unaccustomed palate could not distinguish one from the other, they are not interchangeable to a sensitive Erophagus, and most of them are highly sensitive. It is probable that the decided taste which each individual shows for the liquid secreted by a given person could be explained by an analysis of the liquid itself, if our knowledge of chemistry were more exact. It is reasonable to suppose that every organism requires certain juices to complete and maintain itself. The person who can supply those juices becomes indispensable. It is not surprising that an Erophagus should become desperately attached to that person and establish relationships as lasting and as tender as our love. These relationships are based, not on sexual pleasure, but on the exchange of perfectly assorted liquids.

It is easy to understand that such powerful sentiments should produce modesty. Hence the armlets. When two Erophagi withdraw to a room, as the travellers observe, it is always for one of these brachial feasts, which they call unions, and which are, as a matter of fact, a kind of union in normal cases, because the position of these breasts enable the Erophagi to enjoy their pleasures simultaneously. The great Erophagi novelists have no objection to describing sexual relations, and these books are permitted to children, but the description of a brachial feast is considered obscene, and the best authors avoid it.

It is not difficult to imagine the dramas which our travellers would witness, and which would permit them to study the sentimental life of a people so different from ourselves. The fundamental reason for amorous complications with the Erophagi, as with ourselves, is unshared feeling. Sometimes an Erophagus will have a great desire for the liquid of another, but the latter would have no feeling for the liquid secreted by the former. Then there would be the spectacle of an unfortunate human being, hungry and thirsty, importuning a reluctant Erophagus who would find the scene of an unshared brachial feast boring and ridiculous. In certain cases sickness and age would bring about profound changes in the composition of the liquids and destroy relations which had hitherto seemed solid. In other cases a relationship which had begun by an intense mutual delight in this exchange of liquids would become difficult and painful, because one of the lovers, tired of a too familiar savour, would look elsewhere for new sensations, whereas the other, endowed with a more constant taste, would ask nothing better than that their relationship should continue.

Pierre Chamberlan would notice with interest that the usual duration of a passion among the Erophagi is about the same as with ourselves. It varies considerably, and oscillates between a week and ten years. Certain Erophagi who are restless or blasé need a new liquid almost every day. But Anne would discover old couples still thirsting for each other after fifty years of happiness. What are fundamentally relationships of nourishment become the basis of spiritual unions, of tender affections and friendships. Marriage among the Erophagi, whose legal forms resemble our own, is always based on such feelings and never on sexual relations, which are entirely free. Nevertheless, jealousy, among them as among ourselves, often assumes extreme forms and concentrates upon actions which are regarded with indifference by normal people. For example, some Erophagi would prevent their wives from making love with a stranger, just as certain husbands in our countries prevent their wives from dining alone with a man friend. But legal adultery does not exist, unless there has been an exchange of liquids and the parties have been caught in the act of having a brachial feast.

The consequences, so far as the education of children is concerned, are curious, since the children are in the charge of the state, and married life rests upon an entirely different basis. Differences of sex play no part in the marriages of the Erophagi. A man may marry a man, or a woman a woman. In many cases, however, when a marriage takes place between people of different sex, sexual relations may complete those of nourishment, perhaps thereby rendering the union more perfect. But that is always a secondary matter, just as a common liking for certain foods may be an additional bond between two lovers among us.

To sum up: the ideas which give its value to love, that is to say, the idea of sin and the idea that only a given individual can satisfy us, though associated with a different desire in the minds of the Erophagi, produce the same results as with us. The romantic story of nutrition follows with them practically the same course as the romantic story of reproduction does with us. Their art, which is very remarkable, has been entirely inspired by the need to sublimate impossible thirsts.

The religion of the Erophagi is also a sublimation of this instinct, a phenomenon which Paul Valéry divined, without knowing the Erophagi, when he said: "Hunger and thirst have not degenerated into sentiment and idolatry. Why? But sex has become a demigod, perhaps even God."

Having reached this point in my reflections on the Erophagi, I decided not to write their story.

THE HERO HAD A FATHER

By Richard L. Neuberger

EIGHT YEARS AGO THE MOST PUBLICIZED MARRIAGE EVER TO TITILLATE the tabloid-addicts took place at the estate of Dwight W. Morrow in Englewood, New Jersey. Every feature of the event was blazoned across the front pages. All persons blessed with vision, and gifted with the ability to read, knew what the bride, Miss Anne Morrow, ate for breakfast, and approximately how many drops of sweat glistened on the brow of the groom, Colonel Charles A. Lindbergh.

The diligent and assiduous newspapers omitted to record only one aspect of the spectacle. They forgot to note that the son of the first man ever to attack the capitalistic system on the floor of Congress had just been joined in holy wedlock with the daughter of a partner in the firm of J. P. Morgan and Company.

Incongruities are grist in the mill of the American press. A thousand editors have dipped their pens in stardust to describe the presumably superlative paradox of the engagement of the son of Franklin D. Roosevelt to the daughter of one of the Liberty League-loving du Ponts. Yet the forthcoming matrimony of young Mr. Roosevelt and blonde Miss du Pont is as the Adirondacks to the Himalayas—so far as incongruities are concerned—when compared with the nuptials of Charles A. Lindbergh and Anne Morrow.

Applying the standard of paternal politics to both betrothals, the disagreement between Franklin D. Roosevelt and Eugene du Pont would be paled into profound friendship and concordance by the bristling dissidence between Charles Augustus Lindbergh, Sr. and Dwight W. Morrow.

Lindbergh assailed Wall Street so tenaciously the newspapers claimed he was "hipped" on the subject. Morrow symbolized Wall Street only slightly less than did Rockefeller or J. Pierpont Morgan themselves.

The father of Anne Morrow was a partner in J. P. Morgan

and Company. He was active in the great banking firm during the World War, and sincerely believed the Morgan loans to the Allies were justified in the cause of patriotism and national defense. He was a staunch advocate of "preparedness." Dwight Morrow lived to give his daughter in marriage to the son of a man who once said, " 'Preparedness' has been seized on by the war-munition lords as a substitute for 'armament,' because 'armament' would suggest what was really meant."

In the opinion of Dwight Morrow, "wild-eyed Bolshevik" was too favorable a designation for the author of so seditious a sentiment. Lindbergh, in turn, regarded "war profiteer" as the proper label for Morrow.

Representative Charles A. Lindbergh, Sr. of the Sixth Minnesota District was not present when Anne Morrow became Mrs. Charles A. Lindbergh. He died three years before his only son thrilled the world by flying alone across the Atlantic. . . .

"Son," Congressman Lindbergh told his boy in the autumn of 1917, "in war times it is not safe to think unless one travels with the mob."

Seven months later sixteen-year old Charles A. Lindbergh, Jr. saw his father pelted with rotten eggs and forced to flee for his life from the fury of a mob. The crowd resented Lindbergh's contention that the World War would fail to make the world safe for democracy. "Traitor! Hang him!" the mob shrieked.

The elder Lindbergh had withdrawn from Congress to run for Governor of Minnesota. In the Republican primaries he opposed the incumbent, J. A. Burnquist. Lindbergh's opposition to the War was a national issue and super-patriots in every state howled for his head. Editors as far away as Cape Cod and Puget Sound insisted that Minnesota should not be governed by a "traitorous skunk." In addition, Lindbergh was the official candidate of the Non-Partisan League, whose members were characterized by Burnquist as "vipers."

For bitterness and violence, the campaign was without parallel. Looking back upon it almost a generation afterwards, Senator Ernest Lundeen of Minnesota declared that Lindbergh and his followers were "intellectually lynched."

And some of the lynching was almost actual.

Once a mob became so violent Lindbergh had to be barricaded

in the jail of a nearby town to protect him from being torn to pieces. On another occasion a farmer driving his car for him was beaten until he was a mass of welts. A speaker in the village of Hinckley read a portion of an address in which Lindbergh attributed the War to commercial and financial rivalries; the speaker was stripped, tarred and feathered, and dragged out of the county, more dead than alive. In New Richland the "War Board" refused to permit Lindbergh's adherents to hold a meeting; they tramped out in the country to convene at the farm of an aged veteran of the Civil War. The sheriff followed with the town vigilantes, broke up the meeting, and clubbed these "disloyal snakes."

To declare openly for Lindbergh was to risk drowning in a torrent of ridicule and invective. At the high school in Little Falls the boys hooted and jeered, and cried out that "Slim" Lindbergh's Dad was a "traitor." Several Chicago newspapers suggested that Lindbergh should offer his services to the Kaiser.

Lindbergh was continually trailed by secret-service men. He was suspected of all sorts of reprehensible activities, particularly because of his denunciations of the Espionage Act. He declared that the Espionage Act was modeled after the old Sedition Laws repealed by Thomas Jefferson. If the American people were actually in favor of the War, Lindbergh demanded to know why they could not be permitted freedom of Speech.

Senator Robert La Follette of Wisconsin came to Minnesota to speak in behalf of the Non-Partisan League candidates. At St. Paul he said, "We had grievances against Germany." The Associated Press quoted him as saying, "We had no grievances against Germany." This misquotation nearly cost La Follette his seat in the Senate. Months later the Associated Press apologized for its error.

The treatment of Lindbergh fitted into this pattern. Sixteen-year old "Slim" saw his father hanged in effigy, and watched as Government agents confiscated the plates of his father's book, *Why Your Country Is at War*. For criticizing the munitions traffic, his father was branded a "delinquent and dastard."

The mob spirit was rampant in the North Star State. Meetings for Lindbergh were almost extra-legal. Vigilantes broke up dozens of his speeches. Several times he was shot at, and once he and "Slim" and a friend were pursued by riders wearing black hoods. The friend was driving Lindbergh's car.

"Don't drive so fast," Lindbergh said. "They will think we are afraid of them." He turned to "Slim" and smiled, "Don't be scared, boy."

Some of Lindbergh's advisors warned him that his continued strictures against the causes of the War were ruining his career. He replied that his career would surely be ruined if he suppressed his honest convictions on the main issue of the day. Repeatedly he reiterated the statement he had first uttered in 1915, "Speculations and loans in foreign fields are likely to bring us into war. . . . The war-for-profit group has counterfeited patriotism." He said that some day history would vindicate his claims.

On primary day Lindbergh lost by only 49,000 votes out of a total of 350,000 ballots cast. Without any newspaper support, with a great proportion of his meetings broken up either by police or self-appointed viligantes, with his campaign financed only by the contribution of farmers and workers, Lindbergh polled more than 150,000 votes.

Several times in later years he ran again for public office. He never was successful. In 1920 he even failed to win back his old seat in Congress. The super-patriots had stamped the brand of the traitor on him too deeply. In the public mind they had gouged the impression that Lindbergh was an enemy of his country. During his lifetime this unjustified mark was never completely erased. Today the people of Minnesota regard Lindbergh as a prophet. They have heard his prediction that the World War would not end war echoed ominously in the tramp of marching feet on almost every continent. But until Lindbergh's death in 1924, the stigma of disloyalty attached to his career. Those who excoriated him for his condemnation of the armament industry had done their job with *éclat*. By constant association of Lindbergh's name with such adjectives as "traitorous," "disloyal," and "seditious," they succeeded in convincing thousands of voters that the rangy, solemn-visaged Viking was actually a menace to American institutions.

As late as 1923—five years after the Armistice—Lindbergh was still looked upon as a "dangerous" and "subversive" character. That year he was a Farmer-Labor candidate for Senator, and traveled around the state in his son's first airplane, a creaky Government "Jenny." The tall lad leaned against the plane or tinkered with the motor while Lindbergh, Sr. addressed the picnic or meeting they had flown to attend. Dozens of times "Slim" listened to his father advocating minimum wage laws, public ownership of electric power, and collective bargaining for workers. He heard his father denounce the horror of war and the intolerance of the Ku Klux Klan, and more than once he picked up handbills warning the electorate to beware of the glib-tongued agitator, Charles A. Lindbergh.

The handbills didn't bother to add the "Sr." to Lindbergh's name. The enemies of the stubborn pacifist scarcely knew that he had a son. "Slim" was entirely inconspicuous so far as politics were concerned. Carburetors and spark plugs interested him more than taxation and war profits. In 1923 he had just attained his majority; at last he could vote for his father—that was about all citizenship meant to him them.

One afternoon following a speech in which the elder Lindbergh had been continually heckled and interrupted, the plane started to dip and falter while they were flying over an old farm. With difficulty "Slim" landed on the slope of a hill. Both father and son were shaken and jolted. "Slim" climbed out and examined the craft. He whistled as he picked up one of the cables fixed to the wings; it had been neatly severed with a wire-cutter.

Lindbergh told his boy that the chopped cable signified what it meant to champion an unpopular cause. "Slim" nodded gravely, then trudged to the farmhouse to get tools to repair the damage.

Charles A. Lindbergh was born in Stockholm, Sweden, in January of 1859. He was only a year old when his father, August Lindbergh, resigned his seat in the Rickstag, the Swedish parliament, and immigrated to the United States.

Liberalism in the Lindbergh family did not originate with Charles. It was part of his legacy. August Lindbergh's principal achievement in the Rickstag had been the passage of a law outlawing the whipping-post. He had been horrified by the spectacle of bleeding backs and groaning men in the public square of every Swedish village.

In America—just at the outbreak of the Civil War—August Lindbergh and his family trekked by prairie schooner from St. Louis to Melrose, Minnesota. There they settled near other pioneers from the Scandinavian Peninsula.

Adversity dealt them an early blow. Hauling a giant log to the mill to be sliced into boards, August slipped and fell into the grinding fury of the circular saw. His left arm was cut off at the shoulder and his side was gashed and scarred. It was three days before a doctor could be brought from St. Cloud. Charles applied cold water from the well to the terrible wound in his father's shoulder to stop the flow of blood.

August Lindbergh's son learned the meaning of nerve and courage from that incident. Two generations later a surgeon told Congressman Lindbergh he had to undergo a dangerous abdominal operation but would be unable to take an anesthetic. Lindbergh sent for his friend, Lynn Haines, and talked over the banking situation with him during the entire operation, which lasted almost two hours.

August sent his son to law school at the University of Michigan, and after graduation Charles got a job as a legal clerk for a bank. One day he was dispatched to foreclose on a farmer who had failed to meet the payment on a chattel mortgage. The farmer had several children, and Charles suggested that he sell his team to take care of the payment. The young lawyer helped him get a good price for the horses, and the next day he turned over the money to his employer.

The banker was furious. "I didn't tell you to go and collect the money," he stormed. "I wanted the goods and farm. Just for this you're fired!"

Charles looked at him. "All right," he replied.

Lindbergh entered private practice. He began to occupy a leading rôle in the farmers' co-operative movement, and he wrote numerous essays on the banking and currency situation. Everyone in the county knew him as "C.A." a tall, serious young man with stubborn resistance to any opposition to his ideas. Perhaps this obstinacy was the reason for his estrangement from Evangeline Land after they had had a son, Charles Augustus Lindbergh, Jr., in 1902.

Four years after the birth of his boy, Lindbergh was elected to Congress. He served there for a decade. Reviewing those ten years in the hurly-burly of Washington politics, Senator Lundeen recently stated, "In eighty years of Minnesota history many Congressmen and Senators have come to Washington from the North Star State. The most able and distinguished of them all was Charles A. Lindbergh."

Lindbergh arrived on Capitol Hill with the customary high hopes of the idealist in politics. Within a month he saw himself and the other newcomers shackled by the wainropes of the stilted procedure in the House. After two years of this parliamentary runaround—in which he spoke only when the party whips generously allotted him five or six minutes time—Lindbergh's friend Haines asked him if his faith in the people was as firm as ever.

"Yes," he answered, "and my pity has increased a thousand-fold."

There was a sad-eyed young Congressman from Nebraska in whom Lindbergh found a fellow spirit. Together, he and George Norris formed the spearhead of the insurrection which stripped "Uncle Joe" Cannon of his autocratic powers as Speaker of the House. Lindbergh's friends warned him that incurring the displeasure of the grumpy little Speaker was political suicide. He disregarded their admonitions and with Norris held the floor against the most crushing political juggernaut ever to roll along the aisle of the lower chamber.

When the Democrats substituted the tyranny of the caucus for the Republicans' tyranny of the Speakership, Lindbergh and Norris again assailed the majority and were deprived of their choice committee assignments. Several Minnesota newspapermen commented that "C.A." Lindbergh was apparently inviting political martyrdom at the earliest possible moment. He even refused to employ the time-honored methods of patronage. When the postmaster of Little Falls died, Lindbergh had the right to choose his successor. Instead, he left the decision to a referendum of the voters. Here was a solar plexus smash to the bulwark of party politics. Partisans in all sections of the country condemned this Minnesota upstart who threatened the very foundations of the spoils system. A few commendatory letters from Civil Service advocates were the mete of Lindbergh's reward for his innovation.

In the House Lindbergh was the perennial objector. He wrote doggerel poetry satirizing the Republican tariff, and he introduced a motion to impeach the members of Wilson's Federal Reserve Board. He brought down upon his head the wrath of virtually every newspaper in America when he spoke for hours against including paper and wood pulp on the free tariff list between the United States and Canada. He was instrumental in voicing the demands of the Populists, and he joined with Norris, La Follette, and a Boston lawyer named Louis Dembitz Brandeis in organizing the Republican Progressive League. At the same time that Brandeis was writing his articles on "Other People's Money" in *Harper's Weekly*, Lindbergh published a book, *Banking and Currency and the Money Trust*. Several Congressmen commented on the similarity of the conclusions reached by the scholarly Jewish lawyer and the blunt-spoken Viking from Minnesota.

Private banking was Lindbergh's *bête noir*. The currency question was almost a phobia with him. He sailed so fiercely into every banking proposal of the majority that a conservative Republican said if Charley Lindbergh had been on earth when the plan of salvation was offered, he would have moved to amend it. These single-handed forays against Wall Street earned the Lindbergh the title of the "Lone Fighter." His attacks on the banks took him into the deepest waters of radicalism yet ventured in Congress; he even went beyond the depths braved by La Follette and Norris. On one occasion Lindbergh actually turned his back on Capitalism and endorsed the principles of Debs: "Not many of those who criticize Socialists know the first principles of Socialism. Socialism and Socialists are libeled and slandered by the false and by the ignorant only, for no one who has studied Socialism can for a single moment question that it has a program whereby, if it could be followed out and put into execution, this world would be cleared of much of its misery and degradation."

Lindbergh uttered these words in an era in which Socialism was in as great disrepute as Communism is now. Socialism was the target of every red-hunt. Socialists were suspected of arson, rape, and murder. Over their champagne and *hors d'oeuvres* the gay blades of Washington society talked in shocked tones of "that wild man from Minnesota." Lindbergh was regarded as a fanatic. Yet there were people who listened to his interminable discussions of the money issue, and open-minded editors read the articles written by himself and Brandeis. At last the Pujo Resolution passed the House, and a calm little lawyer named Samuel Untermyer put Morgan, Carnegie, and Rockefeller on the stand and pried them loose from the innermost secrets of American finance. While the masters of banking were being subjected to Untermyer's verbal inquisition, Norris declared on the floor of Congress, "When the true history of Congressional action on the so-called 'Money Trust' is written, it will be found that the Gentleman from Minnesota (Mr. Lindbergh) is entitled to more credit than any other Member."

Charles, Jr. watched many of his father's outnumbered attacks on the fortresses of industry and banking. Frequently he accompanied his father on trips of investigation and inquiry. He was twelve years old when the Congressman took him on a canoe journey through the headwaters of the Mississippi to observe the damage done to farm lands by a faulty reservoir system. Father and son lived in a pup tent and cooked their meals over an open fire. After the outing Lindbergh said his boy had "good stuff" in him.

Lindbergh was not content to learn things by hearsay. He donned dilapidated clothes to visit the slums of New York and Chicago; he wanted to see for himself the conditions in the tenements and rookeries. He told his colleagues that there were people in the nation's greatest cities living in more filth and dirt than did the livestock on his farm back in Minnesota.

Few Congressmen worked harder than Lindbergh. He tried to read every bill—a task made impossible by the deluge of laws poured into the hopper at each session. He used to get to his office at five in the morning, just when the buglers at the Washington Army cantonment were blowing reveille. The Congressman put Charles to work in a corner of his office addressing franked envelopes. One day a clerk suggested that the boy adopt a more efficient method of copying the names he was writing. Charles wheeled on him, "You can't tell me what to do! You're just working here for my father."

From across the room the Congressman looked up. "There isn't anyone in this office working for anyone else. We are all working here together. Don't forget that, son."

Lindbergh had more political enemies than anyone in the House, except possibly George Norris. Yet he was personally popular. Even the Corinthian pillars in the temple of New England conservatism liked the solemn Swede who loped through the halls with his equally somber son scampering to keep pace with him. There was one stalwart of party regularity who constantly objected whenever a Member sought unanimous consent to be absent. Lindbergh told this Representative he wanted permission to be away for several days. The objector thought a moment. "I have to be consistent about this, 'C.A.' " he said. "But I'll tell you what to do. I am going to luncheon today at 12:30. That will be the time for you to make your request of the Chair."

Lindbergh was also popular in his district. Five times he was elected to the House. He knew thousands of voters by their first names. He would stride into the general store in a little village, seat himself on a cracker box, munch a handful of crumbs from the hardtack barrel, and proceed to talk for an hour on the money question. When he finally departed, he had added ten or twelve firm friends to his list of adherents. His constituency was composed largely of farmers, and he knew he could depend on them. On one occasion he was re-elected without opposition. In 1912—the year of Wilson's triumph—he overwhelmed his Democratic adversary by a more than two-to-one margin.

Everyone in Minnesota said that "C.A." was certain to be either a Senator or the Governor. But they ventured their predictions without taking into consideration the holocaust just beyond the horizon.

The World War changed the course of many people's lives— yet no fortunes were changed more swiftly than those of the Lindbergh family. As early as 1915 the Congressman warned, "Each loan brings us a little nearer to the brink of maelstrom." To those who pooh-poohed his fears, he said, "It is my belief we are going in as soon as the country can be sufficiently propagandized into the war mania." He prophesied that the time was not distant when the advocates of peace would be "stoned from the platform and free speech strangled by hordes of furious men who in their secret hearts are still at one with those stoned men . . . The whole nation, pulpit and all, will take up the war cry and shout itself hoarse, and mob any honest man who ventures to open his mouth, and presently such mouths will cease to open."

Two years later in the city of Duluth every hall was denied to Lindbergh. He could not even speak on a street-corner. He was almost a culprit because he expressed his honest convictions on the causes motivating America's entrance into the War. From a potential governor or senator, he was reduced to an ex-Congressman suspected of disloyalty and sedition. He was shunned in the streets, and several times a trolley car emptied of passengers when he boarded it. Who wanted to ride with a Hun? In one address Lindbergh said, "To seek to apply 'national honor' with no thought of existing conditions and without view of the general welfare is weakness instead of strength, foolhardy instead of brave, traitorous rather than patriotic." But the voters had a different opinion, and Lindbergh's political career was washed away in a torrent of hatred and abuse. A devoted minority always clung to him, but he died still regarded by many as a traitor to his country. "Slim" Lindbergh's father did not live to see his prophecies come true.

He predicted that the War would culminate in an orgy of militarism and destruction—but he did not live to see Hitler, Stalin, and Mussolini transform Europe into an armed camp.

He predicted the War would result in economic disaster—but he did not live to see the crash and panic of 1929.

He predicted the War would not make the world safe for democracy—but he did not live to see the aftermath of the great struggle result in less democracy than there ever was in the world before. There were a lot of other things this rangy Viking liberal never lived to see.

He did not see his demands for minimum wages and collective bargaining become the platform of a President re-elected by the most overwhelming vote in the history of the Republic.

He did not see his demands for strict neutrality—voiced as early as 1915—whipped into law and passed with the decisive approval of the people of his adopted country.

He did not see his boy fly the Atlantic and become the idol and hero of those who had scorned him as a "traitor" and "Bolshevik."

He lived ahead of his time . . .

"C.A.'s" advocates have not always been the advocacies of his son. Several years ago Colonel Lindbergh appeared before a Senate Committee and protested the taking of the air-mail contracts from private companies, although "C.A." had continually claimed all transportation should be a public enterprise.

Colonel Lindbergh has found his associates among the families high in industry and banking and commerce—not among the Swedish farmers and shopkeepers who were his father's friends.

No one will ever know what Congressman Lindbergh would say to this. He died while his boy was still a struggling mechanic and novice aviator.

Yet last year in Nazi Germany, where he was inspecting the vast military machine of Hitler and Goering, there glimmered through Colonel Lindbergh's personality a gleam of his father's militant pacifism.

The great flier deplored the use of aerial science as a weapon of war, rather than as an instrument of peace. He condemned the martial spirit engendered in Europe, and he denounced the start of a madcap and barbaric armament race. The speech was so enlightened that Hitler refused to recognize Colonel Lindbergh at the Olympic Games.

An aged farmer in Minnesota, reading the Colonel's remarks, looked up from his newspaper and pushed back his glasses. "You know," he said slowly, " 'Slim' sure sounded like 'C.A.' when he told those Nazi war-lords where to head in at."

The Lone Eagle has been praised by kings and extolled by diplomats. But maybe that compliment was about the best of all.

THE OLD SCHOOL TIE

By EDWARD ACHESON

THE UNITED STATES, AS ALL ENGLISHMEN CAN TELL YOU AND MOST do, is a new country. It has, as yet, no tradition: it has enunciated no ideals: and admittedly. For what further proof is necessary than that benighted America still lacks the one visible and most blatant sign of all inner and spiritual grace—the Old School Tie.

In the "more advanced civilization" (i.e. England) this bit of neckwear, ghastly as its color scheme often is, serves at least a fourfold purpose. It fulfills the function of a caste mark like the decoration of a Hindu's forehead, the boast of a rigid and inexorable stratification. It constitutes within its folds a code of ethics as inflexible as Hammurabi's. It supplies its wearers with an unquestioned and unquestionable philosophy of life. And most important of all, it gives to England, and hence the Empire, a complete and unofficial, yet all-pervading, method of government.

Incidentally and parenthetically, it also comprises the most entertaining blind spot in the Englishman's sense of humor. For the suave and bemonocled Londoner who reserves his best-bred smile of contempt for Americans with luncheon-club lapel-buttons, can see nothing naïve in announcing by means of the stripes on his cravat that he managed in the dimming past to graduate from prep-school, or that he once contributed a mediocre oar to a losing Oxford crew.

Yet, in this as in other branches of sociology and politics, the Englishman's instinct is eminently sound. For the Old School Tie, far from being a smiling matter, undoubtedly ranks as one of the most potent institutions in contemporary British life. Measured against it The Church of England seems superfluous, for in itself it comprises a pragmatic religion: it makes a sorry also-ran of the influence of any Masonic order: against the gossamer of its ramifications, the alleged machinations of the Third Internationale reveal the clumsy hand of the amateur. Shrouded by official unrecognition, there is nothing like it under the sun: only the function performed by the Bolshevik Party within the political and economic framework of the Soviet Union can be said to resemble it. Yet the methods of the Bolshevik Party are direct if anything: the essence of the Old School Tie is indirection—"and influence brought to bear."

And that influence is staggering. The Old School Tie makes Prime Ministers in England, and war outside: it directs foreign policy and most of the stock companies: it fashions society in its own image and society to its own ends. Without it the Ruling Class would lose its adjective overnight and the star of national ascendency would drop in the west like a plummet. Verily, verily, it has been said—"the web of British destiny is spun with the threads of the Old School Tie."

Yet as personal adornment the actual cravat (in contradistinction to the metaphysical tie) is usually not highly intriguing. The great prep school of Eton, for instance, contents itself with a black tie crossed by diagonal blue stripes; blue with white double stripes for its great rival, Harrow. Neither employs electric blue, not even Alice, or baby—just blue. The sort of tie anyone might purchase in an uninspired moment. As a matter of fact, this problem of unintentional misrepresentation was placed squarely before a very special Old-School-Tie clerk. "Suppose," he was asked, "a forgotten man tried to buy an Eton tie—?" Apparently that was a poser; "It's a mistake anyone might make," he was prompted. And the matter was cleared up for him instanter. "Not a gentleman, sir," he smiled.

But, of course, it was inevitable even among gentlemen that such a successful idea should attract imitators. It did—in droves. Regiments adopted distinctive neckwear, one design for officers, naturally, and another for men. Clubs have ties—all of them—boating clubs, cricket clubs, fox-terrier clubs, every imaginable club. Probably the most socially exclusive club tie in England is a demented rainbow of red gold and brown stripes called I Zingari; its overwhelming importance is proven by the fact that any self-respecting Briton can bring himself to be seen dead in it. The Tank Corps has a tie, and pretty bad it is, too, combining brown, red and green. Its wearers, with the sentiment inherent in their calling, translated it, "Through mud and blood to the Green Fields."

These ties, as one might expect, are fairly sacred. Witnesses will not soon forget the expression on the face of a Guards Officer who saw his regimental tie together with Eton, Harrow, an Oxford double Blue and I Zingari, all displayed for sale on Fifth Avenue under the sacrilegious title, "Imported Neckwear."

Against the threat of exactly this type of desecration a number of these ties have been patented—actually patented. The Bank of India tie, which with perhaps unconscious candor displays white elephants on a blue background, is registered at the Patent Office. Indian princes and potentates were quick to get the idea and a number of them have neckties of peculiar design registered for their exclusive use—sort of a one-man Old-School idea. The detectives' cricket club at Scotland Yard has a necktie of its own. And so has the inspection department of the Air Ministry. The identity of the latter tie is one of the great hush-hush matters of the Empire. It is blue with little red quesion marks but that fact is guarded like the golden apples in the west. The indiscreet official who disclosed the secret in his cups is probably at this very moment looking for himself with all the ardor of an outraged bloodhound.

There are, of course, less mysterious ties. Hospitals have them. But you can't get an "Old St. Mary's" by merely having peritonitis within those ancient walls. The cravat is reserved for those who earn or learn there. Even business houses have ties, and a number of them are patented. The neckwear reserved for the exclusive use of the officials of the British-American Export Tobacco Company brings the thing perilously near home.

But Indian Maharajahs and police sports clubs, rowing boat associations and Oxford, banks, tobacco companies and I Zingari, are, when all is said and done, merely variations on a central theme. The Old School Tie is the basis, the reality which lends significance to the others. And the Old School Tie is important only because it is the recognized badge of the Ruling Class. It has nothing whatsoever to do with education: otherwise the University ties would be more valuable. It does not concern itself with individual capability or achievement—its unlovely designs are available to every student. But it does stand for a caste. It proclaims, in effect, that the possessor is not, thank God, as other men.

To less favored nations (e.g. the United States) that must worry along without its benefits, the spiritual aspect of the Cult of the

Cravat is practically unbelievable. But Stanley Baldwin, ironmaster, and Prime Minister of England, himself a graduate of Harrow and hence an "Old Harrovian" can be cited as vivid witness that the unbelievable in all its maudlin majesty is vitally true. Wrote Mr. Baldwin, "When the call came to me to form a Government one of my first thoughts was that it should be a Government of which Harrow should not be ashamed. I remembered how in previous Governments there had been four or perhaps five Harrovians and I determined to have six . . . I will, with God's help do nothing in the course of an arduous and difficult career, which shall cause any Harrovian to say of me that I failed to do my best to live up to the highest ideals of the school."

Than that quotation nothing could better exemplify the charming simplicity of the system: nothing could demonstrate more nicely its practical manifestations. Just picture for a moment the proportions of the riot that would break out in the United States if a President cheerfully announced, that, other considerations to the contrary notwithstanding, he was determined to appoint to his cabinet at least six old school-chums from, say, Groton, Andover, or for that matter, the Dayton, Ohio, Public High School Number Seven. Habitually Americans have condoned some fairly sharp practices among their politicians, but even Mr. Tweed in his veriest heyday would have hesitated to permit himself the Baldwin frankness.

However, it is actually the other side of the equation that holds the greatest interest for foreign observers. If Mr. Baldwin wishes to indulge a starry-eyed attachment to the institution which fifty-one years ago was paid to educate him, that aberration can be attributed to a purely personal peculiarity. What lends social significance to the emotion is the fact that six of his old schoolmates were slated for cabinet posts admittedly and avowedly because they *were* his old schoolmates.

True it can be argued that in practice Mr. Baldwin departed lamentably from the course his conscience dictated: he appointed only five Harrovians while including six men from the great rival prep-school Eton. But the principle is unimpaired. Here are two preparatory schools, out of some one hundred and fifty, between them supplying eleven members of the Baldwin Cabinet of twenty-one.

Nor is the present instance an isolated phenomenon. One-third of all Cabinet Ministers in the last hundred years have come from either Eton or Harrow. Those two schools have supplied twelve of the nineteen Prime Ministers during the same period. Today His Majesty's Ministers, numbering in all fifty-eight, can boast twenty-five Eton and Harrow men; of the fifty-five ranking officials of the foreign service, from Chargé d'affaires to Ambassador, Eton alone claims twenty-eight as well as ten of the thirty-four Governors and Governors-General. Parliaments change, of course, but Eton and Harrow usually manage to fill about a third of the benches. The House of Lords simply shimmers with the better Old School Ties, as do the exclusive clubs, bank directorates, boards of charitable foundations and other institutions which can boast either pomp or circumstance. In every field of endeavor or privilege, provided only that the stakes are high enough, the Old School Tie makes the running. If it be the right tie, its wearer is gratuitously presented with an inside track; if wrong or absent, the chances are infinitely weighed against the contender's ever getting to the post.

The conclusions are therefore obvious. Either the type of education provided by the "great" schools is so overwhelmingly superior that its beneficiaries are uniquely equipped to handle the vaster problems of the nation, or—if not—and I believe very few would care to support that thesis—then the virtual monopoly of the positions of power by the sometime-students of the "great" schools, has, at least to the untutored eye of an American inquirer, a number of the earmarks of a highly successful racket.

This ungenerous impression is further enhanced by any inquiry into the historical background of the educational system. Of course, at the outset, it must be remembered that the schools are a purely British product and hence their development is characterized by a purely British logic which tends to confuse the unwary. The French, for instance, hampered by their inelastic methods of reasoning, seem incapable of grasping the fact that the "Great Public Schools" of England aren't public at all, but private, strictly private. Knowing that the older institutions were founded "to educate the poor and indigent scholars of the neighborhood," it seems paradoxical to the methodical Gallic intellect that these schools should now draw their clientele exclusively from the wealthiest elements in the four corners of the Empire.

But to the British (accustomed from youth to quoting prices in fractional parts of a non-existent coin) the minor nonsequiturs of the public school system are neither clearly apparent nor vastly important. They speak of the "Great Public Schools," in juxtaposition to "the others" without any definite agreement as to which "the great" ones are. Almost always, however, Eton, Harrow, Rugby and Winchester are included. Usually the term is applied to ten or twelve schools which together enroll about six thousand or 11% of the prep-school boys of the country. But the prep-school boys amount to only 2% of the male youth of the nation. Hence the boys from the "Great Public Schools" account for but two tenths of one per cent of the population. Yet this one fifth of one per cent, habitually and as though by divine right, rules the country. Over the last century they, these "Old Boys" of the "Great Public Schools," have occupied exactly half the seats in the House of so-called Commons.

From which it would seem that the proper Old School Tie is not only a necessary but an almost infallible Open-Sesame, and it would be natural to assume that the number of applications for admission to this Royal Road is enormous.

But it isn't. Harrow and Eton have waiting lists, as every other successful school has, but their waiting lists are worked out on an even more modest basis than most, namely, that one in three of all accepted candidates will fail to put in an appearance. Since a number of boys are entered at birth or on speculation before, the calculation fails to bear out the theory that every ambitious parent in the British Isles is panting to have a little Etonian in the home.

Pant he may, but never, if he has a modicum of common sense, will he allow his eagerness to betray him into applying unless he be pretty well assured that the application will be accepted. For to be turned down is fatal, and in its complete fatality lies the key to the smooth functioning of the system. The "outsider," who recognizes himself as such, doesn't even apply, for fear of having that appellation hung around his neck for life. In London today one of the wealthiest, most charming and successful of the young Socialite business men was "turned down by Harrow"; that was twenty years ago; it is still the first thing that you are told about him—in whispers.

The proper procedure for a doubtful parent is to approach one of the all-powerful house masters, and do a bit of "talking around the subject." In discussing the Derby or morganatic marriages, the house master may toss in the interesting fact that the school lists, oddly enough, are chuck-a-block full for the next fifty-two years. The sad but wiser parent will then approach a house master of a second-flight institution, then a third and fourth, until if the cards be stacked against his scion, the boy lands up in some school no one ever heard of and the Ruling Class is thereby relieved of the necessity of "looking out for him." Since, as has been clearly demonstrated by agony column standards, one "Old Boy" is always worth any dozen "young men."

And remember that this winnowing process takes place when a boy is ten years old or less. The "Great Public Schools" are prep-schools, not universities. If a man graduates first in his class from Harvard or Oxford, Cambridge or Yale, there is a fair basis for assuming that he is a capable fellow: perhaps it is in the public interest to put him in a position to govern. But who, bar a psychologist skilled in clairvoyance, could select the nation's best brains from a group of boys applying for admission to school, boys whose ages range from ten on down through zero, into an embryonic stage.

Obviously it can't be done on merit. Equally obviously no such attempt is made. The future Old Etonians or Old Harrovians are chosen first of all from a limited financial class: not every family in that rough island can afford a thousand to fifteen hundred dollars per annum to educate even its whitest hope. And secondly, from a limited social class, since, of course, the sons of Old School Boys are given preference, provided their fathers have earned or retained the ante. Out of which family-school traditions develop and we find eight generations of Bridgewaters wearing Harrow's funny looking straw hats. The Hamiltons, the Churchills and Gordons also historically go to Harrow. Eton has an even more imposing list of great names for the very good reason that being near Windsor it tends to be Tory and Royalist as against Harrow's Whig or Liberal background. Bearing in mind that Eton is twice the size of Harrow, a British Cabinet can almost always be classified as to party by the proportion of Eton to Harrow men. And so can a family. Those which keep changing schools every four or five generations eventually get the reputation of being politically flighty.

But usually they don't. And family tradition, coupled to the other three determinants, cost, the method of house master selections and the impeditive fear of being "turned down," these four combined produce the Old School Tie, and the Old School Tie is responsible for England and the English as she and they are known.

So completely true is this relationship of cause and effect that it is usually assumed without being given the dignity of a premise. In South America, when they swear "on the word of an Englishman," they mean the word of a Public School Boy; they must if they've ever put any credence in the oath of a cockney fish monger. And when the world praises the adenoidal modulations of the "English accent" it is referring to habits of speech in the Great Public Schools: the world does not include the equally British noises emitted by an agitated North Country coal-miner; or, if it does, it has never listened to a North Country coal-miner expressing agitation.

Hence the peculiar paradox—that when an "alien" speaks of "the British" he automatically excludes ninety-nine and four-fifths per cent of the male population, along with most of the women. And does so perfectly unconsciously. So effective is the Old School System.

And it follows as the night the day, that the chief by-product of the system should be snobbery, snobbery of such a colossal, unmitigated variety that it must be seen to be believed. Take the gentleman who wrote to the London *Daily Telegraph*, suggesting "that it would be a good thing if the Old Boys of our Great Public Schools made it a rule invariably to accost anyone of whatever age whom he sees wearing his School Tie: this might prevent those who have no right to wear these ties from attempting to assume a virtue which they lack."

Notice, if you please, the meticulously unsplit infinitive, "invariably to accost" and the subtlety of the last line. The writer doesn't suggest that his plan would prevent those "bounders" from *assuming* the virtue—they couldn't, of course—but from *attempting* to assume. And if the noun "virtue" seems a somewhat unfortunate choice, refer to the London *Daily Express* which will demonstrate editorially that in fact the word conveys a gross understatement. For "the Public School Code," according to the *Express*, "embraces the Ten Commandments, it also embraces the Lord's Prayer. the

Sermon on the Mount, and Kipling's *If*." From which even the most caviling will readily see that living up to this ethic, (even without the *If*) isn't a mere virtue, it's a veritable miracle.

Yet virtue or miracle, an ideal or a matter of practical politics, hereditary theory or racket, there stands the Old School Tie, placidly running the Church Bazaar and the Empire, foreign trade and the village cricket match. Recent vagaries in English foreign policy, such as the Hoare-Laval sell-out and the Mediterranean fleet fiasco, begin to assume a certain demented logic if interpreted in terms of Public School Tradition. The Foreign Office, which is furthest removed from the vulgar influence of public opinion, is most inexorably bound up with the Old School Tie. And older and hence more influential men entered the service before 1919: before 1919 an applicant had to have two qualifications, first a private income, second to "be known to the Secretary of State or recommended to him by men of standing and position." Naturally one-third of the personnel came from Eton: naturally thirty-seven per cent held hereditary titles; naturally "no member of the Foreign Office had ever been traced who attended any school in this country other than a Public School"; and naturally and rightfully, John Bright characterized the whole pageant as "a gigantic form of outdoor relief for the aristocracy."

For what, pray, could an airy abstraction like a League of Nations mean to the toddlers who drew their social science from the Playing Fields of Eton. The voices of the ten million Englishmen and women who voted "yes" in the Peace Ballot sounded only faintly in the Foreign Office, with just sufficient strength to cause a momentary deviation from the realistic policy of the politics of power. But Vansittart, the Old School Tie and Common Sense muddled through in the nick of time and the wrong was righted. England was successfully lined up for the quick march which will land her honorably at the threshold of the next war.

But the Old School Tie, like the Tank Corps cravat, will be all the brighter for a bit more blood. The Old Etonians will make the recruiting speeches, and well. The Old Harrovians will command in the field, and the Old Wychamists (William of Wycham founded Winchester) will direct from London and be knighted for it. Those are the traditions of the particular Schools within the general framework of the Old School Tradition as a whole.

And when the pictures of the Old Boys, who have gained distinction either through death or a peerage, are published in the *Illustrated London News* you will discover that it isn't at all tactless to accuse a man openly of being an "Old Haberdasher." Actually the accusee, if he be a peer and not a casualty, will be delighted that his true worth as a graduate of the Haberdashers' Aske's School at Hampstead has been appreciated. By the same token Old Albanians, Manchurians and Perseans aren't ancient foreigners at all, but sometime students of St. Albans, Manchester and the Perse School, respectively. The jargon becomes esoteric with the Old Carthusians who aren't monks, but beneficiaries of the type of education dealt out at Charterhouse, which was founded by the Carthusian Order. The name Old Salopian has no Freudian content; it is derived from the Roman attempt to pronounce Shrewsbury. The boys from Westminster call themselves Old Elizabethians after the Great Queen, and the Old Stoics aren't Greeks, but hail from Stowe School. Graduates of St. Bee's are, unhappily, called "Old Beghians."

And there are, of course, schools, whose products aren't Old Anythings. The board schools corresponding to our public schools either don't have Old School Ties or more usually have Ties that don't count. Too, at the other end of the scale are private ventures of which the clientele doesn't boast, such as the one advertised in the *London Times* as "Home School for Retarded Sons of the Very Upper Classes": adding reassuringly, "Three vacancies."

But the board schools are outside the charmed circle. A man must be a Disraeli or a Labour Leader to "make good" with such a handicap. Old Grammarians (from the Chelsea Grammar School) Old Stoics, Etonians, Harrovians and Wychamists, together with the four or five thousand other "Public School Boys," all these start from scratch. Provided only that they're not "too bright," that they don't do what "isn't done," or think it, that they ride straight, don't try to get divorced ladies presented at Court, and stay away from Sir Stafford Cripps' Socialist League, provided in a word that they play the game and live up to the Code, they will be "taken care of."

Because, when all is said and done, the tradition as a whole is greater than any of its parts, no matter how great that part may be. The Old School Tie is a "virtue." which, like the Calvinist

Grace, descends with no rhyme and less reason. But it blankets its chosen with a shining anonymity through which no personality can permanently penetrate. An Old Carthusian may become a saint, or a columnist, a foreign secretary, a whiskey baron, or even, theoretically, a poet—yet, those modifications are merely transient; fundamentally, historically and obituarily, his significance, if any, is derived from the fact of his Old Carthusianship.

And Mr. Baldwin, who "in a long and arduous career" has proven so many things, can be called upon to prove this final conclusion. The Prime Minister was coming up to London in the train. A fellow-passenger opposite lowered his copy of the *Times*. "I beg your pardon," said the stranger, "but you're an Old Harrovian, are you not?"

Mr. Baldwin, gratified, said he was.

"Quite. Quite. I was very nearly sure. Yes—you were—let me see now—you left in '86, or was it '87?"

"Five," Mr. Baldwin corrected.

"To be sure. Certainly. You were in Small Houses, if I'm not mistaken. Then you went up to the Head's. Am I right? Ah, I thought so. And you roomed with—with, I mean to say, that lanky chap, Thingame Minor."

Mr. Baldwin smiled and nodded. The fellow-passenger was charmed with himself. "Absolutely—Oh, quite. I remember perfectly. And I'll call your name in just a moment. Don't tell me. It was—what I mean is, your name—something like Bailey or Bancroft—no, no, hold on—it has a 'win' in it."

"Baldwin," the Prime Minister supplied, "Stanley Baldwin."

"Of course, of course. Baldwin. It was right on the tip of my tongue. Well, well—and tell me, Baldwin, since you left school, what have you been doing with yourself?"

SO SMELLS DEFEAT

By George Antheil

THE METROPOLIS ITSELF WILL REMAIN PRACTICALLY UNTOUCHED.
That famous super-super Big Bertha saddled upon that equally
famous super-super dreadnought (designed especially to float it)
will hit New York just once, thereby hardly justifying its great
cost. The several nondescript hits of the third visit of the enemy
bombing squadron will do even less damage. It will almost seem as
if the enemy had been more than especially desirous of keeping
the great prize of New York City intact and had confined itself
instead to attacks designed rather to demoralize than to destroy.
There will remain, of course, a few awe-inspiring reminders of
the recent war as, for instance, that enormous big hole large
enough to enfold a whole ocean liner; this hole will remain in
the middle of Broadway and 116th Street for five years and dis-
close deep down the torn entrails of abandoned subways, gas
and water mains and dead electric cables. That part of Broadway,
however, will now have been closed to traffic for quite a number
of years. There will be a shattered skyscraper near the Public
Library; some will claim that this was the work of the sea-going
Big Bertha; they will prove that the shell had barely missed the
Empire State Building which still stands majestically but minus
its coat of gold and silver, but the posthumous memoirs of a foreign
air-commander will show that it was the work of a single bombing
plane. There is another whopping big hole (although not as large
as the one up on Broadway) at 59th and Madison. The American
Flag will still be flying at the top of the Empire State and the
Chrysler buildings.

BUT we shall *now* be paying heavy indemnities to foreign nations. It is almost two years since our defeated armies disbanded.
Our money shall just have begun to tremble and flutter into paper,
and there will be much talk of moratoriums and the betrayal of
our great war-dead by wicked and unpatriotic statesmen. It will

564

be claimed that we signed peace treaties before there was actually any need to do so.

After three years everybody will still be wearing overcoats bought long before the war, most of them threadbare and fashioned in the style of ten years ago. The greatest and most sumptuous of our hotels will soon be forced to economize in ways that would once have seemed grotesque; for instance, they will unscrew at least half of their electric light bulbs and so leave their great corridors in semi-darkness. They will also take up their rich red carpets and remove the expensive brass handles from the doors of their rooms. If they neglect to do this thousands of hobnail boots will destroy the carpets and the expensive brass doorknobs will disappear in the departing pockets of starving guests.

Vast hordes of returning soldiery will swell beyond any comparison available today the already tremendous ranks of the unemployed and there will be petty looting and stealing everywhere although the city police will have already long ago doubled its strength. Policemen, moreover, will walk in twos.

To add to the general fever of speculation the Dollar will drop in value, and an English Pound will soon be able to buy ten instead of five American Dollars. Everyone will say that the worst has happened and that the Dollar can drop no lower. But the following week it will be twenty Dollars to the Pound. One will witness the wildest days of market speculation this country has ever seen. Foreigners will flock to New York City. Our Dollar will drop steadily day after day until it reaches 50, then 100, then 1000 to the English Pound. Prices will be as unstable as quicksilver; to illustrate: one may be seated in a great restaurant, a proud restaurant that has fed generation upon generation of our very greatest families. Perhaps you yourself are now studying the menu. The waiter will snatch it out of your hands. When he hands it back each item will be marked with a new price according to the latest stock-market returns. Newspapers will be printed upon the cheapest possible paper and will only carry news about the falling Dollar, possible moratoriums, and loans to be attempted of foreign and richer powers.

Then after a few weeks the Dollar will *really* begin to slip. Newspaper headlines will scream "POUND $136,900." Day after day newspapers will carry only these large screaming number headlines. Newspapers will be sold only by ghastly war-wounded for there will be no jobs left for the little enterprising newspaper boys of other days. College students will sell gum, pencils, and shoestrings in the restaurants, otherwise they will not eat. The mistresses and daughters of the former rich will likewise be unable to eat unless they find for themselves a rich foreigner, of which, fortunately for them, there will now be many in New York. Thousands of women, never accustomed to work, will haunt the streets, giving themselves for a single square meal. The Pound will reach the million mark, one million Dollars for one Pound! Householders will secure their vegetables through barter or buy them with suitcases filled full of the new Dollars the presses in Washington are now printing in carload lots. School children will be admitted to school only if they bring coal or food to every lesson.

The city will be swamped with a deluge of magazines so astonishingly and forthrightly filthy that the old *Brevities* of 1933 will seem in comparison like a Sunday school weekly.

A thousand insignificant restaurant-cafés will enjoy the most temporary of existences, all of them with nothing to eat, but with plenty to drink. They will all be designed to accommodate the new and vicious camaraderie of the times.

This camaraderie will be very *peculiar*, decidedly *queer*. Five million soldiers have been fighting in the field for five years without women, and twenty million women have been sitting at home with no companionship but that of very young boys and very old men.

Quite of its own accord new friendships have solidified, friendships cemented under dangerous conditions, dangerous pressures, and in devil-take-care times.

"Tomorrow everyone may be dead." New sexual habits will have been formed and firmly established. The two long separated sexes will at last come together almost as strangers.

These new frightening loves and perversions, habits too long continued to be broken, will then only too often end in suicide. Certain cafés will be full of elegant and beautiful women who are not women but men. There will also be cabarets full of handsome young men who beneath their faultlessly trim dinner jackets and tuxedos will be women.

Many, many churches will be closed. The small towns will be

drained of their youth who will go on the march in numbers away beyond anything ever dreamed of after the famous 1929 depression. Millions upon millions of boys will grow up never even having known what the word "work" means. Curious, mad, dadaist-futuristic art movements will spring up and many "intellectuals" having nothing better to do, will take enthusiastic part in them. Curious as these strange art movements may be, they will, nevertheless, be true mirrors of the mad times they reflect. There will be in addition many insane, pathological crimes, all of a shockingly macabre tendency. Meanwhile the Dollar will reach 1,000,-000,000 to the Pound.

Purely Republican and Democratic political parties will have disappeared. Replacing them will be neither one extreme right nor one extreme left party but ten separate parties of every political shade of the rainbow. Shattered into small fragments, the nation's political strength will now be ever weak and faltering, the Constitution will be changed, and our new Congresses will go into a frenzy of ineffectual lawmaking. Among the new political parties will be the Republican-Socialist Party, the Republican-Democratic Party, the National-Socialist Party, the Communist-Democratic Party, and the All-American Blueshirts.

A mass murderer will appear in Reading, Pa., and to the horror of everyone it will be discovered that he has sold human flesh at his meat shop for over one whole year. Meat however will have been tremendously scarce and one will hardly be too astonished with the little-too-inventive Reading butcher. Butter and eggs will be at a premium. Substitute food will appear; synthetic sugar (with a bitter taste!), synthetic bread (that will crumble in the mouth like chalk) and synthetic coffee (the less said the better!). The Pound will now bring 100 billion Dollars at the banks, and one million American Dollars will hardly buy a single match to light a cigarette. Everyone will now say that the Dollar cannot possibly depreciate any lower. Foreigners of every description will flood New York; they will bring with them Pounds, Marks, Francs or Liras. A thousand transient shops will open and close; they will sell valuables obtained apparently from nowhere; in reality they will be but the go-betweens of the richest homes of Fifth and Park Avenues; the situation will eventually grow so corrupt that the state will take over the pawnbroking of the nation and

a tremendous government pawnshop will eventually be set up in
Madison Square Garden. In this enormous place, seething with
booths, departments, and officials, almost every last householder
will bring his last remaining valuables; he will have to do this in
order to eat, for his fat little bank account of other days will be
now so valueless that it no longer will buy him even a crust of
bread. Country estates originally worth $160,000 will be sold for
100 Pounds Sterling.

Over the entire breadth of the country one will never see a
newly painted house and in New York City many of the older
frame buildings in the poorer section of the city will, through lack
of repairs, literally fall apart. These abandoned properties will then
be gradually taken over by the homeless of whom there are by
this time millions. They will from the remaining tin, board, and
beams construct fantastic and dadaistic structures. The homeless
will now be so numerous that it will now be dangerous to try to
drive them out. For all these many years everyone has refused
to pay any but the most minimum of rents and many middle-strata
homes have declined point-blank to pay any rent at all, but they
have not been evicted; there are already too many of them and
one cannot very well evict the ragged, the poor and the sick. Of
the latter there will be, of course, a great many and rich foreign
governments will send us their relief organizations with many
welcome boatloads of canned milk, potatoes, meat and medicines.
And we will need to take alms from everybody who will give.
Meanwhile our politicians and bankers will sail for abroad in order
to try to negotiate loans . . . loans that will be negotiated at
tremendous premiums, loans that neither they, nor we, whom
they represent, ever really intend to pay. There will be, in particular, some great foreign power who will have profited more
than the other powers through this last of great wars to end wars,
and this power, in consequence, will be puffed up beyond all en-
durance by its new importance and will, accordingly, simply beam
with goodwill upon all mankind. We will nick this country for a
loan every time we get the chance, putting this cash quickly into
buildings, concrete, factories, and homes for the homeless . . .
unmovable property that can never be taken away from us.

Our hotel lobbies will now be so full to brimming with pan-
handlers and get-rich-quick little shots, ready to sell us anything

from a sack of potatoes to a scrapped battleship, that we will be utterly sick of them.

Fat little profiteers speculating successfully with the country's meagre foodstuffs will be sitting in every cabaret, all of them giving expensive dinners to the successful little actresses of the moment.

There will also be "strategic zones." The immediate vicinity of New York will find itself in several of these and every time we journey to Philadelphia, we shall be stopped at Trenton, New Jersey, by a dapper little foreign lieutenant who will make his way through the coaches of our train followed by two unsmiling soldiers both armed to the teeth. He will then demand of each of us "Passport!" and he will do so without a smile or without flinching an eye to your banter. No one will be able to move anywhere without his "papers"; these identifications will have to be stamped and passed by both the foreign government and our own. We will laugh bitterly every time we see one of these detestable foreign uniforms and we will laugh bitterly often, for they will be everywhere.

The situation will now grow rapidly worse. Wives who have remained faithful to us during the whole long war will no longer be able to see their children or shell-shocked husbands starving and often indeed will they go either directly upon the streets, or become the mistresses of those greasy little gentlemen who speculate in humanity's necessities to secure for you the very same necessities these little gentlemen speculate with. Prostitution will increase. To cross Park Avenue after one o'clock at night will be the signal for a snake-line of girls to run and encircle you. Fifty girls holding hands! Among them you will distinguish a former motion picture actress, a former society girl, and three girls from your home town.

Gangsters will disappear because money has become the sign of a sign and all valuables, except jewels, will either be too bulky to steal or too difficult to convert into foreign exchange. Thieving will revert rather to petty larceny, the stealing of vegetables, bread, and small finery. If the left-overs of gangsterism should kidnap someone and hold him for a 50,000 Pound ransom, they would have to get a large truck to cart it off; the ransom must be paid in American dollars for it will be forbidden to obtain foreign exchange money at any American bank. This alone will make kidnapping a well-nigh impossible undertaking; it would take the kidnappers well-nigh a month to count the ransom Dollars just to make sure that they had not been short-changed. One or two large gangs will persist, but they will devote themselves to robbing the few remaining bank vaults still filled with American valuables. A few foreigners with too much foreign valuta in their pockets will be held up and murdered but wise foreigners will quickly learn how to walk about with no foreign valuta in their pockets. Travelers' Checks, issued upon foreign banks and countersigned at the time of tender, will be in use everywhere.

But a new type of crime will spring into being, the crime of desperation, inhibition and inability to cope with the new life dictated by national defeat and the consequent new economic conditions. These crimes will be the crimes of those who were never intended to be criminals; they will be stupid, ridiculous, and terribly ineffectual crimes. Various American families will, of course, react differently. One family will take to the new situation as a duck takes to water whilst the other will go down brittle and unbending. One family will take off their coats and dig; the family next door will not remove their white collars, waiting, hoping, intriguing, until these same white collars can be laundered no more, and their coats and trousers may be repaired no longer. College professors will be the hardest hit. Many of these ancient specimens, once intellectuals, writers, or lecturers in their own right, will now peddle some little book or another they have written; they will appear regularly in the hotel lobbies, restaurants and cafés; all of them will be mendicants but apparently making a living from that which they sell. The alms given them will still be the true alms of compassion and they will be given by those who still have respect, even though misguided, for learning.

An intellectual ferment, having nothing else to do but to sit around and hatch, will increase until it is fever hot; people will, year after year, mope about and evolve the most *recherché* theories about everything. Out of this feverish muddle will arise many new political faiths, art-movements, philosophies, and their accompanying pamphleteers; new "intellectual" magazines printed upon the cheapest paper will be sold in every bookshop, and perhaps the only new and booming industry will be the printing of cheap books. New bookshops will spring up like mushrooms. In St. Louis a dictator will arise, and a little group of fanatics will arise about him. He will be put into jail, of course, but here he will find time to write a revolutionary book later destined to sweep the nation into flames. The book will be Chauvinist to extreme and revive in spirit the old Ku Klux Klan.

No loaves of bread will be displayed in bakery shop windows. (There will no longer be any necessity to advertise this commodity.) Eatables will be obtained only by punched cards and several armed policemen will stand in every foodstuff establishment to prevent rioting. The food will be miserably inadequate. Everyone will slowly come to know what protracted hunger means. The new generation of American girls will be ugly. One will be hard put to it to select a beauty chorus for the new Broadway Revues . . . the Revues, of course, will never falter but appear eternally, year after year, without fail; they will be the last to disappear among the souvenirs of pre-war American life. But our popular songs will no longer be sappy-lovey-dovey but will be hard and brittle and very much to the immediate point; they will point blank beg the little girl to spend just one night with the gentleman entertaining her. Brutality and actuality will have been substituted for June-dream sentimentality. The youth of New York will lose its interest in sports and partake of vicious amusements more in keeping with the blood-sprayed atmosphere of our recently returned battalions. Dangerous clubs well hid from the police and meeting in obscure apartments will permit every kind of orgy which will take place in these secret hide-outs and murder and suicide societies will satisfy the thrill-lust of those who have just spent five years behind the machine guns. Those who have flown five years above a hostile front will no longer have a stomach for that special whimsey fare of 1936 afforded by public libraries carefully censored plays or the well-meaning intentions of matronly entertaining societies. The returning heroes will have done with the Ladies-Aid-tea-shoppe type of entertainment. The taste for blood rather will find its vent in the formation of secret societies meeting weekly to saw off the top of a living man's skull merely to watch the brain throb as the victim slowly dies. Ladies of the Street will offer their dubious services for the merest cigarette money but they will also murder you at the drop of a hat if you unnecessarily flash valuta. But if you go home with them, you will find that they will take you to their former homes upon

East End Avenue, and their mothers, brothers and fathers will receive you with the most perfect equanimity while you stay the night. Pride will have disappeared with morality, and there will be nothing left but hunger.

Meanwhile practically all of the world's rich scum and riff-raff will loll about in our gigantic Park Avenue apartments, paying but $25 monthly for them in valuta. These apartments will be filled with parasitic friends, loot from the remaining shops, and any number of temporary mistresses.

Upon this apparently endless desert of American misery there will eventually appear a new mirage . . . the old paper dollar will disappear and its place will be taken by a new Gold Dollar.

But years of additional misery will come and go. The new generation will grow up furious and questioning; they will camp in the country and harden themselves and will become countryside Spartans and detest the city strongholds reeking, for them, of desolation and corruption. They will hold fanatically together and organize into thousands of secret societies upon thousands of American countrysides; they will manufacture forbidden machine guns, train secret troops, and suddenly and at the right moment thrust forward a new leader, perhaps this very same "dictator" so unsuccessful in that *coup* at St. Louis so many years ago. The nation, just beginning to raise itself out of sickness and desolation and fully ready for the excitement of a new creed will now perhaps experience a new thrill . . . that ancient thrill of power and united strength which comes from within. The new movement will be Chauvinist to extreme and various Leftist parties, now thoroughly alarmed, will band together, thrust and parry, and cause many bloody internal and secret strifes. There will be, for a time, unending intrigues, political killings and wholesale imprisonments; no one will be able to think, eat, sleep or discuss anything but the politics and *coups* of the hour. The new would-be dictator will adapt the symbols and rigamarole of the American Indians; in his paradoxical and Chauvinistic fervor he will claim that the ancient Red Man is the only real and valuable essence of true Americanism and that all other races and inhabitants of this continent should emulate him and him only. The new dictator will adapt totem poles for standards and will "go back" to the Spartan doctrines of the American Indian and soak his preachings in blood. He will call his armies, as they grow, by the names of American Indian tribes. And, as time passes, he will become one of the strongest dictators in the world, the rest of the world having grown, in the meantime, politically weak and torn by internal strife and unemployment. He will laugh at existing agreements forced out of us by foreign powers in the years of our misery and defeat. He will manufacture, against treaty-agreements, thousands of airplanes, and will train thousands of young pilots to fight in them. He will develop new and secret killing devices of which no foreign power has ever dreamed, and against which, therefore, they hardly can be prepared. This may be America. It was Germany, 1918-1934. So smells defeat.

THREE DEAD GEESE

By VINCENT SHEEAN

WE HAVE HAD AN INTERNATIONAL CONFERENCE ON OUR LAKE. THAT is, a number of great men, aided by a number of smaller men, accompanied by a horde of men of all sizes, have been meeting in solemn conclave to settle the future of Europe. The event is not new. Indeed, the same great and little men have met dozens of times before in the past fifteen years, and the future of Europe still seems rather unsettled. In view of this celebrated fact, it occurred to me, as a puzzled dweller on the shores of the lake, to inquire among the people closest to the scene of deliberations—i.e., the other dwellers on the shores of the lake—whether any results of the meeting had been perceived.

I started with Pietro. He raises chickens and geese.

"What do you think of the Conference at Stresa, Pietro?" I asked.

"Ah, Madonna!" he said. "What a lot of trouble for nothing! For five days the policemen and secret agents poisoned my life. I couldn't go out on the lake in my boat, couldn't get to market at Intra, at Lesa, at Stresa, couldn't sell my geese or chickens or eggs, and who is going to pay me back the three hundred lire I have lost, I want to know? My eggs are not like the storage eggs they buy in the big hotels out of boxes. My eggs come from hens. I told the policeman, but they don't care. They would just as soon see all the eggs rot and the meat spoil. I had killed three geese and five chickens for the market at Lesa, and there were all the eggs besides. At least three hundred lire I have lost this week, and the Conference won't pay me back."

"Ah, well, Pietro, that's a great pity, but you know the Conference had other things to think of. They wanted to make peace between nations."

"S-ss-ss-ss! Peace between nations! They might begin by making a little peace here on our lake, for example! Who ever asked them to come here with their aeroplanes and their armies of policemen? Every time I put my nose out of doors somebody asks me to show my papers. The aeroplanes are making me deaf, and I can't get from my house to the farm without being stopped by twenty secret agents, all foreigners, too, from Naples and Sicily and Rome! They can't even understand Italian, not the way I speak it. Is that what they call peace? It's not much different from war."

"Well, there is some difference," I maintained. "At least they don't kill you."

"No," said Pietro—a reasonable man. "They don't kill me. But when they get through their peace meetings there will be another war, sooner or later, and then they'll catch up on the killing. And what for, I'd like to know? All I want to do is get to market three times a week and sell my chickens and geese and eggs. It is not very much, but it is all I want. Why can't they let me alone? I pay my taxes, every year more taxes, and look what they do with the money! Spend it on gasoline to put in a lot of aeroplanes to make me deaf! Millions of lire they have spent this week over at Stresa, and then they won't even let me go to market."

It was obvious that Pietro's severe financial loss had deflected his view of the great assembly. Economic interest does occasionally influence opinion, even on Lago Maggiore. I passed on to Enrico, who, as a stonemason, was less likely to have been financially involved in the historic event.

"How do you feel about the Conference, Enrico?"

Enrico spat violently on the cobblestones of the village street.

"I got a job over at Baveno last week," he said. "It's the first job I have had for about a year and a half, and I was glad to get it.

"Then, on Monday, all these brigands from the south fell on us and declared martial law. I tried to explain that I had a new job and needed the money, but the damned foreigners couldn't even understand what I was saying, and they wouldn't let me go across the lake. So I've lost my job, I suppose. I don't know when I can get another one.

"I tried to argue with the *Maresciallo*. He is a Neapolitan and talks like a horse. All he did was shout and whinny and bellow at me, and then they threw me out of the police station and I had to go home. Thank God I have a field with some vegetables in it, or we would have starved long ago."

"I know that you've had a hard time," I said, "but I was wondering what you thought of the Conference itself."

"*Gran Dio!* What do I know about the Conference? All those people meet and talk and talk and talk, and I lose my job; that's all I know. I tell you, when their war begins I am going to escape from it if I have to swim all the way to Switzerland."

Enrico's view—although a very common one—was not particularly illuminating. I went back to my house, where Maria, the cook, was stewing some vegetables for soup.

"What is your opinion of the Stresa Conference, Maria?" I asked, sitting down on the only chair in the kitchen. She looked up from the stove, her face flushed and startled.

"I don't think about such things, Signor," she said. "I know there is going to be a war, and the boys don't like it, but I don't understand why. There are too many aeroplanes on the lake; they give me a pain in the head, just here. Seven aeroplanes make too much noise. We are not used to noise around here. And then all the policemen . . ."

I let her explain the various local annoyances for some time. I had heard it all before, but once Maria starts she is not easy to stop.

"But the Conference, Maria?" I asked at last. "What about it?"

"The aeroplane factory down at Sesto Calende is working overtime," she said. "There are lots of jobs down there now, only the secret police make so much trouble for the people that work there that many of the boys would rather not have the jobs. I suppose they have to make a lot of aeroplanes for the war. I don't remember the other war very well."

From these and other conversations I concluded that my friends along the lake regarded the great Conference chiefly as a source of annoyance, nugatory in itself but a disturbing influence in the arrangement of their lives. They had lost money; they had lost jobs; they could not go out on the lake to fish; the aeroplanes gave them headaches. With the fatalistic pessimism of old races, they were sure that war would come and the congress of sublime intellects assembled together at Stresa seemed to them no more than an expensive, silly episode along the inevitable road.

I tried a more knowing type, our Signor X., who has travelled much and owns property.

"How can anything good come of it?" Signor X. asked quietly, sucking at his pipe and looking out across the garden wall towards the motionless blue water. "We have seen so many of these meetings, and after each one there is a short time in which they talk as if the war had been put off again. But in the meantime the taxes go up, the army increases, more aeroplanes are built, more ships, more guns. My grandson, who is twelve, says he hopes they will wait until he is old enough to go. He is in training already, and I am afraid he will find out that it is not so much fun as he thinks. Out of our village of not more than thirty houses, twenty-four men died in the last war, and not a single family is better off for it, Signor. How can we believe what they say at their conferences?"

I went to Stresa itself, to the hotel where the French and British delegations lived. Its great hall was given over to a scene familiar to anybody who has ever visited a conference: newspaper correspondents by the score, milling around, with clumps of them coagulated here and there upon some pompous figure representing Diplomacy. Across the scene there ambled majestically the Right Honourable Ramsay MacDonald, shaking his leonine head at the press, or stopping, once in a while, to say something meaningless in a voice of Shakespearean deliberation. When he said, "It is a nice day," he delivered the words as if they were Marc Antony's funeral oration over Caesar, conscious, as always, that his slightest word marked a Historic Moment.

I looked for a certain Carlo, a waiter who comes from one of the villages on our side of the lake.

"What do you think of it, Carlo?"

"Well, I tell you," said Carlo in the fluent English of Biarritz, Cannes and San Remo, "I don't think we make so much money as some people they think. The hotel is full, that is true, but these diplomat don't pay full price, not what they would pay if they was, now, honeymoon couples, or good pay like what we used to have in the old days. And stingy—! They never remember to tip anybody. Maybe they believe in the signs that say tips are abolished. I don't know. Anyhow I think the Regina Palazzo, where the journalists are, will make more money than we do. The journalists, now, they drink, and anyhow the bar make some money, and then journalist are not so stingy. And they easier to wait on, too. These people here, all these diplomat, they make a lot of trouble and they never satisfied. Still, I guess maybe we make some money, only not as much as people say."

"But Carlo, you don't think this conference has been called just so the hotels can make money?"

Carlo's shoulders went up and his hands went out; he grinned; even his ears moved with amusement.

"What the hell else it good for, you tell me?" he asked.

Turning from these conversations to the communiqués and the statements given by great men to the press, I was more puzzled than ever. How can any human event, observed from whatever different points of view, be so diversely interpreted? There was one bouncing French ambassador who proclaimed, at the end of the Stresa convention, that it represented "the greatest step towards peace taken since 1918." What did he mean by "greatest"? What did he mean by "step"? What, above all, did he mean by "peace"? And then all these telegrams between prime ministers, these speeches a day or so later at Geneva, these editorial ecstasies in the official newspapers? In the balance of reality, in the actual count of fact upon fact, it seemed to me that the whole of the words spilled out in three or four languages at the end of the historic meeting weighed less than the three geese and five chickens, the eggs and vegetables, that Pietro had been unable to sell because he could not go to market. And the most unanswerable question propounded was also Pietro's: who will ever give him back the three hundred lire he lost? Who will get Enrico another job? What is to compensate Maria for her headache?

Such things are beneath the notice of the great. They have long since lost themselves in such a labyrinth of covenants, compacts, protocols, guaranties, clauses and annexes, that in their paper paradise they have come to regard life, specific life, as an impertinent interruption.

If the great men of Stresa wanted a souvenir of their historic meeting, there is a very suitable one they could have, and in triplicate, too, so that neither Paris, Rome nor London need feel slighted. Pietro killed three geese for the market to which he was not allowed to go.

TOKEN OF ESTEEM

By Harlan Ware

CHARLES MINNON CAME UP OUT OF THE SECOND BASEMENT, ALONG the greasy passageway between the help's kitchen and the storeroom, and went out of the hotel into the balmy air of a late spring evening. It was seven o'clock and he took a deep breath; for this was freedom. Out on the street at seven o'clock! He hadn't been on the street at seven o'clock in the evening more than a dozen times or so in twenty-five years.

As a matter of fact, he hadn't been out where ordinary people could see him between the hours of eleven a.m. and midnight in more years than he cared to remember. He had worked for Mr. Ashcraft, senior, and now for Mr. Kenneth Ashcraft, all these years—a quarter of a century would have gone by this coming Tuesday since he came there as a bus boy, so hungry at the time that he wanted to work near food.

And now this had happened: he had left early on the night of an important banquet because he could wait no longer to tell his family that he was going to receive a token of esteem.

He thought he'd take a bus. Naturally he hadn't taken a bus in years. One does not wait for buses at midnight, and at ten in the morning he was in too much of a hurry. But tonight he got aboard a Fifth Avenue bus and looked hungrily out at the shops and buildings—so many of them were new since the last time he rode on a bus.

He was home. He climbed the stairs. Outside his own door he could hear the deep voice of his son. He felt embarrassed. His hands were unsteady with the key. He opened the door.

There they were.

There they were, the three of them. Mabel, and his son, and Harriette.

"Well—Dad."

His son was embarrassed, too. Shook hands with him. Then Harriette came up and kissed him, he went over to Mabel and she kissed him, and they all sat down.

"You're home early," said Mabel.

"I thought I would," he explained. "There was an important banquet but I let the boys handle it. I thought, here it is the first night you—you—children are home, and why should I stay there and slave ——"

"Now he is getting some sense," Mabel said.

Then Harriette came over to the chair and sat down on the arm and touched his ear. It was like having some strange young girl sitting on the arm of his chair. He could feel his face get red.

He thought maybe this was a good time to tell them.

"It isn't so bad when you know all you do is appreciated. If it wasn't appreciated it would be too hard—too many hours, too much smell of food. But I've got some news to tell you now that just about makes it all right with me."

"A raise?" said Mabel.

"Not exactly a raise, though I could probably get a raise if I asked for it."

"You ask for it," said Mabel.

"They gonna give you a stick pin or something?" asked his son, his lips sneering.

Funny what words can do to a man, words and the expression on another person's face. All of a sudden Minnon felt the loneliest man in the world; his body grew damp; maybe he was going to have a brain hemorrhage, like the chef had; for when his son said that about the stick pin, something happened inside of Minnon that seemed to cut him off from those three in the room, and from the hotel, so that he was completely alone for a minute, unable to reach anybody, or make anybody understand anything, or get any help from anybody. It was like a man running and running until his heart burst inside him, and there wasn't any race to begin with; or like a man daring dangers of some kind for no reason; or like a man named Minnon who had given up twenty-five years of his life, in a trade, and had got nothing for it but a five-room apartment and three strangers who lived with him.

Because it would be hard to say that they were going to give him a banquet and a watch now, with his son sitting there grinning that way.

"What is it they are going to do for you?" asked Mabel, her voice hard.

He had to tell them now; there was no way out. He tried to make it sound fine and splendid.

"Why," he said, "Mr. Ashcraft himself—and I've heard even his father is going to try and be there (and this was a lie, because he hadn't heard any such thing)—they are going to give me a nice banquet on Tuesday and a token of esteem."

His son laughed harshly. "A banquet! I suppose they think you will enjoy a banquet. That'll be quite a novelty for you—they'll probably give you some of that salad you made up."

"What's the token of esteem?" asked Mabel.

"A gold watch."

He had never heard anything sound so small and trivial and unimportant as that gold watch, just then. He couldn't say it so it would sound as big to him as it had when he first heard of it; there wasn't any way to bring the words out and make it sound like a gold watch; what he said sounded like some kind of a trinket from a novelty store.

Harriette spoke up then.

"They would," she said bitterly. "That's just what they would do, isn't it, mother?—give him a gold watch when gold watches aren't even in! Gold watches haven't been in for as much as ten or twenty years. Why, gold watches went out with those high wheeled bicycles. You'd think if they were going to give you a watch at all they could at least give you a platinum watch, which is in, instead of a gold one, which is absolutely out, isn't that right, Mother?"

Minnon tried to defend it. "Oh, it isn't as bad as that. You see a lot of gold watches around. Mr. Ashcraft carries one, himself—Mr. Ashcraft, senior."

"But not Kenneth, I'll bet you. Kenneth is too smart and up-to-date and all that . . ."

There was no point arguing it out any longer. Any kind of a watch, gold or platinum, was hardly enough to trade for twenty-five years of a man's life, and he might as well face it. Twenty-five years of a man's life—that was one-third, or maybe almost half; and a man's life is all he's got that he knows about which is worth having—for sure. And then he began to think other thoughts that were strange in his head.

He began to think the kind of thoughts that Orloff, the "bolsheviki" chef, must have been thinking up to the time he had the brain hemorrhage. He tried to stop them and think of something else but he couldn't. By the time they really got hold of him so that nothing else would come into his mind, Mabel was asleep beside him, with her back to him. He could reach out and touch Mabel with his fingers, and yet he couldn't either. It seemed startling and immoral to be sleeping beside her. Tonight sleeping beside Mabel was sleeping with a strange woman he hadn't met before.

Everything Mabel said about that hotel had hatred in it. This had been going on for years, and it had taken him all this time, until tonight, to notice it.

And his son: "Maybe they'll give you a stick pin." Sitting there with a disdainful grin on his face, so that you felt as if you'd burst your heart in a race that nobody ran but you . . . and gold watches weren't even in! Those were crushing things to think of. You work twenty-five years of your life—as no man works outside of a big hotel—and they give you your own salad, at a banquet, and a gold watch that isn't even in!

He reached out and touched Mabel's shoulder. She turned sleepily, moving her face toward him.

"U-m-m-m?"

"You know what Orloff said one time I should do when they gave me that watch?"

"Oh, Orloff!"

"No, you'll like this, Mabel. Listen. This is funny. Except that a dead man said it. Orloff said I should take that watch in my hand and throw it against the mirror in the ballroom and crack it in a thousand pieces and tell them they could take their hotel . . ."

His voice sounded like someone else's voice, almost like Orloff's, talking there in the dark to that strange woman who was really Mabel, and it gave him the oddest, wild feeling when she said, sitting up:

"If you did a thing like that you'd lose your job!"

That wild feeling was burning inside his chest and in his mind, too, when he woke up in the morning. Some other times when he had got angry at night he could remember going to sleep still angry, only to wake up in the morning and feel easy again, as if it weren't worth fighting about. But this morning was different. It was still there.

His family had finished breakfast, of course, and he was relieved about that. He didn't know what he could possibly talk to them about during breakfast. It was all he could do to get out the few sentences that were necessary before he went out the door. He wouldn't be home tonight until late, as usual. If it were too late he would stay at the hotel—and they needn't expect him until Friday. It was the Waste Material Dealer's banquet, and though they didn't sound like it, they were very important men. Four dollars a plate. He went out remembering the scornful look on his son's face; four dollars a plate didn't impress him. He was not interested in how much a plate anybody paid for a banquet . . .

He met Mr. Ashcraft as he went into the hotel.

"Charles," said Mr. Ashcraft, pleasantly, inclining his head.

"Wait a minute," said Charles. "Pardon me, but wait a minute Mr. Ashcraft."

"Yes?"

"You called me about that chef the other day."

"Yes?"

"Did anybody tell you Orloff didn't quit?"

"What's that?"

"Orloff—he died!"

"Yes—too bad. How's the new man?"

"He's all right."

"By the way, did Orloff have any family?"

"Just a wife. He never had time to have any family."

Mr. Ashcraft thought that was a joke. He laughed, patted Charles on the shoulder, and they separated.

For a little while Charles was calm. Mr. Ashcraft was famous for having a wonderful sense of humor, and Charles had made him laugh; but after a while he thought that it really wasn't such a funny thing when a man had worked too long every day to have time to raise a family.

"I'll throw your God damned watch against the wall!"

Charles heard himself saying these words out loud. It frightened him. It was Orloff saying them over his shoulder. It was Orloff's big fists clenched at his sides.

After a minute of standing there the fear left him and he had only his anger, and then his anger left him and he had only that loneliness. Then he saw a bus boy named Joe. Joe was a Polish bus boy with a nice clean face, and he thought things were important. He thought it was important not to break dishes. He thought it was important to be promoted to be a waiter. He thought if he could some day get to be the headwaiter in the main banquet room that he would not want anything else. He would want to be the headwaiter in the main banquet room for as much as a year, maybe, or two years, and then he wouldn't care what happened. He had never told Minnon that, but anyone could tell by the way Joe took orders.

Standing there with the anger gone out of him and feeling only the loneliness, Minnon watched Joe work—and saw himself when he was Joe's age, working with careful hands in this same kitchen. And so he called out:

"Joe, I want to see you in my office."

Joe stood beside the desk like a soldier waiting for an order, and you could tell by the way he was poised that, no matter what it was, he would do it.

"You are a bright boy, Joe, a very bright boy. Why don't you leave here and get a job in a store, or in a shop or somewhere."

Joe looked stunned. "But I do my work. Mr. Minnon—don't I do my work?"

"It isn't that. Don't you suppose you would like some other work better; some place where you can go farther? If you stay here the highest you can go is this office."

When he got through Joe was almost crying. Joe said that Mr. Minnon's job was a wonderful job. Joe said he wouldn't ever ask for any job as swell as Mr. Minnon's. He said if he could get up to where Mr. Minnon was in even thirty years, no matter how hard he had to work, or how many hours, no matter if he did get all worn out and nervous—no matter what—he wouldn't ask any more than that, or expect any more than that of—God, and that was an honest fact!

And so Joe went back to being careful with the dishes and hurrying up to finish whatever he was doing faster and better than any other bus boy could finish what he was doing—which was the way to get to be a Captain in the banquet room with a lot of nigger waiters jumping to attention when you spoke to them . . .

And Minnon, feeling a coolness come into his brain, sat in his office and tried to remember his anger, and wondered why he had had it, and in the end put the blame on a dead man where it belonged.

He was glad he was thinking different thoughts when the inter-office memo came. It made his hands tremble when he read it:

Mr. Kenneth Ashcraft
To Charles Minnon:
Mr. Ashcraft has noted that you will have completed twenty-five years of service next Tuesday and has planned to give you a little dinner in the Grey Room at six o'clock. Mr. Ashcraft left for Chicago this morning and did not think to tell you when he saw you earlier today, but he wants you to keep the evening free.
Jane Howell, Secretary to
Kenneth Ashcraft

Well, that was something after all, wasn't it? Here he was in a place that to many people would be about the finest place in the world, and the man who owned it all was going to give a dinner, just for him ——

Then Charles saw how it was. He thought of the twenty-five years again, and the three strangers who lived with him at his house, and saw how this inter-office memo came about. *"Mr. Ashcraft did not think to tell you when he saw you earlier today—"* Mr. Ashcraft would not have thought of it at all if someone had not reminded him, Mr. Ashcraft would have gone off to Chicago and the dinner would never have happened. Probably he would not be back in time now, and the auditor or somebody would rise and say ——

No! He had thrown away twenty-five years for this man who did not remember when he saw him that he was going to give him a dinner! He would not be persuaded out of his just anger by the dinner or even by the token of esteem!

There was not more time to think then. Cooks came up from the downstairs kitchens—food for the luncheons began to steam on the steam tables; over and around him drifted the hot odors of food. He walked through the kitchen and cooks lifted up traytops for his practiced eye to take in the food that waited. They would be doing this again at six-thirty. And again tomorrow at the same hour—and every day, including half the Sundays, for as long as he could live.

All those wild thoughts came back inside him with a rush when the luncheon was over. Mr. Ashcraft's face rose in his mind. "Charles," he had said, pleasantly. Not even for a fleeting second had Mr. Ashcraft thought: "Here is a man who has given me twenty-five years of his life, not just for the money—" Somebody ought to wake Mr. Kenneth Ashcraft up. Somebody ought to jolt him so that he would realize that down in the depths of this hotel were people, like Minnon, who gave him more than any man who hired men could expect of the men he hired—but no one ever would wake Kenneth Ashcraft up to this realization unless Charles Minnon did it on the evening when they commemorated his twenty-five years of service with that token of esteem.

Well, he would do it. Maybe, from getting so mad and staying mad so long, he would have a brain hemorrhage, too, like that chef, and die, but he couldn't help it.

Here, he would draft out a speech. He had five days yet. Even if Ashcraft wasn't back and the auditor was the host he would make them a speech they would always remember.

He would tell them about all the men who worked too many hours—and about the women. He would name all the men and women who had died during the twenty-five years he had been with the hotel. Some of them had died there, some on subways on the way home, some on subways on the way to work, and a few had died in bed. He would tell them about that.

He would tell them what it was like, by God, to trade twenty-five years for a token of esteem! He would tell them so they would always remember his words, even if they only got it second hand.

He took up a pencil. Even the pencil was greasy with food. He wiped it off on a napkin. He took a nice, clean sheet of yellow order paper and he began to write. He filled page after page. He let his assistant pay off the waiters and make the check-up; he just moved the unaccustomed pencil along on the yellow paper and put down words that were strange words to come from him.

And then he read it over. He saw it was wrong. It was too long, and too angry. It would have to be shorter and cooler, and work up to the place where he threw the watch against the wall, so that the bravest part of the speech and the crack of the watch against the wall would happen all at once. He would have to take the bitterest words and select them carefully, and use only those words which would cut the deepest; he would have to make this mean something more than just an angry slap . . .

He worked on it every day and he had not quite finished it on Tuesday morning. But he would have it done in time. It was a masterpiece. He felt that, himself. It was only about three hundred words long but it said everything that all the men before him had half-thought for the same reasons. It would be awful to stand there saying those words while faces all around him got whiter and whiter, and Mr. Ashcraft, or the auditor—well, he just couldn't imagine how they would take it. He had charged them with the crime of robbing a man of twenty-five years of his life—for nothing; of taking from him all of the pleasures of living he might have had during that long time; he would make them see that they had murdered those twenty-five years out of him, as they had murdered years out of the chef. . . . There had never been said anywhere in the world such a speech as that.

He went home early and took a bath. The three strangers were there and they knew what was going to happen; that is, they knew he was going to his own banquet. But they didn't know what he was going to do there. He was going to wait until afterward to tell them; they could all pack up then and go somewhere, if they wanted to. Go somewhere together for a few days and get acquainted for the first time.

When he came out of the bedroom shaved, and neat, and his hair combed down, they looked amused. It was easy to bear their amusement because of what he would have to tell them when he came home. It would be only a few hours when he came home. They wouldn't be so amused then. They would respect him. He narrowed his eyes and looked at them hard. He wondered if one of them would say: "But where is the money coming from now?" If one of them did he knew which one it would be. The one who would say that would be Mabel.

"We're going out to a movie," Mabel said.

That surprised him. Mabel must have gone to a good many movies all these nights while he was working, but that she should go to a movie tonight, and maybe not be home when he came back—that surprised him. While this tremendous thing was happening to him at the hotel they would be sitting in some dark theatre not thinking about him at all, or his problems, or how he felt, or anything at all about him, just as they probably had done for all these years.

"I wish you'd be home when I get here."

He knew he couldn't bear it to come in filled with that great speech and have no one to repeat it to.

He would want to repeat it to them just as he said it, and he would be able to—word for word—because he knew it by heart, now.

"Please be home when I get here," he said.

"To see that watch?" His son grinned. "I can wait."

"If we aren't here," said Mabel, placidly, "we'll see the watch in the morning."

"I'm just asking this of you," Minnon was stern. "I'm asking you to come home from your movie and be here when I get home at eleven o'clock. I've got a special reason that I want you here."

For a minute he thought he was going to hate them, too, for being so self-sufficient, and if he had hated them, then it would be true that he hated everybody, the hotel, and these three, and Mr. Ashcraft. He would be worse than Orloff.

Maybe his face showed them something.

"We'll be home."

The lobby looked like any other night. People were coming in and going out. The clerks were trying to remember the faces of people who had been there before. The bell captain was calling, "Front, boy!" It was all just the same. That surprised him a little. It surprised him still more to think that it would be just the same in the morning.

He went directly to the banquet floor, and checked his hat and coat, like any other guest, and went into the Grey Room. And there they were, all the employees he worked with—dressed up now, and looking different; there they all were—all but Mr. Ashcraft.

Palms. Well, that was nice. They only brought the palms up when it was a three-fifty dinner or more. And place-cards on the table! And the pent-house service, too, with the gold edge! They were trying now to give him something for murdering twenty-five years of him—gold service. And a menu!

The print shop had made a menu, just for him, on a gold card! Dinner, commemorating twenty-five years of service—Charles Minnon—. Was his salad on it? Was it? *Salad Surprise!*

Maybe he was getting a little sentimental and soft up to then. Maybe he was thinking he couldn't say all of that speech he had written, or actually couldn't throw the gold watch at the wall; maybe, because all his friends were here, these people he had worked with, and they looked so pleased for him, and shook hands with so much honor for him, maybe up to then he might have broken down. It was for fear of this that he hadn't told his family, or anyone, what he was going to do; but when he saw that salad, all the rage and fire and anger and wild feeling, came burning up again inside his breast. For if he had done anything he had at least invented a salad, a salad which Orloff had said was a stroke of genius, and in spite of everything, they might have served it, out of honor to him—they might at least show him that they remembered he had made it first——

Back of the palms an orchestra set up the first soft strains of some music and Mr. Kenneth Ashcraft and—and his father came in; and Kenneth Ashcraft's father was leaning on his son's arm and he could hardly walk. . . . He was sick. In his eyes, and on his face, you could see he was sick; but he smiled at Minnon and shook his hand. He looked at Minnon in a friendly way, as if they shared some memories that these others couldn't know. And later, his son helped him to his feet, and he braced his hands on the top of the table, palms down, and made a speech in an uncertain voice.

". . . from a little hotel, to this great establishment, from one kitchen to fifteen kitchens, from one hundred rooms to more than a thousand, we have done that, Minnon and the old employees and I. And now some of you are carrying on the same old policies so that we have the finest hotel in the world and serve the finest food. And we have got joy out of it, out of our work, and that is a lot to a man; for if a man does not enjoy his work then life is surely pretty empty for him. . . . I ate a salad in the Savoy in London and it was called Salad a la Minnon, and I was proud to know that that salad had been first made right here in our hotel ——"

The lights went down and four waiters came in with a big tray with a huge salad bowl on it, and there were little electric lights garnishing the edges; and everybody in the room applauded, because they knew this was Charles Minnon's salad.

Then Kenneth Ashcraft got up.

"Charles Minnon has worked here twenty-five years tonight. This is a fine thing. I take great pleasure, Charles Minnon, in presenting to you this token of esteem."

Minnon opened the little box and saw what was inside, and put it down, and then moved it so the waiter could serve his salad. He looked in the box again to make sure it was platinum. And then, with difficulty, he made his speech:

"I just always want to work for you, that's all."

PIM AND POOH

By Ferdinand Czernin

MY POLICE DOGS WERE GETTING TO BE FAMOUS IN THE COUNTRY round about us. People from all directions were again announcing their desire for one of Diana's puppies. I could have sold fifty of them at least for five pounds apiece. I was quite proud of myself as a breeder of police dogs.

But when her litter was brought forth—Diana was by nature ardent—not a single police dog was in it. There were just little bundles of wool of all colors and sizes. It naturally followed that nobody wanted one.

I did succeed in placing five. One was taken by the butcher in Arusha. His eyes are bleary now and his approval depends upon whether you smell of raw meat. Mrs. Gansenheim who came to these parts to shoot elephants took a fancy to another. He had a brilliant career, and went all the way across the ocean with her to Chicago. A third is still acting as watch dog over on the farm of old Miss Parkins, who is so nervous and terribly afraid of the blacks. Hamisi disposed of another, and a fifth went into the civil service. He has been drafted to carry the surveyor's tripod for his theodolite from farm to farm.

The sixth I couldn't find a home for. I offered him to all my friends, but they always seemed to be ready with some excuse. The few that were persuaded to look at him soon turned away again. "Pooh" they said, at least giving him a name.

Heaven knows he was no beauty. Pale yellow is hardly ever a good color for a dog, and it isn't everyone that cares for a curly tail. But these points wouldn't have mattered so much if it hadn't been for the floppy Dachshund ears, the crinkled brow and the crooked legs. From the size of his paws when he was a puppy we knew he would get to be as big as a St. Bernard. All things considered, the name of Pooh did seem to suit him perfectly.

It was just at this time when I was robbing Diana of one child after another that Tom came for a visit. Tom being a lover of animals, I made up my mind to give him Pooh. But nothing came of it, because he himself arrived with a baby black ape that he had bought somewhere over in Kenya from a native. The man had had the little thing tied with a string. In a fit of temper Tom had untied him, paid five shillings for him and since then had been keeping him inside his jacket. He had a lot more laundry, always having to change his shirt, but still he had stuck by the infant. He didn't want to shut him up, and if he gave him the run of his farm, he would be sure to meet one of the herds of black apes wandering in that part of the country. And you know how wild things behave in the presence of tame young ones.

When he found that we didn't have any apes around my farm, Tom wanted to turn his ward over to me. His purpose may have been confirmed just then by the reaching out of a hairy little hand from inside his jacket towards his bowl of coffee. But when I refused firmly, not wanting to put our friendship to any unnecessary strain, he seemed to give up the idea.

However, when he left the next day, he "forgot" to take the little thing with him. Hours later I found the baby tied to a bed-post in Tom's room. His leash was long enough for him to have got the soap from the washstand, and by the time I came into the room he was in a pretty bad way, only just able to lift his little white eyelids. It was a lengthy cure with castor oil that kept him alive.

During his illness of course we got to know each other so much better that afterwards I didn't have the heart to do away with him. So I decided to leave it all to fate. I just planted him out in the sunshine in front of the house and came back into my room. If he ran away he would run away. If he stayed, well then for Heaven's sake he would stay.

When I looked out again to see how things were going, he and Pooh were tearing through the brown grass together. Near by, Diana lay basking, apparently undisturbed by her son's new friendship. So I too resigned myself, and the little ape was taken in as a member of my household. I called him Pim after an old aunt of mine. It seemed quite natural.

Pim's habits improved a lot through his friendship with Pooh. He no longer cared for stuffy shirts. When he was cold or tired he would cuddle up beside Diana. She adopted him quite. Most likely her body was very glad to be rid of its over heavy burden.

All during the day Pim was free—free to romp through the rooms, into the garden and back again, to smash the flower bowls, and to bite off the buds of the Marechal Niel that I was so proud of. But along towards sundown I used to put him in a cage. I couldn't very well let him run the dangers of our night. But he didn't like his prison. In the beginning we had a struggle every evening to get him to slink behind his bars. For a while we were able to lure him with bananas. But as he grew older he didn't seem to be so greedy, or else his character was stronger, for he would take to a tree top, just to sit and make fun of us. There would be a good long chase which he really enjoyed immensely, before we could corner him and make him surrender. Often the night would set in before we got him. Then out would come the torch light and lanterns. Mfupi, like the half monkey that he was himself, would clamber up a tree to get him. Then there would be piercing shrieks and last desperate attempts at flight. But in reality Pim and Mfupi both got a lot of fun out of it.

At last quite by chance I found the simple way to catch him. Pooh was actually being chastized for some one of his numerous crimes, when in the midst of it Pim came headlong. Clamoring, screeching, he threw himself against me and clutched my arm as hard as he could. He didn't stop his protest till Pooh was out of reach. Then suddenly he let go of me, to gallop after him.

From that time on there were no more evening hunts. Pooh was a good dog and came when you called him. Every evening we had a mock execution. Quick as a flash, Pim would be at hand to let himself be caught, while Pooh the traitor wagged his tail. After a little while though, Pim grew to know what it meant for him. He used to get terribly excited. He would dance up and down on some high branch, shake the limb till the leaves flew, only to give in at last to come to the rescue of his friend.

Schiller once composed a poem to Damon. But Pim was greater than the Greek. He repeated his sacrifice daily. Pretty soon it was enough just to call Pooh at sunset for Pim to come galumping. Sad-eyed, chattering, gnashing his teeth, he would let himself be locked in his cage.

In this way the two of them grew up together and got to be

inseparable. Together they went on journeys of discovery in the bush, together they high jinked, and invented their games.

The grandest of the games was a kind of race. The clearing in front of the house stretches out about half a mile. Then comes the bush, all interlaced with lianas. Pooh had learned from Pim how to find his way in the undergrowth, to crawl beneath the creepers, climb up on old tree trunks and leap down again. It was his only chance of getting ahead in there. He never really liked it. The dark was uncanny to him and as a dog he wanted elbow room. He wasn't an ape to climb the lianas, to jump from one branch to another. That was all very fine if you could do it. But being a dog did have its advantages. In the open he covered the ground faster than the ape could with his short legs and long arms that always seemed to be getting in the way. The dog could tear straight ahead. He didn't turn somersaults, didn't get all out of breath.

The difference was annoying to both sides. So the race was invented. Pim would slink away from the house until he got to about the middle of the clearing. Then he would stand up to yell some bad words back to Pooh, who never waited to argue about it, but, ears flopping, would tear after him. If Pooh caught up with him, Pim would get a good hiding. The next minute they would stroll quite peaceably back to the house together. If Pim reached the bush first, Pooh would have to crawl in after him, slither through lianas, climb tree trunks, and face the terrors of being shut in the dark.

Not all of their games were so harmless, One morning at breakfast I caught sight of them off in the distance. Pooh had his head in the air. Very affected, very self-conscious, he was stepping high, vainglory written all over him. I couldn't see what he was carrying, but it looked like a log of wood. Pim was capering beside him, every now and then with one hand to the ground. With the other he held on to one end of the queer looking log. On they came. Pooh, tail wagging, laid a fat, full grown puff-adder at my feet.

One of the deadliest of our African snakes, the puff-adder is hardly ever more than a foot and a half long, but it gets to be as thick as a fighter's arm. On account of its shape, it can't give chase. It just lies in wait on a forest cut or path, looking for all the world like a fallen branch. Its bite is always fatal but if you

can evade its first attack you have it at your mercy, for its strength
is fairly spent with the one effort.

Gone was any appetite that I had had for ham and eggs. I gave
vent to my feelings in a lecture—Bad! You mustn't touch! No
matter where you find it. Even if it does look dead. Puff-adder I
tell you, puff-adder! The rottenest, meanest, deadliest.

You'll just drop dead, that's all . . . No, you can't have it.
Drop it! . . . Don't ever dare to touch another . . . Bad Pim!—
bad Pooh! Now get out of here! Both of you!

They made off—disgruntled, blighted. They had counted on a
different reception, a little praise, recognition. Hardly out of reach,
Pim jabbered his protest. I buried the snake, and proceeded to
forget about it.

Two days later, Hamisi confided the news that Pim had brought
him a puff-adder. My first thought of course was to see if they had
had the nerve to open the grave. But the peace was undisturbed.
What was the mystery then? Where were they finding these puff-
adders?

I was soon to have the answer when taking a walk over the
farm, the two of them with me as usual. Pooh was baying idioti-
cally into a deserted wart hog hole. Pim was a little ahead of me,
loafing through the tall grass. Suddenly he leaped high, took a few
quick steps forward, and began to bounce up and down like a
rubber ball, beating the air with his long arms, chattering like mad.
Pooh, already bored with what he had been doing, came tearing
up to bark furiously at something in the grass. Pim began to
pull up sod and lumps of earth, to grab for stones and pieces of
wood—anything possible to pelt whatever it was they saw.

Scenting trouble, I ran over to them. And there was a big puff-
adder, erect, ready to leap any second. Pim kept on throwing
everything in reach. Just when I had made up my mind to do
something about it too, the snake flew through the air. Pim hopped
to one side, and the big fat sausage flopped down with a thud on
the earth. Quick as a flash Pim set to work again. Grabbing a
stick he belabored the adder, that now lay helpless in the grass.
Pooh stood by in yelping ecstasy. And when it was all over—when
Pim had laid hold of the reptile, in his rage to hurl it again and
again to the ground, he took his part in the fight and bit deep into
the lifeless body.

Once more the conquerors, bearing their victim, set out on a march of triumph. They would, I am certain, have dragged him three times around the walls of Troy. But well as I understood their feelings, I wanted to do something to put an end to the mischief once and for all. So this time, Pooh got a thrashing, Pim a box on the ears, and the adder described a semi-circle into the brook.

But a lot of good it did. Though no more adders were laid at my feet, Hamisi told me that every now and then they would still bring one home. More capital punishment was out of the question, lacking *corpus delicti*, and they took great care that I shouldn't have it.

In such and other sins and follies—drinking out of ink wells, killing chickens, breaking dishes—these two lived the first years of their lives.

Pooh did get to be enormous. He was bigger than his mother and still growing. Almost as big, Pim was stronger and much more intelligent. Many a time I feared for Pooh when they got into one of their fights. The poor fellow always got the worst of it now. Though at the start, Pim would sometimes good naturedly let Pooh throw him, he could always have the upper hand whenever he wanted it. The match would end as a rule by Pim getting a throttle hold on Pooh, choking the eyes out of his head. Then with Pooh stretched on the ground, his sides heaving and tongue hanging out, Pim would sit close by, quietly waiting for him to come to. Later in absolute harmony, they would saunter off together to think up some more trouble. At times, when I couldn't stand it any longer, I used to interfere, chase Pim away from his quarry. But no good ever came of it. Pim would retreat, scolding, only to get hold of Pooh for revenge later on, when he was sure of being undisturbed. Pooh never escaped the ordeal. So I gave up. It must be said in Pim's defense that he never was the one to begin. Swaggering, Pooh would always gambol up, give his friend a smart nip in the ribs or run him down, or provoke him in some other way, until he got what was coming to him. He never seemed to object to it. And Pim never really injured him. Just the same I always felt uneasy for fear that some day, not out of meanness, but because he himself didn't know how strong he was, Pim might end by murdering his brother.

Besides being really devoted to the dog, Pim was very attached to Hamisi who returned his affection in full. He always had something good saved up for Pim to eat and always forgave him his bad turns. Under the circumstances maybe it wasn't very noble of Hamisi to lay the blame for everything on Pim—for every torn table-cloth, every broken dish, every theft in the store-room—but such is nature in the raw. And Pim was hardly ever punished, for in spite of Hamisi's air of innocence I couldn't be sure that he wasn't the culprit himself. But when it did happen, I know that Hamisi managed to ease his conscience towards Pim, rewarding him handsomely from my supplies. So I was the loser in any case.

It was the year when we were having a terrible time with the drought. The rain had been due for weeks but not a drop had fallen. The hunched up mounds were black from grass fires. Dispirited, the trees drooped their leaves. Our brook narrowed to a wretched little trough in the middle of a broad bed of sand. If now and then a cloud would appear on the horizon, long before it came over us the sun would consume it. Out in the steppe our biggest watering place was dried up, and the thirsting cattle would wander in droves or alone across the country.

At this time a weird unrest seemed to come over Pim. He sat for hours way up on the highest limb of the old cedar tree before the house, giving out clear little longing calls. At times, apparently without any reason, he would scramble down to cling to my hands. Distractedly, he would try to tell me of his trouble. In the middle of a game with Pooh he would stop, raise himself upright, as if to listen. Then he would climb, as if life depended upon it, back to his place in the tree top. For Pooh it was really too hot to play, so he didn't take this queer behavior too much to heart. He would just stretch out in the shade and try to sleep.

As the days passed Pim's nervousness increased. He even lost his appetite. He would sit up in the cedar nearly all day long. And one fine morning he was gone.

Ever since he had grown big enough to take care of himself, he hadn't been sleeping in his cage. With his sharp teeth and strong arms he could really have given a hard time even to his mortal enemy, the leopard. So for months he hadn't known the shame of his prison. He had been sleeping as a rule in one of the papaya trees near the drive.

I first missed him when he didn't come to help me with breakfast. Pooh came, but he lacked the whole-hearted interest of other mornings. His gaze, instead of fastening to my plate, shifted from time to time. The prod of his cold nose seemed not so much the usual request for bacon. It was more the demand that I bestir myself to do something about Pim. I began trying to reassure both of us by simply saying there was no cause for worry at all. Pim had gone for a picnic in the bush. He had been delayed and would probably come back to us any minute. But somehow I wasn't convinced of my own story.

When Hamisi came to say that he hadn't seen Pim that morning at all, then I was panic stricken. We started to search the grounds. In my imagination I saw the body, torn by the leopard, lying under some bush. I depicted the horrible struggle.

But thinking it over coolly, there was much to refute what I feared. For instance, there were no signs of a struggle near the papaya. We surely should have heard something if there had been one in the night, for Pim wouldn't have let himself be carried off by the leopard without a sound.

Only one possibility remained. Pim had heard the call of the wilderness and had followed it deep in the night—had forgotten me, Hamisi, and even Pooh, to return to his inheritance. There was nothing very comforting in the thought, for I felt sure that, free, he wouldn't live to enjoy life very long. Pooh was even more disconsolate than I. He wandered about all day, as if trying not only to find his friend but to understand the fate that had taken him away.

People living in cities have animals too, and care for them possibly as much as we who share our lives with them out here. But their company, their talk is all we have. And as our comrades they are rather more our equals than a Pekingese in the rococo drawing room of some lonely woman . . .

That night rain fell. Not much, but enough to cool the air a little—to make it possible to stay outside. Soon after breakfast I started off to wander through the coffee trees. The poor wrinkled leaves had already begun to smooth out and to shine dark green. Pooh came with me of course. He seemed to be cured of yesterday's sorrow. He nosed around the country as usual after hares and dick-dicks, stirred up cranes, and chased them in full hue and cry, when they flew low, croaking and rustling their wings. Now and then he would come back to me and go to heel in perfect form, till something new attracted his attention, when off he woud tear again.

Pretty soon we came to the end of the Shamba, the land under plough, to the place where the brook falls over some rocks down into a hollow. Normally it makes a beautiful deep green swimming hole, but that day the fall was so infinitesimal that it almost faded away in mid air. It had been the scene of some glorious battles. There Pooh had revenged himself for much ignominy. He loved the water, while Pim distinctly feared it and could only be pulled or pushed into the pool against his will. But as he plunged then into what water there was, to cool himself after his hunt, Pooh didn't seem to be weighed down with memories. When he had enough, had shaken the water out of his coat, rolled himself in rotten leaves, we strolled off again in the direction of the house.

Before you come to the coffee crop, the path leads across a bit of land that I had cleared to use for setting out young coffee trees. The old roots had all been dug up, cut, and piled neatly around the little clearing. But the drought had done for the plan. The land was fallow. A pity. Now the termites were already at it, rebuilding their demolished strongholds. It was an ideal stalking ground for Pooh. Under the crowns of the felled trees, an oribi was often to be found, lying sound asleep. And lately an old wart sow had taken to bringing her young there. Pooh couldn't get close to her of course, but he had all the fun of stirring her up and seeing the young ones run for the bush, squealing. The sow would follow after them, grunting, turning back every now and then.

Under the circumstances, I wasn't surprised when Pooh, yelping his delight, bolted away from my side. I didn't even look up, but just kept on boring with my stick into a termite hill, hoping to find the queen and to thwart the founding of a new state. It was only when I heard a familiar chattering that I turned around to look. Pooh was trotting back, and with him was Pim the truant, for all the world as if nothing whatever had happened. But when he came close to me, Pim did a little dance, just to show how glad he was, before hanging on to my leg and starting to tell me all about it. I was much too happy to see him to have the heart to scold. Hand in hand, we sauntered home, Pooh cavorting all around us, and barking himself hoarse. All the way to the house, Pim was telling me about his adventures. He seemed so pleased to be with us again, just the same as ever, that I forgot the worry and sadness that we had had on his account. If only I had understood what he told me, how different everything might have been.

The first thing at home was Hamisi's noisy welcome. Then came the feast and the merry-making, in honor of the prodigal son. Instead of the fatted calf, we had bananas, sugar, corn cobs and nuts. And from the kitchen, Pim appeared with an open can of California peaches, having, as Hamisi declared, stolen them . . .

Pooh, during all this time, felt very much neglected. His efforts to call attention to himself and to start a wrestling match fetched him a box on the ears by his friend. Much injured, he took to the shade and pretended to sleep, holding his eyes tight shut.

Luncheon brought the three of us together again as usual, on the verandah under the big red and white striped umbrella. During the afternoon the sun beat down as hot as ever, cutting out any idea of a walk. I lazed in a wicker armchair with a book, waiting for the evening. Pooh snored. Pim clawed the fleas out of his hide. The rays of the sun singed the land, and the air flimmered, the shine of the white flagstones hurt. The letters began to dance before my eyes. I closed my book and my lids, and fell asleep.

When Pim's shouting awoke me, the sun was low. Among other things one learns in the bush to wake up instantly, to give up that wonderful twilight state that usually precedes return to reality. Often too much depends upon the few short seconds. When I opened my eyes, Pim was standing up out in the clearing, calling to Pooh, who was already chasing away as hard as he could go. At the edge of the bush—something I had never seen before as long as I had been on the farm—a big herd of black apes was loafing around. And there was Pooh answering the call of his friend at top speed. Realizing his danger, I grabbed my stick and ran after him. All the time, Pim was getting closer and closer to the herd, turning somersaults, yelling, then standing up to call again.

Most of the apes retreated into the bush before the strange animal they saw tearing towards them. Screeching, the mothers grabbed their young. Barking their fear and anger, the aged limped along after. A few of the young ones, their curiosity getting the better of fear, here and there stopped still, standing up to look at the nearing enemy. Then falling back on all fours, they ran all the faster to make up the time their curiosity had cost them.

But one old male was not in so much of a hurry to leave. As if he wanted to cover the retreat of the herd, he stayed behind, barking, grunting, going back step by step, always stopping to look around for the others. Just before the bush, Pim caught up with him. But the old fellow didn't understand his leaps and bounds. He just kept looking at Pooh, now only a few yards away.

Pooh came full tilt, obviously in high feather to have won his face again. From the force of contact, the old ape was bowled over. By the time Pooh, recovered, came dancing along to Pim for the usual sparring, the stranger stood ready to take up the struggle in earnest.

A second later they were at each other, for as soon as Pooh came into the reach of his long arms, the ape went for him, silently, murder in his eye. His first bite tore a gash in his flank. Pooh yelped and snapped for the chest of the old fellow, who in turn dug his fangs into Pooh's neck. And there they were rolling in the grass.

Pim stood by, screaming. He tried tugging at the ape and when he saw that it didn't do any good, he ran to meet me, crying in a pitiful sort of way. By the time I reached them, both of the fighters were covered with blood. At the first blow, my stick broke across the old ape's back. I shouted to Hamisi, who had run after me, to get my gun. And then I did what I could to separate the two, hitting with pieces of wood that were lying around. But it was no use. Each had a terrible hold on the other.

Gasping, otherwise silent, they rolled over the grass. When a piece of flesh, where teeth had been buried, would give way, the jaws would snap deeper down in the body. Both turned and strained for the throat of the other, but as yet neither succeeded. That would be the end of course. For one second, the ape loosed his great yellow teeth from Pooh's flank to snap at my stick, only to dig them, groaning, into the neck. Pooh had taken a firmer hold on his chest. With the strength of his great arms, he pulled Pooh's ears, clawed his eyes and tore at his nostrils.

The two of them rolled into a little hollow close to the bush. I was still trying to separate them, no matter which one I hit. It was impossible to aim, they were so mixed up. Pim had joined in coaxing and crying, pulling and shoving. We both had one idea— to get them apart before they reached the bush. We knew that once in there, Pooh would be done for. The ape's arms seemed to be working with less power. His breathing thrashed his sides. With tremendous effort he lifted his heavy form, pressed away from Pooh with all four limbs, tore, reared, and was free. But before he could quite reach the bush, Pooh had him by the throat. The old ape's one idea now was to get away. Pooh, jaws locked in his fighting spirit, was dragged in with him.

That really finished it.

For a while, in the underbrush, in the tangle of lianas and logs, the struggle flared up again. I could just see the two bodies wind together, unwind, join. I could hear their rattling, gasping, coughing—accompanied by the uproar of the apes that were watching the fight from the trees. In his despair, Pim was clambering up and down the branches. Once he came back to me, tugged at me, crying out and gnashing his teeth. By this time I had almost sickened. Powerless to save him, I had to listen to Pooh, not five steps away, fighting for his last breath of life. I threw myself against the bush. The flexible lianas, thick as an arm, would give way an inch or two and then hold stronger than a steel grating.

At last Hamisi came with the gun. Lying out flat I could see the two animals. Their movements had grown tired, but still they were fighting, clinging. It was impossible to hit one without the other. Finally the brown body loosed itself from the yellow. I shot, and kept on shooting. I only noticed later that I had emptied the whole magazine.

When the sound of the shots died away, the voice of stillness was very audible in that virgin forest. It was broken only at intervals by a terribly tired rattle.

Working with a pocket knife, hands bleeding, we tore a passage through the undergrowth. Pim reached his friend long before us. We took quite a while to cover the few yards that separated us from the dying. When we came, Pooh was dead. Pim's hands were crimson. Never have I seen in any countenance an expression of despair to equal his when he held them, stained as they were, before his eyes. Despair and horror.

We dragged the torn body into the clear. We knotted and slung a bier, and carried Pooh home. The same evening, we buried him down by the swimming hole.

By the green light of the lamp, Pim and I sat late into the night and thought of Pooh. From time to time, he would look at his hands, turn to me, and press himself against me, chattering softly. My fingers stroked his big head. "Poor boy. It wasn't your fault. You couldn't help it." When I went to bed, long after midnight, I gave my hand to Pim for the last time.

The next morning he was gone. But he used to come back from time to time, so long as the herd of apes was in the neighborhood. He would wander around, as though he were taking leave of all the things that were familiar to him. He would climb the old cedar tree, scuttle across the gravel in front of the house, tear a ripe papaya from some branch, saunter through the garden, then disappear again into the bush. He wouldn't let anyone touch him, not even Hamisi.

At last the rains began. The steppe greened again, and the droves of beasts returned to their old grazing grounds. The herd of apes went away too. Pim went with it, and only Hamisi really believes that some day he will come back.

THE MONUMENT

By IRWIN SHAW

"I DO NOT WANT ANY OF HIS OWN BRAND," MC MAHON SAID FIRMLY. He blew on a glass and wiped it with deliberate care. "I have my own opinion of his own brand."

Mr. Grimmet looked sad, sitting across the bar on a high stool, and Thesing shrugged like a salesman, not giving up the fight, but moving to a new position to continue the attack. McMahon picked up another glass in his clean, soft bartender's hands. He wiped it, his face serious and determined and flushed right up to the bald spot that his plastered down hair couldn't cover. There was nobody else in the bar at the front part of the restaurant.

It was three o'clock in the afternoon. In the rear three waiters stood arguing. Every day at three o'clock the three waiters gathered in the back and argued.

"Fascism," one waiter said, "is a rehearsal for the cemetery."

"You read that someplace," another waiter said.

"All right," said the first waiter, "I read it someplace."

"An Italian," the third waiter said to the first waiter. "You are without a doubt one lousy Italian."

Mr. Grimmet turned around and called to the waiters: "Please reserve discussions of that character for when you go home. This is a restaurant, not Madison Square Garden."

He turned back to watching McMahon wiping the glasses. The three waiters looked at him with equal hate.

"Many of the best bars in the city," Thesing said in his musical salesman's voice, "use our own brand."

"Many of the best bars in the city," McMahon said, using the towel very hard, "ought to be turned into riding academies."

"That's funny," Thesing said, laughing almost naturally. "He's very funny, isn't he, Mr. Grimmet?"

"Listen, Billy," Mr. Grimmet said, leaning forward, disregarding Thesing, "listen to reason. In a mixed drink nobody can tell how much you paid for the rye that goes into it. That is the supreme beauty of cocktails."

McMahon didn't say anything. The red got a little deeper on his cheeks and on his bald spot and he put the clean glasses down with a sharp tinkle and the tinkle went through the shining lines of the other glasses on the shelves and sounded thinly through the empty restaurant. He was a little fat man, very compact, and he moved with great precision and style behind a bar and you could tell by watching him whether he was merry or sad or perturbed, just from the way he mixed a drink or put down a glass. Just now he was angry and Mr. Grimmet knew it.

Mr. Grimmet didn't want a fight, but there was quite a bit of money to be saved. He put out his hand appealingly to Thesing. "Tell me the truth, Thesing," he said. "Is your own brand bad?"

"Well," Thesing said slowly, "a lot of people like it. It is very superior for a product of its type."

"Varnish type," McMahon said, facing the shelves. "Carefully matched developing fluid."

Thesing laughed, the laugh he used from nine to six. "Witty," he said, "the sparkling bartender." McMahon wheeled and looked at him, head down a little on his chest. "I meant it," Thesing protested. "I sincerely meant it."

"I want to tell you," Mr. Grimmet said to McMahon, fixing him with his eye, "that we can save seven dollars a case on our own brand." McMahon started whistling the tenor aria from *Pagliacci*. He looked up at the ceiling and wiped a glass and whistled. Mr. Grimmet felt like firing him and remembered that at least twice a month he felt like firing McMahon.

"Please stop whistling," he said politely. "We have a matter to discuss."

McMahon stopped whistling and Mr. Grimmet still felt like firing him.

"Times're not so good," Mr. Grimmet said in a cajoling tone of voice, hating himself for descending to such tactics before an employee of his. "Remember, McMahon, Coolidge is no longer in the White House. I am the last one in the world to compromise with quality, but we must remember, we are in business and it is 1939."

"Thesing's own brand," McMahon said, "would destroy the stomach of a healthy horse."

"Mussolini!" the first waiter's voice came out from the back of the restaurant. "Every day on Broadway I pass forty-five actors who could do his act better."

"I am going to tell you one thing," Mr. Grimmet said with obvious calmness to McMahon. "I am the owner of this restaurant."

McMahon whistled some more from *Pagliacci*. Thesing moved wisely down the bar a bit.

"I am interested in making money," Mr. Grimmet said. "What would you say, Mr. McMahon, if I ordered you to use Thesing's own brand?"

"I would say, 'I am through, Mr. Grimmet.' Once and for all."

Mr. Grimmet rubbed his face unhappily and stared coldly at the waiters in the back of the restaurant. The waiters remained silent and stared coldly back at him. "What's it to you?" Mr. Grimmet asked McMahon angrily. "What do you care if we use another whiskey? Do you have to drink it?"

"In my bar, Mr. Grimmet," McMahon said, putting down his towel and the glasses and facing his employer squarely, "in my bar, good drinks are served."

"Nobody will know the difference!" Mr. Grimmet got off his stool and jumped up and down gently. "What do Americans know about liquor? Nothing! Read any book that is published on the subject!"

"True," Thesing said judicially, "The general consensus of opinion is that Americans do not know the difference between red wine and a chocolate malted milk."

"In my bar," McMahon repeated, his face very red, his wide hands spread on the bar, "I serve the best drinks I know how to serve."

"Stubborn!" Mr. Grimmet yelled. "You are a stubborn Irishman! You do this out of malice! You are anxious to see me lose seven dollars on every case of liquor because you dislike me. Let us get down to the bedrock of truth!"

"Keep your voice down," McMahon said, speaking with great control. "I want to remind you of one or two things. I have worked for you since Repeal, Mr. Grimmet. In that time, how many times did we have to enlarge the bar?"

"I am not in the mood for history, McMahon!" Mr. Grimmet

shouted. "What good is a bar as long as the *Normandie* if it is not run on a businesslike basis?"

"Answer my question," McMahon said. "How many times?"

"Three," Mr. Grimmet said, "all right, three."

"We are three times as big now as we were six years ago," McMahon said in a professor's tone, explaining proposition one, going on to proposition two. "Why do you think that is?"

"Accident!" Mr. Grimmet looked ironically up to the ceiling. "Fate! Roosevelt! The hand of God! How do I know?"

"I will tell you," McMahon said, continuing in the professional vein. "People who come into this bar get the best Manhattans, the best Martinis, the best Daiquiris that are made on the face of the earth. They are made out of the finest ingredients, with great care, Mr. Grimmet."

"One cocktail tastes like another," Mr. Grimmet said. "People make a big fuss and they don't know anything."

"Mr. Grimmet," McMahon said with open contempt, "it is easy to see that you're not a drinking man."

Mr. Grimmet's face reflected his desperate search for a new line of defense. His eyebrows went up with pleasure as he found it. He sat down and spoke softly across the bar to McMahon. "Did it ever occur to you," he asked, "that people come into this place because of the food that is served here?"

"I will give you my final opinion of Greta Garbo," the first waiter's voice sounded out defiantly. "There is nobody like her."

For a moment McMahon looked straight into Mr. Grimmet's eyes. A slight bitter smile played at one corner of his mouth. He breathed deeply, like a man who has just decided to bet on a horse that has not won in fourteen races. "Shall I tell you what I think of the food that is served in your restaurant, Mr. Grimmet?" McMahon asked flatly.

"The best chefs," Mr. Grimmet said quickly, "the best chefs in the city of New York."

McMahon nodded slowly. "The best chefs," he said, "and the worst food."

"Consider," Mr. Grimmet called. "Consider what you're saying."

"Anything a cook can disguise," McMahon said, talking now to Thesing, disregarding Mr. Grimmet, "is wonderful here. Anything with a sauce. Once I ate a sirloin steak in this restaurant . . ."

"Careful, McMahon," Mr. Grimmet jumped off his stool and ran around to face McMahon.

"What can be done to disguise a sirloin steak?" McMahon asked reasonably. "Nothing. You broil it. Simply that. If it was good when it was cut off the steer, it's good on your plate. If it was bad . . ."

"I pay good prices!" Mr. Grimmet yelled. "I'll have no allusions . . ."

"I would not bring a dog into this restaurant to eat sirloin steak," McMahon said. "Not a young dog with the teeth of a lion."

"You're fired!" Mr. Grimmet pounded on the bar. "This restaurant will now do without your services."

McMahon bowed. "That is satisfactory to me," he said. "Perfectly satisfactory."

"Well, now, everybody. Boys!" Thesing said pacifically. "Over a little thing like our own rye. . . ."

McMahon began taking off his apron. "This bar has a reputation. It is my reputation. I am proud of it. I am not interested in remaining at a place in which my reputation will be damaged."

McMahon threw his apron, neatly folded, over a towel rack and picked up the little wooden wedge on which was printed, in gold letters, "William McMahon, *In Charge.*" Mr. Grimmet watched him with trouble in his eyes as McMahon lifted the hinged piece of the bar that permitted the bartenders to get out into the restaurant proper.

"What is the sense," Mr. Grimmet asked as the hinges creaked, "of taking a rash step, Billy?" Once more Mr. Grimmet hated himself for his dulcet tone of voice, but William McMahon was one of the five finest bartenders in the city of New York.

McMahon stood there, pushing the hinged piece of the bar a little, back and forth. "Once and for all," he said. He let the hinged piece fall behind him.

"I'll tell you what I'll do, Billy," Mr. Grimmet went on swiftly, hating himself more and more, "I'll make a compromise. I will give you five dollars more per week." He sighed to himself and then looked brightly at McMahon.

McMahon knocked his shingle thoughtfully against the bar. "I will try to make you understand something, Mr. Grimmet," he said, gently. "I am not as fundamentally interested in money as I am fundamentally interested in other things."

"You are not so different from the rest of the world," Mr. Grimmet said with dignity.

"I have been working for twenty-five years," McMahon said, knocking the shingle that said, "William McMahon, *In Charge*," "and I have constantly been able to make a living. I do not work only to make a living. I am more interested in making something else. For the last six years I have worked here night and day. A lot of nice people come in here and drink like ladies and gentlemen. They all like this place. They all like me."

"Nobody is saying anything about anybody not liking you," Mr. Grimmet said impatiently. "I am discussing a matter of business principle."

"I like this place." McMahon looked down at the shingle in his hand. "I think this is a very nice bar. I planned it. Right?" He looked up at Mr. Grimmet.

"You planned it. I will sign an affidavit to the effect that you planned it," Mr. Grimmet said ironically. "What has that got to do with Thesing's own brand?"

"If something is right here," McMahon went on, without raising his voice, "people can say it's William McMahon's doing. If something is wrong here they can say it's William McMahon's fault. I like that, Mr. Grimmet. When I die people can say, 'William McMahon left a monument, the bar at Grimmet's Restaurant. He never served a bad drink in his whole life.'" McMahon took his coat out of the closet next to the bar and put it on. "A monument. I will not have a monument made out of Thesing's own brand. Mr. Grimmet, I think you are a dumb bastard."

McMahon bowed a little to the two men and started out. Mr. Grimmet gulped, then called, his words hard and dry in the empty restaurant. "McMahon!" The bartender turned around. "All right," Mr. Grimmet said. "Come back."

McMahon gestured toward Thesing.

"Any liquor you say," Mr. Grimmet said in a choked voice. "Any godamn whiskey you want!"

McMahon smiled and went back to the closet and took his coat off and took the shingle out of his pocket. He went back of the bar and slipped on his apron, as Thesing and Grimmet watched.

"One thing," Mr. Grimmet said, his eyes twitching from the strain, "one thing I want you to know."

"Yes, sir," said McMahon.

"I don't want you to talk to me," Mr. Grimmet said, "and I don't want to talk to you. Ever."

Thesing quietly picked up his hat and stole out the door.

"Yes, sir," said McMahon.

Mr. Grimmet walked swiftly into the kitchen.

"I will tell you something about debutantes," the first waiter was saying in the rear of the restaurant, "they are overrated."

McMahon tied the bow in his apron strings and, neatly, in the center of the whiskey shelves above the bar, placed the shingle, "William McMahon, *In Charge*."

DEUTSCHLAND ÜBER ALLES

By J. L. CAMPBELL

THE GIRLS ALL SAT IN THE ROOM DOWNSTAIRS, ALL EXCEPT CLARA, who roamed about, wringing her hands and praying and mumbling to herself. "Ach, she's nutty, that's what she is, nutty as hell!"

Frau Schratt would have sent her off to a hospital, got rid of her somehow, but she couldn't today. Nobody knew what to do today. Through the closed shutters the voices of the passers-by sounded high and excited. From far off came the sound of cheering, and the roar of the airplanes above the town never ceased.

"Ach, Gott! Ain't the darkness never coming?" Louise twisted her handkerchief. It seemed a year since yesterday and a century since last week when everybody was gay and happy. If only Frau Schratt would let them go out and see the Führer! It was bound to be a wonderful sight, what with all the college students and school children lining the streets and shouting and saluting like they had been told to do. If only they could get out now then they'd come back full of life and ready to work as usual. There was bound to be a lot doing after dark, troops had been pouring into Vienna all day long. A dull booming made the windows rattle.

"What's that?" Susie grabbed Louise's arm.

"It's only cannon. My God you're ignorant. Don't you know they always fire cannon for heroes?"

"Sure I do, but sometimes they fire 'em when there ain't any heroes, when they're just fighting." Susie hadn't lived through the revolution for nothing. That was a long time ago but she never would forget it. She had spent two days behind an upturned kitchen table at the end of an asphalt passage. She had seen people shot down, lots of them. One fellow had had his arm blown off but he had held his rifle between his knees and gone on firing just the same.

"What do you think, Greta, do you think things will be better for Austria now that the Germans have come?"

All the girls looked up to Greta. A fellow had once given her an apartment with three rooms and a balcony. She was famous too, her photo had been in the newspapers, advertising a bust developer.

"How should I know? All I know is that it'll be better for us girls. It's always better where there's soldiers. Why I know a girl who makes heaps of money—piles of it—just following wars about—and she's nothing to look at either." Greta cast an approving glance at her own full figure. The door squeaked. Clara stood there. She didn't come in, she just stood there, pale and gaunt. "I am the resurrection and the light!" Her voice was hollow, only her eyes reflected the madness in her head.

"The hell you are! Get upstairs, you're crazy!"

But Clara did not move.

"He's coming! Christ is coming back to us!"

"Ach, go to bed, go to bed and shut up!"

"Ssh! Ssh! Listen!" Clara's voice was no more than a whisper. She wore only a nightgown, her dark hair fell in lank strands about her face. "They are writing His name in letters of fire across the sky!"

"Listen, Clara!" Greta got up and patted her on the shoulder. "Just listen. Those ain't angels writing nobody's name in the sky. They're airplanes, army airplanes, see? And if you don't go upstairs and stay quiet in your room they'll drop a bomb on you, so help you God!"

Clara moved her head slowly back and forth. "Yes, that's right . . . God is my help. . . ." The roar of an airplane drowned her voice. Louise and Susie began to whimper.

"Make her go upstairs somebody. . . . She's blasphemous and I'm superstitious . . . Christ!"

"Christ!" Clara's eyes blazed again. "He's coming for us girls! Our bridegroom is coming for us now. Put on your raiment for Christ! Get ready for the Lord!"

"Shut up! Shut up! Shut up!" Louise couldn't stand it. That's all, she just couldn't stand it.

"Clara!" Frau Schratt's voice filled the hall. The stairs creaked beneath her tread. "You come here." She wasn't going to stand any nonsense. Clara turned. She was accustomed to obeying Frau Schratt, she did so now. She climbed the stairs clinging to the rail. Her breath coming through her teeth made a whistling sound.

"Jesus is coming for us, Madam, He is coming for us all. Maybe He'll come in a chariot of fire, and maybe He'll come like a beggar asking for help, but He's coming."

"Ach, yes, sure, sure. . . . Now you lie down and take a rest first. . . . I'll tell you when He gets here." Frau Schratt made Clara lie down on the sofa in her own room. It was a big room with a stained pink carpet and faded brocade curtains. Over the bed hung a carved cupid, a bow of ruby ribbon tied around its neck. No amount of fresh air could ever rid Frau Schratt's room of the combined smell of stale tobacco, powder, perfume and humanity. As soon as Clara was quiet, Frau Schratt poured herself out a drink of Schliebervitz from a tiny pressed glass carafe that stood on her dressing table. The hot liquid burned her throat. She did not drink as a rule but today was different, she had to be ready for anything. Would the Nazis close her house? Would her taxes go up? Thank God none of her girls had Jewish blood. Not that she was frightened. Emergencies meant nothing to her, her life had been made up of emergencies. She knew how weak men can be, so Hitler couldn't frighten her. She wasn't afraid of Hell, only she wished she had got Clara away. The girl was as mad as a tick. There was no telling what she might do or say and there was no use asking for trouble. She glanced over at the sofa. Clara lay quite still, her eyes closed. Well, she'd get her out of the house in the morning rain or shine, war or peace.

At last the cheering seemed to have ceased, only now and then one heard a distant shout. Two sparrows fluttered and chirped on the window ledge as though nothing were happening in Vienna at all. The clock on the high porcelain stove struck five o'clock. At the same moment an old man, in his shirt sleeves, appeared at the window across the street and began practicing on a cornet. He had practiced there every evening for ten years and, as a rule, his appearance was a signal for Frau Schratt to draw her curtains. But this evening she did not draw them. She had never spoken to him in her life but, somehow, his familiar appearance gave her confidence. The sun sank lower and lower. It cast long rays lighting up the spots upon the carpet. Every one of those spots had a history. That one near the dressing table had been made by a Hungarian officer. Frau Schratt could see him now, standing up there, half-naked and pouring Tokay over the floor, wonderful Tokay too, a hundred years old! He had said he was making his spot of home in a foreign land. A big, fat manufacturer from Linz had made that spot near the door. He'd had a drop too much and cut his head. My God he'd bled like a pig! Then there were those boys from America! What fun they'd had that night! One of them played an accordion and all of them sang. That was just after the War. They had made friends with some Austrian soldiers and they had all had drinks together and put their arms around each other and spilled beer and called each other "comrade" and swore they never would fight again so help them God!

All the spots, all the spots, each with its story of the past!

The sun had set, the room was almost in darkness when Frau Schratt got up to draw the curtains. She paused for a moment and gazed into the street. Already the lights were lighted. A group of men was standing at the upper corner. She could not hear their voices but something about their backs was ominous. They were all of them young. One of them seemed to have cut his face, he kept dabbing it with a handkerchief but his companions paid no attention to him. The old musician had stopped playing. He was leaning out of the window and watching them, too, half furtively. Suddenly the men began hurrying down the street, not running, but faster than walking. When they passed the house Frau Schratt noticed that several of them carried sticks, rather heavy, short sticks. One of them bent down and picked up a stone from the gutter. It didn't take them a minute to pass. They turned into Mariahilfer Strasse. There was a moment's silence. Frau Schratt peered after them, her left hand, covered with flashy rings, gripped the heavy brocade curtain. A moment later there was a crash of glass, screams and cries, "Jude! Jude!" She saw people running across the end of the street. A woman fell. Her hair was streaming down her back. She held up her arm to protect her face. An old man stumbled into view. He wore a big round fur hat. One of the young men knocked off his hat and kicked him. The old man fell against the wall. He had two long greasy curls—one on each side of his face. Why it was old Goldfarb! Frau Schratt knew him well. He owned the dress shop at the corner. Many a time he'd threatened to have her house closed. He didn't like his son Emanuel coming here each Friday. Everything that he could do to annoy her he had done and she had always hated him. But she did not hate him now. Oh,

God, what were they doing to him! They were around him like angry hornets. The old musician across the street looked over and said "Nazi!"

She nodded her head. It was the first time they had ever spoken. Then she drew her curtains and hurried downstairs. She could hear the girls talking.

"Shut that front door and come inside!"

The girls scrambled into the narrow hall. They were pale and frightened.

"None of you girls have got anything to bother about. Keep quiet and stay inside." She hustled them into the big room. There was a green carpet on the floor and the walls were lined with mirrors. They could hear more shouting and glass smashing. The roar of the airplanes began again.

"It's the Jews they're after." Louise's voice was thin, the rouge on her cheeks looked almost black against her pale face.

"Sure it is."

"Did you hear his head crack? I could hear it plain as anything, it sounded like a pistol shot." Greta put her hand on her heart. Her kimono had slipped from off one shoulder. "People oughtn't to treat people that way!"

"Hold your tongue!" Frau Schratt glared. "And let me tell you that from now on the first one of you that begins talking and blabbing about things you don't understand will get out of my house so quick she won't know what's hit her. Remember that! I mean it!" She paused. "I got enough to worry me without you pullets borrowing trouble."

The girls listened to her stump upstairs. No one spoke for a moment. In the long mirrors the huddled group was reflected over and over as though they were dotted across all Austria.

"Jesus!" Greta was the first to speak. "I need a drink!" She called down to the basement. An old woman in a blue apron and cracked shoes brought up beer for them all. That looked natural anyway. Frothy and yellow and natural.

"Say, that was old Goldfarb. Do you think they killed him?" Louise whispered. She didn't want Frau Schratt to hear. "What do you suppose has happened to Emanuel?" None of them had seen him. Maybe he'd got away, left the country. All night long Jews had been in flight.

"They say there's six hundred of 'em on that old iron barge down in the Danube. You know, the one down there where we went to swim last July. They say they wanted to get across to Czechoslovakia, but the Czechs wasn't having any, they wouldn't let 'em land, so they're just left there in the middle of the river."

"Poor devils! God, I never liked Jews much before but, somehow, now they don't seem so bad."

"Oh, Emanuel never was a bad sort. He was always the perfect gentleman with me if I do say it—of course he wasn't much to look at and he wasn't over-generous either—but he was fair. I've always said that and I'll say it now." Greta wiped the beer from her lips with her tongue.

They could still hear people running and shouting and glass smashing, sometimes from far away and sometimes quite near by. Mariahilfer Strasse was full of Jewish shops.

"Now I suppose I'll never get that evening dress he promised me."

"Did he promise you an evening dress?"

"Sure he did." Greta nodded. "It was a French evening dress, or rather a copy of a French evening dress. My God, it was good-looking!"

"What color was it?"

"Green, what you call pea green, my favorite color."

"Pea green?" Susie looked puzzled. She was a country girl. "Which pea green?"

"Pea, peagreen, you poor nut. There's only one."

"No there ain't. There's all sorts of green in peas—dark green, clear green. It depends if they're raw or canned or cooked—my mother always puts in a pinch of soda to make 'em brighter. . . ."

"Yes, that's right, and some spring onions too—Ach, but they're good! Little June peas!" Louise could almost taste them. Soon all the girls were talking about food, food and cooking, that is, all except Greta. She had been a model, her bust had been advertised, she felt superior and besides, she couldn't help thinking about Emanuel Goldfarb. He was getting to like her a lot, he might have given her an apartment if all this hadn't happened. Oh, gee, them airplanes made a noise! He had always said he'd give her an apartment as soon as his old man was out of the way. He was a proper old orthodox and no mistake, long curls, fur hat and religious as hell.

"What's that?"

Everybody stopped talking at once. There it was again. Somebody was tapping at the window. No one spoke, no one breathed. The tapping continued. Suddenly it was drowned by the roar of an airplane flying very low, just above the houses. It must have been carrying a searchlight too. A streak of white light flashed like lightning through the crack between the heavy curtains. There was a banging at the front door. Susie screamed. Her beer upset. It made a great wet patch on the carpet. Frau Schratt hurried downstairs. Clara followed her on to the landing and peered over the bannisters. She clutched the railing, her head bent forward, her eyes shining.

"Who are you, and what do you want?"

"Let me in! Let me in, Frau Schratt, for Christ's sake open the door! It's me, Emanuel!"

Frau Schratt opened the door. Emanuel Goldfarb half fell into the hall. Sweat was streaming down his face, his coat was torn, his trousers were covered with mud.

"Hide me! For the love of God hide me. . . . I've never done anybody any harm . . . they're after me. . . . Everything's gone . . . everything's destroyed. . . . Hide me! For Christ's sake hide me!"

Frau Schratt slammed the door and bolted it. "What in the devil do you mean by coming here? We can't hide you! We're women, we can't hide you! Why don't you go to your own people. . . ."

"My own people! They're dead. . . . The streets are full of blood. . . . They're beating up women and children and old men . . . everybody . . . and all the merchandise, all the beautiful merchandise . . . is thrown into the gutter . . . fifty years of hard work and economy . . . my poor old father . . . and it's all gone. . . . Ach, Gott! Ach, Gott! Aie! Aie! Aie!" He beat his breast. "Have pity . . . they're after me, they will crucify me! They'll crucify me!"

He was on his knee groveling, weeping. They could hear men running up the streets, hoarse voices yelling death and destruction. Greta grabbed Emanuel's hand. She had to half drag him up the stairs. Already people were beating on the door. There was a wardrobe on the second landing. Somehow Greta got Emanuel on top of it, behind a heap of old hatboxes and rubbish. "Stay there, don't move or you'll knock everything off! Christ!" She tried not to look as though she'd been running when she got downstairs. Frau Schratt was just opening the door. They would have broken it down if she hadn't unbolted it.

"Well, gentlemen, what is it? We're closed tonight? What. . . ." But they didn't wait for her to finish. Half a dozen rough-looking men pushed her aside. More wanted to push in but Frau Schratt managed to get the door shut before they could. The men wore swastika bands pinned on their sleeves. Their eyes were bloodshot and the sweat, pouring down their cheeks, was not from fright.

"We're the police."

"Well, I'm always friends with the police. What do you want?"

"A dirty Jew ran in here a minute ago. We want him."

"Somebody ran in here?" Frau Schratt looked around at the girls inquiringly. They were huddled together like frightened sheep. They all shook their heads as though they had never heard of a Jew. "Nobody's come in here. I told you the house was closed for tonight."

"Get out of the way!" One of the men gave Frau Schratt a push. It was too much. She knocked his arm aside.

"Get out of the way, hell! This is my house! Do you hear? My house, and if you want anything in it remember your manners!"

The man stepped back. "Look here! We don't want to make any trouble. We saw a Jew come in here and we're going to get him if we have to tear the house down."

There was no alternative. Two of the men guarded the door, the others went with Frau Schratt. They were a long time searching the house. Greta thought they'd never finish. Once she thought they'd found Emanuel. Upstairs, downstairs, heavy boots tramping, doors slamming, at last they came back. They seemed in a little better humor.

"I guess we made a mistake. He ain't here."

"I told you he wan't here. Now, just to show there's no ill feeling will you all have a beer on the house?" If these were the police of the future better get on the good side of them. Frau Schratt never missed an opportunity if she could help it. They all went into the parlor. The men wouldn't sit down, they didn't pay much attention to the girls but they didn't look suspicious as before. The old woman in the blue apron and the cracked shoes brought up the beer. She smiled a toothless, half-frightened smile as she passed the tray.

One of the men held up his glass. "Heil Hitler!"

The other men held up their glasses. "Heil Hitler! Heil Hitler! Heil Hitler!" Their voices were very deep.

"Praise Christ!" It was Clara. Everybody turned. She came forward, her finger to her lips, smilingly, excitedly. When she reached the middle of the room she stopped and looked around mysteriously. "S-s-s-h! Do you know who we've got upstairs?" Her voice was no more than a whisper. "Christ! He's come! I've seen him! He's waiting upstairs! He's on the wardrobe! Hallelujah!"

"Clara!" But Frau Schratt was too late. No use putting her hand over the girl's mouth now. The men were halfway up the stairs.

It didn't take them long to find Emanuel. He wasn't a small man but he looked tiny when they dragged him down the stairs and on the way to eternity. He didn't cry out or make any sound. Blood trickled down his left temple. His collar was torn and flapped slightly like a humble flag of truce. The front door banged. There was a sort of scrambling noise outside and then everything was silent.

Susie was the first to speak. Her voice was unnatural. "Say, he's left his hat." It had rolled into a corner. She picked it up and began to straighten it. Her fingers were trembling. "Wan't his face awful . . . did you notice? . . . It was . . . pea green. . . ."

"Shut up, you damned fool!" Greta picked up one of the men's glasses and drank it down without stopping for breath. Then she wiped her mouth on the back of her hand and turned on the radio. *Deutschland Über Alles* filled the room with blatant triumph.

Upstairs Clara rocked back and forth on her knees, praising the Lord for His merciful kindness.

THE BRONZE BAFFLER

By HART STILWELL

THE OTHER DAY I TOOK A FAT, MIDDLE-AGED FRIEND OF MINE OUT on a lake to teach him to catch bass. All he knew about bass was what he had read in the papers.

"Now you do it like this," I said, taking a rod and demonstrating the cast. "You bring the rod back behind you, then you whip it smartly forward, releasing tension on the reel spool with your thumb as you do so. Get the idea?"

"Sure," he said. "Give me that rod."

Well, he released the tension at the wrong time, and the bait went flying out behind him, instead of in front of him. It sank slowly to the bottom as he untangled the line. Then when he started reeling in he said, "I've hooked the bottom."

But it wasn't the bottom. It began to move. He clamped down on that line in a way that almost gave me heart failure, and for five minutes he and that bass fought on a no-give and no-take basis. By some miracle the line and the hooks held, and soon he had a seven-pound bass flopping in the boat.

It was the biggest bass I ever saw caught in that lake.

And fish as I would, I could catch nothing all morning that in any way resembled it. That big bass had been lying down near the cool bottoms, just letting the world roll by, when he saw the plug settle. Then as it started up off the bottom, he decided to eat it. That was all.

But the incident fits neatly into the entire history of my bass fishing, and gives body to the pet theories which I have worked out about this most uncertain of sports.

I have come to the conclusion that the black bass is fundamentally a lonely, moody, unpredictable fish that would as soon eat his own children as the next man's. I think he has a split personality and suffers at times from delusions of persecution.

The whole uncertain situation surrounding his actions may

stem from his home life, which to me seems practically void of emotional outlets.

I know of no other line of reasoning that would account for the things he does.

If you decide to sally forth in quest of bass, therefore, console yourself with the thought that intelligence, experience, and skill will probably be a handicap to you in the long run.

I come to this conclusion because I probably catch fewer bass than anybody else in the country. This gives rise at times to annoying situations. But it also brings about quite a bit of amusement and some satisfaction, so that I conclude it is good for the general health of the nation, and I make no complaint.

I merely chronicle the things I have seen.

Like most other anglers who have fished for years, I have developed some very definite theories. Most of them are probably wrong. But they are about as good as the next man's set of theories when it comes to figuring out this big-mouth rascal that won't stick to any set of customs or conventions in spite of having been on the planet several millions of years.

I have come to the conclusion, for instance, that if I take somebody out upon the water with the idea of teaching him to catch bass, he will almost invariably catch more bass than I do. This has happened so frequently that I can no longer attribute it to chance.

It is Theory No. 1 in the Stilwell System of Not Catching Bass. It is humiliating to me at times, but apparently there is nothing I can do about it. In the old days when I was a rank amateur I caught a lot of bass myself, but now that I can pitch that plug up into the pocket where I want it, and can drop the fly on the water as gently as a floating leaf, why the bass just sits and looks at me with a cold and fishy stare.

Furthermore, I have observed that most of the really worthwhile bass I have ever hung on the stringer were hooked when I was lighting a cigarette, holding the rod over my shoulder, or looking across the lake, dreaming of a tall mug of beer.

This gives rise to Theory No. 2, or the Indifference Theory of Bass Fishing.

There is, however, a deep-seated grain of logic behind these happenings, and before I have done I will try to tear down to it and bare it to the public gaze.

But the facts as they are result in making the black bass a great leveler. I know the country is full of experts, and I have seen some of them in operation. It is a thing of pure joy to watch the easy flow of line and rod as they cast. But take any one of them and put him out in a boat with a dub that never saw a bass before, and I will put my money on the dub.

I think we should nose about some, before we go farther, and throw a bit of light on the home life and personal habits of the bass. Along in the spring of the year the male bass begins to feel the urge for a home. He swims about here and there and picks out a good spot. Then he clears it off by gently fanning it with his tail until he has it clean and neat as a pin. When this bit of home making is done, he swims off in quest of a mate who will come and share his little house and lot.

He has to use care in this matter. If he approaches a prospective bride that is a year or two older than he, there is a definite possibility that he might suddenly find himself being eaten, instead of being lovingly flattered and given a chance to reproduce his kind. He is himself a person of uncertain impulses, and should he run across some shy little thing that is too trusting, his urge to eat may overcome his urge to reproduce his kind, and he might eat her. It is all very disconcerting, looking at it strictly from the point of view of romance.

But somehow love will triumph, and he will find himself strutting about the place with a female of the species hovering over the nest, depositing ten or twelve thousand eggs. The male lavishes his seed and care on these eggs, and guards them with his life, while his woman swims away without a thought of the future of the race, content simply to eat.

The male bass will sit for hours and days, touching not a bite of food, simply fanning those jellylike eggs. He will furiously attack anything that comes near his home. And it is at such times that almost everybody, even an expert, can catch bass, for the male will smack any sort of fantastic plug that is thrown within a dozen feet of his home.

It is at such times, therefore, that the law protects him from plugs, but with the true inconsistency of our lawmakers, leaves him completely at the mercy of the man with a minnow. In the minds of a lawmaker there is something sacred about the man who fishes with a minnow, **and it is against** Blackstone and the Ten Commandments to pass a law that will keep him under control.

In due time the eggs hatch and the little bass, so tiny that they are hardly visible to anything except the papa bass, start swimming around. They begin eating at once. They will eat anything smaller than themselves, including their brothers and sisters. This is a habit bass never outgrow. If some of the tiny bass lag behind the others in their growth, they are promptly eaten, thus maintaining the species at its prime level.

Fish hatchery men handling these little fish (which are known as fry) have discovered some strange things about them. For instance, if they put three hundred fry that are hatched out on Friday in a jar with three hundred fry that are hatched the following Monday, in a few hours they will find a grand total of only three hundred fry in the jar. The Monday hatch has all disappeared. This probably demonstrates the evils of being hatched on Monday, as the astrologists **would** perhaps say. This disappearance puzzled hatchery men **for a time,** until they figured out that the bigger fry simply ate the smaller ones, in true bass tradition.

The papa bass follows the mass of fry around, still eating nothing himself. The fry string out in a line from three to ten feet long and a couple of feet across. There might be eight or ten thousand of them, and woe unto any perch or other small fish that would try to make a meal of them while papa bass is on guard. The fry continue growing, and as they grow, they split up into smaller groups. When they split, the papa bass follows the larger mass each time.

This goes on for some time, until finally the paternal urge weakens under the gnawing hunger that cannot be permanently ignored and the general confusion of trying to pick the larger group. When this stage is reached the papa bass just sails into them and lets his hunger assert itself. He gobbles down as many as he can catch.

This is Lesson No. 1 to the little bass, and from then on it's a continued series of lessons, all the same—learning what will eat them and what not to eat.

The bass is the No. 1 fresh water fish of this country because he is found from the frozen lakes of Canada to the mudholes along the Rio Grande and from the swamps of Florida to the rocky ridges of California. Wherever there is a much as a tubful of water that doesn't freeze solid in winter, you will find him. He can stand up and thrive under conditions that will tax the durability of a carp or catfish. And it is nearly impossible to fish out a bass hole.

The bronze back will strike at anything that moves, no matter how dizzy its color or ridiculous its shape. Then again he won't touch anything, no matter if it is handed to him on a silver platter by an expert.

He is strictly an individualist, and has his own ideas about things, these ideas varying from day to day at an alarming pace. These facts contribute to making him the great leveler, and the kingpin of fresh water fish.

I started fishing for bass many years ago, and I used to walk out to the bank of a little lake in front of my home and scare the bass out from the shore, then catch them on a fly rod metal spinner as they swam away. Such fantastic luck can hardly be imagined. Yet I caught them. I would not cast until I saw one run out from the bank. Only a rank dub would have tried it.

I would come home at night and announce that we would breakfast on bass the next morning. Then I would sally forth at dawn and bring them in. I never failed—until years later when I began to absorb all the technique about handling a fly rod, and picked up a few of the expert's tricks in bass fishing.

Now I wouldn't take a fifty-fifty wager that I could catch a bass in a week in any waters I should choose to tackle. I have been chastened and humbled and beaten by this fish for so many years and on so many occasions that I freely and frankly admit I know nothing in the world about him. All I know is that the most fish are caught, ordinarily, by people who shouldn't catch them.

Bass are quite gullible fish until they begin to grow a bit older. Anybody can catch small bass, even an expert. Anybody can catch a bass that has never been caught before. But it takes a rank dub to catch a big, seasoned bass.

I know of one bass in a hatchery that became quite tame. His name was Corky. He would follow the hatchery man around and look at him with a soulful eye, waiting for his food. He would come to get it like a dog. And he learned a lot of tricks. He learned that when anybody walked along the edge of the hatchery bank, they would scare frogs out into the water. So he would swim right along beside them and get his frogs. But unfortunately, a bigger bass ate Corky one day.

I had a bass spotted myself once, and he was practically tame. We were on extremely cordial terms, for I always handled him with great care and released him uninjured after every catch. His name was Charley, and he lived just a short cast from the spot where I kept my boat.

I used to get into the boat and glide away from Charley without disturbing him on the outward trip, then if I had a fairly good day I would leave him alone when I returned. But if everything else went badly, I would drop a plug or a bug or a fly out there and snag Charley at the end of the day. He always responded and always gave me a nice brisk bit of action before I brought him abroad, and then released him to battle again. He was a playful rascal, and would frequently smack the bait with his tail just for the fun of it.

Somebody eventually caught him and fried him. It was one of the sadder moments of my fishing career when I found him dead and gone.

Charley was an exception, for most bass learn quite quickly not to take hold of things with hooks in them. If you want to see how they catch on, drop out to a fish hatchery some day when the hatchery superintendent decides to take out two or three of the fish to look at them.

On the first cast with a bass bug there will be a mad rush of fish for it as it touches the surface, and two or three of the bigger ones will strike at it instantly. Five or six bass will follow their pal to see what is happening to him, or perhaps still hoping for another whack at that bug he robbed them of.

The next cast will bring one or two bass on a dash for the lure. But on the third cast the chances are about fifteen to one the bronze fellows will simply stare at the bug and let it go at that. Likewise the fourth and fifth and seventh and twentieth casts will bring the same indifference. The bass have looked and learned. They are smart enough to see that there is something screwy about a tiny bug manhandling a three-pound bass for five minutes and then jerking him right out of the water.

That is about what happens in the wild and woolly waters.

You go fishing and snag a lot of little fellows, under the legal size limit. You carefully put them back, but they remember those plugs. As they grow they might occasionally slip and hit another plug. But you land only one out of three or four bass that strike, since they have quite a knack of coming out of the water and shaking hooks loose. So the schooling goes on. Those that throw the plug are learning about the ways of Man.

The bass learns what that thing is that you are operating with such nicety up on top of the water, or down in it. You can give the lure all the trick jerks that the book calls for, and still he will only smile as he lies and watches. For he knows.

People devote a vast amount of thought and study and time to working out fishing systems that will trick bass. They go deeply into the science of color combinations, form and movement, and of timing. They try to fathom the mental processes of a bass, and there are anglers who claim they can tell you when a bass strikes whether he is doing so out of anger, or because he is hungry.

They will tell you, "now a bait falling on the water should lie still for perhaps eight or nine seconds, during which time the bass thinks it is dead. Then when you move it gently, the bass concludes it is only wounded, and decides to eat it . . ." and so on.

I have a friend who practically dedicates his life to this sort of thing. And he is only one among hundreds of thousands of bass anglers who have determined to learn all there is about the art.

This friend will cast a floating plug and then count ten seconds. He counts it by his watch, too. Nothing slipshod about him. Then he gives the bait a gentle twitch. He counts ten seconds more and gives it another twitch. Then two seconds and two twitches. Then he works it toward him for about ten feet (the escape approach to bass psychology) and he stops again, this time for five seconds.

He has a regular formula with a dozen or so variations, adaptable to different water and weather conditions. He is an expert.

Yet the two biggest bass ever caught on a fishing trip on which he and I went were hauled into the boat by a fellow we took along on a trip once. This man had done practically no bass fishing or fishing of any kind for that matter.

He tossed out a floating plug and promptly had a backlash. While he sat there in the boat untangling the line a great big bass came up and leisurely swallowed the plug which the little waves were jiggling on top of the water. The fisherman went on about his business of untangling the line, while the bass would leap prodigiously, then make a run here or there. Finally, the fisherman untangled the line and cranked in the big fish.

Not more than a half-hour later he threw the same plug up in a tree. It hooked on a small limb not far from the water and he started jerking to get it loose. After four or five vigorous jerks the bait came loose and slapped down on the water. And a big bass was waiting there for it, gobbling it down the second it hit.

"I seem to have a knack for this," he said.

"Pure skill," we assured him.

Those were the only two decent bass we caught on that trip.

Still my friend, the expert, fishes with his watch, and I give the bait those same pretty little jiggles that make it look so realistic from above.

Once in a while I get to fishing "off guard" and tie into something big. Maybe I'm shifting my feet in the boat, or day dreaming about rivers in far away lands, or chatting about something—entirely forgetful of the bait out there. Meantime I am imparting an entirely different set of wiggles to it—and I am suddenly astonished to find myself fast to a big one.

These continued recurrences of bass catches that do not seem logical force me to the conclusion that they are actually logical.

I have worked out my own theory, which is probably wrong and which doesn't help me much, even though it should be right.

It seems to me that since almost all anglers who really know how to handle their tackle follow rather definite, set methods of working lures, the bass inevitably arrives at the point where he recognizes the lure by these known actions. The bass sees so many phony mice being worked just a certain way—a way that makes them look really good to the man in the boat—that he doesn't fall for the trick any more.

As an old fisherman friend of mine said, the big question is, "How do they look to the fish?"

Well, when a dub takes hold of an outfit, he does things to the bait that are entirely different from the pet series of jerks and retrieves of the good angler. And the dub gets astonishing results at times. He gets the same kind of results that an expert frequently gets when he forgets his fishing and is thinking of something else.

It would seem, then, that the best system for snagging them is a complete absence of system. Just try to do something different every time you cast a bait.

At least that's my theory, and you can take it or leave it.

On top of that you must remember that the bass is the most unpredictable of creatures, and that he will strike when you least expect him to, and behave like a spoiled child when you really are doing some powerful urging. He just refuses to get up and recite his piece at the proper time.

So if you want to fish for Mr. Bass, you simply get hold of an outfit and go out to the water and throw a bait to him. Go out there with an open mind on bass fishing and a headful of dreamy thoughts about some far away South Sea island with a palm tree and maybe a pretty girl on it. When you throw the bait out on the water just amuse yourself by seeing what dizzy things you can make it do.

Whether you take a casting rod outfit, or a fly rod rig, my suggestion to you is to tackle bass fishing without theories, without study, and without much hope. You are more likely then to get game—and if you don't, you still have had a good time.

A SNAKE OF ONE'S OWN

By JOHN STEINBECK

IT WAS ALMOST DARK WHEN YOUNG DR. PHILLIPS SWUNG HIS SACK to his shoulder and left the tide pool. He climbed up over the rocks and squashed along the street in his rubber boots. The street lights were on by the time he arrived at his little commercial laboratory on the cannery street of Monterey. It was a tight little building, standing partly on piers over by the water and partly on the land. On both sides the big corrugated iron sardine canneries crowded in on it.

Dr. Phillips climbed the wooden steps and opened the door. The white rats in their cages scampered up and down the wire, and the captive cats in their pens mewed for milk. Dr. Phillips turned on the glaring light over the dissection table and dumped his clammy sack on the floor. He walked to the glass cages by the window where the rattlesnakes lived, leaned over and looked in.

The snakes were bunched and resting in the corners of the cage, but every head was clear; the dusty eyes seemed to look at nothing, but as the young man leaned over the cage the forked tongues, black on the ends and pink behind, twittered out and waved slowly up and down. Then the snakes recognized the man and pulled in their tongues.

Dr. Phillips threw off his leather coat and built a fire in the tin stove; he set a kettle of water on the stove and dropped a can of beans into the water. Then he stood staring down at the sack on the floor. He was a slight young man with the mild, preoccupied eyes of one who looks through a microscope a great deal. He wore a short blond beard.

The draft ran breathily up the chimney and a glow of warmth came from the stove. The little waves washed quietly about the piles under the building. Arranged on shelves about the room were tier above tier of museum jars containing the mounted marine specimens the laboratory dealt in.

Dr. Phillips opened a side door and went into his bedroom, a book-lined cell containing an army cot, a reading light and an uncomfortable wooden chair. He pulled off his rubber boots and put on a pair of sheepskin slippers. When he went back to the other room the water in the kettle was already beginning to hum.

He lifted his sack to the table under the white light and emptied out two dozen common starfish. These he laid out side by side on the table. His preoccupied eyes turned to the busy rats in the wire cages. Taking grain from a paper sack he poured it into the feeding troughs. Instantly the rats scrambled down from the wire and fell upon the food. A bottle of milk stood on a glass shelf between a small mounted octopus and a jellyfish. Dr. Phillips lifted down the milk and walked to the cat cage, but before he filled the containers he reached in the cage and gently picked out a big rangy alley tabby. He stroked her for a moment and then dropped her in a small black painted box, closed the lid and bolted it and then turned on a petcock which admitted gas into the killing chamber. While the short soft struggle went on in the black box he filled the saucers with milk. One of the cats arched against his hand and he smiled and petted her neck.

The box was quiet now. He turned off the gas for the airtight box would be full of gas.

On the stove the pan of water was bubbling furiously about the can of beans. Dr. Phillips lifted out the can with a big pair of forceps, opened the beans and emptied them into a glass dish. While he ate he watched the starfish on the table. From between the rays little drops of milky fluid were exuding. He bolted his beans and when they were gone he put the dish in the sink and stepped to the equipment cupboard. From this he took a microscope and a pile of little glass dishes. He filled the dishes one by one with sea water from a tap and arranged them in a line beside the starfish. He took out his watch and laid it on the table under the pouring white light. The waves washed with little sighs against the piles under the floor. He took an eyedropper from a drawer and bent over the starfish.

At that moment there were quick soft steps on the wooden stairs and a strong knocking at the door. A slight grimace of annoyance crossed the young man's face as he went to open. A tall lean woman stood in the doorway. She was dressed in a severe dark suit—her straight black hair, growing low on a flat forehead, was mussed as though the wind had been blowing it. Her black eyes glittered in the strong light.

She spoke in a soft throaty voice, "May I come in? I want to talk to you."

"I'm very busy just now," he said half-heartedly. "I have to do things at times." But he stood away from the door. The tall woman slipped in.

"I'll be quiet until you can talk to me."

He closed the door and brought the uncomfortable chair from the bedroom. "You see," he apologized, "the process is started and I must get to it." So many people wandered in and asked questions. He had little routines of explanations for the commoner processes. He could say them without thinking. "Sit here. In a few minutes I'll be able to listen to you."

The tall woman leaned over the table. With the eyedropper the young man gathered fluid from between the rays of the starfish and squirted it into a bowl of water, and then he drew some milky fluid and squirted it in the same bowl and stirred the water gently with the eyedropper. He began his little patter of explanation.

"When starfish are sexually mature they release sperm and ova when they are exposed at low tide. By choosing mature specimens and taking them out of the water, I give them a condition of low tide. Now I've mixed the sperm and eggs. Now I put some of the mixture in each one of these ten watch glasses. In ten minutes I will kill those in the first glass with menthol, twenty minutes later I will kill the second group and then a new group every twenty minutes. Then I will have arrested the process in stages, and I will mount the series on microscope slides for biologic study." He paused. "Would you like to look at this first group under the microscope?"

"No, thank you." He turned quickly to her. People always wanted to look through the glass. She was not looking at the table at all, but at him. Her black eyes were on him but they did not seem to see him. He realized why—the irises were as dark as the pupils, there was no color line between the two. Dr. Phillips was piqued at her answer. Although answering questions bored him, a lack of interest in what he was doing irritated him. A desire to arouse her grew in him.

"While I'm waiting the first ten minutes I have something to do. Some people don't like to see it. Maybe you'd better step into that room until I finish."

"No," she said in her soft flat tone. "Do what you wish. I will wait until you can talk to me." Her hands rested side by side on her lap. She was completely at rest. Her eyes were bright but the rest of her was almost in a state of suspended animation. He thought, "Low metabolic rate, almost as low as a frog's, from the looks." The desire to shock her out of her inanition possessed him again.

He brought a little wooden cradle to the table, laid out scalpels and scissors and rigged a big hollow needle to a pressure tube. Then from the killing chamber he brought the limp dead cat and laid it in the cradle and tied its legs to hooks in the sides. He glanced sidewise at the woman. She had not moved. She was still at rest.

The cat grinned up into the light, its pink tongue stuck out between its needle teeth. Dr. Phillips deftly snipped open the skin at the throat; with a scalpel he slit through and found an artery.

With flawless technique he put the needle in the vessel and tied it in with gut. "Embalming fluid," he explained. "Later I'll inject yellow mass into the venous system and red mass into the arterial system—for blood stream dissection—biology classes."

He looked around at her again. Her dark eyes seemed veiled with dust. She looked without expression at the cat's open throat. Not a drop of blood had escaped. The incision was clean. Dr. Phillips looked at his watch. "Time for the first group." He shook a few crystals of menthol into the first watch glass.

The woman was making him nervous. The rats climbed about on the wire of their cage again and squeaked softly. The waves under the building beat with little shocks on the piles.

The young man shivered. He put a few lumps of coal in the stove and sat down. "Now," he said. "I haven't anything to do for twenty minutes." He noticed how short her chin was between lower lip and point. She seemed to awaken slowly, to come up out of some deep pool of consciousness. Her head raised and her dark dusty eyes moved about the room and then came back to him.

"I was waiting," she said. Her hands remained side by side on her lap. "You have snakes?"

"Why, yes," he said rather loudly. "I have about two dozen

rattlesnakes. I milk out the venom and send it to the anti-venom laboratories."

She continued to look at him but her eyes did not center on him, rather they covered him and seemed to see in a big circle all around him. "Have you a male snake, a male rattlesnake?"

"Well it just happens I know I have. I came in one morning and found a big snake in—in coition with a smaller one. That's very rare in captivity. You see, I do know I have a male snake."

"Where is he?"

"Why right in the glass cage by the window there."

Her head swung slowly around but her two quiet hands did not move. She turned back toward him. "May I see?"

He got up and walked to the case by the window. On the sand bottom the knot of rattlesnakes lay entwined, but their heads were clear. The tongues came out and flickered a moment and then waved up and down feeling the air for vibrations. Dr. Phillips nervously turned his head. The woman was standing beside him. He had not heard her get up from the chair. He had heard only the splash of water among the piles and the scampering of the rats on the wire screen.

She said softly, "Which is the male you spoke of?"

He pointed to a thick, dusty grey snake lying by itself in one corner of the cage. "That one. He's nearly five feet long. He comes from Texas. Our Pacific coast snakes are usually smaller. He's been taking all the rats, too. When I want the others to eat I have to take him out."

The woman stared down at the blunt dry head. The forked tongue slipped out and hung quivering for a long moment. "And you're sure he's a male."

"Rattlesnakes are funny," he said glibly. "Nearly every generalization proves wrong. I don't like to say anything definite about rattlesnakes, but—yes—I can assure you he's a male."

Her eyes did not move from the flat head. "Will you sell him to me?"

"Sell him?" he cried. "Sell him to you?"

"You do sell specimens, don't you?"

"Oh—yes. Of course I do. Of course I do."

"How much? Five dollars? Ten?"

"Oh! Not more than five. But do you know anything about rattlesnakes? You might be bitten."

She looked at him for a moment. "I don't intend to take him. I want to leave him here, but—I want him to be mine. I want to come here and look at him and feed him and to know he's mine." She opened a little purse and took out a five dollar bill. "Here! Now he is mine."

Dr. Phillips began to be afraid. "You could come to look at him without owning him."

"I want him to be mine."

"Oh, Lord!" he cried. "I've forgotten the time." He ran to the table.

"Three minutes over. It won't matter much." He shook menthol crystals into the second watch glass. And then he was drawn back to the cage where the woman still stared at the snake.

She asked, "What does he eat?"

"I feed them white rats, rats from the cage over there."

"Will you put him in the other cage? I want to feed him."

"But he doesn't need food. He's had a rat already this week. Sometimes they don't eat for three or four months. I had one that didn't eat for over a year."

In her low monotone she asked, "Will you sell me a rat?"

He shrugged his shoulders. "I see. You want to watch how rattlesnakes eat. All right. I'll show you. The rat will cost twenty-five cents. It's better than a bull fight if you look at it one way, and it's simply a snake eating his dinner if you look at it another." His tone had become acid. He hated people who made sport of natural processes. He was not a sportsman but a biologist. He could kill a thousand animals for knowledge, but not an insect for pleasure. He'd been over this in his mind before.

She turned her head slowly toward him and the beginning of a smile formed on her thin lips. "I want to feed my snake," she said. "I'll put him in the other cage." She had opened the top of the cage and dipped her hand in before he knew what she was doing. He leaped forward and pulled her back. The lid banged shut.

"Haven't you any sense," he asked fiercely. "Maybe he wouldn't kill you, but he'd make you damned sick in spite of what I could do for you."

"You put him in the other cage then," she said quietly.

Dr. Phillips was shaken. He found that he was avoiding the dark eyes that didn't seem to look at anything.

He felt that it was profoundly wrong to put a rat into the cage, deeply sinful; and he didn't know why. Often he had put rats in the cage when someone or other had wanted to see it, but this desire tonight sickened him. He tried to explain himself out of it. "It's a good thing to see," he said. "It shows you how a snake can work. It makes you have a respect for a rattlesnake. Then, too, lots of people have dreams about the terror of snakes making the kill. I think because it is a subjective rat. The person is the rat. Once you see it the whole mater is objective. The rat is only a rat and the terror is removed."

He took a long stick equipped with a leather noose from the wall. Opening the trap he dropped the noose over the big snake's head and tightened the thong. A piercing dry rattle filled the room.

The thick body writhed and slashed about the handle of the stick as he lifted the snake out and dropped it in the feeding cage. It stood ready to strike for a time, but the buzzing gradually ceased. The snake crawled into a corner, made a big figure eight with its body and lay still.

"You see," the young man explained, "these snakes are quite tame. I've had them a long time. I suppose I could handle them if I wanted to, but everyone who does handle rattlesnakes gets bitten sooner or later. I just don't want to take the chance." He hated to put in the rat. She had moved over in front of the new cage; her black eyes were on the stony head of the snake again.

She said, "Put in a rat."

Reluctantly he went to the rat cage. For some reason he was sorry for the rat, and such a feeling had never come to him before. His eyes went over the mass of swarming white bodies climbing up the screen toward him. "Which one?" he thought. "Which one shall it be?" Suddenly he turned angrily to the woman. "Wouldn't you rather I put in a cat? Then you'd see a real fight. The cat might even win, but if it lost it might kill the snake. I'll sell you a cat if you like."

She didn't look at him. "Put in a rat," she said. "I want him to eat."

He opened the rat cage and thrust his hand in. His fingers found a tail and he lifted a plump, red-eyed rat out of the cage. It struggled up to try to bite his fingers and failing hung spread out and motionless from its tail. He walked quickly across the room, opened the feeding cage and dropped the rat in on the sand floor. "Now, watch it," he cried.

The woman did not answer him. Her eyes were on the snake where it lay still. Its tongue flicking in and out rapidly, tasted the air of the cage.

The rat landed on its feet, turned around and sniffed at its pink naked tail and then unconcernedly trotted across the sand, smelling as it went. The room was silent. Dr. Phillips did not know whether the water sighed among the piles or whether the woman sighed. Out of the corner of his eye he saw her body crouch and stiffen.

The snake moved out smoothly, slowly. The tongue flicked in and out. The motion was so gradual, so smooth that it didn't seem to be motion at all. In the other end of the cage the rat perked up in a sitting position and began to lick down the fine white hair on its chest. The snake moved on, keeping always a deep S curve in its neck.

The silence beat on the young man. He felt the blood drifting up in his body. He said loudly, "See! He keeps the striking curve ready. Rattlesnakes are cautious, almost cowardly animals. The mechanism is so delicate. The snake's dinner is to be got by an operation as deft as a surgeon's job. He takes no chances with his instruments."

The snake had flowed to the middle of the cage by now. The rat looked up, saw the snake and then unconcernedly went back to licking his chest.

"It's the most beautiful thing in the world," the young man said. His veins were throbbing. "It's the most terrible thing in the world."

The snake was close now. Its head lifted a few inches from the sand. The head weaved slowly back and forth, aiming, getting distance, aiming. Dr. Phillips glanced again at the woman. He turned sick. She was weaving too, not much, just a suggestion.

The rat looked up and saw the snake. He dropped to four feet and backed up, and then—the stroke.

It was impossible to see, simply a flash. The rat jarred as though under an invisible blow. The snake backed hurriedly into the cor-

ner from which he had come, and settled down, his tongue working constantly.

"Perfect!" Dr. Phillips cried. "Right between the shoulder blades.
The fangs must almost have reached the heart."

The rat stood still, breathing like a little white bellows. Suddenly he leaped in the air and landed on his side. His legs kicked
spasmodically for a second and he was dead.

The woman relaxed, relaxed sleepily.

"Well," the young man demanded, "it was an emotional bath,
wasn't it?"

She turned her misty eyes to him. "Will he eat it now?" she
asked.

"Of course he'll eat it. He didn't kill it for a thrill. He killed
it because he was hungry."

The corners of the woman's mouth turned up a trifle again. She
looked back at the snake. "I want to see him eat it."

Now the snake came out of his corner again. There was no
striking curve in his neck, but he approached the rat gingerly,
ready to jump back in case it attacked him. He nudged the body
gently with his blunt nose, and drew away.

Satisfied that it was dead, he touched the body all over with
his chin, from head to tail. He seemed to measure it and to kiss it.
Finally he opened his mouth and unhinged his jaws at the corners.

Dr. Phillips put his will against his head to keep it from turning
toward the woman. He thought, "If she's opening her mouth, I'll
be sick. I'll be afraid." He succeeded in keeping his eyes away.

The snake fitted his jaws over the rat's head and then with a
slow peristaltic pulsing, began to engulf the rat. The jaws gripped
and the whole throat crawled up, and the jaws gripped again.

Dr. Phillips turned away and went to his work table. "You've
made me miss one of the series," he said bitterly. "The set won't
be complete." He put one of the watch glasses under a low power
microscope and looked at it, and then angrily he poured the contents of all the dishes into the sink.

The waves had fallen so that only a wet whisper came up through
the floor. The young man lifted a trapdoor at his feet and dropped
the starfish down into the black water. He paused at the cat, crucified in the cradle and grinning comically into the light. Its body was

puffed with embalming fluid. He shut off the pressure, withdrew the needle and tied the vein.

"Would you like some coffee?" he asked.

"No, thank you. I shall be going pretty soon."

He walked to her where she stood in front of the snake cage. The rat was swallowed, all except an inch of pink tail that stuck out of the snake's mouth like a sardonic tongue. The throat heaved again and the tail disappeared. The jaws snapped back into their sockets, and the big snake crawled heavily to the corner, made a big eight and dropped his head on the sand.

"He's asleep now," the woman said. "I'm going now. But I'll come back and feed my snake every little while. I'll pay for the rats. I want him to have plenty. And sometime—I'll take him away with me." Her eyes came out of their dusty dream for a moment. "Remember, he's mine. Don't take his poison. I want him to have it. Good-night." She walked swiftly to the door and went out. He heard her footsteps on the stairs, but he could not hear her walk away on the pavement.

Dr. Phillips turned a chair around and sat down in front of the snake cage. He tried to comb out his thought as he looked at the torpid snake. "I've read so much about psychological sex symbols," he thought. "It doesn't seem to explain. Maybe I'm too much alone. Maybe I should kill the snake. If I knew—no, I can't pray to anything."

For weeks he expected her to return. "I will go out and leave her alone here when she comes," he decided. "I won't see the damned thing again."

She never came again. For months he looked for her when he walked about in the town. Several times he ran after some tall woman thinking it might be she. But he never saw her again—ever.

AN ADVENTURER RETIRES

By HILAIRE DU BERRIER

THE PEOPLE WHO PUBLISH "ADVENTURE MAGAZINES" AND WRITE THE scenarios for Gary Cooper's films, may Allah spit on their upturned faces as they pray.

To you who sigh while Ronald Colman leads a cavalry charge across some foreign plain or swaggers, uniformed, through a market place where the camels wear bells and a muezzin comes out on a minaret calling true believers to their prayers, I'll tell you something:

Ronald and Gary get paid for acting that stuff but adventurers get in trouble for doing it.

Messrs. Cooper and Colman and Gable show you the end as it isn't, and when his day's work is over Mr. Colman leaves the "papier-mâché" setting that represents the bombed town we were in or the port where we had fever.

He washes his make-up off and goes back to a fine home in Beverly Hills and wonders whether to toss off a cocktail alone or spend another buck and invite someone to have one with him.

That's adventure as it ought to be, but I'll tell you something about it as it is; it's learning to speak ten languages but to say: "I am happy," in none of them.

It's having every meal come as a pleasant surprise. It's loneliness and worry and a lousy life. It's ending up in cursed little ports of heat with a fever and beard and ragged shoes and no money.

When you had money you threw it away on anyone that would have a drink with you, and when you haven't there's no one around to say: "Come on, old horse, and sit down."

The end of most every adventure is in some port that you can't get out of, in a room that you can't pay the rent on, looking at a book of pictures and a couple of medals, and using Black Flag for talcum powder.

I used to think adventure was being a dashing young man with

639

a grin on his face who rode through life, figuratively speaking, singing a song and throwing a sword in the air. I thought it was following armies into a captured town and looking on workaday men as crusaders looked on a peasant.

Also I thought it was whispers and moonlight and green palm trees and blue seas and dark places and promises and one woman whose eyes would sparkle like the flash of sunlight on bayonets, but it wasn't.

Adventure is waiting in some God-awful land for a Negro or a Chinaman or a Rumanian to get ready to see you and then waiting for your pay or your contract or a battle or a chance to get out.

The one thing in a war you never learn is the joy of sacking a captured town, or marching in with the drums rolling and tanks roaring up and down the streets, because if there's a chance of capturing any towns it's a certainty they won't be hiring you.

Your only experience along that line will be taking a last look at some place you've become attached to and smashing everything you can't take with you before you pull out.

Every town you leave that way you'll look back at and remark that it never looked beautiful before and you'll never get a chance to look at it again. In a few days the retreat will become a rout and when the show is over you'll never dare come back.

Aside from a few men like himself a soldier of fortune has no friends. When they leave a war the group scatters to live as best they can till they meet at the next one, maybe on the same side and maybe not.

Other men talk "shop" when they get together, and a soldier of fortune can't talk their shop; he's a rank outsider.

American consuls and respectable workaday citizens despise him. Never tell them you knew Wehib Pasha when he was pushing Graziani back down along the Webbi-Shebelli or that you have seen all those ports on the posters of where ships go.

They think you haven't any right to have been there and will hate you for having cheated them, or else they'll call you a bloody liar and say "Adventurer" in a different tone than they reserve for Ronald Colman and Errol Flynn.

There is a story about an American who was captured and condemned to be shot in South America, so he sent for his consul and said: "For God's sake do something; telephone Washington, cable the President—do something for me!" And the consul said: "Now, see here, old chap; what do you want to bother the State Department about this for?"

Don't let anyone tell you women are romantic and will be won by the stories you bring back from the far places. Security is the only State adventurers never know and that's the only one women want to live in.

When I close my eyes I think of that sweltering cargo boat plowing through heat and the Red Sea on the way to Abyssinia.

Frenchmen, Arabs, Greeks, Armenians, a Pole, some Swiss, a couple of Negroes, and God only knows what else were off with high spirits to where the papers said a war was going to be. They were the merriest bunch of fighting, spitting, swearing, drinking, bottle-smashing cutthroats a man could meet.

A bearded French colonial spit contemptuously at a fish and said: "A whole shipload going to Abyssinia and not a lifeboat full will come back," but no one gave a damn. Every man thought he was going to be in the lifeboat and what might happen to the others didn't matter.

Two men died on the way—*mais tant pis;*—someone has to die.

In Abyssinia we ate eggs that smelled and drank milk from a cow that was sick. Our cook boy had syphilis and when we lifted our eyes from our food they fell on a leper, but it was better than Monte Carlo.

This is typical adventure; you live like a native for eleven months and stick your money in the Bank of Ethiopia, saving silver thalers so you can go back to a little village in central France where you left your books and a paint box, and the next thing you know you find yourself in Djibouti.

With a sun-burnt curve of sea front before you and the Somaliland desert behind, you sit down to think it over. When the Italians arrived in Addis Ababa they took the bank.

The charred hulk of a French liner, half-submerged, sticks out of the water like a grim memorial to disaster. Haile Selassie passed it when he left that port for the last time.

You get fever in Djibouti but you haven't the price of quinine, and quinine is the rent you pay on life.

There's a telegraph office but they don't send telegrams collect. Mail leaves twice a month.

You live in an Arab's house and day after day you watch the waterfront shimmer in the heat with the Belgian officers who are stranded with you and remark that Djibouti is the home of derelicts.

The decayed boats fall to pieces along the beach and waves wash through the ribs of a rotting Arab dhow in the shallows. You wonder if you could make that dhow float before your letter comes.

You get thin in the heat and can't eat or sleep or bother to shave or even wash, and when the fever comes you think you're looking at the world through the "prop" of a pursuit job again.

Then something gets in your eyes and your eyes get sick, but a bottle of Optraex costs fifteen francs—and you're an adventurer waiting for a letter, you're not Dick Halliburton.

When you get in trouble in a strange land there's nothing to do but wait or connive your way out as best you can. If you go to your consulate you'll have to get yourself out anyway, plus some more trouble for having bothered the consul, so you go down to the brothel for the French army instead where you know you'll get sympathy and a café-turk even if you haven't fifteen francs.

You may even get the loan of a hundred-franc-note in the French brothel.

I think the third republic must have been paying those women, because everyone I knew borrowed from them. They didn't seem like prostitutes; they were old comrades:

Twice a month a white boat came for a day and you watched it sail off with tears in your eyes; then you went to the *bureau de poste* to see if you had a letter.

If the day happened to be Sunday they opened the *poste* anyway. What the hell! Little Madame Beau and the man with the handle-bar mustache hadn't had anything to do for two weeks except play with the pet lion they had chained to the door. Lieutenant Duguy used to wet postage stamps on the lion's tongue.

From the post office everyone went into seclusion to read their mail. The riff-raff went to Riga's hotel and the elite went to the honky-tonk.

The girls knew what you were expecting in the post and who from; they knew everyone's business, and they could tell by your face whether it came or not. If it didn't they said: "Better luck on the next boat," and gave you their *L'Illustration* to read.

When the letter eventually came you gave them the stamps.

The tables and seats in that co-educational center were set in concrete so the soldiers couldn't throw them at each other. The beer was warm because Docteur Huchon said iced drinks would give you dysentery. A black boy sat on the floor and pulled a cord to swing the mat-fans suspended from the ceiling, and every half-hour he tossed a bucket of water across the cement floor to cool it off.

Bearded soldiers, dirty Somalis, turbaned Arabs, the foreign community, and Madame learned to lift their feet unconsciously and let the tidal wave with its fleet of match boxes, cigarette butts, burnt matches, and crumpled packages of Gitane-bleu sail under and then put their feet down again without taking their eyes from a last month's *Paris-soir*. I'll be damned if I call that adventure.

Out of desperation you hook up with a Cherif from Yemen. The Imam is building up an army of sorts, and the Cherif takes you to Hodeidah.

Hodeidah is pretty bad too, but it's also better than Monte Carlo. Instead of kissing fat ladies' hands for tea you kiss the Koran, and the Koran can't talk.

Just about the time you forget what the taste of ice and the face of a woman is like a military mission of Italians comes in to work for nothing and you find out you're going to get your pay in Paradise. *C'est l'aventure, mes amis. Que voulez-vous?*

You reach Port Said on the deck of a freighter and the British Intelligence Officer who comes aboard treats you like a Prince, a launch at your service and everything. It's a pleasure to help a man like that.

When you reach Alexandria you're a bloody adventurer and probably a spy—and you can't get off. All of your life will be like that.

In Greece you don't click, so you go to Turkey. Turkey has gone nationalist too. They don't trust you and wouldn't want you if they did, but you meet a lovely lady on the boat.

After the months in Abyssinia and Somaliland and Yemen your heart is hungry and that woman tosses a hand-grenade in your scheme of things. She comes into your life like spring to a barefoot army. To change her annexation to *de jure* from *de facto*, you ask her to marry you.

It's time to be serious now. No more flying out in bombers to shake night up like a cocktail, or running across the map to the places where wars are and color and noise and boasting and the variousness of adventure. You're going to get married and have a little boy and play with electric trains.

It's going to make you dull in time and narrow of vision. It's the road that leads to a job in an office, but it's worth it for that woman.

And you know what she says? She says: "Marry you, Hal? I wouldn't marry you if you were the last man on earth, but I'll tell you what I will do. I'll go to Bucharest and Budapest and Vienna with you."

Arm in arm you lean over a ship's side and watch Istanbul, like a water-color frontispiece from *Arabian Nights*, disappearing in the distance.

There is sunlight on the water and sunlight on the minarets. There must be a million minarets all straight and white and slender, shimmering in the light and pointing straight to Allah. Life is all poetry and color and one woman and many minarets. The beauty of it makes you feel your heart has just taken a bath and become clean again, like the Caaba stone on the Day of Judgment.

Adventure is months of loneliness with sometimes the loan of a few days of beauty. The stories you tell in the cafés when it's all over are only the highlights with the long months sifted out.

The next consul you meet has something to say about immoral young ne'er-do-wells who live with women they aren't married to. He'd be jealous if you lived with a goldfish.

Eventually a day comes when the end of your money is in sight again and the lovely lady of a little while throws a kiss from a train window and then the train pulls out. You wander back to a hotel room suddenly gone all empty.

From it you go to a coffee house gone all empty too. Life has become like an evacuated town and its streets are silent.

A revolution starts in Spain and you pack your bags. The lady marries a lawyer and goes to adventure films in the movies.

The first side you try won't have you because Italians are running the show and they have your name on the list, from Abyssinia, so you shrug your shoulders and join the other. At best a soldier of fortune is only a military prostitute, until he becomes a General or gets the Legion of Honor.

As soon as you get yourself in you start thinking of your friends and remember how George cabled you twenty pounds when you were broke in Geneva, so now you repay the favor by getting George in with you.

Two weeks later when you bury George, Hugh says casually: "Thank God we won't have jittering-George with us to put me in a state of chronic nerves anymore."

Spain gets you down. Every street is no man's land when someone is likely to pick you off from a window. You never know who the enemy is or where. The Russians will try to get you shot to strengthen their own position and some *agent provocateur* will try it so he can collect on you.

If you go home with a senorita you are likely to get your throat cut, and if you make a forced landing behind the enemy lines you are sure to get it cut, but that's all right. You don't expect a war to be Utopia.

However one day your plane crashes and the anarchists want to shoot you for sabotage. That's the end.

When you get out of Spain you find the globe has suddenly become smaller. You can't go to Italy or Germany now. You've worked for the Reds in Spain so none of the Balkan kingdoms will have you. Portugal will take your finger prints if you go there, and if you go to Austria you'll be shadowed.

An American military attaché and his assistant become friendly. They're fine fellows and you like them, but when you get through telling them all about the anti-aircraft fire in Spain they assign an informer to find out if you are up to anything new, and you find yourself in trouble for knowing what you told them. You can't win!

Somehow you don't mind the breach of friendship and the lack of faith that puts you on the "outside," but you do feel insulted that they belittle your intelligence by assigning such a dumb informer to report on you; only a lieutenant too.

In the eyes of your countrymen if you don't work you aren't respectable. Your consulates regard you as an undesirable who is likely to cause them a lot of writing and ruin some bridge games someday. You are never a potential friend who may be able to help them.

The man who is a pariah and an outcast in the eyes of his countrymen becomes a dangerous international character in the eyes of the authorities of whatever country he is traveling in. Your passport has too many stamps and visas. Obviously you are a master mind serving Paris or Rome or Berlin or Moscow, depending on what country you are in.

They make inquiries at your consulate and the reply is almost sure to plant you in the enemy camp. Why is it our officials abroad are so quick to remember a man's obligations to his country and so sure to forget a country's obligation to a man; that as long as a man is honest and labors to acquire respect and position even though it is in another land in an unconventional manner it is his country's obligation to at least not harm him? Besides, it's poor business. Anything should be better than having him on relief.

You try working for an African potentate for awhile and you decide to leave that job for Hubert Julian. One phase of your work is being photographed in uniform with "the Prince." These pictures are captioned: "His Highness, the Nawaub, and Chief-of-Staff, in London," and sent back to Africa to convince his wife's family that he is busy.

That Nawaub trusted no one. If he sent you on a mission he sent someone else to watch you and another man to watch your watcher.

He never told you what all the mysterious conferences were about until he got in trouble; then he sent you to get him out, and you never knew what "deal" he was transacting on the side until someone had sold him a gold brick and he would call on you to try to get his money back.

Whenever he went out in public you went along to give him face, and at first you would try to give the impression he was "your man" when people stared at you. That never worked. He was a tall Negro, straight as a ramrod and with the air of one who is accustomed to command.

He could stand up and look an English butler right in the eye. Best thing to do when he insisted on going into exclusive restaurants with you was address him as Your Highness, loud enough for everyone to hear. That pleased him, satisfied the head waiter and excused you.

A hundred pounds was nothing if he felt like giving a small party, but to get your pay you had to sell him a brass crown studded with red and green glass, that you found in a theatrical costumer's window.

From being Chief-of-Staff, Military Adviser, and Chief of Protocol to H. H., the Nawaub of T——, you drift into the most logical business for a soldier of fortune at large. It's the arms and munitions game.

A true soldier loves a gun as an Arab loves a horse. It's a pleasure to talk guns and touch guns. Guns are power. They are the bricks empires were built with, but don't let Senator Nye deceive you into thinking there is big money or easy money selling them.

To get votes you have to fight something. Big Bill Thompson picked on the King of England and Hitler baited the Jews. Mussolini attacked the savages, and there weren't any other windmills left for Senator Nye. Besides, they don't make guns in North Dakota.

Since Nye and Cordell Hull put Skoda and Schwartzlauser and Vickers on their feet and left the Mauser market to the little countries with cheap money and peasant labor you have to wait months in a hotel lobby; you have to bribe, lie, drink, talk and give dinners to close a small deal at one per cent profit.

A Jew in Anvers is buying your guns and swears they're for some little banana country in South America, so you present his papers and apply for the permit of exportation.

Someone in the war office finds out the papers are faked and the guns are destined for Spain. Someone else gets the profit and you clear out for China.

China is the dream of every soldier of fortune who hasn't been there.

Every stranger who arrives in China is regarded as either an adventurer or a missionary, except Mrs. Harkness. She comes to chase baby pandas and she's a business woman.

If you say you're an aviator looking for a job, Bert Hall's reputation still packs enough wallop to knock you colder than a mother-in-law's kiss, but that's nothing against Bert—in China.

It's a mystery why the American Consulate goes to such expense and trouble checking up on new arrivals in the Orient without doing anything to check up on the Russians they send out to do the checking.

Climbing into the pale of respectability in Shanghai is like trying to crowd into a lifeboat that's already full, with someone from the Treasury Department, or another department, waiting to hit you over the head with an oar.

In all fairness to everyone, it's very logical. I'm not telling you this to complain; I'm only telling you to forget adventure and be a mug. Get a job that works you so hard and pays so little no one will envy you; then you'll be okay. If you wander beyond your own horizon you'll be a "black sheep" in the next one.

The men who control American business in Shanghai are old-timers and most of them have a history that has both B. O. and halitosis, but now they are figures in the community and are rated by their race horses.

A new-comer has first to overcome the whispering campaign that he is in the dope business, if he's a business man, and a spy, if he is trying to sell military equipment or work for the government.

Within a week the rickshaw coolies in front of the Cathay are saying: "Look out for that guy. The American consulate is watching him."

An official, when asked about an exporter who is trying to "break in," says: "We haven't anything on him yet, but give us some time. He'll end badly." And so our national prestige stays where we put it.

No one has to worry about the soldier of fortune who gets a job with the Chinese government. He won't last. The man above him will be a returned student who has been waiting for this chance and the men below him will be Chinese who consider it a loss of face to accept any advice from a foreigner. The two put the screws to the man in the middle.

The man in the consulate who furnishes your reference makes about one-third the pay of a third-rate aviator, and the Russian who furnishes him with his information knows what to furnish and how much if he wants to keep having his expense accounts okay'd.

You figure out the answer.

If you go to Paradise you're lucky you won't need a passport. The British would probably go in for nothing, but you would have to buy a visa, and then when you got it you'd get your book stamped: "Not good for travel in Heaven."

I give up! China or Chile, the end is the same. There's always something.

Prometheus was an adventurer. He didn't want to live as other men, so he started a revolution in his way. He revolted against drabness and darkness and the monotony of things as they were.

What happened to Prometheus for longing for color and warmth and fire happens to all of us.

I've had enough! I'm going to leave dash and color and romance to Carl Laemmle's war-scarred towns with a soda fountain and a damned good restaurant behind them.

There's a little village in the Alps Maritimes where the mayor wears blue pants with patches on the knees, and red wine is a franc and a half a bottle. Maybe I can be a **gendarme**.

Sure, it's been a great show, **going** to bed in one capital and waking up in another. When Generals sent for me I never knew whether it was to give me a decoration or have me shot.

In less than two years I was under fire in three wars, in three countries, on three continents. There were soldiers marching and planes falling and guns pounding away at little white towns, but there was only one short space of happiness and contentment.

I've almost forgotten what it was like, standing on the balcony of the Grand Geubi, watching the little Emperor send his armies out.

The night Franco moved his Moors up to the gates of Madrid and captured the streetcar terminus seems like a crazy dream now, and the day P. Y. Wong called me in his office, up in Hankow, and sacked me under charge of espionage seems pure flattery to my importance and doesn't matter.

All the memories and cities and strange places were wasted because there isn't anyone now to whom I can say: "Do you remember?"

Back in Paris the old friends linger over coffee and liqueurs and amuse the friends with the stories. When the stories are finished they call for their hats and sticks and gloves and go out in the night and home. My home is in the café, and when I leave I go out in the night.

It's been a fine show, for everyone but me!

Now I'd like a job as a lighthouse keeper somewhere where it's warm, or a night watchman some place where the light isn't too bad for reading.

When I was young I prayed: "Give me a short life in the saddle, Allah; not a long life by the fire!" But Allah is wise. Allah O akbar!

THE SCENT OF FEAR

By Jack Melville

FEAR OR PANIC CAUSED BY FEAR IS RESPONSIBLE FOR AT LEAST NINETY per cent of all accidents. This is particularly true of such accidents as occur in the Great Outdoors. Frequently we pick up a newspaper and read of someone lost in the forest who died of exposure or starvation or both. Do you know—it is very doubtful if one out of a thousand of these people actually died of either exposure or starvation? They died of FEAR that these things would happen to them. There is a vast difference between the actuality and the fear of it. Let us take the case of those people who have presumably starved to death while lost in the woods. In most cases they have passed on in less than two weeks, and yet—how about that great colored heavyweight fighter, Harry Wills?

Years ago Wills was a jockey. Every year he went to Hot Springs and fasted for thirty-one days in March to keep his weight down. Later, when he entered the fight game, he continued his yearly fast to help him keep in condition. Now, retired from the ring, he still does his thirty-one day fast in March JUST BECAUSE IT MAKES HIM FEEL SO GOOD. Or how about the great Irish leader, Terrance McSweeny, Lord Mayor of Cork. In 1924, he fasted for twenty-four days on a hunger strike, and again starting September, 1934, he held a hunger-strike fast for the astounding time of seventy-five days. Everyone has heard of Mahatma Ghandi and the different times he has fasted for almost unbelievable periods of time. These men were NOT AFRAID OF STARVING. People who are lost in the woods become frightened and then panicky because they think they are starving to death. They think this so hard they give up fighting, lose control of themselves and then the dread becomes a reality.

It is strange what people will do when they discover they are lost. Take the first time I was lost as an example. I was about four-teen or fifteen years old at the time and living at Sault Ste. Marie,

Michigan. In November I went hunting deer at a little place called Dollarville, some fifty miles west of the Sault. This particular day I left our hunting camp at the railroad before daylight and headed north. There were a couple of feet of snow on the ground and light snow was falling as I left the railroad. As the morning advanced the snow came faster and faster. A north wind came up that drove the snow before it in great clouds. Before I realized what was happening I was in the middle of a real blizzard. It behooved me to forget deer hunting and find my way back to shelter. Then, to my dismay, I suddenly discovered that in the blinding swirl of the storm I had lost all sense of direction. For a while I was so frightened at what might happen to me that I had a first-class case of panic. Blindly I started to run as fast as I could in the direction I thought might be toward home. The more I ran the more panicky I became. I suddenly stumbled upon a snowshoe trail of someone who was going the same way I was. I rushed along this trail. In a little while I came to a place where the trail I was following joined another very faint trail made by snowshoes. This trail was all but obliterated by windswept snow. Two other men out in this unsettled wilderness ahead of me and going the same way I was? Impossible! I had been traveling in a circle! I dropped in the snow overcome by sheer exhaustion and the horror of my predicament.

As I lay gasping for breath I remembered one of my father's pet warnings. Many times he had said to me, "Son, if you ever get lost, first thing to do is to sit down quietly and *know you're all right.* Then think over where your back trail is, in what direction you were headed when you started out and what you did as you went along. If it all comes back to you in good shape—why, start out quietly and backtrack. If it doesn't seem clear, then stay where you are and build a fire with lots of smoke. You will be found in plenty of time. Above all, Son, remember there is nothing to fear."

I suddenly realized that I had been acting like a perfect fool. I got rather shakily to my feet, adjusted my snowshoes which had become loose, found an old stump, dusted the snow off it and sat down. Quietly I tried to figure out exactly where I was. My wanderings had covered every point of the compass but I knew I was north of the railroad and also that I should be south of the Tehquamenon River. So far so good. It was impossible to backtrack on the snowshoe trail. It was snowing so hard that the trail of an hour ago was completely out of sight. I had no compass and there was no sun. By the time all this had passed through my mind it was nearly three o'clock in the afternoon. Black darkness was less than an hour away. My decision was to stay right where I was for the night. It would be easy to obtain my directions from the sun the next morning.

I dropped a small spruce tree with my belt axe. Quickly I built a lean-to, made a bough bed in its shelter, gathered plenty of firewood and built a good fire. Before dark I was as comfortable as a bug in a rug. In spite of the fact that the temperature was far below zero I had a very decent night's sleep.

Next morning the blizzard had let up considerably. There was no sun but, by placing the point of my knife blade on my thumb nail I could see a faint shadow pointing, I knew at that time in the morning, to the northwest. Knowing my directions, it was not difficult to find my way home. I had carried no food with me on that hunt as I had planned to be away for the day only. If reason had not come to my rescue I could easily have become more and more panic-stricken until all sense left me. Remember, that particular stretch of woods I was in was of dense spruce coverage, without any outstanding landmarks and was at least a hundred miles long by fifty wide. Plenty of room to wander for weeks without finding the way to safety.

So many people who go into places where wild life still abounds are fearful of being attacked by wolves. For a number of years I was an official wolf trapper for Algonquin Park, Ontario. Many times the question has been asked me, "Will wolves attack human beings?" The answer is, "No, they will not." The newspaper, the Sault Ste. Marie, Ontario, *Star,* has a standing reward of one hundred dollars for anyone who brings in an authentic story of a human being attacked by wolves. This reward has been in effect for at least thirty years that I personally know about without ever having to be paid. The Canadian Government had a commission, which for a number of years made a careful investigation of all stories of such attacks and has yet to find one that is authentic. Personally, I have had many experiences with wolves under various circumstances. One of the most common fallacies is that it is almost sure death to meet a wolf or wolf pack on the ice of a lake in a storm, but in January, 1929, I had the following experience. That morning I had started across Lake Traverse in a blinding blizzard. My lead dog, Chico, followed close to my heels. My parka hood was pulled far out over my face, leaving a small opening to see through. Suddenly Chico crouched beside me snarling, whining and showing a brave front to real fear. I threw back my hood and found that I had walked into the middle of a large pack of wolves. The closest was not over seventy-five yards away. I did not have a weapon of any sort and did not need one. Those wolves were far more frightened of me than I was of them and they certainly cleared out in a hurry. Exceptionally deep snows that year had made food very scarce and these wolves were nearly famished.

Except, perhaps, for the larger members of the bear family, such as the brown, polar and grizzly, I know of no animals in North America that will molest anyone unless molested first by that person. I have great doubts that even the larger bears will go out of their way to trouble human beings. There really is no cause for fear of animals day or night.

Speaking of fear of animals brings up an interesting question. Why is it that a mother wolf or deer, or in fact almost any wilderness mother, when she hears or smells danger approaching, will quickly hide her young and run away?

Again we come to that little word that plays such an important part in our lives—Fear. When an animal or human being is frightened the body gives off a very strong odor that is exceedingly irritating to other animals. These forest mothers know that when they are frightened FEAR-SCENT will betray their hiding place. They also know that their babies are too young to be frightened and therefore do not have any fear-scent. That is the reason they hide their young and then away they run, leaving a heavy fear-scent trail for their enemy to follow. They really are not cowardly but offer themselves as decoys in order to protect their young.

Perhaps this little story will illustrate what I mean when I say that forest babies do not have fear-scent. One bright, warm day in early spring I was riding my pony back to my cabin from White Partridge Lake. Trotting ahead of me were several of my half-wolf sled dogs. On either side trotted several others while in the rear were more, some ten or twelve altogether. What breeze there was blew directly into our faces. We were ascending a long, easy grade up a sand hill. The ground on either side of the road was covered with ground pine and moss. I was riding along singing and talking to the dogs when suddenly I looked down at the ground right beside my pony and my heart almost stopped beating. Without a sound I dove headlong out of the saddle right on top of a tiny fawn, gathered him up in my arms and was back in the saddle before those wolf-dogs knew what it was all about. Wolf-dogs have about as keen a sense of smell as any animal living and yet five or six of them had passed within less than three feet of that fawn without scenting it. The fawn was too young to realize fear.

It is that fear-scent which causes dogs to attack people who seemingly have not molested them. One of my best friends up North was a little, hard-boiled French Canadian by name of Frank. He was one of the Rangers and a grand trail companion. When I first knew Frank there was only one thing in heaven or earth he was afraid of and that was a dog. He would walk a hundred yard half-circle to keep away from the dog kennels as he came into camp, and of all the dogs he feared Chico most. Chico was my team leader, one-quarter husky and three-quarters timber wolf. He was, also, my favorite dog and as such had the run of the place. Of course Chico caught the fear-scent and would go for Frank every time he saw him and try to tear him to pieces. Frank would drop his gun and run for the nearest tree. For about six months this state of affairs went on until Frank gradually became accustomed to Chico and, I guess, the dog became accustomed to Frank. Slowly, as Frank's fear-scent lessened, friendship grew up between them. I'll admit it took almost a year, but at the end of that time, while he still feared other dogs, Frank liked Chico pretty well. Chico returned Frank's friendship.

One day Frank was coming through the woods trail headed for my cabin. He had almost reached it when, suddenly, without warning, two of my meanest wolf-dogs, who had broken loose from the kennels, leaped out of the brush at his throat and pulled him to the ground. He struck out blindly but had no chance against those wild, snarling huskies. It surely looked as if his fear of dogs had been a premonition and that the end had come. Then came a crashing in the bushes and seemingly out of nowhere flashed Chico like a streak of light and lit squarely in the middle of the fight, slashing right and left, fangs tearing at throats and thighs. He was a hundred pounds of fighting fury gone mad. That scrap didn't last long. In a minute both of Frank's attackers were in full flight. Strange as it may seem, from that mixup Frank lost all sense of fear of dogs. Chico's defense of him made so great an impression that he found belief and trust that practically worked a miracle. It is interesting to note that Frank now has a fine dog team of his own and some of the dogs were noted bad actors before he acquired them.

For many years I raised, trained and raced sled dogs. After much experimenting and spoiling many good dogs by bad methods I, at last, found that a dog will respond quickly both in friendship and in training when he is approached without fear. Make no mistake there. A dog cannot be bluffed. No one can fool him for a minute who approaches him with a fearless exterior and a quaking heart. A person in that condition gives off fear-scent in great quantities. God gave man dominion over all animals. Why not use that God-given right? Actually root out all sense of fear before approaching a dog, or any animal for that matter, then with quiet, gentle firmness proceed with his training. You will be surprised at the results. All animals hate fear-scent.

Several years ago I spent one day in Ottawa. I had come down from my cabin at Traverse on business and was driving back that evening. In the late afternoon I found time to pay a quick visit to a friend of mine who had a team of racing huskies. While we were at his kennels I noticed a large cage, some six by eight feet, set off by itself. Peering into its dark recesses I first saw two green, glaring eyes. Gradually, as my own eyes became accustomed to the darkness, I made out the form of a young timber wolf, eight or nine months old, crouched in the farthermost and darkest corner.

"Where in heaven's name did you pick her up?" I asked my friend.

"Oh," he replied. "A friend of mine gave her to me about six months ago. He thought I could use her for breeding purposes. It's no go, though, for I can't tame her. She's wild as a coot. Don't seem to be able to knock any sense into her head at all."

I looked at her fine, well-shaped head. Her eyes, in spite of the expression of terror, showed a longing for understanding. It was my good luck that made me know she was worthwhile. I heard myself saying, "By Jove, I sure wish she was mine. I could use her to real advantage."

My friend grinned at me. "You're welcome to her," he said, "if you can handle her but you'll have to prove it before you can take her away."

"You're on," I said. "Please leave me absolutely alone with her for an hour or so and then come back."

As soon as he had gone I studied the wolf carefully from the outside of the cage. She was a frightened little thing. I worked myself into the mental condition where I not only had no fear of her but felt sorry for her, loved her and wanted her friendship. Then I sat down and leaned my back against the heavy screen of the cage door and started singing softly to myself in a monotone. That is one of the quickest and most successful ways to lull fear and establish friendly relationship with any animal you wish to tame. In about ten minutes I got up, opened the cage door and stepped inside. Slowly I sat down near the door with my back to the wall, humming all the time and seemingly, not paying any attention to the cringing animal whose burning, fear-filled eyes never wavered in their continuous glaring at me.

Softly I kept on humming, careful to pay her no attention. Every few minutes I edged a little closer to her. When I was only about three feet from where she crouched, I spoke softly to her in a monotone. It really did not matter what I said as long as my voice showed sincere friendliness and had no trace of fear in it.

It took me over a half-hour of slow edging along that floor before I arrived close enough to touch her, or what is more to the point, for her to reach me. Still half-humming, half-talking to her, I sat perfectly still for a while. Then slowly I reached out my hand in front of her nose, then over her head and let my fingers rub her just behind the ears—where dogs love to be rubbed. At my first touch she cringed and trembled, wrinkled her nose, but made no move to bite me. The rubbing continued for a minute or two and then slowly I took my hand away.

I repeated this caress again and again. Then I rubbed her forehead, nose and back, humming to myself as I worked. The fear glaze in her eyes gradually gave way to a look of doubt, then wonder, as understanding began to dawn. At last she allowed her head to rest on my knee. Her trembling stopped and she snuggled closer.

Her eyes closed as, with an almost human sigh, she relaxed her body against mine, just like a little child who yearned for love and understanding from someone she could trust. For some time we sat there together.

I was so interested in this new and fascinating friendship that I did not notice my friend approaching until I heard him exclaim, "Well, I'll be a son of a river hog." At his first words, the wolf, startled, sprang to her feet and sank her teeth into my arm in a swift, slashing rip. Naturally she was on the defensive and, in her terror, attacked the thing closest to her. That happened to be me. Luckily I had on a heavy coat but even at that it was mighty painful.

"Easy, girl—steady—it's all right, pet," I managed to say quietly and then told my friend to get away from us and stay. He had done enough damage. The wolf, trembling, crouched in the far corner of the cage, expecting man-made punishment which was the only treatment she had known in her short time in captivity. I realized how futile such punishment would be and so, talking to her softly, I gradually moved over beside her again. It was more than twenty minutes later that her head once more rested on my knee. I sat there for a while, then, with a brisk ruffling of her shaggy fur, got to my feet and walked out of the cage.

From my friend I procured a dog collar and short leash. Without difficulty I placed the collar around the wolf's neck and led her to the little roadster. My friend drove me back to my cabin. That night we traveled over a hundred and fifty miles with the wolf sitting on the floor of the car, her head, most of the time, resting on my knee. She wore no muzzle nor was there any need for one. It was but a few weeks before she was my shadow and slept across the foot of my bed at night. All this would have been utterly impossible if, at any time, my voice or manner had showed one iota of fear or even if I had entertained any thought that would cause fear-scent.

When my son was three years old he had an old southern Negress as a nurse. One of her favorite methods of punishing him when he was naughty and his mother and I were not around was to lock him in a dark closet. She told him that the goblins who inhabited the darkness would get him if he so much as peeped. This punishment planted and fostered an unreasoning fear of the dark that, as time went on, became a very terrible complex which continued

long after we rooted out the cause and removed "Mammy." When
he was ten years old I took him with me to the big woods of
Canada to live. It was a new life and environment. In daytime or
in the lamplight of the cabin he was happy and absolutely fearless
and loved his new life dearly. At night in the darkness of the forest
he suffered terrible tortures from fear. He not only had his goblins,
witches and other denizens of darkness to worry about but also our
actual wild animal neighbors such as wolves, bears, etc. In vain I
tried to show him that in reality there was nothing to harm him or
to be afraid of. The teachings of the old Negress were too deeply
rooted, seemingly, to ever be eradicated.

At last a plan came to my mind that seemed as though it might
be a solution to the problem. About fifty feet from the kitchen
door was the woodpile. Purposely I waited until well after dark to
fill the woodbox. Then, Son carrying the lantern, we went together to bring in the next day's supply of wood. At the end of
each trip I would laughingly remind him that there was nothing to
be afraid of at the woodpile. After a few weeks I dared him to go
with me but leave the lantern behind. His teeth chattered from
fear—but he went. From then on we worked in the dark for weeks
until he found out that there really was nothing to fear. Every
little woods noise we investigated thoroughly so that he would
learn to read from the sound exactly what made it and why. At
last came the time when he went alone to the woodpile and brought
back his load. I'll admit he made a very quick trip but we were
both mighty proud of that feat. After that first trip alone he never
again let me help him fill the woodbox and he always worked at
night. He found that his fear of the dark was without foundation.
By the time he had reached the age of twelve he had entirely overcome the darkness complex and was going on canoe cruises of
from two days to three weeks duration, alone, sleeping out under
the stars, miles from anyone.

All the terrible menace his frightened young mind conjured out
of darkness had been very real to him. Only through the continual
contact with darkness and facing those imaginary foes did he finally
come to the full realization that there really was nothing to fear
and that he was as safe from harm in the dark as in the light.

The dictionary defines FEAR as "an emotion excited by threatening evil or impending pain, accompanied by a desire to avoid or

escape from it." It is usually the fear that a canoe will tip over that causes the occupant to move suddenly in the wrong direction and thereby upset it. The fear of drowning, when suddenly thrown into the water, causes one to struggle frantically and, incidentally, force himself under. It is an interesting, scientific fact that a baby, until he is twenty-four hours old, can swim. After it reaches the age of twenty-four hours it starts to realize fear and then it sinks. Fear is really the mental hazard of "Crossing your bridges before you come to them." The realization of this fact will cause fear to be conquered and disappear. When this Greatest Menace is removed the victory gives a confidence that insures the removal of all lesser menaces.

THREE SKELETON KEY

By GEORGE G. TOUDOUZE

MY MOST TERRIFYING EXPERIENCE? WELL, ONE DOES HAVE A FEW in thirty-five years of service in the Lights, although it's mostly monotonous routine work—keeping the light in order, making out the reports.

When I was a young man, not very long in the service, there was an opening in a lighthouse newly built off the coast of Guiana, on a small rock twenty miles or so from the mainland. The pay was high, so in order to reach the sum I had set out to save before I married, I volunteered for service in the new light.

Three Skeleton Key, the small rock on which the light stood, bore a bad reputation. It earned its name from the story of the three convicts who, escaping from Cayenne in a stolen dugout canoe, were wrecked on the rock during the night, managed to escape the sea but eventually died of hunger and thirst. When they were discovered, nothing remained but three heaps of bones, picked clean by the birds. The story was that the three skeletons, gleaming with phosphorescent light, danced over the small rock, screaming. . . .

But there are many such stories and I did not give the warnings of the old-timers at the *Isle de Sein* a second thought. I signed up, boarded ship and in a month I was installed at the light.

Picture a grey, tapering cylinder, welded to the solid black rock by iron rods and concrete, rising from a small island twenty odd miles from land. It lay in the midst of the sea, this island, a small, bare piece of stone, about one hundred fifty feet long, perhaps forty, wide. Small, barely large enough for a man to walk about and stretch his legs at low tide.

This is an advantage one doesn't find in all lights, however, for some of them rise sheer from the waves, with no room for one to move save within the light itself. Still, on our island, one must be careful, for the rocks were treacherously smooth. One misstep and down you would fall into the sea—not that the risk of drowning was so great, but the waters about our island swarmed with huge sharks who kept an eternal patrol around the base of the light.

Still, it was a nice life there. We had enough provisions to last for months, in the event that the sea should become too rough for the supply ship to reach us on schedule. During the day we would work about the light, cleaning the rooms, polishing the metalwork and the lens and reflector of the light itself, and at night we would sit on the gallery and watch our light, a twenty thousand candle-power lantern, swinging its strong, white bar of light over the sea from the top of its hundred twenty foot tower. Some days, when the air would be very clear, we could see the land, a thread-like line to the west. To the east, north and south stretched the ocean. Landsmen, perhaps, would soon have tired of that kind of life, perched on a small island off the coast of South America for eighteen weeks, until one's turn for leave ashore came around. But we liked it there, my two fellow-tenders and myself—so much so that, for twenty-two months on end with the exception of shore leaves, I was greatly satisfied with the life on Three Skeleton Key.

I had just returned from my leave at the end of June, that is to say mid-winter in that latitude, and had settled down to the routine with my two fellow-keepers, a Breton by the name of Le Gleo and the head-keeper, Itchoua, a Basque some dozen years or so older than either of us.

Eight days went by as usual, then on the ninth night after my return, Itchoua, who was on night duty, called Le Gleo and me, sleeping in our rooms in the middle of the tower, at two in the morning. We rose immediately and, climbing the thirty or so steps that led to the gallery, stood beside our chief.

Itchoua pointed, and following his finger, we saw a big three-master, with all sail set, heading straight for the light. A queer course, for the vessel must have seen us, our light lit her with the glare of day each time it passed over her.

Now, ships were a rare sight in our waters for our light was a warning of treacherous reefs, barely hidden under the surface and running far out to sea. Consequently we were always given a wide berth, especially by sailing vessels, which cannot maneuver as readily as steamers.

No wonder that we were surprised at seeing this three-master heading dead for us in the gloom of early morning. I had immediately recognized her lines, for she stood out plainly, even at the distance of a mile, when our light shone on her.

She was a beautiful ship of some four thousand tons, a fast sailer that had carried cargoes to every part of the world, plowing the seas unceasingly. By her lines she was identified as Dutch-built, which was understandable as Paramaribo and Dutch Guiana are very close to Cayenne.

Watching her sailing dead for us, a white wave boiling under her bows, Le Gleo cried out:

"What's wrong with her crew? Are they all drunk or insane? Can't they see us?"

Itchoua nodded soberly, looked at us sharply as he remarked: "See us? No doubt—if there *is* a crew aboard!"

"What do you mean, chief?" Le Gleo had started, turned to the Basque, "Are you saying that she's the 'Flying Dutchman'?"

His sudden fright had been so evident that the older man laughed:

"No, old man, that's not what I meant. If I say that no one's aboard, I mean she's a derelict."

Then we understood her queer behavior. Itchoua was right. For some reason, believing her doomed, her crew had abandoned her. Then she had righted herself and sailed on, wandering with the wind.

The three of us grew tense as the ship seemed about to crash on one of our numerous reefs, but she suddenly lurched with some change of the wind, the yards swung around and the derelict came clumsily about and sailed dead away from us.

In the light of our lantern she seemed so sound, so strong, that Itchoua exclaimed impatiently:

"But why the devil was she abandoned? Nothing is smashed, no sign of fire—and she doesn't sail as if she were taking water."

Le Gleo waved to the departing ship:

"*Bon voyage!*" he smiled at Itchoua and went on. "She's leaving us, chief, and now we'll never know what ——"

"No she's not!" cried the Basque. "Look! She's turning!"

As if obeying his words, the derelict three-master stopped, came about and headed for us once more. And for the next four hours the vessel played around us—zigzagging, coming about, stopping, then suddenly lurching forward. No doubt some freak of current and wind, of which our island was the center, kept her near us.

Then suddenly, the tropic dawn broke, the sun rose and it was day, and the ship was plainly visible as she sailed past us. Our light extinguished, we returned to the gallery with our glasses and inspected her.

The three of us focused our glasses on her poop, saw standing out sharply, black letters on the white background of a life-ring, the stenciled name:

"*Cornelius-de-Witt, Rotterdam.*"

We had read her lines correctly, she was Dutch. Just then the wind rose and the *Cornelius de Witt* changed course, leaned to port and headed straight for us once more. But this time she was so close that we knew she would not turn in time.

"Thunder!" cried Le Gleo, his Breton soul aching to see a fine ship doomed to smash upon a reef, "she's going to pile up! She's gone!"

I shook my head:

"Yes, and a shame to see that beautiful ship wreck herself. And we're helpless."

There was nothing we could do but watch. A ship sailing with all sail spread, creaming the sea with her forefoot as she runs before the wind, is one of the most beautiful sights in the world—but this time I could feel the tears stinging in my eyes as I saw this fine ship headed for her doom.

All this time our glasses were riveted on her and we suddenly cried out together:

"The rats!"

Now we knew why this ship, in perfect condition, was sailing without her crew aboard. They had been driven out by the rats. Not those poor specimens of rats you see ashore, barely reaching the length of one foot from their trembling noses to the tip of their skinny tails, wretched creatures that dodge and hide at the mere sound of a footfall.

No, these were ships' rats, huge, wise creatures, born on the sea, sailing all over the world on ships, transferring to other, larger ships as they multiply. There is as much difference between the rats of the land and these maritime rats as between a fishing smack and an armored cruiser.

The rats of the sea are fierce, bold animals. Large, strong and intelligent, clannish and seawise, able to put the best of mariners to shame with their knowledge of the sea, their uncanny ability to foretell the weather.

And they are brave, these rats, and vengeful. If you so much as harm one, his sharp cry will bring hordes of his fellows to swarm over you, tear you and not cease until your flesh has been stripped from the bones.

The ones on this ship, the rats of Holland, are the worst, superior to other rats of the sea as their brethren are to the land rats. There is a well-known tale about these animals.

A Dutch captain, thinking to protect his cargo, brought aboard his ship—not cats—but two terriers, dogs trained in the hunting, fighting and killing of vicious rats. By the time the ship, sailing from Rotterdam, had passed the Ostend light, the dogs were gone and never seen again. In twenty-four hours they had been overwhelmed, killed and eaten by the rats.

At times, when the cargo does not suffice, the rats attack the crew, either driving them from the ship or eating them alive. And studying the *Cornelius de Witt*, I turned sick, for her small boats were all in place. She had not been abandoned.

Over her bridge, on her deck, in the rigging, on every visible spot, the ship was a writhing mass—a starving army coming towards us aboard a vessel gone mad!

Our island was a small spot in that immense stretch of sea. The ship could have grazed us, passed to port or starboard with its ravening cargo—but no, she came for us at full speed, as if she were leading the regatta at a race, and impaled herself on a sharp point of rock.

There was a dull shock as her bottom stove in, then a horrible crackling as the three masts went overboard at once, as if cut down with one blow of some gigantic sickle. A sighing groan came as the water rushed into the ship, then she split in two and sank like a stone.

But the rats did not drown. Not these fellows! As much at home in the sea as any fish, they formed ranks in the water, heads lifted, tails stretched out, paws paddling. And half of them, those from the forepart of the ship, sprang along the masts and onto the rocks in the instant before she sank. Before we had time even to move, nothing remained of the three-master save some pieces of wreckage floating on the surface and an army of rats covering the rocks left bare by the receding tide.

Thousands of heads rose, felt the wind and we were scented, seen! To them we were fresh meat, after possible weeks of starving. There came a scream, composed of innumerable screams, sharper than the howl of a saw attacking a bar of iron, and in the one motion, every rat leaped to attack the tower!

We barely had time to leap back, close the door leading onto the gallery, descend the stairs and shut every window tightly. Luckily the door at the base of the light, which we never could have reached in time, was of bronze set in granite and was tightly closed.

The horrible band, in no measurable time, had swarmed up and over the tower as if it had been a tree, piled on the embrasures of the windows, scraped at the glass with thousands of claws, covered the lighthouse with a furry mantle and reached the top of the tower, filing the gallery and piling atop the lantern.

Their teeth grated as they pressed against the glass of the lantern-room, where they could plainly see us, though they could not reach us. A few millimeters of glass, luckily very strong, separated our faces from their gleaming, beady eyes, their sharp claws and teeth. Their odor filled the tower, poisoned our lungs and rasped our nostrils with a pestilential, nauseating smell. And there we were, sealed alive in our own light, prisoners of a horde of starving rats.

That first night, the tension was so great that we could not sleep. Every moment, we felt that some opening had been made, some window given away, and that our horrible besiegers were pouring through the breach. The rising tide, chasing those of the rats which had stayed on the bare rocks, increased the numbers clinging to the walls, piled on the balcony—so much so that clusters of rats clinging to one another hung from the lantern and the gallery.

With the coming of darkness we lit the light and the turning beam completely maddened the beasts. As the light turned, it successively blinded thousands of rats crowded against the glass, while the darkside of the lantern-room gleamed with thousands of points of light, burning like the eyes of jungle beasts in the night.

All the while we could hear the enraged scraping of claws against the stone and glass, while the chorus of cries was so loud that we had to shout to hear one another. From time to time, some of the rats fought among themselves and a dark cluster would detach itself, falling into the sea like a ripe fruit from a tree. Then we would see phosphorescent streaks as triangular fins slashed the water —sharks, permanent guardians of our rock, feasting on our jailors.

The next day we were calmer, and amused ourselves teasing the rats, placing our faces against the glass which separated us. They could not fathom the invisible barrier which separated them from us and we laughed as we watched them leaping against the heavy glass.

But the day after that, we realized how serious our position was. The air was foul, even the heavy smell of oil within our strong-hold could not dominate the fetid odor of the beasts massed around us. And there was no way of admitting fresh air without also admitting the rats.

The morning of the fourth day, at early dawn, I saw the wooden framework of my window, eaten away from the outside, sagging inwards. I called my comrades and the three of us fastened a sheet of tin in the opening, sealing it tightly. When we had completed the task, Itchoua turned to us and said dully:

"Well—the supply boat came thirteen days ago, and she won't be back for twenty-nine." He pointed at the white metal plate sealing the opening through the granite—"If that gives way—" he shrugged—"they can change the name of this place to Six Skeletons Key."

The next six days and seven nights, our only distraction was watching the rats whose holds were insecure, fall a hundred and twenty feet into the maws of the sharks—but they were so many that we could not see any diminution in their numbers.

Thinking to calm ourselves and pass the time, we attempted to count them, but we soon gave up. They moved incessantly, never still. Then we tried identifying them, naming them.

One of them, larger than the others, who seemed to lead them in their rushes against the glass separating us, we named "Nero"; and there were several others whom we had learned to distinguish through various peculiarities.

But the thought of our bones joining those of the convicts was always in the back of our minds. And the gloom of our prison fed these thoughts, for the interior of the light was almost completely dark, as we had to seal every window in the same fashion as mine, and the only space that still admitted daylight was the glassed-in lantern-room at the very top of the tower.

Then Le Gleo became morose and had nightmares in which he would see the three skeletons dancing around him, gleaming coldly, seeking to grasp him. His maniacal, raving descriptions were so vivid that Itchoua and I began seeing them also.

It was a living nightmare, the raging cries of the rats as they swarmed over the light, mad with hunger; the sickening, strangling odor of their bodies —

True, there is a way of signaling from lighthouses. But to reach the mast on which to hang the signal we would have to go out on the gallery where the rats were.

There was only one thing left to do. After debating all of the ninth day, we decided not to light the lantern that night. This is the greatest breach of our service, never committed as long as the tenders of the light are alive; for the light is something sacred, warning ships of danger in the night. Either the light gleams, a quarter hour after sundown, or no one is left alive to light it.

Well, that night, Three Skeleton Light was dark, and all the men were alive. At the risk of causing ships to crash on our reefs, we left it unlit, for we were worn out—going mad!

At two in the morning, while Itchoua was dozing in his room, the sheet of metal sealing his window gave way. The chief had just time enough to leap to his feet and cry for help, the rats swarming over him.

But Le Gleo and I, who had been watching from the lantern-room, got to him immediately, and the three of us battled with the horde of maddened rats which flowed through the gaping window. They bit, we struck them down with our knives—and retreated.

We locked the door of the room on them, but before we had time to bind our wounds, the door was eaten through, and gave way and we retreated up the stairs, fighting off the rats that leaped on us from the knee deep swarm.

I do not remember, to this day, how we ever managed to escape. All I can remember is wading through them up the stairs, striking them off as they swarmed over us; and then we found ourselves, bleeding from innumerable bites, our clothes shredded, sprawled across the trapdoor in the floor of the lantern-room—without food or drink. Luckily, the trapdoor was metal set into the granite with iron bolts.

The rats occupied the entire light beneath us, and on the floor of our retreat lay some twenty of their fellows, who had gotten in with us before the trapdoor closed, and whom we had killed with our knives. Below us, in the tower, we could hear the screams of the rats as they devoured everything edible that they found. Those on the outside squealed in reply, and writhed in a horrible curtain as they stared at us through the glass of the lantern-room.

Itchoua sat up, stared silently at his blood trickling from the wounds on his limbs and body, and running in thin streams on the floor around him. Le Gleo, who was in as bad a state (and so was I, for that matter) stared at the chief and me vacantly, started as his gaze swung to the multitude of rats against the glass, then suddenly began laughing horribly:

"Hee! Hee! The Three Skeletons! Hee! Hee! The Three Skeletons are now *six* skeletons! *Six* skeletons!"

He threw his head back and howled, his eyes glazed, a trickle of saliva running from the corners of his mouth and thinning the blood flowing over his chest. I shouted to him to shut up, but he did not hear me, so I did the only thing I could to quiet him—I swung the back of my hand across his face.

The howling stopped suddenly, his eyes swung around the room, then he bowed his head and began weeping softly, like a child.

Our darkened light had been noticed from the mainland, and as dawn was breaking the patrol was there, to investigate the failure of our light. Looking through my binoculars, I could see the horrified expression on the faces of the officers and crew when, the daylight strengthening, they saw the light completely covered by a seething mass of rats. They thought, as I afterwards found out, that we had been eaten alive.

But the rats had also seen the ship, or had scented the crew. As the ship drew nearer, a solid phalanx left the light, plunged into the water and, swimming out, attempted to board her. They would have succeeded, as the ship was hove to, but the engineer connected his steam to hose on the deck and scalded the head of the attacking column, which slowed them up long enough for the ship to get underway and leave the rats behind.

Then the sharks took part. Belly up, mouths gaping, they arrived in swarms and scooped up the rats, sweeping through them like a sickle through wheat. That was one day that sharks really served a useful purpose.

The remaining rats turned tail, swam to the shore and emerged dripping. As they neared the light, their comrades greeted them with shrill cries, with what sounded like a derisive note predominating. They answered angrily and mingled with their fellows. From the several tussles that broke out, they resented being ridiculed for their failure to capture the ship.

But all this did nothing to get us out of our jail. The small ship could not approach, but steamed around the light at a safe distance, and the tower must have seemed fantastic, some weird, many-mouthed beast hurling defiance at them.

Finally, seeing the rats running in and out of the tower through the door and the windows, those on the ship decided that we had perished and were about to leave when Itchoua, regaining his senses, thought of using the light as a signal. He lit it and, using a plank placed and withdrawn before the beam to form the dots and dashes, quickly sent out our story to those on the vessel.

Our reply came quickly. When they understood our position how we could not get rid of the rats, Le Gleo's mind going fast, Itchoua and myself covered with bites; cornered in the lantern-room without food or water, they had a signal-man send us their reply.

His arms, swinging like those of a windmill, he quickly spelled out:

"Don't give up, hang on a little longer! We'll get you out of this!"

Then she turned and steamed at top speed for the coast, leaving us little reassured.

She was back at noon, accompanied by the supply ship, two small coast guard boats, and the fire boat—a small squadron. At twelve-thirty the battle was on.

After a short reconnaissance, the fire boat picked her way slowly through the reefs until she was close to us, then turned her powerful jet of water on the rats, The heavy stream tore the rats from their places, hurled them screaming into the water where the sharks gulped them down. But for every ten that were dislodged, seven swam ashore, and the stream could do nothing to the rats within the tower. Furthermore, some of them, instead of returning to the rocks, boarded the fire boat and the men were forced to battle them hand to hand. They were true rats of Holland, fearing no man, fighting for the right to live!

Nightfall came, and it was as if nothing had been done, the rats were still in possession. One of the patrol boats stayed by the island, the rest of the flotilla departed for the coast. We had to spend another night in our prison. Le Gleo was sitting on the floor, babbling about skeletons and as I turned to Itchoua, he fell unconscious from his wounds. I was in no better shape and could feel my blood flaming with fever.

Somehow the night dragged by, and the next afternoon I saw a tug, accompanied by the fire boat, come from the mainland with a huge barge in tow. Through my glasses, I saw that the barge was filled with meat.

Risking the treacherous reefs, the tug dragged the barge as close to the island as possible. To the last rat, our besiegers deserted the rock, swam out and boarded the barge reeking with the scent of freshly cut meat. The tug dragged the barge about a mile from shore, where the fire boat drenched the barge with gasoline. A well placed incendiary shell from the patrol boat set her on fire.

The barge was covered with flames immediately and the rats took to the water in swarms, but the patrol boat bombarded them with shrapnel from a safe distance, and the sharks finished off the survivors.

A whaleboat from the patrol boat took us off the island and left three men to replace us. By nightfall we were in the hospital in Cayenne. What became of my friends?

Well, Le Gleo's mind had cracked and he was raving mad. They sent him back to France and locked him up in an asylum, the poor devil; Itchoua died within a week; a rat's bite is dangerous in that hot, humid climate, and infection sets in rapidly.

As for me—when they fumigated the light and repaired the damage done by the rats, I resumed my service there. Why not? No reason why such an incident should keep me from finishing out my service there, is there?

Besides—I told you I liked the place—to be truthful, I've never had a post as pleasant as that one, and when my time came to leave it forever, I tell you that I almost wept as Three Skeleton Key disappeared below the horizon.

THE VILLAGES ARE THE HEART
OF SPAIN

By JOHN DOS PASSOS

1. VILLAGE BEHIND THE LINES

FIRST IT WAS THAT THE DRIVER WAS LATE, THEN THAT HE HAD TO go to the garage to get a mechanic to tinker with the gasoline pump, then that he had to go somewhere else to wait in line for gasoline; and so, in pacing round the hotel, in running up and down stairs, in scraps of conversation in the lobby, the Madrid morning dribbled numbly away in delay after delay. At last we were off. As we passed the Cibeles fountain two shells exploded far up the sunny Sastillana. Stonedust mixed with pale smoke of high explosives suddenly blurred the ranks of budding trees, under which a few men and women were strolling because it was Sunday and because they were in the habit of strolling there on Sunday. The shells hit too far away for us to see if anyone were hit. Our driver speeded up a little.

We passed the arch of Carlos Third and the now closed café under the trees opposite the postoffice where the last time I was in Madrid I used to sit late in the summer evenings chatting with friends some of whom are only very recently dead. As we got past the controlposts and sentries beyond the bull-ring, the grim exhilaration of the besieged city began to drop away from us, and we bowled pleasantly along the Guadalajara road in the spring sunlight.

In a little stone town in a valley full of poplars we went to visit the doctor in charge of the medical work for the Jarama front. He was a small dark brighteyed young man, a C. P. member I imagine; he had the look of a man who had entirely forgotten that he had a life of his own. Evidently for months there had been nothing he thought of, all day and every day, but his work. He took us to one of his base hospitals, recently installed in a group of old buildings, part of which had once been a parochial school. He apologized for it; they had only been in there two weeks, if we came two weeks later we'd see an improvement. We ate lunch there with him, then he promptly forgot us. In spite of the rain that came on, we could see him walking up and down the stony court inside the hospital gate with one member of his staff after another talking earnestly to them. He never took his eyes off whoever he was talking to, as if he were trying to hypnotize them with his own tireless energy. Meanwhile we tried to stimulate our driver, a singularly spineless young man in a black C. N. T. tunic, the son of a winegrower in Alcazar de San Juan, to fix the gasoline pump on the miserable little Citroen sedan we had been assigned to. At last the doctor remembered us again and as our driver had gotten the pump into such a state that the motor wouldn't even start, he offered to take us to the village to which we were bound, as he had to go out that way to pick a site for a new base-hospital. We set out in his Ford, that felt like a racing-car after the feeble little spluttering Citroen.

Rain was falling chilly over the lichengreen stone towns and the tawny hills misted over with the fiery green of new wheat. Under the rain and the low indigo sky, the road wound up and down among the great bare folds of the upland country. Late in the afternoon we came to a square building of lightbrown stone in a valley beside a clear stream and a milldam set about with poplars. The building had been a monastery long ago and the broad valley lands had belonged to the monks. As we got out of the car larks rose singing out of the stubby fields. The building was a magnificent square of sober seventeenth century work. In the last few years it had been used as a huntingclub, but since July, 1936 none of the members of the club had been seen in those parts. A family of country people from Pozorubio had moved out there to escape the air-raids and to do some planting.

They invited us in with grave Castilian hospitality and in a dark stone room we stood about the embers of a fire with them, drinking their stout darkred wine and eating their deliciously sweet fresh bread. With his glass in his hand and his mouth full of bread the doctor lectured them about the war, and the need to destroy the Fascists and to produce as much food as possible. Wheat and potatoes, he said, were as important as machinegun bullets in war.

"I am an illiterate and I know more about driving a mule than international politics. That is all my parents taught me," the tall dark thinfaced man who was the head of the family answered gravely. "But even I can understand that."

"But it's so terrible, gentlemen . . ." the woman broke in.

"There are no more gentlemen or masters here," said the man harshly. "These are comrades."

"How soon will it be stopped? It can't last all summer, can it?" asked the woman without paying attention to the man. Tears came into her eyes. Three little girls and a half-grown boy, standing in the shadows behind their Mother whose face was streaked with tears in the firelight, all turned their black eyes fixedly on the doctor's face.

"The war will stop when the fascists are driven out of Spain," said the doctor. "After all it's for these children, and all our children, to make life better for them . . ." he added looking into one face after another. Then he explained how the country people must tell everybody in the village to send to Madrid to the Department of Agriculture for free seed potatoes and that they must use the milldam to irrigate the fields. Then we gravely wished them good health and went out to the car and were off into the rainy night again.

We stopped at their village, Pozorubio, to load up on bread. We went into the bakery through a dimly lit stone doorway. The baker was at the front, so the women and young boys of the family were doing the baking. The bread had just come out of the oven. "Yes you can buy as much as you want," the women said. "We'd have bread for Madrid if they'd come and get it. Here at least we have plenty of bread." We stood around for a while in the dry dim room talking and looking into the fire that glowed under the ovens. As we got back into the car with our arms piled high with the big flat loaves the doctor was saying bitterly, "And in Madrid they are hungry for bread; it's the fault of the lack of transport and gasoline . . . we must organize our transport." Then he snapped at his Belgian chauffeur, "We must get back to headquarters fast, fast." You could see that he was blaming himself for the relaxed moment he'd spent in the warm, sweetsmelling bakery. As the car lurched over the ruts of the road across the hills, furry black in the rainy night, there went along with us in the smell of the bread something of the peaceful coziness of the village, and country people eating their suppers in the dim

roomy stone houses and the sharp-smelling herbs in the fires and
the brown faces looking out from the shelter of doorways at the
bright stripes of the rain in the street and the gleam of the cobbles
and the sturdy figures of country women under their shawls.

2. VILLAGE ON THE VALENCIA ROAD

Fuentedueña is a village of several hundred houses in the province of Madrid. It stands on a shelf above the Tagus, at the point
where the direct road to Valencia from Madrid dips down into
the river's broad terraced valley. Above it on the hill still tower
the crumbling brick and adobe walls of a castle of Moorish work
where some feudal lord once sat and controlled the trail and river-
crossing. Along the wide wellpaved macadam road there are a few
wineships and the barracks of the civil guard. The minute you step
off the road you are back in the age of packmules and twowheeled
carts. It's a poor village and it has the air of having always been
a poor village; only a few of the houses on the oblong main square
with their wide doors that open into pleasant green courts have
the stone shields of hidalgos on their peeling stucco fronts. The
town hall is only a couple of offices, and the telephone on the wall
that links the village to Madrid. Since July the real center of the
town has been on another street, in the house once occupied by
the pharmacist, who seems to have been considered hostile, because
he is there no more, in an office where the members of the socialist
(U. G. T.) Casa del Pueblo meet. Their president is now mayor and
their policies are dominant in the village. The only opposition is
the C. N. T. syndicalist local which in Fuentedueña, so the socialists claim and I think in this case justly, is made up of small store-
keepers and excommission merchants, and not working farmers
at all. According to the mayor they all wear the swastika under
their shirts. Their side of the story, needless to say, is somewhat
different.

At the time of the military revolt in July the land of Fuentedueña
was held by about ten families, some of them the descendants, I
suppose, of the hidalgos who put their shields on their houses on
the main square. Some of them were shot, others managed to
get away. The Casa del Pueblo formed a collective out of their
lands. Meanwhile other lands were taken over by the C. N. T. local.
Fuentedueña's main cash crop is wine: the stocks in the three or

four bodegas constituted the town's capital. The Casa del Pueblo, having the majority of the working farmers, took over the municipal government and it was decided to farm the lands of the village in common. For the present it was decided that every working man should be paid five pesetas for every day he worked and have a right to a daily liter of wine and a certain amount of firewood. The mayor and the secretary and treasurer and the muledrivers and the blacksmith, every man who worked was paid the same. The carpenters and masons and other skilled artisans who had been making seven pesetas a day consented, gladly they said, to taking the same pay as the rest. Later, the mastermason told me, they'd raise everybody's pay to seven pesetas or higher; after all wine was a valuable crop and with no parasites to feed there would be plenty for all. Women and boys were paid three fifty. The committees of the U. G. T. and the C. N. T. decided every day where their members were to work. Housing was roughly distributed according to the sizes of the families. There was not much difficulty about that because since the fascist airraids began people preferred to live in the cavehouses along the edges of the hill than in the big rubble and stucco houses with courts and corrals in the center of town, especially since one of them had been destroyed by a bomb. These cavehouses, where in peacetime only the poorest people lived, are not such bad dwellings as they sound. They are cut out of the hard clay and chalky rock of the terraced hillsides facing the river. They have usually several rooms, each with a large cone-shaped chimney for light and to carry off the smoke of the fire, and a porch onto which narrow windows open. They are whitewashed and often remarkably clean and neat. Before the civil war the housedwellers looked down on the cavedwellers; but now the caves seem to have definite social standing.

The village produces much wine but little oil, so one of the first things the collective did was to arrange to barter their wine for oil with a village that produced more oil than it needed. Several people told me proudly that they'd improved the quality of their wine since they had taken the bodegas over from the business men who had the habit of watering the wine before they sold it and were ruining the reputation of their vintages. Other local industries taken over by the collective are the bakery and a lime kiln, where three or four men worked intermittently, getting the stone from a quarry immediately back of the town and burning it in two small adobe ovens, and the making of fiber baskets and harness which people make from a tough grass they collect from the hills round about. This was a spare time occupation for periods of bad weather. After wine the crops are wheat, and a few olives.

The irrigation project seemed to loom larger than the war in the minds of the mayor and his councillors. Down in the comparatively rich bottom land along the Tagus the collective had taken over a piece that they were planning to irrigate for truck gardens. They had spent thirteen thousand pesetas of their capital in Madrid to buy pumping machinery and cement. A large gang of men was working over there every day to get the ditches dug and the pump installed that was going to put the river water on the land before the hot dry summer weather began. Others were planting seed potatoes. An old man and his son had charge of a seed-bed where they were raising onions and lettuce and tomatoes and peppers and artichokes for planting out. Later they would sow melons, corn and cabbage. For the first time the village was going to raise its own green vegetables. Up to now everything of that sort had had to be imported from the outside. Only a few of the richer landowners had had irrigated patches of fruits and vegetables for their own use. This was the first real reform the collective had undertaken and everybody felt very good about it, so good that they almost forgot the hollow popping beyond the hills that they could hear from the Jarama river front fifteen miles away, and the truckloads of soldiers and munitions going through the village up the road to Madrid and the fear they felt whenever they saw an airplane in the sky. Is it ours or is it theirs?

Outside of the irrigated bottom lands and the dryfarming uplands the collective owns a considerable number of mules, a few horses and cows, a flock of sheep and a flock of goats. Most of the burros are owned by individuals, as are a good many sheep and goats that are taken out to pasture every day by the village shepherds under a communal arrangement as old as the oldest stone walls. Occasional fishing in the river is more of an entertainment than part of the town economy. On our walks back and forth to the new pumping station the mayor used to point out various men and boys sitting along the river bank with fishing poles. "All members of the C. N. T.," he'd say maliciously. "You'd never find a socialist going out fishing when there was still spring plowing to be done." "We've cleaned out the fascists and the priests," one of the men who was walking with us said grimly. "Now we must clean out the loafers." "Yes," said the mayor. "One of these days it will come to a fight."

3. FISHING VILLAGE

In San Pol, so the secretary of the agricultural coöperative told me with considerable pride, they hadn't killed anybody. He was a small, schoolteacherylooking man in a worn dark business suit. He had a gentle playful way of talking and intermingled his harsh Spanish with English and French words. San Pol is a very small fishing village on the Catalan coast perhaps thirty miles northeast of Barcelona. It consists of several short streets of pale blue and yellow and whitewashed houses climbing up the hills of an irregular steep little valley full of umbrella-pines. The fishingboats are drawn up on the shingly beach in a row along the double track of the railway to France. Behind the railway is a string of grotesque villas owned by Barcelona business men of moderate means. Most of the villas are closed. A couple have been expropriated by the municipality, one for a coöperative retail store, and another, which had just been very handsomely done over with a blue and white tile decoration, to house a municipal pool parlor and gymnasium, public baths and showers, a huge airy coöperative barber shop and, upstairs, a public library and readingroom. On the top of the hill behind the town a big estate has been turned into a municipal chicken farm.

The morning I arrived the towncouncil had finally decided to take over the wholesale marketing of fish, buying the catch from the fishermen and selling it in Barcelona. The middleman who had handled the local fish on a commission basis was still in business; we saw him there, a big domineering pearshaped man with a brown sash holding up his baggy corduroys, superintending the salting of sardines in a barrel. "He's a fascist," the secretary of the coöperative said, "but we won't bother him. He won't be able to compete with us anyway because we'll pay a higher price."

Then he took me to see a little colony of refugee children from Madrid living in a beautiful house overlooking the sea with a rich garden behind it. They were a lively and sunburned bunch of kids under the charge of a young man and his wife who were attending to their schooling. As we were walking back down the steep flower-lined street (Yes, the flowers had been an idea of the socialist municipality, the secretary said smiling) it came on to rain. We passed a stout man in black puffing with flushed face up the hill under a green umbrella. "He's the priest," said the secretary. "He doesn't bother anybody. He takes no part in politics." I said that in most towns I'd been in a priest wouldn't dare show his face. "Here we were never believers," said the secretary, "so we don't feel that hatred. We have several refugee priests in town. They haven't made any trouble yet."

He took me to a fine building on the waterfront that had been a beach café and danceplace that had failed. Part of it had been done over into a little theatre. "We won a prize at the Catalonia drama festival last year, though we're a very small town. There's a great deal of enthusiasm for amateur plays here." We had lunch with various local officials in the rooms of the choral society in a little dining room overlooking the sea. Far out on the horizon we could see the smoke of the inevitable non-intervention warship.

And a fine lunch it was. Everything except the wine and the coffee had been grown within the town limits. San Pol had some wine, they said apologetically, but it wasn't very good. First we had broad beans in olive oil. Then a magnificent dish of fresh sardines. My friends explained that the sardine fishing had been remarkably successful this year, and that fish were selling at war prices so that everybody in town had money in his pocket. They fished mostly at night with floating nets. The boats had motors and great batteries of acetylene lights to attract the fish to the surface. The difficult part of the business was to tow the net around the fish and scoop them up without losing them. After the sardines we had roast chicken from the village chickenfarm, with new potatoes and lettuce. Outside of fish they explained new potatoes were their main cash crop. They sold them in England, marketing them through the coöperative of which my friend was secretary. He had been in England that winter to make new arrangements. The coöperative was a number of years old and a member of the Catalan alliance of coöperatives. Of course now, since the movement, they were more important than ever. "If only the fascists would let us alone." "And the anarchists," somebody added . . . "We could be very happy in San Pol."

We drove out of town in the pouring rain. As the road wound up the hill we got a last look at the neat streets of varicolored stucco houses and the terraced gardens and the blue and white and blue and green fishing boats, with their clustered lights sticking out above their sterns like insect eyes, drawn up in a row along the shingle beach.

4. THE MEN AT THE TELEPHONE

Barcelona. April 29. The headquarters of the unified Marxist party (P.O.U.M.). It's late at night in a large bare office furnished with odds and ends of old furniture. At a bit battered fake Gothic desk out of somebody's library Nin sits at the telephone. I sit in a mangy overstuffed armchair. On the settee opposite me sits a man who used to be editor of a radical publishing house in Madrid.

We talk in a desultory way with many pauses about old times in Madrid, about the course of the war. They are telling me about the change that has come over the population of Barcelona since the great explosion of revolutionary feeling that followed the attempted military coup d'état and swept the fascists out of Catalonia in July. "You can even see it in people's dress," said Nin from the telephone laughing. "Now we're beginning to wear collars and ties again but even a couple of months ago everybody was wearing the most extraordinary costumes . . . you'd see people on the street wearing feathers." Nin was wellbuilt and healthylooking and probably looked younger than his age; he had a ready childish laugh that showed a set of solid white teeth.

From time to time as we were talking the telephone would ring and he would listen attentively with a serious face. Then he'd answer with a few words too rapid for me to catch and would hang up the receiver with a shrug of the shoulders and come smiling back into the conversation again. When he saw that I was beginning to frame a question he said, "It's the villages . . . They want to know what to do." "About Valencia taking over the police services?" He nodded. "What are they going to do?" "Take a car and drive through the suburbs of Barcelona, you'll see that all the villages are barricaded . . . The committees are all out on the streets with machine guns." Then he laughed. "But maybe you had better not." "He'd be all right," said the other man. "They have great respect for foreign journalists." "Is it an organized movement?" "It's complicated . . . in Bellver our people want to know whether they ought to move against the anarchists. In other places they are with them . . . You know Spain."

It was time for me to push on. I shook hands with Nin and with a young Englishman who also is dead now, and went out into the rainy night. Since then Nin has been killed and his party suppressed. The papers have not told us what has happened in the villages.

But already that April night the popular movement in Catalonia seemed doomed, hemmed in by ruthless forces of worldpolitics too big for it. Perhaps these men already knew it. They did not have the faces of men who were betraying their country or their cause, but there was no air of victory about them.

The trade union paper had just been installed in a repaired building where there had once been a convent.

The new rotary presses were not quite in order yet and the partitions were unfinished between the offices in the editorial department. They took me into a little room where they were transmitting news and comment to the trade union paper in the fishing town of Gijon in Asturias on the north coast clear on the other side of Franco's territory. A man was reading an editorial. As the rotund phrases (which perhaps fitted in well enough with the American scheme of things for me to accept) went lilting through the silence, I couldn't help being swept by the feeling of the rainy night and the working men on guard with machine guns and rifles at sandbag posts on the roads into villages, and the hopes of new life and liberty and the political phrases pounding confused and contradictory in their ears; and then the front, the towns crowded with troops and the advanced posts and trenches and the solitude between; and beyond, the old life, the titled officers in fancy uniforms, the bishops and priests, the pious ladies in black silk with their rosaries, the arab moors and the dark berbers getting their revenge four hundred and fifty years late for the loss of their cities, and the profiteers and businessmen and squareheaded German traveling salesmen; and beyond again the outposts and the Basque country people praying to God in their hillside trenches and the Asturian miners with their sticks of dynamite in their belts and the longshoremen and fishermen of the coast towns waiting for hopeful news; and another little office like this where the editors crowded around the receiving set that except for blockade-runners is their only contact with the outside world. "How can the new world full of confusion and crosspurposes and illusions and dazzled by the mirage of idealistic phrases win against the iron combination of men accustomed to run things who have only one idea binding them together, to hold on to what they've got; how can the new world win?" was what I'd liked to have asked the editors of the labor paper in Gijon over the short wave set.

There was a sudden rumble in the distance. The man who was reading stopped. Everybody craned their necks to listen. There it was again. "No it's not firing, it's thunder," everybody laughed with relief. They turned on the receiver again. The voice from Gijon came feebly in a stutter of static. They must repeat the editorial. Static. While the operator tinkered with the adjustments the distant voice from Gijon was lost in sharp crashes of static. Black rain was lashing against the window.

LEININGEN VERSUS THE ANTS

By Carl Stephenson

"UNLESS THEY ALTER THEIR COURSE AND THERE'S NO REASON WHY they should, they'll reach your plantation in two days at the latest."

Leiningen sucked placidly at a cigar about the size of a corn cob and for a few seconds gazed without answering at the agitated District Commissioner. Then he took the cigar from his lips, and leaned slightly forward. With his bristling grey hair, bulky nose, and lucid eyes, he had the look of an aging and shabby eagle.

"Decent of you," he murmured, "paddling all this way just to give me the tip. But you're pulling my leg of course when you say I must do a bunk. Why, even a herd of saurians couldn't drive me from this plantation of mine."

The Brazilian official threw up lean and lanky arms and clawed the air with wildly distended fingers. "Leiningen!" he shouted. "You're insane! They're not creatures you can fight—they're an elemental—an 'act of God!' Ten miles long, two miles wide—ants, nothing but ants! And every single one of them a fiend from hell; before you can spit three times they'll eat a full-grown buffalo to the bones. I tell you if you don't clear out at once there'll be nothing left of you but a skeleton picked as clean as your own plantation."

Leiningen grinned. "Act of God, my eye! Anyway, I'm not an old woman; I'm not going to run for it just because an elemental's on the way. And don't think I'm the kind of fathead who tries to fend off lightning with his fists, either. I use my intelligence, old man. With me, the brain isn't a second blindgut; I know what it's there for. When I began this model farm and plantation three years ago, I took into account all that could conceivably happen to it. And now I'm ready for anything and everything—including your ants."

The Brazilian rose heavily to his feet. "I've done my best," he gasped. "Your obstinacy endangers not only yourself, but the lives of your four hundred workers. You don't know these ants!"

Leiningen accompanied him down to the river, where the Government launch was moored. The vessel cast off. As it moved downstream, the exclamation mark neared the rail and began waving its arms frantically. Long after the launch had disappeared round the bend, Leiningen thought he could still hear that dimming, imploring voice, "You don't know them, I tell you! *You don't know them!*"

But the reported enemy was by no means unfamiliar to the planter. Before he started work on his settlement, he had lived long enough in the country to see for himself the fearful devastations sometimes wrought by these ravenous insects in their campaigns for food. But since then he had planned measures of defence accordingly, and these, he was convinced, were in every way adequate to withstand the approaching peril.

Moreover, during his three years as a planter, Leiningen had met and defeated drought, flood, plague and all other "acts of God" which had come against him—unlike his fellow-settlers in the district, who had made little or no resistance. This unbroken success he attributed solely to the observance of his lifelong motto: *The human brain needs only to become fully aware of its powers to conquer even the elements.* Dullards reeled senselessly and aimlessly into the abyss; cranks, however brilliant, lost their heads when circumstances suddenly altered or accelerated and ran into stone walls, sluggards drifted with the current until they were caught in whirlpools and dragged under. But such disasters, Leiningen contended, merely strengthened his argument that intelligence, directed aright, invariably makes man the master of his fate.

Yes, Leiningen had always known how to grapple with life. Even here, in this Brazilian wilderness, his brain had triumphed over every difficulty and danger it had so far encountered. First he had vanquished primal forces by cunning and organization, then he had enlisted the resources of modern science to increase miraculously the yield of his plantation. And now he was sure he would prove more than a match for the "irresistible" ants.

That same evening, however, Leiningen assembled his workers. He had no intention of waiting till the news reached their ears from other sources. Most of them had been born in the district; the cry "The ants are coming!" was to them an imperative signal for instant, panic-stricken flight, a spring for life itself. But so great was the Indians' trust in Leiningen, in Leiningen's word, and in Leiningen's wisdom, that they received his curt tidings, and his orders for the imminent struggle, with the calmness with which they were given. They waited, unafraid, alert, as if for the beginning of a new game or hunt which he had just described to them. The ants were indeed mighty, but not so mighty as the boss. Let them come!

They came at noon the second day. Their approach was announced by the wild unrest of the horses, scarcely controllable now either in stall or under rider, scenting from afar a vapor instinct with horror.

It was announced by a stampede of animals, timid and savage, hurtling past each other; jaguars and pumas flashing by nimble stags of the pampas, bulky tapirs, no longer hunters, themselves hunted, outpacing fleet kinkajous, maddened herds of cattle, heads lowered, nostrils snorting, rushing through tribes of loping monkeys, chattering in a dementia of terror; then followed the creeping and springing denizens of bush and steppe, big and little rodents, snakes, and lizards.

Pell-mell the rabble swarmed down the hill to the plantation, scattered right and left before the barrier of the water-filled ditch, then sped onwards to the river, where, again hindered, they fled along its bank out of sight.

This water-filled ditch was one of the defence measures which Leiningen had long since prepared against the advent of the ants. It encompassed three sides of the plantation like a huge horseshoe. Twelve feet across, but not very deep, when dry it could hardly be described as an obstacle to either man or beast. But the ends of the "horseshoe" ran into the river which formed the northern boundary, and fourth side, of the plantation. And at the end nearer the house and outbuildings in the middle of the plantation, Leiningen had constructed a dam by means of which water from the river could be diverted into the ditch.

So now, by opening the dam, he was able to fling an imposing girdle of water, a huge quadrilateral with the river as its base, completely around the plantation, like the moat encircling a medieval city. Unless the ants were clever enough to build rafts, they had no hope of reaching the plantation, Leiningen concluded.

The twelve-foot water ditch seemed to afford in itself all the security needed. But while awaiting the arrival of the ants, Leiningen made a further improvement. The western section of the ditch ran along the edge of a tamarind wood, and the branches of some great trees reached over the water. Leiningen now had them lopped so that ants could not descend from them within the "moat."

The women and children, then the herds of cattle, were escorted by peons on rafts over the river, to remain on the other side in absolute safety until the plunderers had departed. Leiningen gave this instruction, not because he believed the non-combatants were in any danger, but in order to avoid hampering the efficiency of the defenders. "Critical situations first become crises," he explained to his men, "when oxen or women get excited."

Finally, he made a careful inspection of the "inner moat"—a smaller ditch lined with concrete, which extended around the hill on which stood the ranch house, barns, stables and other buildings. Into this concrete ditch emptied the inflow pipes from three great petrol tanks. If by some miracle the ants managed to cross the water and reach the plantation, this "rampart of petrol" would be an absolutely impassable protection for the besieged and their dwellings and stock. Such, at least, was Leiningen's opinion.

He stationed his men at irregular distances along the water ditch, the first line of defense. Then he lay down in his hammock and puffed drowsily away at his pipe until a peon came with the report that the ants had been observed far away in the South.

Leiningen mounted his horse, which at the feel of its master seemed to forget its uneasiness, and rode leisurely in the direction of the threatening offensive. The southern stretch of ditch—the upper side of the quadrilateral—was nearly three miles long; from its center one could survey the entire countryside. This was destined to be the scene of the outbreak of war between Leiningen's brain and twenty square miles of life-destroying ants.

It was a sight one could never forget. Over the range of hills, as far as eye could see, crept a darkening hem, ever longer and broader, until the shadow spread across the slope from east to west, then downwards, downwards, uncannily swift, and all the green herbage of that wide vista was being mown as by a giant sickle, leaving only the vast moving shadow, extending, deepening, and moving rapidly nearer.

When Leiningen's men, behind their barrier of water, perceived the approach of the long-expected foe, they gave vent to their suspense in screams and imprecations. But as the distance began to lessen between the "sons of hell" and the water ditch, they relapsed into silence. Before the advance of that awe-inspiring throng, their belief in the powers of the boss began to steadily dwindle.

Even Leiningen himself, who had ridden up just in time to restore their loss of heart by a display of unshakable calm, even he could not free himself from a qualm of malaise. Yonder were thousands of millions of voracious jaws bearing down upon him and only a suddenly insignificant, narrow ditch lay between him and his men and being gnawed to the bones "before you can spit three times."

Hadn't his brain for once taken on more than it could manage? If the blighters decided to rush the ditch, fill it to the brim with their corpses, there'd still be more than enough to destroy every trace of that cranium of his. The planter's chin jutted; they hadn't got him yet, and he'd see to it they never would. While he could think at all, he'd flout both death and the devil.

The hostile army was approaching in perfect formation; no human battalions, however well-drilled, could ever hope to rival the precision of that advance. Along a front that moved forward as uniformly as a straight line, the ants drew nearer and nearer to the water-ditch. Then, when they learned through their scouts the nature of the obstacle, the two outlying wings of the army detached themselves from the main body and marched down the western and eastern sides of the ditch.

This surrounding maneuver took rather more than an hour to accomplish; no doubt the ants expected that at some point they would find a crossing.

During this outflanking movement by the wings, the army on the center and southern front remained still. The besieged were therefore able to contemplate at their leisure the thumb-long, reddish black, long-legged insects; some of the Indians believed they could see, too, intent on them, the brilliant, cold eyes, and the razor-edged mandibles, of this host of infinity.

It is not easy for the average person to imagine that an animal, not to mention an insect, can *think*. But now both the European brain of Leiningen and the primitive brains of the Indians began to stir with the unpleasant foreboding that inside every single one of that deluge of insects dwelt a thought. And that thought was: Ditch or no ditch, we'll get to your flesh!

Not until four o'clock did the wings reach the "horseshoe" ends of the ditch, only to find these ran into the great river. Through some kind of secret telegraphy, the report must then have flashed very swiftly indeed along the entire enemy line. And Leiningen, riding—no longer casually—along his side of the ditch, noticed by energetic and widespread movements of troops that for some unknown reason the news of the check had its greatest effect on the southern front, where the main army was massed. Perhaps the failure to find a way over the ditch was persuading the ants to withdraw from the plantation in search of spoils more easily attainable.

An immense flood of ants, about a hundred yards in width, was pouring in a glimmering-black cataract down the far slope of the ditch. Many thousands were already drowning in the sluggish creeping flow, but they were followed by troop after troop, who clambered over their sinking comrades, and then themselves served as dying bridges to the reserves hurrying on in their rear.

Shoals of ants were being carried away by the current into the middle of the ditch, where gradually they broke asunder and then, exhausted by their struggles, vanished below the surface. Nevertheless, the wavering, floundering hundred-yard front was remorselessly if slowly advancing towards the besieged on the other bank. Leiningen had been wrong when he supposed the enemy would first have to fill the ditch with their bodies before they could cross; instead, they merely needed to act as stepping-stones, as they swam and sank, to the hordes ever pressing onwards from behind.

Near Leiningen a few mounted herdsmen awaited his orders. He sent one to the weir—the river must be dammed more strongly to increase the speed and power of the water coursing through the ditch.

A second peon was dispatched to the outhouses to bring spades and petrol sprinklers. A third rode away to summon to the zone of the offensive all the men, except the observation posts, on the near-by sections of the ditch, which were not yet actively threatened.

The ants were getting across far more quickly than Leiningen would have deemed possible. Impelled by the mighty cascade be-

hind them, they struggled nearer and nearer to the inner bank.
The momentum of the attack was so great that neither the tardy
flow of the stream nor its downward pull could exert its proper
force; and into the gap left by every submerging insect, hastened
forward a dozen more.

When reinforcements reached Leiningen, the invaders were half-
way over. The planter had to admit to himself that it was only
by a stroke of luck for him that the ants were attempting the crossing on a relatively short front: had they assaulted simultaneously
along the entire length of the ditch, the outlook for the defenders
would have been black indeed.

Even as it was, it could hardly be described as rosy, though the
planter seemed quite unaware that death in a gruesome form was
drawing closer and closer. As the war between his brain and the
"act of God" reached its climax, the very shadow of annihilation
began to pale to Leiningen, who now felt like a champion in a new
Olympic game, a gigantic and thrilling contest, from which he
was determined to emerge victor. Such, indeed, was his aura of
confidence that the Indians forgot their stupefied fear of the peril
only a yard or two away; under the planter's supervision, they
began fervidly digging up to the edge of the bank and throwing
clods of earth and spadefuls of sand into the midst of the hostile
fleet.

The petrol sprinklers, hitherto used to destroy pests and blights
on the plantation, were also brought into action. Streams of evil-
reeking oil now soared and fell over an enemy already in disorder
through the bombardment of earth and sand.

The ants responded to these vigorous and successful measures
of defence by further developments of their offensive. Entire
clumps of huddling insects began to roll down the opposite bank
into the water. At the same time, Leiningen noticed that the ants
were now attacking along an ever-widening front. As the numbers
both of his men and his petrol sprinklers were severely limited,
this rapid extension of the line of battle was becoming an overwhelming danger.

To add to his difficulties, the very clods of earth they flung into
that black floating carpet often whirled fragments towards the defenders' side, and here and there dark ribbons were already mounting the inner bank. True, wherever a man saw these they could

still be driven back into the water by spadefuls of earth or jets of petrol. But the file of defenders was too sparse and scattered to hold off at all points these landing parties, and though the peons toiled like madmen, their plight became momently more perilous.

One man struck with his spade at an enemy clump, did not draw it back quickly enough from the water; in a trice the wooden haft swarmed with upward scurrying insects. With a curse, he dropped the spade into the ditch; too late, they were already on his body. They lost no time; wherever they encountered bare flesh they bit deeply; a few, bigger than the rest, carried in their hindquarters a sting which injected a burning and paralyzing venom. Screaming, frantic with pain, the peon danced and twirled like a dervish.

Realizing that another such casualty, yes, perhaps this alone, might plunge his men into confusion and destroy their morale, Leiningen roared in a bellow louder than the yells of the victim: "Into the petrol, idiot! Douse your paws in the petrol!" The dervish ceased his pirouette as if transfixed, then tore off his shirt and plunged his arm and the ants hanging to it up to the shoulder in one of the large open tins of petrol. But even then the fierce mandibles did not slacken; another peon had to help him squash and detach each separate insect.

Distracted by the episode, some defenders had turned away from the ditch. And now cries of fury, a thudding of spades, and a wild trampling to and fro, showed that the ants had made full use of the interval, though luckily only a few had managed to get across. The men set to work again desperately with the barrage of earth and sand. Meanwhile an old Indian, who acted as medicine-man to the plantation workers, gave the bitten peon a drink he had prepared some hours before, which, he claimed, possessed the virtue of dissolving and weakening ants' venom.

Leiningen surveyed his position. A dispassionate observer would have estimated the odds against him at a thousand to one. But then such an onlooker would have reckoned only by what he saw— the advance of myriad battalions of ants against the futile efforts of a few defenders—and not by the unseen activity that can go on in a man's brain.

For Leiningen had not erred when he decided he would fight elemental with elemental. The water in the ditch was beginning to rise; the stronger damming of the river was making itself apparent.

Visibly the swiftness and power of the masses of water increased, swirling into quicker and quicker movement its living black surface, dispersing its pattern, carrying away more and more of it on the hastening current.

Victory had been snatched from the very jaws of defeat. With a hysterical shout of joy, the peons feverishly intensified their bombardment of earth clods and sand.

And now the wide cataract down the opposite bank was thinning and ceasing, as if the ants were becoming aware that they could not attain their aim. They were scurrying back up the slope to safety.

All the troops so far hurled into the ditch had been sacrificed in vain. Drowned and floundering insects eddied in thousands along the flow, while Indians running on the bank destroyed every swimmer that reached the side.

Not until the ditch curved towards the east did the scattered ranks assemble again in a coherent mass. And now, exhausted and half-numbed, they were in no condition to ascend the bank. Fusillades of clods drove them round the bend towards the mouth of the ditch and then into the river, wherein they vanished without leaving a trace.

The news ran swiftly along the entire chain of outposts, and soon a long scattered line of laughing men could be seen hastening along the ditch towards the scene of victory.

For once they seemed to have lost all their native reserve, for it was in wild abandon now they celebrated the triumph—as if there were no longer thousands of millions of merciless, cold and hungry eyes watching them from the opposite bank, watching and waiting.

The sun sank behind the rim of the tamarind wood and twilight deepened into night. It was not only hoped but expected that the ants would remain quiet until dawn. But to defeat any forlorn attempt at a crossing, the flow of water through the ditch was powerfully increased by opening the dam still further.

In spite of this impregnable barrier, Leiningen was not yet altogether convinced that the ants would not venture another surprise attack. He ordered his men to camp along the bank overnight. He also detailed parties of them to patrol the ditch in two of his motor cars and ceaselessly to illuminate the surface of the water with headlights and electric torches.

After having taken all the precautions he deemed necessary, the farmer ate his supper with considerable appetite and went to bed. His slumbers were in no wise disturbed by the memory of the waiting, live, twenty square miles.

Dawn found a thoroughly refreshed and active Leiningen riding along the edge of the ditch. The planter saw before him a motionless and unaltered throng of besiegers. He studied the wide belt of water between them and the plantation, and for a moment almost regretted that the fight had ended so soon and so simply. In the comforting, matter-of-fact light of morning, it seemed to him now that the ants hadn't the ghost of a chance to cross the ditch. Even if they plunged headlong into it on all three fronts at once, the force of the now powerful current would inevitably sweep them away. He had got quite a thrill out of the fight—a pity it was already over.

He rode along the eastern and southern sections of the ditch and found everything in order. He reached the western section, opposite the tamarind wood, and here, contrary to the other battle fronts, he found the enemy very busy indeed. The trunks and branches of the trees and the creepers of the lianas, on the far bank of the ditch, fairly swarmed with industrious insects. But instead of eating the leaves there and then, they were merely gnawing through the stalks, so that a thick green shower fell steadily to the ground.

No doubt they were victualing columns sent out to obtain provender for the rest of the army. The discovery did not surprise Leiningen. He did not need to be told that ants are intelligent, that certain species even use others as milch cows, watchdogs and slaves. He was well aware of their power of adaptation, their sense of discipline, their marvelous talent for organization.

His belief that a foray to supply the army was in progress was strengthened when he saw the leaves that fell to the ground being dragged to the troops waiting outside the wood. Then all at once he realized the aim that rain of green was intended to serve.

Each single leaf, pulled or pushed by dozens of toiling insects, was borne straight to the edge of the ditch. Even as Macbeth watched the approach of Birnam Wood in the hands of his enemies,

Leiningen saw the tamarind wood move nearer and nearer in the mandibles of the ants. Unlike the fey Scot, however, he did not lose his nerve; no witches had prophesied his doom, and if they had he would have slept just as soundly. All the same, he was forced to admit to himself that the situation was now far more ominous than that of the day before.

He had thought it impossible for the ants to build rafts for themselves—well, here they were, coming in thousands, more than enough to bridge the ditch. Leaves after leaves rustled down the slope into the water, where the current drew them away from the bank and carried them into midstream. And every single leaf carried several ants. This time the farmer did not trust to the alacrity of his messengers. He galloped away, leaning from his saddle and yelling orders as he rushed past outpost after outpost: "Bring petrol pumps to the southwest front! Issue spades to every man along the line facing the wood!" And arrived at the eastern and southern sections, he dispatched every man except the observation posts to the menaced west.

Then, as he rode past the stretch where the ants had failed to cross the day before, he witnessed a brief but impressive scene. Down the slope of the distant hill there came towards him a singular being, writhing rather than running, an animal-like blackened statue with a shapeless head and four quivering feet that knuckled under almost ceaselessly. When the creature reached the far bank of the ditch and collapsed opposite Leiningen, he recognized it as a pampas stag, covered over and over with ants.

It had strayed near the zone of the army. As usual, they had attacked its eyes first. Blinded, it had reeled in the madness of hideous torment straight into the ranks of its persecutors, and now the beast swayed to and fro in its death agony.

With a shot from his rifle Leiningen put it out of its misery. Then he pulled out his watch. He hadn't a second to lose, but for life itself he could not have denied his curiosity the satisfaction of knowing how long the ants would take—for personal reasons, so to speak. After six minutes the white polished bones alone remained. That's how he himself would look before you can—Leiningen spat once, and put spurs to his horse.

The sporting zest with which the excitement of the novel contest had inspired him the day before had now vanished; in its place was a cold and violent purpose. He would send these vermin back to the hell where they belonged, somehow, anyhow. Yes, but how was indeed the question; as things stood at present it looked as if the devils would raze him and his men from the earth instead. He had underestimated the might of the enemy; he really would have to bestir himself if he hoped to outwit them.

The biggest danger now, he decided, was the point where the western section of the ditch curved southwards. And arrived there, he found his worst expectations justified. The very power of the current had huddled the leaves and their crews of ants so close together at the bend that the bridge was almost ready.

True, streams of petrol and clumps of earth still prevented a landing. But the number of floating leaves was increasing ever more swiftly. It could not be long now before a stretch of water a mile in length was decked by a green pontoon over which the ants could rush in millions.

Leiningen galloped to the weir. The damming of the river was controlled by a wheel on its bank. The planter ordered the man at the wheel first to lower the water in the ditch almost to vanishing point, next to wait a moment, then suddenly to let the river in again. This maneuver of lowering and raising the surface, of decreasing then increasing the flow of water through the ditch was to be repeated over and over again until further notice.

This tactic was at first successful. The water in the ditch sank, and with it the film of leaves. The green fleet nearly reached the bed and the troops on the far bank swarmed down the slope to it. Then a violent flow of water at the original depth raced through the ditch, overwhelming leaves and ants, and sweeping them along.

This intermittent rapid flushing prevented just in time the almost completed fording of the ditch. But it also flung here and there squads of the enemy vanguard simultaneously up the inner bank. These seemed to know their duty only too well, and lost no time accomplishing it. The air rang with the curses of bitten Indians. They had removed their shirts and pants to detect the quicker the upwards-hastening insects; when they saw one, they crushed it; and fortunately the onslaught as yet was only by skirmishers.

Again and again, the water sank and rose, carrying leaves and drowned ants away with it. It lowered once more nearly to its bed; but this time the exhausted defenders waited in vain for the flush of destruction. Leiningen sensed disaster; something must have gone wrong with the machinery of the dam. Then a sweating peon tore up to him—

"They're over!"

While the besieged were concentrating upon the defence of the stretch opposite the wood, the seemingly unaffected line beyond the wood had become the theatre of decisive action. Here the defenders' front was sparse and scattered; everyone who could be spared had hurried away to the south.

Just as the man at the weir had lowered the water almost to the bed of the ditch, the ants on a wide front began another attempt at a direct crossing like that of the preceding day. Into the emptied bed poured an irresistible throng. Rushing across the ditch, they attained the inner bank before the slow-witted Indians fully grasped the situation. Their frantic screams dumbfounded the man at the weir. Before he could direct the river anew into the safe-guarding bed he saw himself surrounded by raging ants. He ran like the others, ran for his life.

When Leiningen heard this, he knew the plantation was doomed. He wasted no time bemoaning the inevitable. For as long as there was the slightest chance of success, he had stood his ground, and now any further resistance was both useless and dangerous. He fired three revolver shots into the air—the prearranged signal for his men to retreat instantly within the "inner moat." Then he rode towards the ranchhouse.

This was two miles from the point of invasion. There was therefore time enough to prepare the second line of defence against the advent of the ants. Of the three great petrol cisterns near the house, one had already been half emptied by the constant withdrawals needed for the pumps during the fight at the water ditch. The remaining petrol in it was now drawn off through underground pipes into the concrete trench which encircled the ranchhouse and its outbuildings.

And there, drifting in twos and threes, Leiningen's men reached him. Most of them were obviously trying to preserve an air of calm and indifference, belied, however, by their restless glances and knitted brows. One could see their belief in a favorable outcome of the struggle was already considerably shaken.

The planter called his peons around him.

"Well, lads," he began, "we've lost the first round. But we'll smash the beggars yet, don't you worry. Anyone who thinks otherwise can draw his pay here and now and push off. There are rafts enough and to spare on the river and plenty of time still to reach 'em."

Not a man stirred.

Leiningen acknowledged his silent vote of confidence with a laugh that was half a grunt. "That's the stuff, lads. Too bad if you'd missed the rest of the show, eh? Well, the fun won't start till morning. Once these blighters turn tail, there'll be plenty of work for everyone and higher wages all round. And now run along and get something to eat; you've earned it all right."

In the excitement of the fight the greater part of the day had passed without the men once pausing to snatch a bite. Now that the ants were for the time being out of sight, and the "wall of petrol" gave a stronger feeling of security, hungry stomachs began to assert their claims.

The bridges over the concrete ditch were removed. Here and there solitary ants had reached the ditch; they gazed at the petrol meditatively, then scurried back again. Apparently they had little interest at the moment for what lay beyond the evil-reeking barrier; the abundant spoils of the plantation were the main attraction. Soon the trees, shrubs and beds for miles around were hulled with ants zealously gobbling the yield of long weary months of strenuous toil.

As twilight began to fall, a cordon of ants marched around the petrol trench, but as yet made no move towards its brink. Leiningen posted sentries with headlights and electric torches, then withdrew to his office, and began to reckon up his losses. He estimated these as large, but, in comparison with his bank balance, by no means unbearable. He worked out in some detail a scheme of intensive cultivation which would enable him, before very long, to more than compensate himself for the damage now being wrought to his crops. It was with a contented mind that he finally betook himself to bed where he slept deeply until dawn, undisturbed by any thought that next day little more might be left of him than a glistening skeleton.

He rose with the sun and went out on the flat roof of his house. And a scene like one from Dante lay around him; for miles in

every direction there was nothing but a black, glittering multitude,
a multitude of rested, sated, but none the less voracious ants: yes,
look as far as one might, one could see nothing but that rustling
black throng, except in the north, where the great river drew a
boundary they could not hope to pass. But even the high stone
breakwater, along the bank of the river, which Leiningen had
built as a defence against inundations, was, like the paths, the
shorn trees and shrubs, the ground itself, black with ants.

So their greed was not glutted in razing that vast plantation?
Not by a long chalk; they were all the more eager now on a rich
and certain booty—four hundred men, numerous horses, and bursting granaries.

At first it seemed that the petrol trench would serve its purpose.
The besiegers sensed the peril of swimming it, and made no move
to plunge blindly over its brink. Instead they devised a better maneuver; they began to collect shreds of bark, twigs and dried leaves
and dropped these into the petrol. Everything green, which could
have been similarly used, had long since been eaten. After a time,
though, a long procession could be seen bringing from the west
the tamarind leaves used as rafts the day before.

Since the petrol, unlike the water in the outer ditch, was perfectly still, the refuse stayed where it was thrown. It was several
hours before the ants succeeded in covering an appreciable part of
the surface. At length, however, they were ready to proceed to a
direct attack.

Their storm troops swarmed down the concrete side, scrambled
over the supporting surface of twigs and leaves, and impelled these
over the few remaining streaks of open petrol until they reached
the other side. Then they began to climb up this to make straight
for the helpless garrison.

During the entire offensive, the planter sat peacefully, watching
them with interest, but not stirring a muscle. Moreover, he had
ordered his men not to disturb in any way whatever the advancing
horde. So they squatted listlessly along the bank of the ditch and
waited for a sign from the boss.

The petrol was now covered with ants. A few had climbed the
inner concrete wall and were scurrying towards the defenders.

"Everyone back from the ditch!" roared Leiningen. The men
rushed away, without the slightest idea of his plan. He stooped

forward and cautiously dropped into the ditch a stone which split the floating carpet and its living freight, to reveal a gleaming patch of petrol. A match spurted, sank down to the oily surface—Leiningen sprang back; in a flash a towering rampart of fire encompassed the garrison.

This spectacular and instant repulse threw the Indians into ecstasy. They applauded, yelled and stamped, like children at a pantomime. Had it not been for the awe in which they held the boss, they would infallibly have carried him shoulder high.

It was some time before the petrol burned down to the bed of the ditch, and the wall of smoke and flame began to lower. The ants had retreated in a wide circle from the devastation, and innumerable charred fragments along the outer bank showed that the flames had spread from the holocaust in the ditch well into the ranks beyond, where they had wrought havoc far and wide.

Yet the perseverance of the ants was by no means broken; indeed, each setback seemed only to whet it. The concrete cooled, the flicker of the dying flames wavered and vanished, petrol from the second tank poured into the trench—and the ants marched forward anew to the attack.

The foregoing scene repeated itself in every detail, except that on this occasion less time was needed to bridge the ditch, for the petrol was now already filmed by a layer of ash. Once again they withdrew; once again petrol flowed into the ditch. Would the creatures never learn that their self-sacrifice was utterly senseless? It really was senseless, wasn't it? Yes, of course it was senseless—provided the defenders had an *unlimited* supply of petrol.

When Leiningen reached this stage of reasoning, he felt for the first time since the arrival of the ants that his confidence was deserting him. His skin began to creep; he loosened his collar. Once the devils were over the trench there wasn't a chance in hell for him and his men. God, what a prospect, to be eaten alive like that!

For the third time the flames immolated the attacking troops, and burned down to extinction. Yet the ants were coming on again as if nothing had happened. And meanwhile Leiningen had made a discovery that chilled him to the bone—petrol was no longer flowing into the ditch. Something must be blocking the outflow pipe of the third and last cistern—a snake or a dead rat? Whatever it was, the ants could be held off no longer, unless petrol could by some method be led from the cistern into the ditch.

Then Leiningen remembered that in an outhouse near-by were two old disused fire engines. Spry as never before in their lives, the peons dragged them out of the shed, connected their pumps to the cistern, uncoiled and laid the hose. They were just in time to aim a stream of petrol at a column of ants that had already crossed and drive them back down the incline into the ditch. Once more an oily girdle surrounded the garrison, once more it was possible to hold the position—for the moment.

It was obvious, however, that this last resource meant only the postponement of defeat and death. A few of the peons fell on their knees and began to pray; others, shrieking insanely, fired their revolvers at the black, advancing masses, as if they felt their despair was pitiful enough to sway fate itself to mercy.

At length, two of the men's nerves broke: Leiningen saw a naked Indian leap over the north side of the petrol trench, quickly followed by a second. They sprinted with incredible speed towards the river. But their fleetness did not save them; long before they could attain the rafts, the enemy covered their bodies from head to foot.

In the agony of their torment, both sprang blindly into the wide river, where enemies no less sinister awaited them. Wild screams of mortal anguish informed the breathless onlookers that crocodiles and sword-toothed piranhas were no less ravenous than ants, and even nimbler in reaching their prey.

In spite of this bloody warning, more and more men showed they were making up their minds to run the blockade. Anything, even a fight midstream against alligators, seemed better than powerlessly waiting for death to come and slowly consume their living bodies.

Leiningen flogged his brain till it reeled. Was there nothing on earth could sweep this devils' spawn back into the hell from which it came?

Then out of the inferno of his bewilderment rose a terrifying inspiration. Yes, one hope remained, and one alone. It might be possible to dam the great river completely, so that its waters would fill not only the water ditch but overflow into the entire gigantic "saucer" of land in which lay the plantation.

The far bank of the river was too high for the waters to escape that way. The stone breakwater ran between the river and the plantation; its only gaps occurred where the "horseshoe" ends of the water-ditch passed into the river. So its waters would not only be forced to inundate into the plantation, they would also be held there by the breakwater until they rose to its own high level. In half an hour, perhaps even earlier, the plantation and its hostile army of occupation would be flooded.

The ranchhouse and outbuildings stood upon rising ground. Their foundations were higher than the breakwater, so the flood would not reach them. And any remaining ants trying to ascend the slope could be repulsed by petrol.

It was possible—yes, if one could only get to the dam! A distance of nearly two miles lay between the ranch house and the weir—two miles of ants. Those two peons had managed only a fifth of that distance at the cost of their lives. Was there an Indian daring enough after that to run the gauntlet five times as far? Hardly likely; and if there were, his prospect of getting back was almost nil.

No, there was only one thing for it, he'd have to make the attempt himself; he might just as well be running as sitting still, anyway, when the ants finally got him. Besides, there *was* a bit of a chance. Perhaps the ants weren't so almighty, after all; perhaps he had allowed the mass suggestion of that evil black throng to hypnotize him, just as a snake fascinates and overpowers.

The ants were building their bridges. Leiningen got up on a chair. "Hey, lads, listen to me!" he cried. Slowly and listlessly, from all sides of the trench, the men began to shuffle towards him, the apathy of death already stamped on their faces.

"Listen, lads!" he shouted. "You're frightened of those beggars, but you're a damn sight more frightened of me, and I'm proud of you. There's still a chance to save our lives—by flooding the plantation from the river. Now one of you might manage to get as far as the weir—but he'd never come back. Well, I'm not going to let you try it; if I did I'd be worse than one of those ants. No, I called the tune, and now I'm going to pay the piper.

"The moment I'm over the ditch, set fire to the petrol. That'll allow time for the flood to do the trick. Then all you have to do is to wait here all snug and quiet till I'm back. Yes, I'm coming back, trust me"—he grinned—"when I've finished my slimming-cure."

He pulled on high leather boots, drew heavy gauntlets over his hands, and stuffed the spaces between breeches and boots, gauntlets and arms, shirt and neck, with rags soaked in petrol. With close-fitting mosquito goggles he shielded his eyes, knowing too well the ants' dodge of first robbing their victim of sight. Finally, he plugged his nostrils and ears with cotton-wool, and let the peons drench his clothes with petrol.

He was about to set off, when the old Indian medicine man came up to him; he had a wondrous salve, he said, prepared from a species of chafer whose odor was intolerable to ants. Yes, this odor protected these chafers from the attacks of even the most murderous ants. The Indian smeared the boss' boots, his gauntlets, and his face over and over with the extract.

Leiningen then remembered the paralyzing effect of ants' venom, and the Indian gave him a gourd full of the medicine he had administered to the bitten peon at the water ditch. The planter drank it down without noticing its bitter taste; his mind was already at the weir.

He started off towards the northwest corner of the trench. With a bound he was over—and among the ants.

The beleagured garrison had no opportunity to watch Leiningen's race against death. The ants were climbing the inner bank again—the lurid ring of petrol blazed aloft. For the fourth time that day the reflection from the fire shone on the sweating faces of the imprisoned men, and on the reddish-black cuirasses of their oppressors. The red and blue, dark-edged flames leaped vividly now, celebrating what? The funeral pyre of the four hundred, or of the hosts of destruction?

Leiningen ran. He ran in long, equal strides, with only one thought, one sensation, in his being—he *must* get through. He dodged all trees and shrubs; except for the split seconds his soles touched the ground the ants should have no opportunity to alight on him. That they would get to him soon, despite the salve on his boots, the petrol in his clothes, he realized only too well, but he knew even more surely that he must, and that he would, get to the weir.

Apparently the salve was some use after all; not until he had reached halfway did he feel ants under his clothes, and a few on his face. Mechanically, in his stride, he struck at them, scarcely conscious of their bites. He saw he was drawing appreciably nearer the weir—the distance grew less and less—sank to five hundred—three—two—one hundred yards.

Then he was at the weir and gripping the ant-hulled wheel. Hardly had he seized it when a horde of infuriated ants flowed over his hands, arms and shoulders. He started the wheel—before it turned once on its axis the swarm covered his face. Leiningen strained like a madman, his lips pressed tight; if he opened them to draw breath. . . .

He turned and turned; slowly the dam lowered until it reached the bed of the river. Already the water was overflowing the ditch. Another minute, and the river was pouring through the near-by gap in the breakwater. The flooding of the plantation had begun.

Leiningen let go the wheel. Now, for the first time, he realized he was coated from head to foot with a layer of ants. In spite of the petrol, his clothes were full of them, several had got to his body or were clinging to his face. Now that he had completed his task, he felt the smart raging over his flesh from the bites of sawing and piercing insects.

Frantic with pain, he almost plunged into the river. To be ripped and slashed to shreds by piranhas? Already he was running the return journey, knocking ants from his gloves and jacket, brushing them from his bloodied face, squashing them to death under his clothes.

One of the creatures bit him just below the rim of his goggles; he managed to tear it away, but the agony of the bite and its etching acid drilled into the eye nerves; he saw now through circles of fire into a milky mist, then he ran for a time almost blinded, knowing that if he once tripped and fell. . . . The old Indian's brew didn't seem much good; it weakened the poison a bit, but didn't get rid of it. His heart pounded as if it would burst; blood roared in his ears; a giant's fist battered his lungs.

Then he could see again, but the burning girdle of petrol appeared infinitely far away; he could not last half that distance. Swift-changing pictures flashed through his head, episodes in his life, while in another part of his brain a cool and impartial onlooker informed this ant-blurred, gasping, exhausted bundle named Leiningen that such a rushing panorama of scenes from one's past is seen only in the moment before death.

A stone in the path . . . too weak to avoid it . . . the planter stumbled and collapsed. He tried to rise . . . he must be pinned under a rock . . . it was impossible . . . the slightest movement was impossible. . . .

Then all at once he saw, starkly clear and huge, and, right before his eyes, furred with ants, towering and swaying in its death agony, the pampas stag. In six minutes—gnawed to the bones. God, he *couldn't* die like that! And something outside him seemed to drag him to his feet. He tottered. He began to stagger forward again.

Through the blazing ring hurtled an apparition which, as soon as it reached the ground on the inner side, fell full length and did not move. Leiningen, at the moment he made that leap through the flames, lost consciousness for the first time in his life. As he lay there, with glazing eyes and lacerated face, he appeared a man returned from the grave. The peons rushed to him, stripped off his clothes, tore away the ants from a body that seemed almost one open wound; in some places the bones were showing. They carried him into the ranch house.

As the curtain of flames lowered, one could see in place of the illimitable host of ants an extensive vista of water. The thwarted river had swept over the plantation, carrying with it the entire army. The water had collected and mounted in the great "saucer," while the ants had in vain attempted to reach the hill on which stood the ranch house. The girdle of flames held them back.

And so imprisoned between water and fire, they had been delivered into the annihilation that was their god. And near the farther mouth of the water-ditch, where the stone mole had its second gap, the ocean swept the lost battalions into the river, to vanish forever.

The ring of fire dwindled as the water mounted to the petrol trench, and quenched the dimming flames. The inundation rose higher and higher: because its outflow was impeded by the timber and underbrush it had carried along with it, its surface required some time to reach the top of the high stone breakwater and discharge over it the rest of the shattered army.

It swelled over ant-stippled shrubs and bushes, until it washed against the foot of the knoll whereon the besieged had taken refuge. For a while an alluvial of ants tried again and again to attain this dry land, only to be repulsed by streams of petrol back into the merciless flood.

Leiningen lay on his bed, his body swathed from head to foot in bandages. With fomentations and salves, they had managed to stop the bleeding, and had dressed his many wounds. Now they thronged around him, one question in every face. Would he recover? "He won't die," said the old man who had bandaged him, "if he doesn't want to."

The planter opened his eyes. "Everything in order?" he asked.

"They're gone," said his nurse. "To hell." He held out to his master a gourd full of a powerful sleeping draught. Leiningen gulped it down.

"I told you I'd come back," he murmured, "even if I am a bit streamlined." He grinned and shut his eyes. He slept.